...LAS · CHAUFFEUR SERVICES · COOKE... ...S
FASHION & ACCESSORIES · FLORISTS · GARDEN D...
...Y & WATCHES · MUSEUMS · MUSIC FESTIVALS · NAN...
...OLO CLUBS · PORTRAITS · PRIVATE BANKS · PROPERT...
...RESTAURANTS & BARS · ANTIQUE & PICTURE RESTO...
...SPECIALIST SHOPS · SPORTING ESTATES · SPORTS CL...
...NES, CHAMPAGNES & SPIRITS · YACHT BROKERS, DE...
...EALERS · ARCHITECTS & DECORATORS · ART & ANTI...
...OUSES · CASINOS · CASTLES & VILLAS · CHAUFFEUR...
...IC EMPLOYMENT AGENCIES · FASHION & ACCESSOR...
...BEAUTY · HOTELS · JEWELLERY & WATCHES · MUSEU...
...ERERS · PICTURE DEALERS · POLO CLUBS · PORTRAI...
...ERS & BLOODSTOCK AGENTS · RESTAURANTS & BAR...
...CONSULTANTS · SPAS & CLINICS · SPECIALIST SHOP...
...NSULTANTS · WINE MERCHANTS · WINES, CHAMPA...
...HT CLUBS · AIR CHARTER · ANTIQUE DEALERS · AR...
...LA TABLE · ARTS DE VIVRE · AUCTION HOUSES · CA...
...HOOLS · COSMETIC SURGEONS · DOMESTIC EMPLO...
...EN DESIGNERS · GOLD CLUBS · HAIR & BEAUTY · HO...
...NANNIES · PARTY ORGANISERS & CATERERS · PICTU...
...ERTY CONSULTANTS · RACING TRAINERS & BLOODS...
...ESTORERS · SCHOOLS · SECURITY CONSULTANTS · S...
...TS CLUBS & GYMS · TRAVEL CONSULTANTS · WINE M...
...KERS, DESIGNERS & BUILDERS · YACHT CLUBS · AIR...
...ART & ANTIQUE FAIRS · ARTS DE LA TABLE · ARTS D...
...UFFEUR SERVICES · COOKERY SCHOOLS · COSMETIC...
...& ACCESSORIES · FLORISTS · GARDEN DESIGNERS...
...S · MUSEUMS · MUSIC FESTIVALS · NANNIES · PART...
...UBS · PORTRAITS · PRIVATE BANKS · PROPERTY CON...
...ESTAURANTS & BARS · ANTIQUE & PICTURE RESTOR...

Europe's Elite 1000

The Ultimate List
1999

First Published in October 1998 by
Cadogan Publications Limited
50 Hans Crescent, London SW1X 0NA, UK
Telephone: +44-171-581 1805

British Library Cataloguing in Publication Data
A catalogue record for this book is available from The British Library
ISBN 0 9534276 0 9

Publisher: Kevin Kelly

Acknowledgements and Picture Credits: See page 320

Colour origination by Graphic Media Management Ltd., Ireland
Printed and bound in Ireland by Betaprint Ltd.

TITLE PAGE: *A garden in Southern France, designed by Alain David Idoux.*
PAGE 4: *A London apartment designed by André de Cacqueray. Photographed by Colin Gates.*

EUROPE'S ELITE 1000
THE ULTIMATE LIST
1999

EDITED BY
SANDRA LANE

CADOGAN PUBLICATIONS

FOREWORD

Having been, for centuries, the cradle of Western culture, Europe remains the source of and the standard-bearer for most of the world's finest luxury products and services.

This unique guide - the first of an annual series - lists the most acclaimed companies and individuals in Europe who are maintaining and building upon that tradition of excellence. It has been researched, written and edited by a team of distinguished contributors, whose specialised, local knowledge has enabled us to give you the definitive, inside story on the very best Europe has to offer.

Recognising the limitations of the many guide books, on a variety of subjects, which already exist, *Europe's Elite 1000* has been created to fulfil two purposes.

First, it has been designed as a source-book, which will provide an invaluable reference-point when travelling to or within Europe, guiding you in the direction of the best, and only the best - the finest hospitality, the best shops, the most exclusive clubs and the most distinguished providers of an enormously broad range of services - all brought together in a single volume.

Second, having been created in this visually arresting format and containing a wide range of editorial features in addition to the Listings, it will make an elegant and long-lasting addition to your library or coffee table.

Whatever your particular interests, as long as you are a lover of the finer things in life, you will not only be inspired by this book but also, we hope, will make many exciting new discoveries throughout its pages.

KEVIN KELLY
PUBLISHER

EUROPE'S ELITE 1000

THE LISTINGS

Europe's Elite 1000 comprises three Listings sections, each of which includes names from all sectors of luxury goods and services: The Elite 1000, 100 Rising Stars and 100 Best-Kept Secrets. Every company or individual proposed for inclusion has been checked and cross-checked by our network of contributors, advisers and contacts, to ensure that its inclusion is merited. The names have been selected on the basis of the current excellence of their products and services, rather than, simply, a high profile or impressive past reputation. Equally, all names have been judged against a pan-European standard of excellence, rather than being selected on a country-by-country basis. All of the entries will be reviewed and updated annually.

THE ELITE 1000

While the Elite 1000 list, naturally, includes the acknowledged 'greats', it also contains many less predictable names. Some readers may, however, be surprised to find certain famous names missing from the list. If they did not qualify, it is because they appear to us to have succumbed either to the temptation of resting on their laurels, rather than constantly reviewing and upgrading their standards, or to the temptation of becoming too commercial and populist.

100 BEST-KEPT SECRETS

While the Elite 1000 listing contains a significant number of names that are well known only to those who are truly 'at home' in Europe or those with a specialised knowledge of a particular sector, this list of Secrets is more of a 'Little Black Book'. Names on this sometimes quirky list constitute real insiders' tips, such as a favourite hideaway hotel, a marvellous beautician or a jeweller who works only to private commission. Some of the names are already well-established but, we believe, deserve to be more widely known.

100 RISING STARS

While some of the Rising Stars may be well-established and may already have achieved considerable success, we believe that they will make it to the very top of their particular field. Others - relative newcomers - may not yet have fulfilled their potential or proved that they have real staying power but their commitment to excellence is unquestioned. Many of these names will make it into the Elite 1000 - perhaps as soon as next year.

HOW TO USE THIS BOOK

Each of the above lists is published in alphabetical order, across all product categories. The names are cross-referenced in three indexes, to enable you to use the book in a variety of ways. For example, if you are travelling to a particular country, you would use the Country Index to discover the best of everything in that country. On the other hand, if you are seeking the best in a certain field - say, jewellers or antique dealers - you would use the Product Category Index, which will list all European names under the relevant category heading. In addition, there is a straight Alphabetical Index of all names which have been included in the Listings sections of the book.

CONTENTS

You never
actually own a Patek Philippe.

You merely look after it

for the next generation.

PATEK PHILIPPE
GENEVE

Begin your *own* tradition.

QUINTESSENTIALLY BIRLEY

Words by Jane Elliott Pictures by Fritz von der Schulenburg

*Regarded by many as the archetypal Englishman,
Mark Birley has, over the last thirty-five years, run the four most
stylish and exclusive private clubs in Europe.*

Much as one might wish, one cannot pretend that an obsession with quality is one of England's national characteristics. Yet it is what drives Mark Birley. Birley is the owner, creator and irresistible force behind four private clubs: Annabel's, the nightclub that for thirty years has transcended trendiness; Mark's Club, his own deceptively simple, luxurious transformation of the English gentleman's club; Harry's Bar, where sublime Italian food is served in beautiful surroundings; and the Bath & Racquets Club, where pampered members can work off the excesses of wining and dining at the other three. Birley's clientele is the world's rich and successful. On any day at Mark's Club or Harry's Bar you might see King Constantine at a table beside Rothschilds, Flicks, a Kennedy, a media mogul, and a plutocrat or two - peppered with the topmost echelons of showbusiness. Birley's clubs provide them with a home-from-home. Yet you will not see paparazzi resident on the pavements outside. No sneaked shots of, for example, royalty in the arms of the latest film star on the dance floor at Annabel's are allowed to be smeared over the pages of the tabloids. Birley polices the privacy of members like the last don of the haute monde; moreover, gossip columnists know that his clubs are their proprietors' own haunts.

A corner of the drawing room at Mark's Club reflects its owner's impeccable taste, with paintings and objects collected over the years by Mark Birley himself.

LEFT: *At Harry's Bar the specially-chosen low tables are adorned with blue rimmed venetian glasses and custom-made linen and the walls hung with Peter Arno cartoons.* BELOW, *left to right: Brilliant chef Alberico Penati with "artist sommelier" Valentino – adored by all comers for his courtly manners – and maître d' Mario, the master of placement.*

Yet, continuing social cachet is the symptom, not the cause, of their success. Beneath the socialite chatter hums a perfectly oiled, consummately professional machine, run to precise instructions.

Birley's clubs have been called "quintessentially English" but, more exactly, they are quintessentially Birley. Each is firmly imprinted with the master's voice - his eye, his palate, his renowned taste. The patron sits at his own table at Harry's Bar, taking in every detail. Let us look at those details: tables at a low height for intimacy, adorned with specially produced linen and blue-rimmed Venetian glasses; white truffles crouching like exotic toads over a perfect glass bowl of arborio rice, awaiting starter's orders for an unforgettable risotto. The walls of ochre Fortuny silk are studded with Birley's unmatchable private collection of Peter Arno cartoons; above them, an old Venetian chandelier, lit to the side by a Burne Jones stained glass window.

Most restaurants boast something called decor - as soon as the place opens, the designer vanishes, having bulk-bought and delivered a complete 'look'. This is not Birley's modus operandum. His clubs grow organically; painstakingly, he develops them over the years. At Mark's Club, one may trace the journey made by this noted collector, from Landseers to Bugatti bronzes. From table lights specially commissioned by the man himself to the absolute comfort of club armchairs, his own taste permeates every inch. At Harry's Bar, too, everything has its own personal history - the tiny silver tops on cups of expresso, to retain heat, or the fluted silver risotto spoons, which Birley found in Milan and of which he is particularly fond: "When one goes missing, we'll notify Palermo."

Mark Birley frequently describes himself as "a most unlikely nightclub owner". That, perhaps, is because Annabel's was never intended to be a nightclub - certainly not in the sweaty, disco sense of the word - at all. In 1962, John Aspinall took over the last private house in Berkley Square and Birley "thought it might be fun" to have a bar in the basement. "At that time, the divine architect Philip Jebb was around and I commissioned him", Birley recalls. "He later told me that he had actually never been in a nightclub - which I thought was rather an advantage." Hence, the dance floor is tucked away at

the back. The secret of Annabel's astonishing longevity as one of the world's top night places is that it is actually a meeting place - somewhere one can eat late at night, which is still rare in London - and eat well at such an hour, which is rarer still. Founder members, who were mainly Birley's friends, still pay the original £5 annual membership fee and the club maintains a sense of personal cohesion. Dukes and foreign potentates, legendary filmstars and playboys, supermodels and those nice ladies in little black dresses, up for the night from the country - at the door, Ted recognises every one of them by name, and they sink thankfully into some of the most comfortable surroundings in London, reassured and exhilarated by the sense of belonging.

Birley's inspiration as a club owner came from unlikely sources. "Many years ago, I used to go to Buck's Club in Clifford Street. There was a boys' table where I used to have lunch practically every day. It wasn't exactly beautifully done, but Buck's was Buck's own club - it was his. If any members of the Committee dared to make a suggestion, they were practically thrown out! People think I look grumpy

ABOVE: *More diplomat than maître d', Bruno runs Mark's Club with exquisite courtesy.* OPPOSITE: *Scenes from Harry's Bar.*

most of the time, but it's nothing to the grumpiness of good old Buck. It was totally autocratic - and it was a very personal thing. When Buck died, the spirit of the club died; the light went out of its eyes."

Autocratic indeed. At work, Birley has been described by a member of his staff as "swift to chide and slow to bless". The man himself, now in his sixties, is six foot four; long of limb, with a deep voice enriched by the sort of Cohiba cigar growl that makes much-divorced American ladies quiver. He is the son of the portrait painter Sir Oswald Birley, whose talent he inherited. "My father taught me how to look at pictures and actually see things. I started drawing really to please him, but then found that I drew quite well." His mother was a noted Irish beauty, whose fiery temperament seems to have burned, as much as warmed, those closest to her. His sister, Maxime de la Falaise, inherited the same fastidious eye and the ability to cast a spell over those in her orbit.

Debutantes are supposed to have mourned when the young Birley announced his engagement to Lady Annabel Vane Tempest Stewart, daughter of Lord Londonderry; much of their life together was lived in the public eye - and certainly in the social pages of the press. Although they divorced - and Lady Annabel had other children by, and married, the late Jimmy Goldsmith - Birley and Lady Annabel remain terrifically close friends. Both have borne the tragedy of the loss of their eldest son, Rupert, drowned off the coast of Africa.

Socially, Birley has a reputation as something of a loner. But if so he is the most besieged loner of all time. Phone calls, parties, dinners, private jet trips - work is play and play is work. At home, he likes to retire in comfort to watch sport - he is passionate about tennis - on a television loud and large enough to drown out any unwitting house guest.

It has been said that the best Italian food in London is at Harry's Bar, the best traditional food at Mark's Club - and the best food of all is at Mark's own house. Often this is a kitchen supper, a perfectly cooked roast chicken for a handful of friends; or a Saturday lunch might start with viscous cold vodka with freshly squeezed juice of key limes before lunch, featuring shepherd's pie, twinned happily with a bottle of Opus One. At Mark Birley's house the ice cream may not only have been made, but the recipe invented, that day.

Birley's friends are international and, when they come to visit, they bring offerings to tempt him: a new source of grappa, a ripe Vacherin, just lapping the edges of the plate; chocolates from Sprüngli; pounds of thin, crisp bacon brought in from New York.

All this tends to make him seem intimidating as a guest, perhaps unfairly. Many a hostess, afraid to entertain the exacting Mr Birley at her table, would be reassured if she knew how much he enjoyed a really good pork pie. This is not to be mistaken for pretension; it is a simple, utterly single-minded search for the best. Just as Captain Scott was trying to attain the South Pole, Mark Birley is looking for the perfect cheese straw.

In private he can be gloriously funny, swapping blue jokes with David Tang, his Hong Kong Chinese friend and apostle and, even more hilariously, telling stories against himself. Occasionally, a wicked prankster emerges. Staying at an exclusive Spanish hotel with friends, Birley found the swimming pool entirely under occupation by sunbathing Germans. Having three whole pounds of finest English sausages in his room as a present for friends - and who does not? - he rose at dawn to relish the horrified cries of the Germans at the sight of raw pink sausages, bobbing in the pool.

There is a remarkable feeling of family in each and every one of Birley's clubs. Fathers and sons work for Mark Birley; decades are notched up by staff. They are serious about what they do and that is why they enjoy it. It shows in the exquisite, old-fashioned courtesy of Bruno at Mark's Club; in Harry's Bar in the smiling professionalism of Mario (who never forgets a name, just as The Boss can be relied on never to remember one), the gentle gravity of Valentino, artist sommelier and, in a different form, in the constantly inventive brilliance of chef Alberico Penati. Not for Birley the cheeky chappie waiter, the maître d' who pretends to be 'cool' at the customer's expense. At the Bath & Racquets Club you will not find sweat-stained, grubby, lycra-clad bodies; Birley has installed a magnificent in-house laundry, so that members are attired in crisp, fresh white shirts and shorts in their own size on each visit. It's the attention to details that distinguishes; his clubs are, as he puts it himself, "pockets of resistance" in a world of mediocrity and of compromise.

Once engaged on something - whether the acquisition of an object, or loyalty to a friend - Birley is unshakeable. Most touching of all is his love for his dogs; stories abound of his inseparable companions Bella, the alsatian, and labradors Jennifer and Flukey. He is a passionate campaigner against the cruelties of the British quarantine laws. Recently, Birley's daughter India Jane returned from living in India with Nina, a mongrel she had adopted from the streets of Calcutta. Birley paid visits to Nina in the kennels, bringing her, since she had never been fed English food, a lamb biryani. From one of London's finest Indian restaurants. **E**

THIS PAGE: *In the dining room at Mark's, the magnificent silver carving trolley is a central feature.*

Without doubt, there are vehicles whose computing power is comparable to that of the BMW 7 Series.

When you start up a BMW 7 Series, you activate 20 MB/s of computing power (for communications a

fety systems as well as engine management). That's more than on Apollo 11's mission to the moon. **The BMW 7 Series.**

Freude am Fahren

CHRISTIE'S MAKES HISTORY

*S*ince 1766, when *James Christie* opened a single office in London and was painted by his friend *Gainsborough,* the property of the famous and the distinguished has passed under the hammer of our auctioneers, who stand in a rostrum originally designed by *Chippendale.* One of our first

clients was *Catherine the Great of Russia.* In 1795, *la Comtesse du* fetched over eight thousand pounds. Two the personal collection of the *Princess*

Barry's jewels, given to her by Louis XV hundred years later we sold the jewels from *Salimah Aga Khan.* Admiral Lord Nelson bought Vigée-Lebrun's portrait of *Emma, Lady Hamilton* and *Queen Victoria* bought a statue as a present for *Prince Albert.* In 1990, *The Duke of Beaufort's* Badminton Cabinet sold for £8,580,000, the highest price ever paid for a piece of furniture.

In 1994 we sold French

furniture from the collection of *Hubert*

de Givenchy; this fetched £17,674,227. *Houghton* have been sold from Christie's *Canterbury Tales* from Wentworth,

Furniture, works of art and pictures from Great Rooms as was Chaucer's *The* which at £4,621,500 was the

highest price ever paid for a printed book. *Leonardo da Vinci's* Codex was sold to

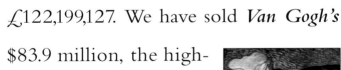

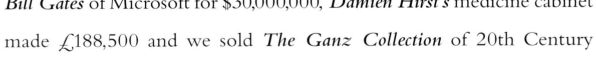

Bill Gates of Microsoft for $30,000,000, *Damien Hirst's* medicine cabinet made £188,500 and we sold *The Ganz Collection* of 20th Century Art in New York for Portrait of Dr. Gachet for

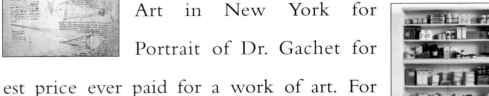

£122,199,127. We have sold *Van Gogh's* $83.9 million, the high- over two hundred years,

est price ever paid for a work of art. For people who buy and sell at Christie's have

been making history. For

advice on buying or selling at auction please call Susie Johnson on (0171) 389 2414.

CHRISTIE'S

AN IRISH GEORGIAN TOWNHOUSE

Words by Sandra Lane Pictures by John Reck

Dublin is famed world-wide for its Georgian architecture.
We step behind the elegant door of this delightful Georgian house.

"Dublin, the second city of the Empire, not in size or population but in precedence, bears all the marks of a capital and in no way compares with the matriarchy of many English provincial towns, for its architectural quality is ranked among the finest Renaissance cities of Europe." So declared the distinguished magazine, *Country Life*, in May 1946.

Today Dublin is undergoing something of a Renaissance. Ireland has Europe's most dynamic economy and the success of this so-called Celtic Tiger has attracted Irish people back, from all over the world, to live here. Its capital has become a lively, cosmopolitan city.

Amongst those who took the decision to return were the owners of this house who, for many years, had lived in the South of France. "On a return visit to Ireland in 1994, I was struck by the many changes, most, indeed, for the better," explains the owner's wife. "Dublin was a fun city, there was vibrant theatre, a lively musical scene and, for my sports-obsessed husband, every possible sporting activity. We decided, then and there, that the time had come to return home.

"The next question was to find a place we really would want to live in. The choice of area was simple. I had always loved the Georgian squares in Dublin with their wonderful gardens and, in

The colour scheme of the drawing room is based on the pale yellow silk damask, specially woven in Lyon. The Louis XV giltwood canapé is signed by Etienne Nauroy and there is a pair of painted Louis XVI giltwood fauteuils by Michel Gourdin. The painting, by Sir Godfrey Kneller (1646-1723), is a full-length portrait of his daughter. PREVIOUS PAGE: The entrance hall has been flooded with light, enhancing its graceful proportions. The seven ormulu lanterns, reproduced after those in the Palace of Fontainebleau, decline in three sizes, becoming smaller as you climb to higher floors.

particular. I loved the scale of some of the later Georgian houses. Not so large that one was obliged to have live-in staff, yet having the space, dimensions and architectural classicism of that gracious era."

The Georgian squares of Dublin have great appeal, not only to the town planner but to anyone who appreciates the value of restraint in the use of exterior ornamentation - the juxtaposition of simple forms and the variety of the treatment of front doors - and of the dignified effect of perfectly balanced internal volumes coupled with rich, yet delicate, stucco mouldings. Above all, these squares (built from 1750 onwards as town houses for wealthy aristocrats and merchants, after the Earl of Kildare built Leinster House to the west of the city centre, declaring "Where I go, society will follow") represent a stage of development in the city which left its mark upon so many great men and formed a background to a brilliant society in the 18th century.

The owners insisted on finding a house that had not been turned into professional offices or apartments. "I really could not face reconstructing a period house that had been chopped about and stripped of all its original charm," the owner's wife declares. Eventually the choice was narrowed down to three, all which had been primarily lived in as homes since the day they were built. The owner of one

The magnificent English Regency dining table was bought in Paris. The fireplace, original to the house, is flanked by a pair of early 18th century Irish consoles, on which stand a pair of large Imari porcelain plates and a 17th century Italian marble bust, one of a pair found in Nice. The antique glass Irish chandelier was original to the house and a family portrait, Le Bourgmestre de Delft painted by Michel Jarszoon Van Miereveld 1567-1641 hangs above the sideboard.

OPPOSITE PAGE: *clockwise from top left: In the son's bedroom, a Napoleon campaign-style bed is complemented by a fine, mahogany Empire wardrobe. The glass chandelier in the study was original to the house; the writing desk is Louis XV and the armchairs are Charles X. Fine antique silver dressing-table accessories* offset a Georgian mirror. In the guest bathroom, an Empire-style vanity unit provides a strong counterpoint to the Regency mirror and Directoire-style wallpaper.

THIS PAGE, *clockwise from right: The formal, courtyard garden is lined with 'winter green' trellis. In the master bathroom, a free-standing bath divides the room into separate bathing and dressing areas; a Picasso takes pride of place above the fireplace. The Provençal-style family living room combines American sofas with garden chairs from Avignon.*

PREVIOUS PAGE: *Georgian-style panelling was added to the master bedroom; the Louis XV overmantel is flanked by a pair of Louis XVI ormulu wall lights. The gilded stool is by Pugin.*

THIS PAGE: *The library was copied from the owners' drawing room in their former London home. The Brazilian mahogany bookcase, one of a set of three, was designed specially for the room by André de Cacqueray.*

agreed to sell. "We immediately fell in love with its great feeling of serenity and marvellous light. It was virtually in the same condition as it was the day it was built," recalls the owner. "A friend of ours, the Knight of Glin, Chairman of the Irish Georgian Society, confirmed our belief that it was a pretty special house and, for the next year, we set about its redecoration."

The choice of decorator was just as straight-forward. André de Cacqueray, an art historian by education, antique dealer by trade and interior decorator by inclination, had become a great friend of the owners while living close to them in London, where they had a lovely apartment in a grand period house overlooking a Kensington garden square. "When they acquired their home in the South of France I had the pleasure of creating a very contemporary home for them. Very stylish but totally different from London," he explains.

The owner's wife describes de Cacqueray as "a French classicist with a strong contemporary feel for colour and with a passion for good fabrics, all things that appeal to my sense of decoration. He is also a total perfectionist," she adds, "and is a wonderful source of skilled artisans, whether it be Polish carpenters in London, silk weavers in Lyon, gilders in Florence or lantern makers in Paris."

"Having come to decorating by way of antiques, André's great talent is his sense of proportion and his ability to create the proper environment for things," she remarks. "He sees interiors as part of life, not as show-pieces, which was perfect for us, because we wanted this house to feel like the family home that it is."

For André de Cacqueray, it was "a marvellous collaboration. The owner's wife has an excellent eye and, indeed, would have made a brilliant interior decorator had she decided to turn her hand to it." She has been a significant collector over many years, acquiring quite a number of first class pieces of Louis XV and XVI furniture from some of the best *ébénists* of the period, some very fine paintings, lots of early prints and architectural drawings and an interesting collection of antiquities, as well as some good quality Irish furniture and pictures.

The collaboration was also, clearly, fun. "As I was still living in France, it was fortuitous that André was doing up an 18th century château just outside Grasse," explains the owner's wife. "So for the next year, while the builders were busy in Ireland carrying out rewiring, plumbing and other essential work, the plans for our Dublin home were discussed over a series of good lunches in Nice, Cannes and across the border in Italy. Room by room, samples were examined, swatches looked at and all the minutiae of our redecoration finalised."

De Cacqueray describes the owners as dream clients. "They are not conventional," he explains. "They are very spirited and enthusiastic and make decisions quickly. Yet, while they are both perfectionists and therefore very intense, they never regret anything - not even mistakes. That is very rare."

The owners brought to the house the items that they had accumulated in past homes. These were absorbed into the new scheme, along with things bought specifically for Dublin. Two of the rooms, the master bedroom and the library, were almost reconstructions of the home they loved in London.

"The Irish are famed for hospitality and their love for conversation, so the dining room, of course, had to be really special," remarks de Cacqueray. Based around an antique Donegal carpet with a spectacular pair of early Irish console tables, it is a marvellous room in which to entertain. The other rooms are a mixture of traditional and contemporary. The drawing room on the first floor is grand in both style and scale without being precious, while the minimalist, downstairs drawing room counter-points the more traditional rooms of the upper floors. To the back of the house a small, classical French garden is entered through a cosy, sun-filled garden room.

"As someone who has moved home many times in a peripatetic life, this town house in Dublin is the end of my decorating career," asserts the owner's wife. "I love the space, the dimensions, the light, the tranquillity, looking out into greenery back and front and, every morning, hearing the song of the birds. In the evening, hearing the clip-clop of the horse-drawn carriages taking the tourists around Dublin's Georgian trail, it is a throwback to more gracious times, yet at the same time, only a stone's throw from the centre of a modern city." ∎

»HAPPY SPORT«®
PRECIOUS AT ALL TIMES

Chopard
GENÈVE

»HAPPY HEARTS«

YOUR CADDIE
WILL DISCUSS TEA.
YOUR CHEF,
TEE.

Where else would it happen? Where else would you find a 5 Red Star Hotel & Country Club that will totally surprise you? Here in a sumptuously restored Georgian estate surrounded by the Arnold Palmer designed golf course that is home to the Smurfit European Open and 300 acres of gardens, walks and Irish countryside. Here is Ireland's finest, most luxurious resort. But here too is a doorman that will make your day. A gardener that will restore your faith in humanity. A chef who will tell you how to avoid the sand trap on the 11th. A caddie who will recommend the lamb. Where else? Where else, indeed...

THE KILDARE HOTEL & COUNTRY CLUB

For a brochure or to book, please call (353) (0) 1 601 7200, Fax (353) (0) 1 601 7299
Email hotel@kclub.ie, golf@kclub.ie. Web http//www.kclub.ie

A part of The Jefferson Smurfit Group plc

Europe's Dream Eighteen

Words by Tom Doak

Attempting to choose the 18 best golf holes in Europe is a hopeless task. Today there are more than 3,500 golf courses bounded by the Atlantic and the Mediterranean, fully one-quarter of them having been built in the last twenty years. No one can know them all, nor produce a list free of personal bias.

But we can lay down some ground rules. Each hole was kept in its proper place in the round - thus the first hole is indeed the opening hole at Machrihanish and the second, at Carnoustie, was compared against second holes throughout the continent. The combined course has four short holes and three par 5s, sprinkled randomly throughout, so it would have the flow of a real 18. Individual holes were chosen based on their playing interest, challenge, beauty and historic significance. The acid test: every one of these holes would be worth the trip to play, whatever you score. My thanks to well-travelled golf writers Phil Hermann of Switzerland and Masa Nishijima from Japan for helping to narrow down the list of candidates.

The 1st at Machrihanish, Scotland - *423 yards par 4*

Golf began in Scotland, so it is only fitting to choose an opening hole from the mother country - especially if it happens to be one of the best in the world, in a remote location unspoiled by the golf tourism explosion of the last decade.

Our round is begun from 'The Battery', a rocky promontory perched twenty feet above the Atlantic surf. In front of us there is a stretch of sandy beach angling away to the left and beyond a rippling fairway. One cannot simply play down the fairway; each golfer must gauge his ability to get the first tee ball airborne and choose how much beach can be carried accordingly. Over-confident - and the second shot of the day will have to be played from the shells on the beach, too safe - and one can easily go through into the 18th fairway, putting the green quite out of reach for the next.

Whereas the tee shot allowed us to choose our own path, the fairway for the approach is relentlessly straight. The green is guarded by a solitary bunker front right - exactly where we'd aim to give us some leeway of hooking the second shot back into the dunes or onto the beach. Whether we take four or six, we'll have had a chance to strike the ball solidly, get ourselves loose and be inspired for the journey ahead.

The 2nd at Carnoustie, Scotland
- 448 yards par 4

Even before Seve Ballesteros and Nick Faldo, celebrated players were a logical choice to consult on how to make a good golf course and the five-times Open champion, James Braid, made a lucrative hobby of course design for thirty years after his glory days as a competitor.

On the strong 2nd hole at Carnoustie, one fairway bunker is so well placed that it carries Braid's name. The straightaway par 4 runs down a wide valley between the dunes and originally provided a relatively generous landing area for good players, until Braid was called in to suggest improvements. His solution: a nasty pot bunker in the left-center of the fairway, 230 yards from the tee. Weaker players don't have to worry about it but not even the touring professionals can carry it comfortably against a stiff breeze, so they're forced to try and squeeze by it in order to reach the green in regulation.

The second shot is more straightforward but almost never short. And, if you think the hole is difficult the first time you play it, wait until you see it with the pin on the back tier of the green, which forces the approach to thread the needle between two flanking pot bunkers! Surely you'll see the pin there for the final round of the Open Championship in 1999.

The 3rd at Royal County Down, Newcastle, Northern Ireland - *473 yards par 4*

Royal County Down, an hour south of Belfast, is one of the world's most majestic settings for golf. Its fairways tread the valleys between 30- and 40-foot sand dunes draped in flowering gorse.

The par-4 3rd is the end of an exhilarating run along the Irish Sea, away from the red-roofed clubhouse. If the wind isn't helping, it will take two full-blooded shots to get home, the first past fringed bunkers on the left of the fairway and the second over cross-bunkers and between a gate of large

PREVIOUS PAGE: *The 1st at Machrihanish, Scotland.* OPPOSITE: *The 2nd at Carnoustie, Scotland.* ABOVE: *The 3rd at Royal County Down, Newcastle.*

dunes 75 yards short of the green. Behind the green rises the most impressive sand dune of all - but fortunately, instead of playing over it, we're ready to turn back and view the Mountains of Mourne.

The 4th at Valderrama, Cadiz, Spain - *520 yards par 5*

Scene of the 1997 Ryder Cup, Valderrama has come to be recognised as the finest golf course on the continent thanks to two men. One is the architect Robert Trent Jones, who first designed it in the early 1970s as a second course for Sotogrande, then continued to refine it at the behest of the new ownership. The other is the owner, Jaime Ortiz-Patiño, who has lavished his full attention on turning it into the finest-conditioned course in Europe.

The 4th is a classic example of designer Jones' belief that par 5 holes should offer substantial risks and rewards. For the Ryder Cuppers it is plainly reachable in two big shots but the last hundred yards must run the gauntlet between cork trees and a small hill to the left, and a pond immediately to the right of the green.

Try for a three or a two-putt birdie and an errant second could result in a six or worse. It's a perfect match-play hole, yielding enormous advantage to the first player who dares and succeeds in reaching the green.

It is also a beautiful green setting, with a gurgling waterfall added by Mr. Patiño beside the putting surface, lulling you to sleep as you try to sink a birdie putt. After our first three holes, your scorecard probably needs one.

RIGHT: *The 4th at Valderrama, Cadiz, Spain.*
ABOVE: *The 6th at St. Enodoc, Cornwall, England.*

5th at Royal Worlington & Newmarket, Mildenhall, England - *170 yards par 3*

One of the great things about golf is that even the average player will occasionally play a shot which a professional would envy. The same is true for golf courses. Though great holes proliferate at championship venues, they may also be found in unlikely spots, thanks to divine inspiration by the architect or to The Creator, who shaped the land. One example is the nine-hole Royal Worlington & Newmarket, home to the Cambridge University golf team.

No short hole is more difficult than the par-3 5th, whose green has been described as resembling a vaulting-horse, with the narrow end pointed back toward the tee. It is of modest length and, thankfully, there is seldom a strong wind about. But only the straightest of shots will suffice, as the green falls away down a bank toward a stream on the right and into a deep, grassy hollow known as 'Mug's Hole' to the left. A single, fatal error with a mid-iron could result in a makeshift game of leap-frog, going desperately back and forth across the sliver of green.

Even a ball on the green is no guarantee of a three, for Mildenhall's greens are both undulating and quick and the 5th is the most severe of the lot. The only consolation for a big score (and suitable trepidation for those who make their par) is that, as it's a nine-hole course, you'll have another crack at the hole later.

The 6th at St. Enodoc, Cornwall, England - *374 yards par 4*

At a modest total length of 6,200 yards, the scenic St. Enodoc course has been dismissed by many as just a 'holiday' course - but the golf has more to offer than views of sandy Daymer Bay.
Certainly its most memorable hole is the par-4 6th, which features the deepest bunker I've encountered on any of the 1,000 courses I've seen around the world. Or perhaps I should say the 'tallest' bunker, for it is really nothing more than the cratered remains of an eroded 40-foot sand dune, situated directly on the line to the hole.

Since the hole is only 374 yards, good players may elect to lay up slightly off the tee, rather than drive to the very base of the dune, from which the bunker rises abruptly. However, it is imperative to

strike solidly from the tee, as the carry over the dune to a green in the bowl behind it would be unthinkable with anything but a lofted iron. The approach is completely blind over a marker-post but, from the tee, a glimpse of the green over the corner of the dune provides some security and, anyway, you're supposed to keep looking at the ball during your stroke, not the target.

Fortunately, I've never actually been in the bunker, so I have no idea how one might escape from it after an errant second. It's a hazard so ruggedly natural that even players who have skirted it are likely to have nightmares afterwards.

The 7th at Sotogrande (Old Course), Cadiz, Spain - *422 yards par 4*

Before Valderrama, there was Sotogrande (Old), Robert Trent Jones' first course of significance on the European continent. Today its flashy younger sister steals the headlines but possibly that is all right with the Old Course, which was conceived as, and remains, a posh and quiet retreat.

Long before Valderrama's 4th was built, the small pond beside the 7th green at Sotogrande was known as Europe's most hypnotic water hazard, with an almost magnetic attraction to disaster. Like the last, this is emphatically a second-shot hole but, here, the trouble is much too plainly in view - the small pond to the right, banked by a natural stone wall, bunkers to the left and behind the green and cork oak narrowing the entrance. It is as dangerous as it is picturesque.

OPPOSITE: *The 8th at Royal Troon, Scotland.*
ABOVE: *The 10th at Kennemer, Zandvoort, Netherlands.*

The 8th at Royal Troon (Old Course), Scotland - *126 yards par 3*

This is both the shortest hole of any on the Open Championship rota and the most deadly, thanks to a tiny green which inspired its moniker, 'The Postage Stamp'. At its narrowest, it is no more than ten paces across, with deep bunkers cut into a sharp dune at the left of the green and a steep fall to the right, with more bunkers cut into the bank.

The hole is short enough for anyone, as the ageless Gene Sarazen can attest. Playing in the 1973 Open Championship - 51 years after his first Open triumph - he holed it in one stroke. This is three less than Greg Norman, for whom it was the only bogey in his final round of 64 that almost stole the Open in 1989, and many less than the 15 recorded by a German golfer in 1950, the highest single-hole score in the history of the Open Championship.

Ironically, the modest length of the hole compounds its maddening difficulty. With an elevated tee and green overlooking the sea, it is completely exposed to the elements and the last thing one really wants to do is to play a lofted iron into the air and see where the wind blows it. A three-quarters punch shot with a less lofted iron is the master stroke but, even for the masters, it takes nerve to play it across the deep bunker hard in front of the green.

Even if the rest of the round is played badly, a three at the Postage Stamp will make a day's golf here a memory for a lifetime.

The 9th at Lahinch, Co. Clare, Ireland - *381 yards par 4*

The site of the annual South of Ireland Amateur Championship, Lahinch is that rarest of combinations - a pleasant, enjoyable holiday course which is also an intriguing test for tournament play of the highest order. Such was the genius of Dr. Alister Mackenzie, who redesigned Old Tom Morris' original Lahinch layout in 1926, before going overseas to achieve greater fame at Royal Melbourne (Australia) and Augusta National.

The 9th is one of several arresting holes devised by Mackenzie, whose new routing takes the golfer through the large sand dunes which had separated the course from the sea. Its dune-top championship tee is the highest point on the golf course and, after we have enjoyed the view for a while and surveyed the holes to come, there is the joy of crashing a drive to an invitingly wide fairway on a shelf below.

But the doctor was more cunning than that. With a deep hollow in the left of the fairway, we are easily tempted to leave the tee shot out to the right for safety. But, once we've driven there, we find that the green is angled toward the left of the fairway and an approach from the right faces the impossible

task of skirting a deep bunker cut into the shoulder of a hill and stopping before it rolls off the left side of the green and down a steep bank to the next tee.

Really, we could have seen all this quite clearly from the tee, if we'd been paying proper attention. Then we'd have realised that, even if the drive didn't carry the hollow, we would have been left with a straight-in approach, where the shoulder of hill above the green cradles our natural fade back toward the hole. In golf, as in life, those who learn from their mistakes prosper.

The 10th at Kennemer, Zandvoort, The Netherlands - *361 yards par 4*

One of the best-kept secrets of golf in Europe is the triumvirate of fine links courses scattered along the North Sea coast between Amsterdam and Rotterdam: Kennemer, Noordwijk and Haagsche. The most easily accessible of the three is Kennemer, a short commuter train ride out from Amsterdam to the seaside suburb of Zandvoort.

From the tee of the 10th one can see nothing but dunes and scrub, a green on the horizon and a marker post to the left. You'll have to trust that, in fact, there is a generous fairway past the marker post, hidden just below sight by the intervening dunes. Whether to play to the left or the right of the post depends on your preference for approaching, as the green is turned sideways, making it wider than deep. Those who have confident distance control of their irons may take the shorter route down the right-hand edge, while others with more trouble stopping their shots quickly

might want to play out to the left and fade the ball into the green's length. Either way, the hole will give you new-found respect for the variety of golf to be found on the Continent.

The 11th at Ballybunion (Old Course), Co. Kerry, Ireland - *443 yards par 4*

Certainly this is the most spectacular hole on our fantasy course; one could scarcely dream up a place more dramatic than Ballybunion, where Tom Watson and Mark O'Meara often stop through for a game on their way to the Open Championship, and where US President Bill Clinton played a round during his 1998 visit to Ireland. The small beach resort on Ireland's west coast is just an hour from Shannon airport and now provides 36 holes of golf to stir the imagination. The par-4 11th plays along an eroded cliff with the Atlantic surf below and to the right. If the tee shot manages to stay on the descending, stair-stepped fairway, the player is rewarded with a thrilling second shot looking down a gun barrel of fairway through a narrow 'V' between the dunes and then slightly back up to a green on a mound. No bunkers are necessary to complicate the hole - if you don't stay on the straight and narrow, the shaved banks of the green make it most difficult to get the ball to sit and stay on the green.

The 12th at Morfontaine, Senlis, France - *520 yards par 5*

A sleepy private golf club in Paris' north suburbs, near Chantilly, Morfontaine is a fine heathland course in the grand tradition of Sunningdale, Wentworth and England's best. Indeed, it may be better than them all, thanks to the brilliant, subtle contouring of greens and hazards performed by Tom Simpson, an artist among golf architects of the 1920s and 1930s.

Morfontaine is not quite of championship length but it still possesses many strong holes, especially the opening pair, of 460 and 225 yards. After these, the par-5 12th may seem like a cream-filled French pastry. At 520 yards it is within reach of two strong shots but overswinging will bring the heathery roughs and pine trees into reach as well. Patience - and three good shots - will leave the chance of a birdie putt on Simpson's subtle green. Read the break carefully so you won't leave frustrated.

The 13th at Hamburger Golf & C.C., Falkenstein, Germany
- *325 yards par 4*

Every good course needs a couple of shorter par 4 holes where placement is rewarded over brute strength - and Mr. Colt's 13th at Falkenstein, in the poshest suburb of Hamburg, certainly fills the bill. From the elevated tee, the strong may be tempted to try and carry a small ridge in front of the green; however, a pulled drive will leave them ricocheting about in the trees, cursing their stupidity. The best placement for the tee shot is, instead, out to the right but a single, nasty fairway bunker requires careful planning before hitting away - whether to play short of it or try to get past? Either way, the second must be a perfectly played pitch to alight on the small sloping green and, ideally, stay below the hole for a reasonable putt.

Despite the international success of their countryman Bernhard Langer, the Germans have yet to take to the game in their masses and, as a result, golf in Germany is as pleasant an experience as one can find - relaxed, sociable and accessible to all.

The 14th at Royal Portrush (Dunluce course), Northern Ireland
- *211 yards par 3*

Most great holes in the United Kingdom have earned a name and that of the 14th at Portrush - 'Calamity' - is a fitting tribute to a hole that makes any player quake in his boots. Tee, green and the pathway in between are perched on the brink of a gargantuan inland range of dunes, with an 80-foot drop-off to the right into the 'War Hollow', a huge valley between here and the pyramidal dunes along the coast.

There is no lay-up fairway for the meek here; unless one opts to aim well out into the dunes on the left for safety, one must play a full-blooded long iron or wood across the rim of the chasm, with about twenty yards of high ground in front of the green as a buffer for those who fall short. Anything to the right is down the grassy cliff, from where the ball may be found and played if one does not suffer from vertigo; still, it is difficult to surmise the correct line back to the green from so far below. Just don't ask how I know.

OPPOSITE, *above: The 11th at Ballybunion, Co. Kerry, Ireland. Below: The 13th at Hamburger Golf & C.C., Germany. THIS PAGE, above: The 14th at Royal Portrush, Northern Ireland. Below: The 15th at Swinley Forest, Ascot, England.*

The 15th at Swinley Forest, Ascot, England - *454 yards par 4*

This is our third consecutive hole designed by the hand of Mr Colt, who pronounced Swinley Forest 'the least bad' of any course he ever designed - proving that Colt would have had more difficulty finding success in today's age of self-promotion.

At only 6,000 yards from its furthest-back tees, Swinley Forest is a course that flaunts all modern conventions of golf. There is no PGA professional, no yardage booklet, not even a par - they prefer to list the old 'bogey' score on the card by which to judge one's progress. (Just as well, as the strict par of 67 or 68 would be beyond the grasp of most). What they have not done without are fine golf holes of all lengths amidst the heather and rhododendrons. The rising fairway of the 15th, pinched by bunkers left and right at just the right spot, and a more severe bunker to the left of the green, is one of its strongest.

Sadly, you'll be fortunate ever to see it, for Swinley is arguably the most private golf club in Britain - a haven for diplomats and executives and Prince Andrew. On weekdays it does cater to some of the country's most élite golfing societies, who get to enjoy the celebrated club lunch, but otherwise guest play is rare.

The 16th at Sperone, Corsica, France - *580 yards par 5*

For most Europeans the island of Corsica is remembered as the birthplace of the Emperor Napoleon. For golfers who have visited it, Corsica will never be forgotten for Sperone, a new resort course which has made an equally bold attempt to conquer the hearts and minds of Europe.

The course features several cliff-top holes with falls of 100 feet to the blue Mediterranean below and, on a clear day, views across to the mainland. Most nerve-wracking of all is the long 16th, which plays right out to the point of land on which the back nine sits. One pull to the left on any of the three shots this hole requires and you'll have your own version of Waterloo.

THIS PAGE: *The 17th at El Saler, Valencia, Spain.* OPPOSITE: *The 18th at The Old Course at St Andrews, Scotland.*

The 17th at El Saler, Valencia, Spain - *218 yards par 3*

Though Robert Trent Jones brought jet-set golf to the Costa del Sol, one Spanish golf architect was already making his mark in his homeland. El Saler, built in 1967 on the heels of Sotogrande, was Javier Arana's magnificent response to Jones' challenge.

One of Arana's beliefs was that the 17th hole should always be a par 3, so that the average golfer behind in a match would have the opportunity to recover with one decisive stroke. The 17th at El Saler, along the Valencia coast, is probably the best testament to this philosophy.

The 18th at The Old Course at St. Andrews, Scotland - *354 yards par 4*

The 18th is the 'Home' hole and there is no more thrilling place to finish than up into the town of St Andrews, the true home of golf. The hole is largely free of hazards, save for the out-of-bounds street along the right boundary and Granny Clark's Wynd, a paved road off which you might have to play your approach after an unlucky drive.

For most visitors, the hole provides the once-in-a-lifetime chance to play before ever-present onlookers, who studiously follow the progress of inbound players while awaiting their own brush with history. The five centuries of golf played over the Old Course are a tangible difficulty here. Ask Doug Sanders, who took a careless five at the last when a four would have made him Open champion in 1970, Seve Ballesteros, whose magnificent three slammed the door on Tom Watson in 1984, or Costantino Rocca, who fluffed his chip into the Valley of Sin to blow his chance of winning in 1995, then holed an impossible putt to get to a play-off. One can rise to the occasion or succumb since, no matter the hazards of any course, golf is a game of largely self-inflicted pressure. The bunkerless 18th on The Old Course gives you the chance to write your own epitaph. **E**

THE AUTHOR
At age 37, Tom Doak has established himself as one of the leaders of the next generation of golf architects, with two of his seven solo designs rating among the top 100 golf courses in the US. He is also a contributing editor to GOLF Magazine (US) and author of The Confidential Guide to Golf Courses, a review of the best courses on five continents.
Doak's company is currently completing planning work for its first project on European soil at the Archfield estate, adjacent to Muirfield, Scotland.

Veuve Clicquot

LA GRANDE DAME

it is in the tradition of our predecessors, who acquired objects as disparate in size as the Elgin Marbles and rare carved gems. The Grand Tourists' acquisitions have always found couriers willing and able to transport them to Northern Europe; it was in this way that the great museums accumulated a large part of their collections.

On at a leisurely pace towards the South. By evening Le Manoir at the Oustau de Baumanière in Les-Baux-de-Provence, a restored 18th century farmhouse, is an ideal place to stay. The swimming pool is deliciously cold on a hot day. For dinner eat leg of baby lamb cooked in pastry, one leg per person. The view out over the strange white rocks of Les Baux village and beyond, to the mysterious Camargue, is breathtaking and the wine cellar beyond imagination.

From here visit Nîmes and wonder at the Coliseum, Avignon and the Palace of the Popes, and drive across the long causeway that traverses the marshes to the walled city of Aigues-Mortes. The Camargue is a place to explore. Flamingos and white horses, wild black bulls and marshland, small villages sheltered from the endless wind in the hollows of the land. There is no need to leave but the Grand Tourist must press on.

Leaving Montelimar and Aix behind, on down the motorway, a road divided by oleandas and blue irises in full flower, to Monaco. Here tourists come to watch celebrities and the Grand Tourists watch the common tourists. The Hôtel de Paris is one of the few truly grand hotels left in the world and Monte Carlo, like Las Vegas, a place built to entertain the rich and the poor tourist alike. The Grill in the Hôtel de Paris is almost perfect; its Louis XV restaurant exceptional. A secret of Monte Carlo is the restaurant in the Mirabeau Hotel, quietly dignified and extremely good, just the sort of place for a Grand Tourist.

Carla's restaurant at La Brique is the other extreme - not even mentioned in the Michelin Guide, this is a point of pilgrimage for all Grand Tourists. Carla insists that you book in advance and arrive on time. She cooks for the twenty people that her restaurant can accommodate and she cooks only for them. She and her one assistant then serve the meal and what a meal it is. La Brique is two hours from Monaco, a drive of immense beauty up the Valley of La Roya. The air is fresh and the silence all-embracing. At Sospel, a small village on the way and a place to break the journey, a waterfall crashes as it falls several hundred feet into the River Roya. Soarge is another small town to visit on the way to La Brique. Only a few miles beyond Brique is the source of the river and Notre Dame des Fontaines, a small chapel with brilliant 15th century frescos - a place of great peace and beauty.

THIS PAGE: *Paris.* OPPOSITE TOP: *The wild horses of The Camargue.* BELOW: *The Roman arena at Nîmes; Monaco, viewed from the Grande Corniche.*

On to Italy, take the motorway to Genoa; the drive is scenic and the road impressive as it burrows through hills and soars over ravines on the edge of the sea. Take time to stop just over the border at La Mortola, the Hanbury Gardens. Recently restored, they are a great curiosity. Genoa has grand hotels but not much else. Nearby, however, are the gardens of the Villa Pallavicini. Lucca is the next stop; within the walled city on the northern fringe of Tuscany only three buildings were constructed after the 18th century. A city best viewed late at night or in the early hours of the morning, when the pavements are still.

If France is the country of food and wine, then Italy is the land of the soul. Play cassettes of Italian operas while driving in Italy. Drink when you're thirsty, eat when you're hungry; eat simply but of the best ingredients, bought in local delicatessens. Picnics are the way to eat in the Tuscan countryside. Be careful of setting up your picnic in fields, however, for there the local prostitutes ply their trade. Sit and eat at the end of a long avenue of cypress trees or close to some crumbling monument. Enjoy the fresh air and the smell of the wild flowers, the bread, the wine, the vegetables, cheese and oil. Take time to enjoy the architecture and fine gardens with which this region abounds.

Avoid Florence. Too many cars, motor scooters and people. Why queue for hours to see other people looking at works of art? Siena in the early morning is cool and calm; a visit to view the manuscripts in the library of the cathedral is worth a dozen crowded hours in Florence's Uffizi Gallery.

Head for Sinalunga, just south of Siena. What is there? Not much: just one of the best hotels in Italy. The Locanda dell'Amorosa at Sinalunga is a perfect base for the Grand Tourist. Large rooms have open log fires, lest the evenings of May still have a wintry chill about them. A dining room where the food is simple but splendid, where the wine is the best. Be sure to make a detour to Bomasco to see the

ABOVE: *The Locanda dell'Amorosa at Sinalunga.* BELOW: *The Tuscan countryside near Florence.* OPPOSITE: *St Peter's Basilica reflected in the Tiber.*

ABOVE: *The Abruzzi countryside.*
TOP: *The cathedral at Orvieto.*

Garden of Goteques.

Stop at Orvieto to see the doorway of the cathedral and then to take a cappuccino in the café opposite that doorway, or find a vantage point on a hill facing the town and watch as the setting sun turns the entire facade to molten gold.

Rome is but two hours away. Stay at the Hotel de la Ville, insist on a room with a large balcony, one the size of a tennis court, then eat your breakfast on that balcony and watch the sunlight as it plays on the domes of the Roman churches. Eat at Piperno in what was formerly the Ghetto. Artichoke Judeaico and then baby lamb cooked in the oven. What a meal that makes washed down with a strong Tuscan wine.

Visit endless palaces and churches, gardens and monuments. The grandest of Tourists once spent years in Rome bringing home to Britain not only its artefacts but its architecture. It is from this city that we derive our law and our culture. Recently, the Palazzo Altemps Museum has been reopened. Built 600 years ago, the palace was turned into a museum 'for a select public' in the 16th century, to house the private collection of Cardinal Marcus Sitticus Altemps. Besides housing the Boncampagne Ludovisi collection, it was, in the 16th century, a great favourite with Grand Tourists. It houses another four collections of sculpture and one dedicated to Egyptian statuary. Most of these collections have not been seen by the public for the last 50 years.

Naples is the next stop, a city filled with museums and churches, amongst the most beautiful, the church of the Lombards. Before arriving at Naples, however, the Gardens of the Parco Della Villa D'Ayala are an important stop to make. Situated at Valva, these landscape gardens are laid out with shady walks. Parterres of box abound with statuary, the most spectacular of which comprises an amphitheatre of stone steps on which numerous busts have been placed backed by box hedges. It is the weirdest sight. At Padula there is the Certosa di San Lorenzo, the grandest of monasteries. An architectural masterpiece, a haven of cool beauty in a rugged landscape. Its main staircase a thing of elegance, its library the envy of anyone who ever enjoyed a book. No Grand Tour would be complete without a visit to Pompeii but do not buy souvenirs, they have gone down in quality in the last 300 years.

After Naples, wind along the Amalfi coast, turn left and head into the countryside of Basilica. Do not linger here. Drive with speed and certainty to the other side of Italy to the Salentine Peninsula and the Pugliese town of Lecce, Italy's most beautiful. There is no metropolitan bustle about Lecce; Puglia is a place of calm, a forgotten land and Lecce is its capital. Puglia is a simple place populated by simple, dignified people; the Tourist barely exists there except in August. The land around Lecce - small

fields with high stone walls, grey swathes of olive trees, rich soil and tobacco plants - is littered with towns and villages; each one has something worth seeing. The Grand Tourist will eat well in Puglia's modest hostelries; the cuisine is dramatically different from other parts of Italy. At Leaucca del Mare there is a butcher who sells baby lamb weaned and fed on the herbs of the countryside. This lamb is much sought after by the greatest French chefs.

Now starts the journey up the Adriatic Coast of Italy to the City of Venice. This journey could take days: stopping at the hill top villages of Abbruzzo and the Marche, the town of Urbino, its castle a Renaissance masterpiece, and then Bolonga, home of the best cooking in Italy. Visit Parma

ABOVE: *The island of San Giorgio Maggiore in the early morning.* BELOW LEFT: *The Chiostro dei Santi Nicolò Cataldo at Lecce.* BELOW: *Venice's Palazzo Ducale*

- Verdi was born in nearby Bassetta - Mantova, the scene for Verdi's Rigoletto, Verona where Juliet's balcony is to be found, and Vicenza, the birth-place of Palladio. Hidden amongst the towns of the Veneto is the perfect small Renaissance town of Sabbioneta. Built by a member of the Gonzag family, it is a microcosm of how a Renaissance city should look. Winter and summer palaces, cathedral, and baptistry, theatre and armoury - none much restored; the place is a perfect secret. Past myriad country villas from the architects of the 16th and 17th century. One of them, Palladio's Villa La Rivella, is available for private rental, a perfect base for exploring the area.

At last on to Venice, across the causeway, out of the car and then by private motor launch to the Monaco Hotel on the Grand Canal. What can be said of Venice? Dismiss the chauffeur and sell the car. Travellers come to Venice and some of them never leave. **E**

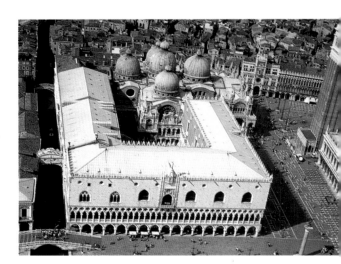

Asprey & Garrard. Now Mary Broughton has
even more of an advantage on her side of the table.

Asprey&Garrard

LONDON

Asprey & Garrard, the two finest names in luxury, have become the single greatest. This marriage of craftsmanship and design, fine jewellery and English living, means that Mary Broughton has certainly doubled her chances. Featured above, the elegant four piece collection in platinum and diamonds is extremely well-matched. Which, as Miss Broughton's pile of chips reveal, is rather more than can be said of her opponents. Tel: 0171 493 6767.

EUROPE'S ELITE 1000

The 1000 names on the following list are the Editors' choices of the finest shops, services and luxury goods that Europe has to offer. We give you an insider's report on each and every one of them.

ABEKING & RASMUSSEN

In 1907 designer and yachtsman Henry Rasmussen, together with mechanical engineer Georg Abeking, established Abeking & Rasmussen near Bremen; its current president (keen sailor Hermann Schaedla) is Henry Rasmussen's grandson. The yard has translated its technical expertise, developed through its construction of commercial and naval vessels, into the building of fine, custom motor and sailing yachts of up to 200ft. Clients have included Gianni Agnelli and American property developer Elizabeth Meyer.

Abeking & Rasmussen
P.O. Box 1160, D-27805 Lemwerder, Germany
Tel: +49-421-67 330   Fax: +49-421-67 33 112

ACCADEMIA EUROPEA

The bigwigs in security-conscious Milan, including Giorgio Armani, use this top-notch agency to supply highly trained and ultra-discreet bodyguards around the clock. Its office is open daily from 09.30 to 22.00.

Accademia Europea -
Sport da combattimento
via Melzo 9, 20129, Milan, Italy
Tel: +39-02-29 40 90 80 Fax: +39-02-29 52 45 88

L'ACIUGHETA

Gianni Bonaccorsi established this remarkable enoteca nearly twenty years ago. Don't be put off by the ultra-touristy exterior for, inside, he sells the greatest Italian wines and specialises in discovering excellent new growths from small vineyards. In one room wines are available for sale to take away; in another, a dozen reds and whites are opened (the list is changed daily) for clients to taste by the glass.

L'Aciugheta
Campo San Filippo e Giacomo 4357,
4509 Castello, Venice, Italy
Tel: +39-041-522 4292   Fax: +39-041-520 8222

ADAM & COMPANY

Despite having been founded only in 1983, this bank has created a style and culture that makes clients feel that it is 100 years old. As well as providing the full asset and liability management service expected of a private bank, Adam & Company holds in great store the old-fashioned courtesies that were once a hallmark of banking. According to Managing Director Ray Entwistle, if that means shooting or fishing with any of the bank's 8,000 clients, it is maintaining a feeling of intimacy and individuality that counts.

Adam & Company Group plc
22 Charlotte Square,
Edinburgh EH2 4DF, Scotland
Tel: +44-131-225 8484   Fax: +44-131-225 5136

ADLER

Leyla, Franklin and Carlo Adler are the descendants of Jacques Adler, born in the Austro-Hungarian Empire, who founded this family firm in Istanbul in 1886. Though based in Geneva since 1972, Adler's designs continue to be inspired by Istanbul's romantic heritage. Baguette diamonds and the innovative combination of coloured stones in the same piece, are Adler trademarks.

Above all, though, a sense of family lies at the heart of its products - guaranteeing total control of every stage of Adler's production, from the selection of stones to the finished product, and ensur-

ing highly personal service in its boutiques within Europe, and the Far East.

Adler
23 rue du Rhône, CH-1204 Geneva, Switzerland
Tel: +41-22-819 8025   Fax: +41-22-819 8020
Also in Gstaad (+41-33-744 6680)
and London (+44-171-409 2237)

ADMIRABLE CRICHTON

Suddenly catering is a buzz business, and bright young things are queuing up to moonlight as waiters and waitresses. Some of the best looking and best-connected are working for Johnny Roxburgh at party organisers, The Admirable Crichton. They will organise every detail of your next bash - from food and flowers to fireworks - all with great flair and efficiency.

The Admirable Crichton
6 Camberwell Trading Estate, Denmark Road,
London SE5 9LB, UK
Tel: +44-171-733 8113   Fax: +44-171-733 7289

ADRIAN SASSOON

Rebelling against sport as an Eton schoolboy, Adrian Sassoon instead became interested in antiques, beginning his business in 18th-century Sèvres and contemporary ceramics in 1992. His range is wide, from interesting collectors' pieces and useable tableware to items of museum quality. He also deals in contemporary British works, including glass furniture by Danny Lane, and acts as an art advisor. For five years he was assistant curator at the J. Paul Getty Museum.

Adrian Sassoon
14 Rutland Gate, London SW7 1BB, UK
Tel: +44-171-581 9888   Fax: +44-171-823 8473
By appointment only

ADRIEN MAEGHT

This internationally renowned gallery has attracted art connoisseurs the world over since before the second World War, with its displays of modern and contemporary artists. Brach and Kandinsky are among those whose works are on show in this unmissable, family-run establishment.

Adrien Maeght

42 rue de Bac, 75007 Paris, France

Tel: +33-1-45 48 45 15   Fax: +33-1-42 22 22 83

AGATA E ROMEO

In this small, simply-decorated restaurant, built on the ancient (350 BC) ramparts of Monte Esquilino, Agata Caraccio, the owner's wife, turns out wonderful cooking based on traditional Roman specialties. Her specialties include a loaf of lettuce with foccacia and Collonata bacon, artichoke 'cake' and grated sheep's milk cheese millefeuilles.

Agata e Romeo

via Carlo Alberto 45, 00185 Rome, Italy

Tel: +39-0644-66 115   Fax: +39-0644-65 824

AGENZIA IMMOBILIARE VALORI

Paolo and Marco Valori have an intimate knowledge of Northern Tuscany's real estate market. In 35 years of business, they have built up a first-class reputation for buying and selling high quality villas, castles, apartments and agricultural estates. They can also help with long and short term rentals.

Agenzia Immobiliare Valori

via Tinto da Battifole 3/5, 50053 Empoli, Italy

Tel: +39-0571-78 433 or +39-055-29 46 36

Fax: +39-055-70 00 06

AEROLEASING

Aeroleasing is a world leader in custom-tailored business jet charters. Since 1966 it has transported, world-wide, key decision makers as well as individual passengers eager to avoid the oversized, overcrowded airports and lack of privacy which are an unavoidable part of regular airline flights. Among the advantages of customised flying are its sound economies, the minimising of waiting and fatigue and the effect - intangible but sure - of a prestigious business tool.

Aeroleasing's extensive fleet offers 20 of the finest and most modern business aircraft for every type of voyage. It comprises luxurious transoceanic jets, such as the Falcon 900 and 900EX,

transcontinental craft such as the Canadair SE, the Falcon 2000 and 20-731, and medium-range jets like the Learjet 45, 35A, 31A, or Citation II. The company operates major maintenance centres in Geneva and Kiev which, combined with the competence of its pilots, ensures outstanding safety. The company's guiding philosophy - the relentless pursuit of perfection - has gained it a worldwide reputation for flexibility and a quality of service which far surpasses that of First Class on commercial airlines.

Thanks to the quality of its operations, Aeroleasing is also retained to provide managment services for many aircraft owned by high net-worth individuals and major international corporations.

Aeroleasing

PO Box 36, CH-1215 Geneva Airport, Switzerland

Tel: +41-22-717 0000   Fax: +41-22-717 0007

AGRY

Situated in tiny premises off the Place Vendôme, Agry has been engravers to the aristocracy since 1825. Catherine Hacquebart, a descendant of the founder, and her small team continue to design family insignia, which can be engraved to order on anything from porcelain to blazer buttons. Her visiting cards and

Ex Libris designs have a Proustian elegance and she will also produce headed note-paper complete with a miniature drawing of your ancestral home.

Maison Agry

14 rue de Castiglione, 75001 Paris, France

Tel: +33-1-42 60 65 10   Fax: +33-1-42 60 48 92

McKEAGUE-GREEN

INTERNATIONAL PLACEMENTS

THE AgenC McKEAGUE-GREEN

This privately owned recruitment consultancy specialises in the international placement of top quality domestic staff and yacht crews.

Working closely with their clients, in the utmost confidentiality, proprietor Jann McKeague-Green and her team have an excellent track record in placing a wide variety of staff (from highly-trained chefs/cooks, butlers/valets, housekeepers and chauffeurs to multi-lingual private secretaries and PAs) with members of British and foreign Royalty, as well as with private households throughout the world. Furthermore, the company offers a crew recruitment service for large motor and sailing yachts.

Recently affiliated with a leading private security service, The AgenC McKeague-Green also provides comprehensive personal and residential security, along with close protection (including diplomatic and high-risk property), remote surveillance, anti-poaching and counter-terrorism services.

In all divisions the AgenC McKeague-Green emphasises discretion and a highly personalised service, maintaining a one-to-one contact with both clients and staff. A word of caution, though: don't ask what any of their butlers saw....it's strictly confidential!

The AgenC McKeague-Green
1st Floor, 50 Hans Crescent, London SW1X 0NA, UK
Tel: +44-171-225 1942   Fax: +44-171-225 1941
Email: agenc@cocoon.co.uk
International Crew Recruitment
Tel: +44-171-225 1962   Fax: +44-171-225 1941
Email: icr@cocoon.co.uk

AIDAN O'BRIEN

This young trainer has made a staggering leap to fame. Still in his 20s, he looks like a young, studious schoolmaster but, set up at the famous Ballydoyle stables and gallops owned by Vincent O'Brien (surprisingly, no relation), Aiden has had over 200 horses under his control for the last three years or so and has dominated Irish racing, as well as having great success in England. The protegé of John Magnier, he has similar talents to his legendary namesake in being equally efffective with both jumpers and flat racers. For instance, in 1997 he won the Champion Hurdle at Cheltenham with *Ishtabrak* and, little over a month later, the 2000 Guineas at Newmarket with *King of Kings*.

Aidan O'Brien
Ballydoyle, Cashel, Co. Tipperary, Ireland
Tel: +353-62-62 615   Fax: +353-62-61 260

AIMO E NADIA

Aimo and Nadia Moroni's eponymous restaurant is now known as a *luogo* (which roughly translates as 'place') rather than a *ristorante*, due in part to its tradition of giving customers the same table that they had on their first visit - a gesture typical of their very thoughtful service. The cooking induces euphoria: In particular Spaghetti with baby onions and peppers or Sea anemones with ricotta and fresh raw tomatoes.

Aimo e Nadia
via Montecuccoli 6, 20100 Milan, Italy
Tel: +39-02-41 68 86

AIX EN PROVENCE FESTIVAL

Aix-en-Provence is a perfect place for a music festival. It's the spirit of the place: the 17th and 18th century buildings and fountains, that special Provençal light, the sweet scent of summer flowers in the courtyard of the Archbishop's Palace, where performances take place, the background hum of cicadas.

The festival has been established for more than 50 years and, following some difficulties during the 1990s, it is now back on course. Its productions command first class directors, conductors and performers (Pierre Boulez, Daniel Harding, Peter Brook) and its programme ranges from early opera to contemporary works.

Festival International d'Art Lyrique
Palais de l'Ancien Archevêché,
13100 Aix-en-Provence, France
Tel: +33-4-42 17 34 34   Fax: +33-4-42 63 13 74

AKELARE

One of the chefs most identified with the movement to rejuvenate Basque cooking,

Pedro Subijana returned to his birthplace after a distinguished career elsewhere in Spain to run this restaurant. Among the items

on his seafood-centred menu, the Chilled tomato cream with sea urchin and soft cheese and his Xangurro with cockle sauce and borage cream are unmissable. The restaurant's blue-themed Art Deco room, run with panache by Perfe Prol, is complemented by wonderful views of the ocean and surrounding countryside.

Akelare
Barrio de Iguerdo, 20008 San Sebastian, Spain
Tel: +34-943-21 20 52   Fax: +34-943-21 92 68

AL PINO

This elegant, glass-walled restaurant affords diners marvellous views of the surrounding vineyards, yet it is just 5 minutes from the Turin-Piacenza motorway. Chef-proprietor Mario Musoni is a genius with risotto - current favourites include frog and herb risotto and one based on zucchini flowers and summer truffles. Musoni's English wife, Patricia, runs the front of house and oversees the wine collection, which includes every wine produced by Angelo Gaja since 1982.

Al Pino
via Pianazza 11, Montescano, 27040 Pavia, Italy
Tel: +39-0385-60 479   Fax: +39-0385-60 479

AL RODODENDRO

Bon viveurs flock to Al Rododendron for its refined but warm ambience (the big round tables help in this respect) and Maria Barale's creative

Piedmontese cooking. Zucchini with truffles, in the spring, truly superb lamb and, in the autumn, wild boar, are among the specialities, while sommelier Carlo dispenses first-class examples of the local Dolcetto, Nebiolo and Barolo.

Al Rododendro
Loc. san Giacamo, Boves, 12012 Cuneo, Italy
Tel: +39-0171-38 03 72   Fax: +39-0171-38 78 22

AL SORRISO

"Liberty with a touch of local colour" is how Angelo Valazza describes the decor of his refined restaurant (a new member of Relais & Châteaux), set in the woods near Novara. Ravioli with seven cheeses and truffles, and Pigeon with balsamic vinegar are among the treats that emanate from the kitchen of his wife, Luisa.

Unlike many Italian restaurants, Al Sorriso's wine list is an eclectic selection of gems from both old and new worlds.

Al Sorriso
via Roma 18, 28018 Soriso, Novara, Italy
Tel: +39-0322-98 32 28   Fax: +39-0322-98 33 28

ALAIN BEZZOLA

Super-smart clients regard Alain Bezzola, one of Geneva's leading specialists in dermatology and aesthetic surgery, as the best 'eye' man in town. Formerly head of the city's University Hospital of Dermatology, he is a master of laser techniques, dermabrasion and collagen, as well as the current hit, Botox.

Alain Bezzola
52 Rue Ernest-Bloch,
CH-1207 Geneva, Switzerland
Tel: +41-22-736 1242   Fax: +41-22-736 2785

ALAIN BLONDEL

Although Alain Blondel specialises mainly in figurative works, he has expertise in most areas of modern art. During his previous training, as an architect, he became fascinated by the art nouveau buildings of Hector Guimard and has consistently championed Guimard's work ever since. A Chevalier des Arts et Lettres, Blondel represents well-established artists working in Spain, France, Britain and Russia and, in 1997, organised a retrospective of Tamara de Lempicka's work which toured Japan.

Galerie Alain Blondel
4 rue Aubray le Boucher, 75004 Paris, France
Tel: +33-1-42 71 85 86   Fax: +33-1-42 78 47 90

ALAIN CHAPEL

Flowers - indoors and out - are the leitmotif of this lovely country inn. This soothing environment is the backdrop for a marvellous restaurant now in the hands of Chapel's widow

Suzanne and his inspired protégé, chef Philippe Jousse. Service is silken smooth and wines sublime. Hard to understand why Michelin doesn't reinstate the third star that Chapel had when he was alive.

Alain Chapel
01390 Mionnay (Ain), France
Tel: +33-4-78 91 82 02   Fax: +33-4-78 91 82 37

ALAIN DAVID IDOUX

This sculptor-turned-garden designer revels in the contrast between the controlled environment of the garden and the wild landscape of the *garrigue* of Provence, where he lives. He employs sculpture (often using 'found objects') to establish perspectives or punctuate a line of vision - a concept that he terms "Land Art". Using plants which are adapted to their surroundings, Idoux's gardens are powerful and simple, with a rugged edge. Current projects include gardens in Salzburg, Marrakesh, Geneva and Malaga.

Alain David Idoux
La Chabaude, chemin de Saint-Massian,
84400 Apt, France
Tel: +33-4-90 04 72 41   Fax: +33-4-90 04 61 78

ALAIN DU ROYER DUPRE

Following his success as a 'provincial' trainer, du Royer was taken on by the Aga Khan and trains (for other owners as well) out of the latter's Chantilly stables. Although he has taken a little time to acclimatise to the big league and has not been very successful for the Aga in England, he has been prolific in France.

Alain du Royer Dupré
3 chemin des Aigles, 60500 Chantilly, France
Tel: +33-3-44 58 03 03   Fax: +33-3-44 57 39 38

ALAIN DUCASSE

Alain Ducasse is the only chef in the world with 6 Michelin stars and his gastronomic temple in Paris is justifiably a mecca for peripatetic lotus eaters - many of whom will already be familiar with his Louis XV restaurant at Monte Carlo's Hôtel de Paris and his rustic-luxe Provençal outpost, La Bastide de Moustiers.

Alain Ducasse
59 avenue Raymond Poincaré, 75016 Paris, France
Tel: +33-1-47 27 12 27   Fax: +33-1-47 27 31 22

Le Louis XV
Hôtel de Paris, MC 98000, Monaco
Tel: +377-92 16 30 01   Fax: +377-92 16 69 21

La Bastide de Moustiers
chemin de Quenson,
04360 Moustiers-Ste-Marie, France
Tel: +33-4-92 70 47 47   Fax: +33-4-92 70 47 42

ALBERTA FERRETTI

Alberta Ferretti, herself the daughter of a dressmaker, makes fairy-tale clothes for grown-up women. Her ethereal slips in delicious colours and textures spirit you back to the days when you wore pretty party dresses to birthday teas. Deeply romantic and utterly discreet, the richness of her clothes is in the details and the almost weightless fabrics. Yet though the clothes look dainty, they are so well cut that even strong-boned women look utterly right in them - women like Andie MacDowell, Sheryl Crow, Kate Winslet and Angelica Huston.

Alberta Ferretti
via Donizetti 48, 20122 Milan, Italy
Tel: +39-02-76 05 91   Fax: +39-02-78 41 90

ALBERTO PINTO

This decorator thinks big. Offer him a 1,000 square metre room to play with and he will be delighted. The first assignment of his career, in 1968, was to decorate Isadora Duncan's house on St Jean Cap Ferrat. Most of his clients are American; the sort of people, he says, "who don't have time to explain their lifestyles". And his style? "To hold on to the past, but throw in a contemporary touch."

Alberto Pinto
61 quai d'Orsay, 75007 Paris, France
Tel: +33-1-45 51 03 33   Fax: +33-1-45 55 51 41

ALBRECHT NEUHAUS

First established in 1965 in Düsseldorf, this distinguished dealer's reputation for discretion and sound advice - not to mention great salesmanship - soon brought him a second branch in Würzburg. His range is wide, embracing sculp-

ture and *objets d'art* from the Middle Ages to the baroque, important European furniture and German gold and silver.

Albrecht Neuhaus Kunsthandel
Heinestraße 9, D-9070 Würzburg, Germany
Tel: +49-931-56 849   Fax: +49-931-54 286

ALDO COPPOLA

Aldo Coppola has had his salon designed by Philippe Starck and his fingers in every fashion pie in the world. As well as working wonders with private clients' hair, his stylists have created the runway looks for designers from Dior to Armani and contribute coiffures to numerous movies and advertising campaigns.

Aldo Coppola
corso Garibaldi 110, 20121 Milan, Italy
Tel: +39-02-657 2685   Fax: +39-02-29 00 66 27

ALFONSO XIII (HOTEL)

Standing between a 12th century Alcazar Palace and a 15th century cathedral, this grand palace is undoubtedly one of Andalusia's jewels. A central courtyard glamorously recaptures Spain's Moorish past and sets the scene for the riches within. 146 sumptuously decorated rooms look out over tiled arcades, huge fountains and a lush, semi-tropical garden.

Hotel Alfonso XIII
San Fernando 2, 41004 Seville, Spain
Tel: +34-5-422 2850   Fax: +34-5-421 6033

ALFRED DUNHILL

Alfred Dunhill made his name by designing clothes for motorists at the turn of the century and his innovations included the first-ever pocket lighter. The brand now looks set for a renaissance under Creative Director Ashley Lloyd-Jennings. Its London flagship store is a club-like haven; antique leather sofas invite you to rest while you have your jewellery polished, your suit steamed or your urgent faxes sent.

Alfred Dunhill
48 Jermyn Street, London SW1Y 6LX, UK
Tel: +44-171-838 8118   Fax: +44-171-290 8655

ALTAÏR

If you are an inveterate nomad, you will feel at home here, in one of Europe's best travel bookshops. Underlining its commitment to the subject, Altair also publishes an award-winning travel magazine of the same name. There is also an impressive selection of books on subjects as diverse as photography, world music and maps.

Altaïr
Balmes 69-71, 08007 Barcelona, Spain
Tel +34-934-54 29 66   Fax +34-934-51 25 59

ALTOPALATO

This is where the smartest of the smart Milanese send their offspring for a comprehensive grounding in the culinary arts. Students are not taught merely how to cook. There are lessons in subjects as diverse as wine (with particular emphasis, of course, on the great Barolos and occasional references to somewhere called Bordeaux), table etiquette and the history of food.

Altopalato
via Ausonio 13, 20100 Milan, Italy
Tel: +39-02-58 11 10 00

L'AMBASCIATA

For 25 years Romano and Francesco Tamani have run this elegant and romantic restaurant; the tables are particularly pretty, adorned with beautiful objects and the wine list is vast. That the likes of Fellini, Zucchero and Natalia Strada have all been regulars is testament to Romano's prowess with traditional Italian dishes (try his pumpkin tortelli and, in winter, his wondrous oxtail stew) and Francesco's charm out front.

L'Ambasciata
via Martiri di Belfiore 33,
46026 Quistello, Mantua, Italy
Tel: +39-0376-61 90 03   Fax: +39-0376-61 82 55

LES AMBASSADEURS

Originally a Rothschild mansion and, in the 70's and early 80s a jet-set dining club, 'Les A', as it is affectionately known, became one of London's smartest casinos (under the aegis of London Clubs International) in 1981. The original Rothschild library, with its magnificent, carved wooden panelling remains intact and the glass-walled restaurant overlooks a pretty courtyard garden. High-rolling members are drawn from all over the world.

Les Ambassadeurs, London, UK
At the time of writing, UK law prohibits the publication of contact details for British casinos. The law is currently under review.

L'AMBROISIE

Ambrosia is what Bernard Pacaud produces from his kitchen. If his *surprises du jour* include his Marjolaine of foie gras, don't miss it. Likewise his Sea bass with rosemary-scented artichokes. As one of the most enchanting restaurants in Paris (parquet floors, shelves full of books and honey-coloured walls draped with Aubusson tapestries) L'Ambroisie invariably attracts a star-studded clientele - Jacques Chirac, for instance, comes here for intimate family dinners. Danièle Pacaud and Pierre le Moullac are splendid front-of-house hosts.

L'Ambroisie
9 Place des Vosges, 75004 Paris, France
Tel: +33-1-42 78 51 45

ALOIS DALLMAYR

A family business since 1700, Dallmayr is one of Europe's great delicatessens. Alois Dallmayr's original grocery shop soon earned them royal warrants all over Europe and the store, with its historical facade, is much loved by Munich's townsfolk as part of their tradition, as well as by a host of foreign admirers - notably the Queen of Thailand. Today a walk through this iconic establishment is an essential part of any visitor's itinerary in the city. In addition to a cornucopia of delicacies, the store stocks the best teas and coffees as well as an impressive array of wines and spirits.

There is an excellent oyster and champagne bar on the premises (prestige cuvées are sold by the glass), as well as a restaurant. The latter, recently redecorated, is a Munich institution, always packed with diners, who come to exchange gossip and enjoy the classical delicatessen specialties: lobster, caviar, smoked salmon and foie gras. Dallmayr also offers a first-rate party catering division, providing a very private service for discerning hosts and hostesses. Finally, the store operates a gift service, sending items all over the world; the boutique on its first floor sells a range of luxurious items for the table and home.

Alois Dallmayr
14-15 Dienerstrasse, D-80331 Munich, Germany
Tel: +49-89-21 350   Fax: +49-89-213 5167
Website: www.dallmayr.de

AMELS

Established in 1918 as a family company building fishing boats, Amels became a significant player in custom yacht construction in the late 1970s. Following a tricky patch in the mid-80s, it was bought by the Damen ship-building concern and, under the leadership of Cor Smits (now Chairman), came right back on song. Specialising in ocean-going steel and aluminium yachts, Amels currently has five projects of over 50m under construction; its dry dock has the capacity to construct vessels up to 120m under cover. Latest launch was the 50m Disdale-designed *Tigre d'Or*, in September 1998.

Amels Holland BV
P.O. Box 1, 8754 ZN Makkum, Netherlands
Tel: +32-5152-32 525   Fax: +32-5152-32 179

AMHUINNSUIDHE

Centred around Jonathan and Lady Marcia Bulmer's ravishing, Scottish baronial castle, Amhuinnsuidhe encompasses 60,000 acres of glens and rocky valleys on the Isle of Harris in the Outer Hebrides. Its six natural freshwater lochs and rivers are a paradise for salmon and sea trout - and thus for fishermen (under the watchful eye of ghillies Alec and Kenny Morrison) and the glens are excellent stalking country. There is an incredible variety of bird life and deliciously sweet oysters can be plucked from the rocks.

Amhuinnsuidhe
Logie Estate Office, Forres,
Moray 1V36 0QN, Scotland
Tel: +44-1309-61 12 08   Fax: +44-1309-61 13 00

EL AMPARO

Spanish Basque cuisine is the basis of Carmen Guasp's exquisite menu here. Local luminaries rave about his flavoursome Red peppers stuffed with codfish; there is praise, too, for the charming vine-covered mews house in which the lucky few dine. Overhanging galleries are filled with flowers, laughter and cosmopolitan conversation.

El Amparo
Puigcerda 8, 82001 Madrid, Spain
Tel: +34-91-431 6456

AMPLEFORTH COLLEGE

Britain's leading Roman Catholic school, founded in 1802 and run by Benedictine monks, Ampleforth is set in beautiful countryside. It has evolved considerably in recent years but retains a resolutely old-fashioned ethos and a belief in holistic education; games, for instance, are still compulsory. Approximately 20 per cent of pupils go on to Oxford or Cambridge University.

Ampleforth College
York YO6 4ER, UK
Tel +44-1439-76 60 00   Fax: +44-1439-78 83 30

AMSTEL INTERCONTINENTAL

This palatial hotel, on the banks of River Amstel, has recently been refurbished at vast expense. Its 111 rooms have been turned into 79 and there is an eight-roomed Royal Suite with bullet-proof glass. Its restaurant is the only one in Amsterdam to hold two Michelin stars.

Amstel Intercontinental
1 Prof Tulpplein, 1018 GX Amsterdam,
The Netherlands
Tel: +31-20-622 6060   Fax: +31-20-622 5808

ANANOV

Andrei Ananov was one of the first jewellers in Russia to set up his own business (under the Communist régime, private jewellery companies were illegal) with a large shop beneath the Grand Hotel Europe. The amiable 53-year-old is the pre-eminent source of jewellery in the style of Carl Fabergé and has a large and loyal clientele all over Europe.

Ananov
Grand Hotel Europe, Mikhaylovskaya ul 1/7,
St Petersburg, Russia
Tel: +7-812-329 6576   Fax: +7-812-329 6578

ANDERSON & SHEPPARD

This tailor resolutely maintains both its élitist mystique and its traditional styling. Since it has some of the world's leading establishment figures - notably Prince Charles - taped, this is hardly surprising. Givenchy's maverick designer Alexander McQueen once worked here and famously stitched a graffiti message into the lining of one of the heir to the throne's suits.

Anderson & Sheppard
30 Savile Row, London W1X 1AG, UK
Tel: +44-171-734 1420   Fax: +44-171-734 1721

ANDRE FABRE

Easily the leading trainer in France, Fabre has won numerous classics on both sides of the Channel; every time he sends a horse to run in England it is expected to win. He trains a huge string of horses (over 200), for owners including the Maktoum brothers, Jean-Luc Lagardaire, the Wildensteins and Madame de Moussac. Before taking up training 20 years ago, Fabre was a leading steeplechase jockey; utterly focused and very hard-working, he eschews the social scene which revolves around racing.

André Fabre
14 avenue de Bourbon, 60500 Chantilly, France
Tel: +33-3-44 57 04 98   Fax: +33-3-44 58 14 15

ANDREW SMITH

Trading under the Havana Horse banner, Smith is active throughout the bloodstock world and probably logs more air-miles than anyone in his trade, on behalf of such clients as Norman Cheng, Gary Seidler and Robert Sangster. Noted for his discreet style (buying privately and only selling at auctions) he "acquires" horses for clients, rather than simply buying them. Many of his acquisitions have gone on to become winners but a major coup was extricating a client from an $8 million deal for *El Gran Señor* after he was narrowly beaten in the Derby.

Andrew Smith
Havana Horse, 20 Kinnerton Street,
London SW1X 8ES, UK
Tel: +44-171-235 1704   Fax: +44-171-235 6389

ANDREW WINCH YACHT DESIGN

"Designing the client's dream yacht." With this ideal Andrew Winch established his business in 1987. Over a decade later, that philosophy has not changed. Luxurious, classically-inspired yachts, ranging in length from 30 to 65 metres, are launched in shipyards from Holland to New Zealand, for clients right across the globe.

Andrew Winch Yacht Design
The Limes, 123 Mortlake High Sreet,
London SW14 8SN, UK
Tel: +44-181-878 8678   Fax: +44-181-878 8704

ANGELA PINTALDI

Donna Karan was so taken with the beautiful young jewellery designer Angela Pintaldi, who lives on the island of Pantelleria, where Giorgio Armani also has a summer house, that she featured her pieces in a show. With this endorse-

ANDRE DE CACQUERAY

André de Cacqueray's ability to "understand how things should look and to create a sympathetic setting for them" stems from his background as an art historian and antique dealer. This London-based decorator has, through word of mouth, quietly staked his claim to a place among Europe's élite - thanks to projects as varied as a grand château near Grasse, a Belgravia mews house (decorated to a strict budget), a Polish country house and a Georgian townhouse in Dublin (featured in this book).

As befits the descendant of a page-boy at the court of Louis XV (who had the temerity to scratch his initials on a pane of glass at Versailles - graffiti which is visible to this day), de Cacqueray is particularly at home with classical French furniture and fabrics. However, his references are widely-based and he has recently completed a house on the south coast of England in a Long Island style and a Belle Epoque hunting lodge in Austria.

De Cacqueray's clients praise both his perfectionism and his deceptively easy-going style and acknowledge that he has inspired them to a better understanding of their own objects, spaces and lifestyles. A great believer in the value of Cardinal Mazarin's words, "Semplice ma Pomposo", the personable de Cacqueray declares, "One's interior should be a timeless cocoon".

André de Cacqueray
227 Ebury Street, London SW1W 8UT, UK
Tel: +44-171-730 5000   Fax: +44-171-730 0005

ment, Pintaldi's work - an exotic melange of, amongst other things, amber, rock crystal, ivory and pearls; carved, rough-hewn and suspended from simple clasps or twists of silk - has rapidly attracted a cult following amongst style sophisticates, including Isabella Rosellini, Annette de la Renta and Victoria de Rothschild.

Angela Pintaldi
Piazza Sant'Erasmo, St Pietro all'Orto 9,
20121 Milan, Italy
Tel: +39-02-26 55 12 95   Fax: +39-02-76 01 46 05

ANGÉLIQUE DE FOLIN

This porcelain painter's work has such grace and vibrancy that you can almost imagine the butterflies on her Charles X-style hot chocolate service taking flight around you. She is also a very talented miniaturist, designing services with exquisite oriental horse and elephant motifs. Her fabric designs are equally fresh and minutely detailed, particularly her ducks on the tablecloths of Paris' Tour d'Argent restaurant.

Angélique de Folin
1 rue de Bellechasse, 75007 Paris, France
Tel: +33-1-45 61 48 20

ANGELO CAROLI HEALTH CLUB

Flab is a four-letter word for the fashionocracy who patronise this über-chic Milanese gym. On first joining the club, every member is assigned a personal trainer who supervises all workouts and monitors progress as the months go by.

Angelo Caroli Health Club
via Senato 11, 20121 Milan, Italy
Tel: +39-02-76 02 85 17   Fax: +39-02-78 20 87

ANGLO-GERMAN CLUB

Decorated with Old Master paintings and silk-covered sofas - and housed in a beautiful old villa in Hamburg's smartest area - this private club is modelled closely on its English counterparts. The city's conservative élite particularly appreciates the fine quality of its cuisine (men only at lunch time, and a strict dress code at all times) and regularly use its private rooms for discreet parties and dinners.

Anglo-German Club
Harvesterhudeweg 44, D-20149 Hamburg, Germany
Tel: +49-40-45 01 55 12

ANITA SMAGA

As elegant as the women she dresses, Anita Smaga has an impeccable eye for the best of each season's designer collections. The rails of her boutique are full of gems from Valentino, St Laurent, Lacroix, Gucci and Calvin Klein, to name but a few.

Anita Smaga
51 rue du Rhône, CH-1204 Geneva, Switzerland
Tel: +41-22-310 2655   Fax: +41-22-311 5680

ANGELICA FRESCOBALDI

Decorator Angelica Frescobaldi operates out of fascinating premises in the courtyard of an old house, where she sells antiques, ornaments and furnishings. In this studio, she designs a range of lamps, frames and small items of furniture, as well as one-off commissions - all produced, using largely forgotten artisanal techniques and materials, by her exclusive network of Italian craftsmen. In her limited free time, this in-demand decorator travels widely with her young family - and is never without a notebook, in which she collects ideas and inspiration. Working with a client base that includes some of Milan's most prominent lawyers and bankers, Frescobaldi describes her style as "classical, with a contemporary twist".

Angelica Frescobaldi
via del Carmine 7, 20121 Milan, Italy
Tel/Fax: +39-02-87 79 47

ANNABEL'S

For over 35 years Mark Birley's nightclub in Berkeley Square has played host to the very cream of the world's elite. Its continued success is a tribute to its owner's immense style, reflected in the club's refusal ever to fall victim to fashion - either in its decorative style (vaguely, but not too, evocative of an English country house), its cuisine or its dance music. Birley's perfect manners as a host extend to his rewarding founder members' loyalty by charging them the same £5-a-year subscription that they paid upon joining. Another great strength is the extraodinary loyalty of Annabel's staff, some of whom have worked there since the very beginning and have become genuinely loved by members.

Annabel's
Berkeley Square, London W1X 8NR, UK
Tel: +44-171-629 1096

ANNELIE, PIZZI E RICAMI

Since its opening in 1992, this small boutique has been the talk of the town, the place to come for the classiest monogrammed embroidery and the finest - and often costliest - lace. Austrian-born Annelie seeks out the best antique examples, ensuring a constant supply of rare and exquisite pieces.

Annelie, Pizzi e Ricami
Calle Lunga Santa Barnaba, Dorsuduro,
2748 Venice, Italy
Tel: +39-041-520 3277

ANNICK GOUTAL

Since she won the 1986 Prix de l'Excellence Européene, former pianist Annick Goutal has continued to impress with the quality and originality of her scents. Today her perfumes - such as the delicate Eau d'Hadrien (a favourite with Madonna) and the highly charged Passion (Goutal's personal fragrance) - conjure up emotions and memories that strike an immediate chord in the wearer.

Annick Goutal
14 rue de Castiglione, 75001 Paris, France
Tel: +33-1-42 60 52 82
Fax: +33-1-40 71 20 70

ANTHONY D'OFFAY GALLERY

Anthony d'Offay is unusual among major art dealers in neither having a private fortune nor coming from a family of dealers. Having used £260 at the age of 21 to buy the papers of poets from Oscar Wilde's circle, he is now seen by many as Britain's foremost dealer in international contemporary art. He and his wife, Anne Seymour, live in a grand London house, decorated entirely in white for the display of art, and also own the New York house designed by Philip Johnson for Blanchette Rockefeller's collection of contemporary art. Yet, d'Offay remains a mysterious figure, hard to spot even at his own openings.

Anthony d'Offay Gallery
9, 21, 23 and 24 Dering Street,
London W1R 9AA, UK
Tel: +44-171-499 4100   Fax: +44-171-493 4443

ANTICA OSTERIA DEL PONTE

This 300 year-old inn is impossibly romantic. During the winter tables are arranged around the fireplace, while the candle-lit garden provides an equally charming setting in the summer. Ezio and Maurizio Santin's specialities include the definitive risotto with saffron and zucchini flowers, and egg 'in cammiccia' with a foie gras and white truffle sauce. Gourmets and romantics mix here with businessmen and political celebrities.

Antica Osteria del Ponte
Piazza G. Negri 9,
20081 Cassinetta di Lugagnano, Italy
Tel: +39-02-942 0034   Fax: +39-02-942 0610

ANTICHI MAESTRI PITTORI

Giancarlo Gallino was a successful executive in the textile industry before founding his gallery in 1978 - a decision he describes as "the best I ever made". Exhibitions over the years include 13th-and 14th-century Tuscan and Umbrian art and a comparative look at painting and sculpture from the 12th to the 17th centuries.

Antichi Maestri Pittori
via Andrea Doria 19/a,
10123 Turin, Italy
Tel: +39-011-812 7587   Fax: +39-011-812 7612

ANTICHITÀ ALBERTO DI CASTRO

This family-run gallery, established at the end of the last century, is worth visiting just to see the sumptuous and beautifully co-ordinated display space. Alberto di Castro's speciality is rare 16th- and 17th-century marbles and silverwork from Rome and the Lazio. The gallery does not restore works before offering them for sale; as

Alessandra di Castro explains, "The flavour that works acquire over the centuries is as interesting to us as the work itself".

Antichità Alberto Di Castro
Piazza di Spagna 5, 00187 Rome, Italy
Tel: +39-06-679 2269   Fax: +39-06-678 7410

ANTIQUORUM

It is surprising that Antiquorum was established as recently as 1974, since this auction house seems as venerable and precise as some of the timepieces it specialises in selling. Yet, thanks to its youth, it is neither hidebound, nor afraid of innovation, having pioneered

ANOUSKA HEMPEL COUTURE

From subtly elegant suits to the most flamboyant evening gowns, Anouska Hempel's designs reflect her own dramatic style and passion for life and travel; indeed, she began designing out of a desire to create exactly the kind of clothes that suit her own lifestyle. Their deceptively simple designs and rigorous tailoring are counterbalanced by her choice of extraordinary and extravagant fabrics (fine French lace, silk chiffons and organzas over heavy silk crêpes and shot zibelines), meticulous attention to detail and the use of many techniques largely lost to modern manufacturing.

For example, many evening dresses incorporate a bustier, using traditional corsetry skills and yet, with clever cutting and draping, they allow the body to move freely. Hempel believes that "the inside of a dress should be just as important as the outside" and, as well as the "architecture" of her clothes (as she calls it) has a fascination with buttons and bows.

In keeping with the designer's love of drama, colours are drawn from a richly dark palette, reflected also in the dramatic ambience of her Chelsea atelier; its swathes of midnight blue silk, gilded mirrors, candlelight and deeply scented flowers provide a perfect foil for her clothes.

Anouska Hempel Couture
2 Pond Place, London SW3 6QJ, UK
Tel: +44-171-589 4191
Fax: +44-171-584 1800

the selling of wristwatches at auction during the 1980s.

Antiquorum
2 rue du Mont-Blanc, CH-1201
Geneva, Switzerland
Tel: +41-22-909 28 50   Fax: +41-22-909 28 60

ANTONIETTA MAZZOTTI EMALDI

From the town of Faenza (whence faïence originates) comes the hand-painted custom-made pottery of Antonietta Mazzotti Emaldi. Having learned her trade as an apprentice in ceramics, she set up a workshop with her husband, an ancient majolica expert. Patrons of her delicately-hued pieces, featuring Renaissance, mythological and floral motifs, include the Italian President's staff and the American Embassy.

Antonietta Mazzotti Emaldi
Villa Emaldi, via Firenze 240, 48018 Faenza, Italy
Tel: +39-0546-43 199   Fax: +39-0546-43 156

ANTONIO RAVA

After restoring the Palazzo Barberini for the Italian Ministry of Culture, trained architect Antonio Rava set up his own business in 1984 with three partners. While Studio Rava specialises in the restoration of modern art (and advises on hanging and transportation techniques) it also has an in-depth knowledge of older works of art. Working primarily for the public sector, Rava also undertakes limited private commissions.

Studio Rava
via Castilione 6 bis int. 4, 10132 Turin, Italy
Tel: +39-11-819 3739   Fax: +39-11-819 1542

ANTICO SETIFICIO FIORENTINO

Now owned and run by members of the Pucci family, this company has been continuously

hand-weaving silk on the same premises for over 300 years. Today's production - much of it made to order for the likes of the Agnellis, the Gettys and the Queen of Denmark - includes silk damask, brocades, and silk lampass, all woven to the original Renaissance patterns on hand looms. Most of these looms date from the 18th century, although one was designed by Leonardo da Vinci. Other typically Florentine fabrics are woven on 19th-century mechanical looms. The yarns used are specially prepared and dyed by hand, without chemicals, since modern yarn cannot be used on antique looms.

Antico Setificio Fiorentino
via L. Bartolini 4, 50124 Florence, Italy
Tel: +39-055-21 38 61   Fax: +39-055-21 81 74

APICIUS

Discreetly decorated in the modern style, this restaurant is named after the famous chef of Roman times and features the inventive and much-praised cooking of Jean-Pierre Vigato. Among many masterful dishes, his *Foie gras de canard poêlé en aigre-doux aux radis noirs* is a revelation. Madame Vigato oversees the front door with immense charm.

Apicius
122 avenue de Villiers, 75017 Paris, France
Tel: +33-1-43 80 19 66   Fax: +33-1-44 40 09 57

L'ARCHIDUC

One of Europe's best and most intimate jazz venues, this piano bar was opened by Jean-Louis Hennart in 1937 and the décor remains unchanged. Frequented in the early years by Miles Davis and Jacques Brel, it continues to attract jazz legends. Despite never advertising, it is packed to the rafters every night. Get there early as no advance tickets can be purchased.

L'Archiduc
8 rue Antoine-Dansaert, 1000 Brussels, Belgium
Tel: +32-2-512 0652

ARNYS

This boutique has been sartorial heaven for intellectual dandies since it opened in 1933. Every item - a stylistic blend of formal elegance and landed gentry-style comfort - is made exclusively for the shop. Its most famous creation is the Corbusier jacket, created for the architect himself more than 40 years ago.

Arnys
14 rue de Sèvres, 75007 Paris, France
Tel: +33-1-45 48 76 99

ARS ROSA

Blue-blooded Milanese with deep pockets beat a path to Bettina Rossi's tiny shop, for her exquisite, 100 per cent hand-made linens, lingerie and

children's clothes, as well as made-to-measure bras and briefs. Benevolent Signora Rossi has been dispensing her wares personally to the likes of Maria Callas and Princess Michael of Kent since she founded the company in 1952.

Ars Rosa
8 via Montenapoleone, 20121 Milan, Italy
Tel: +39-02-76 02 38 22   Fax: +39-02-76 02 22 86

ART BASEL

This event, established in 1967, is for serious buyers; over 250 exhibitors travel from around the world and the selection process is scrupulous. The main section comprises leading contemporary galleries, while 'Statements' is a subsidised section for younger artists, 'Video-Forum' is devoted entirely to that medium, and photography and graphic art also feature prominently. According to a director of London's Anthony d'Offay Gallery, long-term exhibitors, "It is the only European contemporary art fair that American curators feel unable to miss."

Art Basel
Schweizer Mustermesse,
CH-4021Base, Switzerland
Tel:+41-61-686 2020   Internet: www.art.ch.
Annually for five days in June

ARABELLA LENNOX-BOYD

The Best Garden Award at the 1998 Chelsea Flower Show is the latest jewel in this designer's crown. Italian-born Lady Lennox-Boyd sees her work as a vocation and is fired by the philosophy that a garden is "all about space, history, flair and people as well as plants". Despite her many prestigious commissions (for Sir Terence Conran and the Duke of Westminster, among others), it is her own plot

at the early 19th-century house in Lancashire, that she shares with her husband, former MP Sir Mark Lennox-Boyd, that she describes as her "great work of art".

Arabella Lennox-Boyd
45 Moreton Street, London SW1V 2NY, UK
Tel: +44-171-931 9995   Fax: +44-171-821 6585

ART COLOGNE

Art Cologne, which began 30 years ago, focuses on the choicest of Modern Masters, leaving cutting-edge contemporary art to its rivals. Until recently, Art Cologne was known for its large number of exhibitors and for visitors in excess of 80,000. These have now been reduced to a more manageable scale and new vetting procedures introduced, both with very favourable results.

Art Cologne
Cologne Exhibition Centre, Rhineside Halls,
D-50532 Cologne, Germany
Tel: +49-221-821 2907   Fax: +49-221-821 3446
Every November

ARTEMIDE

Founded in 1959 by Ernesto Gismondi and Sergio Mazza, Artemide is a showcase for the 20th century's leading lighting designers. It carries the work of Ettore Sottsass, Michele de Lucchi and Gismondi Sapper (examples of which are also found in the world's major design museums) as well as the cutting-edge Metamorfosi concept.

Artemide
Corso Monforte 19, 20100 Milan, Italy
Tel: +39-02-76 00 69 30

ARTHUR SILVA NETTO

Plastic surgeon Arthur Silva Netto divides his time between Milan and his native Rio de Janeiro - perfecting his skills in the Reconstructive Surgery department of the Cancer Hospital there. The author of more than 20 publications about his discipline, he is highly respected both for his aesthetic sense (and special expertise with breasts and noses) and his knowledge of the latest procedures.

Arthur Silva Netto
Galleria del Corso 4, 20122 Milan, Italy
Tel: +39-02-76 02 33 80   Fax: +39-02-78 27 65 11

ARTHUR'S RIVE GAUCHE

Presided over by the vivacious Nicole Codourey, Arthur's is where *le tout* Geneva hangs out, especially late in the evening, when leading Swiss DJs mix good music and the barman mixes great cocktails. At lunchtime, gourmet snacks are served and, for the summer, there is a magnificent terrace overlooking the Rhône.

Arthur's Rive Gauche
29 Rue du Rhône, CH-1204 Geneva, Switzerland
Tel: +41-22-318 60 90   Fax: +41-22-318 60 99.

ARTIOLI

Believed to be the Pope's cobblers, Severiano Artioli and his descendants have been producing hand-made shoes for men of means for 50 years. Some of their materials - kangaroo, ostrich, shark and crocodile - are not for the ultra-conservative but the quality is assured; only one hide in 100 is accepted as being good enough.

Artioli
via Oslavia 3, 21049 Tradate, Italy
Tel: +39-0331-84 13 22   Fax: +39-0331-84 45 64

ARTURO RAMON

Arturo Ramon is a fourth-generation art dealer. The present father and son team show how two different concepts can coexist in complete harmony within two galleries: one works with traditional art and antiques, while the other emphasises modern and contemporary art. Ramon's speciality is Catalan paintings from the late 19th- and first half of the 20th centuries. They regularly hold events - each with a fascinating story behind it - in their house in the old quarter of Barcelona.

Arturo Ramon
Palla 23 and 25,
08002 Barcelona, Spain
Tel: +34-93-302 5970   Fax: +34-93-318 2833

ARZAK

Decorated with charm and hung with old paintings, this is home to Juán Mari Arzak (a third-generation chef and one of Spain's most celebrated) and his daughter Elena. Their fresh and light interpretation of Spanish Basque cooking, with a strong bias towards seafood, is complemented by a magnificent wine list.

Arzak
Alto de Miracruz 21, E-20015
San Sebastian, Spain
Tel: +34-99-43 28 55 93   Fax: +34-99-43 27 27 53

ASHFORD CASTLE

Dating from the 12th century, this property has recently been upgraded. Most of the rooms enjoy spectacular views of Lough Corrib (State Room 430 in the oldest wing, is particularly attractive) and the 300 acre grounds are filled with rare plants.

Ashford Castle
Cong, Co. Mayo, Ireland
Tel: +353-92-46 003   Fax: +353-92-46 260

ASPINALLS

John ('Aspers' to his friends) Aspinall's casino - lately expanded into the next door house - has been setting new aesthetic standards for London gaming houses since its inception. This is the place to see the racier members of the British aristocracy win or lose their shirts against a backdrop, appropriately, of animal art inspired by Howletts, Aspers' game park.

Aspinalls, London, UK
At the time of writing, UK law prohibits the publication of contact details for British casinos. The law is currently under review.

ATELIER LUMONT

Should your cat happen to knock your precious antique vase off the mantelpiece, you should dispatch every piece to Jean-Jacques Coron, ceramics restorer *par excellence*, who took over this repair workshop in 1979. The fact that Coron once re-assembled an 18th-century Sèvres vase for Buckingham Palace should be reassurance enough of his skills.

Atelier Lumont
12 rue Cacheux, 92400 Courbevoie, France
Tel: +33-1-47 89 56 90

ATHLETIQUE CLUB BOULOGNE BILLANCOURT

If horse-riding in the Bois de Boulogne appeals, this is the place. Located on the outskirts of Paris, it's a mecca for well-bred, perfectly manicured Ladies and their equally polished daughters. There are three jumping arenas and some 40 horses. The emphasis is very much on eventing.

Athlétique Club Boulogne-Billancourt
Parc Rothschild, 35 quai Alfonse le Gallo,
92100 Boulogne–Billancourt, France
Tel: +33-1-48 25 59 80

ASPREY & GARRARD

Britain's two most historic jewellers, Asprey and Garrard, were brought together into one business in September 1998, based at the beautiful Bond Street showroom first occupied by Asprey in 1847. Both companies' heritage is steeped in the design and manufacture of beautiful objects - silver, leather goods and *objets d'art*, as well as jewellery - many of them made to private commission, by highly skilled craftsmen in the workshops located above the showroom.

Innovation in design has always been the trademark of both companies, with landmark items, such as Asprey's revolutionary lightweight dressing case (which attracted Queen Victoria's attention at the Great Exhibition of 1851) and Garrard's ornate Cowes Yacht Race Cup (presented for the first time that same year) being created throughout their history. Alongside its classical designs for rare stones, both Asprey & Garrard has a particularly English taste for witty objects - often extravagant versions of utilitarian items - a baby's beaker or a computer mouse in solid silver, for example, or a parquet Cluedo board made of precious woods.

In 1862 Asprey won its first Royal Warrant, just one of many to be awarded to both companies, whose merger makes Asprey & Garrard the strongest English luxury goods company for the 21st century.

Asprey & Garrard
165 New Bond Street, London W1Y 0AR, UK
Tel: +44-171-493 67 67   Fax: +44-171-491 0384

AU PETIT MATELOT

Inventor of the navy pea jacket and one of the oldest shops in Europe, this boutique was France's first maritime outfitter and today, as ever, its aim is to provide men's *habillement* for 'the hunt, voyage, automobile and yachting'. The preponderance of blue clothing, the colour of nobility in France, gives browsers a clue as to its preferred clients. It has a stunning collection of jockey silks.

Au Petit Matelot
27 avenue de la Grande-Armée,
75016 Paris, France
Tel: +33-1-45 00 15 51   Fax: +33-1-40 67 12 95

AUBERGE DE L'ERIDAN - MARC VEYRAT

With its lovely lakeside terrace and gardens set against a wooded hillside, this deeply luxurious inn, with its dreamy views across Lake Annecy, offers welcome respite for the travelling gourmet. With his inspired use of the herbs and rare roots that he gathers himself from the surrounding meadows (spruce bark and juniper berries, for instance, with which he roasts duck), Marc Veyrat's daring cuisine seems suffused with the alpine air.

Auberge de l'Eridan
13 Vieille Route des Pensieres,
74290 Veyrier-du-Lac, France
Tel: +33-4-50 60 24 00   Fax: +33-4-50 60 23 63

L'AUBERGE DE L'ILL

Extending along the river bank, amid flower gardens and weeping willows, the Haeberlin family's restaurant-with-rooms is as pretty as its surroundings. Marc Haeberlin's traditionally-based Alsace cooking is lighter and less classic than you might expect and his mastery of flavours clearly evident in such treats as Pan-roasted frogs' legs with cabbage ragoût. The wine cellar is an education in just how good Riesling can be.

L'Auberge de l'Ill
2 rue de Collonges, 68970 Illhaeusern, France
Tel: +33-03-89 71 89 00   Fax: +33-03-89 71 82 83

AUBERGE DU MOULIN HIDEUX

Charles and Martine Lahire's idyllic 18th-century *auberge*, in the heart of the Ardennes forest, has been a picture-postcard pretty inn for the past 50 years. Chef Christian Ulweling ensures that it is also a culinary staging post, with tempting dishes such as Turbot with basil or Venison in peppercorn sauce, plus game, mushrooms and forest berries in the autumn.

Auberge du Moulin Hideux
1 Route de Dohan, 6831 Noirefontaine, Belgium
Tel: +32-61-46 70 15   Fax: +32-61-46 72 81

L'AUBERGE DU PERE BISE

This romantic, 19th-century inn (with its beautiful, recently opened Villa des Roses annexe) is run with serene efficiency and considerable charm by Charlyne Bise. Her talented chef daughter, Sophie, turns out marvels such as Dublin Bay prawn ice-cream with basil and a glorious Potato and foie gras 'tarte tatin'.

L'Auberge du Père Bise
Route du port, 74290 Talloires,
Talloires, France
Tel: +33-4-50 60 72 01   Fax: +33-4-50 60 73 05

AUBUSSON

The town of Aubusson has been renowned for its hand-woven carpets and tapestries since the 16th century. Early this century, however, artists such as Férnand Leger, Dalì and Picasso gave tapestry-making there a new lease of life. Like them, Robert Four, a fifth generation master weaver, is passionate about carrying on the Aubusson tradition. Besides producing carpets for such clients as the Sultan of Brunei and the Hôtel de Crillon, the company will repair any Aubusson piece.

Aubusson
Robert Four Workshops, 7 rue Madeleine, 23200 Aubusson, France
Tel: +33-5-55 66 15 70 Fax: +35-5-55 66 87 31
Shop: 28 rue Bonaparte, 75006 Paris, France
Tel: +33-1-43 29 30 60 Fax: +33-1-42 44 18 07

AUDEMARS PIGUET

Makers of the world's first luxury sportswatch and playboy's staple, the Royal Oak, Audemars Piguet was founded 120 years ago. Recognition came swiftly for the company, with the British Museum acquiring one of its timepieces after the 1889 Univeral Exhibition of Paris. Still in the hands of its founding families, the company today makes 15,000 watches each year.

Audemars Piguet
6 avenue August Forel,
CH-1110 Morgs, Switzerland
Tel: +41-21-802 4955 Fax: +41-21-845 1400

AUSONE (CHATEAU)

One of the oldest *crus* of Saint-Emilion, Château Ausone was reputedly once the property of the Roman pro-consul and poet Ausonius. Recently taken over by Alain Vauthier (following epic negotiations with his fellow heirs of the Dubois-Challon family) the vineyard's perfect southerly aspect results in a highly perfumed and complex wine of legendary finesse (it was Cole Porter's favourite). The property has particularly beautiful cellars, carved out of an ancient quarry. Ausone '82 will be ripe for drinking in 1999.

Château Ausone
33330 Saint-Emilion, France
Tel: +33-5-57 24 68 88 Fax: +33-5-57 74 47 39

AXEL VERVOORDT

A great showman, Axel Vervoordt runs his business from an extravagantly decorated Renaissance-style château. Although he has a team of 60 people to help him, his approach is very personal; he buys only what he would want in his own home and chooses most items himself. As much decorator as antique dealer, he works hard to bring out the tastes of the owners of the buildings he works on, while inspiring a sense of the house's history.

Axel Vervoordt
Kasteel ës Gravenwezel, St Jobsteenweg, 2970 ës Gravenwezel, Belgium
Tel: +32-3-658 14 70 Fax: +32-3-658 37 81
By appointment only

AZZEDINE ALAÏA

Having created no perfume, no licences, no franchises and making no compromises, Alaïa is treated as something of an oddity in the fashion world. Yet his design and technical skills surpass many of the most media-fêted couturiers – he is able to sew and cut as well as design. His passion for perfection means that his collections are always late, but it's well worth waiting to be among the select few ushered into his *hôtel particulier* in the Marais.

Azzedine Alaïa
7 rue de Moussy, 75004 Paris, France
Tel: +33-1-42 72 19 19 Fax: +33-1-48 87 04 36

BACCARAT

The fact that 40 percent of France's hand-made crystal - ranging from contemporary jewellery to hand-enamelled vases and vast chandeliers - is made by Baccarat in no way compromises this firm's superb quality. For a marriage made in heaven, drink Taittinger champagne from a Baccarat flute, for both brands are owned by the Groupe du Louvre, under the chairmanship of Anne-Claire Taittinger-Bonnemaison.

Baccarat
30bis rue du Paradis, 75010 Paris, France
Tel: +33-1-47 70 64 30 Fax: +33-1-42 46 97 08

BAD DRIBURG

Still owned by the family of Graf Oeynhausen-Sierstorpff after 200 years, this private spa (with its adjoining rehabilitation clinic) today offers the most modern health and beauty treatments. The lovely, half-timbered buildings, 6-hectare park and beautiful surrounding countryside make it a haven for both relaxation and fitness.

Unternehmensgruppe Graf von Oeynhausen-Sierstorpff
Im Kurpark, D-33014 Bad Driburg, Germany
Tel: +49-5353-95 25 16 Fax: +49-5353-95 25 39

BADIA A COLTIBUONO

This ravishing thousand year-old abbey became the residence of the Stucchi Prinetti family two centuries ago. The present châtelaine, Lorenza de'Medici, an acclaimed author on Italian gastronomy, runs cooking classes here during the summer. A restricted number of 'live-in' participants are made privy to her cooking secrets and given an insight into the aristocratic Italian lifestyle.

Badia a Coltibuono
Gaiole in Chianti, 53013 Siena, Italy
Tel: +39-0577-74 94 98   Fax: +39-0577-74 92 35

BADRUTT'S PALACE HOTEL

Set in six acres of private grounds with views of the lake and surrounding mountains, the Palace Hotel remains in the hands of the Badrutt family, who founded it over a hundred years ago, inventing the winter Season in the process. Join the shiny set that stays here

in the winter and you can avoid the throngs on the pistes; the hotel has its own ski school and skating instructors.

Badrutt's Palace Hotel
7500 St Moritz, Switzerland
Tel: +41-81-837 1000   Fax: +41-81-837 2999

BALLINACOR

Lord Jack Ardee, as *The Shooting Gazette* pointed out last year, owns "the best pheasant shoot in Ireland". Two syndicates share it. The first comprises the luckiest inhabitants of the Emerald Isle and the other is headed by the King of Sweden, who shoots roughly every other weekend. The birds are consistently high and there are lots of them. Lord Ardee runs a tight ship and the shoot is well and efficiently conducted. His commercial days are booked well ahead so put yourself on the waiting list immediately.

Ballinacor
Ballinacor House, Greenane, Rathdrum,
Co. Wicklow, Ireland
Tel: +353-404-46 186   Fax: +353-404-46 123
or c/o Humewood Castle
Tel: +353-508-73 215   Fax: +353-508-73 382

BALLYBUNION

This club, founded in 1896 and just 40 miles from Shannon airport, promises golfers the chance to enjoy the roar of Atlantic surf as they play the two 18-hole courses. Tom Watson rates the Old Course, which winds back and forth between the dunes and the sea, as one of the world's top six and its short 8th one of his 'dream 18'. US President Bill Clinton played here during his 1998 visit to Ireland.

Ballybunion Golf Club
Ballybunion, Co. Kerry, Ireland
Tel: +353-68-27 146   Fax: +353-68-27 387

BALLYMALOE COOKERY SCHOOL

In 1983, 20 years after Myrtle Allen opened her country-house restaurant, her son and daughter-in-law, cookery writer Darina Allen, opened their cookery school. In the courses (which range from just one day to a 12-week certificate course) there is great emphasis on local, natural food; vegetables and herbs are grown organically in the huge kitchen garden.

Ballymaloe Cookery School
Shanagarry, Co. Cork, Ireland
Tel: +353-21-64 67 85   Fax: +353-21-64 69 09

BALMAIN

At the design helm of Balmain couture since 1993, Oscar de la Renta has brought glamour and colour back to the label - as well as a sta-

ble of socialite clients from America. With Georgina Brandolini (ex-Valentino) and Gilles Dufour (ex-Chanel) now heading the ready-to-wear division, the house has undoubtledly rejoined the A-List.

Pierre Balmain
44 rue Francois 1er, 75008 Paris, France
Tel: +33-1-47 20 35 34   Fax: +33-1-47 23 40 11

THE BALVENIE

To get to the heart of The Balvenie forget about standard bottlings and head straight for one of the 15 year-old single bottle examples. Pale in colour without any hint of amber, there is a steeliness to the flavour, which adds refinement and elegance to a malt already well endowed in those departments.

The Balvenie
William Grant & Sons, 84 Lower Mortlake Road, Richmond, Surrey TW9 2HS, UK
Tel: +44-181-332 1188 Fax: +44-181-332 1695

BANANA SPLIT

Started by Julian Posner as a schoolboy in 1984, Banana Split has perfected the art of the 'big impact'. Its technicians and designers will go to absolutely any lengths to create the party of a lifetime. Clients are rich and varied, ranging from the Sultan of Brunei to BMW.

Banana Split
Unit 11, Carlisle Road, London NW9 0HD, UK
Tel: + 44-181-200 1234   Fax: +44-181-200 1121

BANK JULIUS BAER & CO. LTD.

With bearer shares listed on both the Zürich and Frankfurt Stock Exchanges, the Julius Baer Group manages more than 90 billion Swiss francs worth of assets for private and insitutional clients from around the world. The group's principal vehicle, Bank Julius Baer, founded in 1890, is one of Switzerland's leading asset management banks. Broad expertise, individual client counselling, continuity and the commitment of the Bär families (holders of the majority of registered shares) are the cornerstone of the company's corporate culture.

Bank Julius Baer & Co. Ltd.

Bahnhofstrasse 36, CH-8018, Zürich, Switzerland

Tel: +41-1-228 5111   Fax: 41-2-211 2560

B. METZLER SEEL. SOHN & CO. KGaA

Germany's oldest family-owned bank has 325 years' experience of providing customised financial services for clients. Today it offers the full range of services of an international investment bank, including asset management and related counselling services for high net-worth individuals. In managing private clients' assets, Metzler invests considerable time and energy building relationships based on mutual trust. Its management style emphasises long-term preservation and growth of capital, while protecting clients from unpleasant surprises - even when the markets are turbulent. Metzler's centuries-old tradition of total independence allows clients' needs to remain its central concern.

B. Metzler seel. Sohn & Co, KGaA

Postfach 20 01 38, D-60605 Frankfurt am Main, Germany

Tel: +49-69-21 04 46 12   Fax: +49-69-21 04 47 77

BANNERMAN

The Bannermans form the perfect team: Isabel is the plantswoman and Julian the highly imaginative designer and builder of grottoes. One of their most high-profile projects is the seven-acre water garden at Waddesdon Manor in Buckinghamshire. Julian has done much work recently for HRH, the Prince of Wales at Highgrove, and John Paul Getty II is another illustrious client.

Isabel and Julian Bannerman

Hanham Court, Hanham Abbots,

Bristol BS15 5NT, UK

Tel: +44-117-961 1202

BARBIZON (RESTAURANT)

In 1959 Alain Deluc's father discovered the beautiful Norman villa on the ege of the Soignes forest that was to become the Barbizon restaurant. After studying with Troisgros and Chapel, Deluc has come into his own with signature dishes like *Compression d'homard et huîtres, vinaigrette aux herbes*. Tables five and six are the most discreet.

Restaurant Barbizon

95 Welriekendedreef, 3090 Jezus-Eik,

Overijse, Belgium

Tel: +32-2-657 0462 Fax: +32-2-657 4066

BAREISS (HOTEL)

Gourmets flock here for the cooking (the restaurant consistently rates among Germany's top 10); nature-lovers come for the 1000 kilometres of hiking trails, children come to be royally entertained in their own house, the Villa Kunterbunt, and all leave this Black Forest refuge with memories of an authentically *gemütlich* ambience, presided over with charming efficiency by the Bareiss family.

Hotel Bareiss,

Gärtenbühlweg 14,

D-72270 Baiersbronn-Mitteltal, Germany

Tel: +49-7442-470   Fax: +49-7442-47 320

BARON'S COURT

The Duke of Abercorn's glorious 5000 acre estate, spanning a valley on the edge of the Sperrin mountains, offers the best stalking and pheasant shooting in Northern Ireland, as well as first-class salmon fishing on a mile-long private stretch of the River Mourne (part of the famous Foyle system). The pheasant are all high-flying and high quality and the deer are unique - a wild herd of pure-bred Japanese sika deer. Head keeper Sam Pollock's work in managing the deer was recently recognised by a Laurent-Perrier Award for wild game conservation.

Baron's Court

Newtownstewart, Co. Tyrone,

BT78 4EZ, Northern Ireland

Tel: +44-1662-66 16 83   Fax: +44-1662-66 20 59

BAROVIER AND TOSO

Listed in the Guinness Book of Records as the oldest industrial dynasty in the world, this firm celebrated its 700th year of artistic glass production in 1995. Today the company combines traditional craftsmanship with sophisticated modern technology to produce its exquisite glass. The traditionally-styled items are the prettiest, although director Jacopo Barovier also commissions pieces from contemporary designers and architects, with considerable success.

Barovier and Toso

Fondamenta Vetrai 28, 30121 Murano, Venice, Italy

Tel: +39-041-73 90 49   Fax: +39-041-527 4385

BARRY JONES

Consultant plastic and reconstructive surgeon, Barry Jones, is Clinical Tutor for endoscopic aesthetic surgery at the Royal College of Surgeons. Enormously respected by his peers, in his private practice Jones is renowned as a 'people person', with a straighforward and serious attitude towards his work. Major operations are undertaken at the state-of-the-art Wellington Hospital.

Barry M. Jones MS FRCS

14a Upper Wimpole Street, London W1M 7TB, UK

Tel: +44-171-935 1938   Fax: +44-171-935 6607

THE BATH & RACQUETS CLUB

Like his other clubs, Harry's Bar, Mark's Club and Annabel's, Mark Birley's Bath & Racquets Club, tucked away in a mews behind Claridge's, is exceedingly discreet, beautifully decorated and perfect in every detail - right down to the immaculately-laundered 'whites' that are provided to members on each visit. But this in no way detracts from the seriousness with which it takes the job of keeping its members in the peak of fitness, with state-of-the-art exercise machines and top-flight personal trainers.

The Bath & Racquets Club
49 Brook's Mews, Davies Street,
London W1Y 1LE, UK
Tel: +44-171-499 9044   Fax: +44-171-629 5166

BAYERISCHER HOF
The great Falk Volkardt may have stepped down from the helm of this superb family-owned hotel but his daughter, Innegrit, is a worthy successor. She has just overseen a five year refurbishment programme (costing some DM50 million) which embraced the guest rooms, all public areas and even the façade. Despite the hotel's size, the atmosphere here is cosy and welcoming and the service outstanding. The hotel also provides an exceptionally high level of security, with tailor-made services available on

request. The Bayerischer Hof's lovely roof garden swimming pool overlooks the rooftops of Munich and the spire of the nearby Frauenkirche. Rooms and suites range in style from Parisian chic to Tirolean manor.

Bayerischer Hof
Promenadeplatz 2-6, D-80333 Munich, Germany
Tel: +49-89-21 200   Fax: +49-89-212 0633

BELTXENEA
A small brass plate at street level is the only indication that this restaurant exists at all. The restaurant has its own interior garden, where tables are much in demand. The Basque-inspired menu includes a highly recommended melon and lobster salad, as well as *Tronc de lluç Ondarroa*.

Beltxenea
Calle Mallorca 275, 08008 Barcelona, Spain
Tel: +34-93-215 3024   Fax: +34-93-487 0081

BENETTI
Established in Viareggio in 1873 by Lorenzo Benetti and originally producing commercial vessels, Benetti was instrumental in the development of today's modern yacht, with the semi-custom Delfino series in the 1960s. When the under-capitalised yard was rescued in 1985 by Paolo Vitelli's Azimut SpA the former family company gained not only financial muscle and sophisticated management but also the capability of constructing in GRP, steel and aluminium, up to 65m in length. 1998 launches include the 54m *Ambrosia*.

Benetti
Sales office: Viale dei Mareschi 14,
10051 Avigliana, Turin, Italy
Tel: +39-011-936 7272   Fax: +39-011-936 7270

BERNARDAUD
Though founded in 1863, this family-run Limoges porcelain company is remarkably forward-looking; its current tableware range is designed by Olivier Gagnère and Hervé Van der Straeten, two leading lights in the decorative arts. A real delight is its Paris salon de thé, where you can choose not just your tea and cakes, but also your porcelain.

Bernardaud
11 rue Royale, 75008 Paris, France
Tel: +33-1-47 42 82 66   Fax: +33-1-49 24 06 35

BERRY BROS & RUDD LIMITED
Trading from the same address in St. James's for 300 years (worth a visit for its atmosphere alone) and still owned by the Berry and Rudd families, this wine merchant is not as fusty as its history might suggest. A wine shop at Heathrow airport with a tasting bar (a glass of Château Latour being an ideal antidote to the rigours of the flight ahead), a highly informative website and Britain's most technically advanced storage facility maintain its edge.

Berry Bros & Rudd Limited
3 St James's Street, London SW1A 1EG, UK
Tel: +44-171-396 9600   Fax: +44-171-396 9641

BERLUTI
Anyone curious to know the price of a pair of *par mesure* women's boots at this famous shoemakers can no longer be in the dark, thanks to the revelations over the ex-French foreign minister Roland Dumas' affairs. Some people, it seems, will risk all to be finely shod. Hand made from a single, seamless piece of leather, Berluti's distinctively proportioned shoes are as comfortable as gloves. The colouring is an art in itself; rich reds or greens are rubbed

into black, creating a subtle patina.

Berluti
26 rue Marbeuf, 75008 Paris, France
Tel: +33-1-43 59 51 10 Fax: +33-1-42 89 57 92

THE BERKELEY
It was at the Berkeley that the Duke of Windsor first courted Mrs Simpson. Though the hotel moved in 1972 to its prime Knightsbridge loca-

tion, it retains its sense of discreet grandeur. Its roof-top health club incorporates a swimming pool, which can be opened to the sky in fine weather, and a state-of-the-art Christian Dior spa. Jean-Jacques Pergant leads an exemplary management team.

The Berkeley
Wilton Place, London SW1X 7RL, UK
Tel: +44-171-235 6000   Fax: +44-171-235 4330

DR BERNARD CORNETTE DE SAINT CYR
Flamboyant Dr Bernard Cornette de Saint Cyr's speciality is deep-tissue lifting of the face by, for example, re-covering cheekbones with fat from the jowls. He claims that his facelifts work right down to the bone rather than just pulling the surface of the skin like the average facelift - all without altering the patient's natural appearance.

Dr Bernard Cornette de Saint Cyr
15 rue Spontini, 75116 Paris, France
Tel: +33-1-47 04 25 02   Fax: +33-1-47 04 60 66

BERTHAUDIN
Fly first class on Swissair or stay at Badrutt's Palace in St Moritz and the chances are that you'll enjoy a Berthaudin wine. As well as being

Switzerland's leading winemaker, Berthaudin - founded in 1936 - is a first-class wine merchant. Claude Berthaudin, son of the founder, directs operations with panache and particularly recommends Hugel (Alsace) Chapoutier (Rhône valley) and Domaine Faveley (Burgundy).

Marcel Berthaudin SA
11 rue Ferrier, CH-1202 Geneva, Switzerland
Tel: +41-22-732 0626 Fax: +41-22-732 8460

BERTHILLON

Tucked away on the Ile St-Louis, this marvellous ice-cream shop gets its fair share of back-packing tourists - but don't let that put you off. You're just as likely to see St. Laurent-clad locals joining the permanent queue; they know it's worth the wait.

Berthillon
31 rue St-Louis en l'Ile, 75005 Paris, France
Tel: +33-1-43 54 31 61

BIENNALE INTERNAZIONALE DI ANTIQUARIATO

The Florence Biennial, now in its 38th year, exhibits Italy's best picture and furniture dealers. It was traditionally held at the Palazzo Strozzi, an architecturally distinguished Renaissance palace currently undergoing restoration, but since 1997 it has been based at the Palazzo Corsini, still inhabited by the Corsini family. This late Florentine-baroque palace's rooms serve as stands for the dealers.

Biennale Internazionale di Antiquariato
Piazza Strozzi 1, 50123 Florence, Italy
Tel: +39-055-28 26 35   Fax: +39-055-21 48 31
In September of every unevenly numbered year

BIENNALE INTERNATIONALE DES ANTIQUAIRES, PARIS

The Paris Biennale is one of the most luxurious art fairs in Europe, featuring sumptuous room-settings of high quality and unusual antiques and *objets d'art*, framed by specially-created Louis XIV mouldings. Over 120 international dealers, such as Luis Alegria, Didier Aaron, Gisèle Croës, Richard Green and Alberto Repossi, show pieces ranging from antiquities to the 1950s.

Biennale International des Antiquaires,
Carrousel du Louvre, 99 rue de Rivoli,
75001 Paris, France
Tel: +33-1-47 20 31 87 Fax: +33-1-47 23 51 83

THE BEST IN ITALY

Having begun as a rental agent for some of Italy's most beautiful, private and secure properties, this company, run by Count Girolamo and the American-born Countess Simonetta Brandolini d'Adda, has added property search and sales to its services. To achieve a perfect fit between purchaser and property, the Brandolinis prefer to meet all clients before embarking on a search and act as liaison between clients, lawyers, notaries and, if

required, local architects, craftsmen, fine art experts and decorators. They hold clients' hands throughout the entire, complex process of finding, buying, restoring and furnishing a property in Italy. Then, if wished, by acting as rental agents, they help to maximise the financial return from the property for the periods during which the owners are not in residence.

The company's rental portfolio currently comprises about 80 properties throughout Italy; for rentals Tom Cruise, Mel Gibson, Sting - and others which the ultra-discreet Brandolinis would not dream of mentioning - will go nowhere else. For clients, they also organise special events and tours - often with access to venues not usually open to the public. So personalised is the service that many clients have become firm friends with the Brandolinis.

The Best in Italy
via Ugo Foscolo 72, 50124 Florence, Italy
Tel: +39-055-22 30 64   Fax: +39-055-229 8912

BIRGER CHRISTENSEN

Furriers to the Royal Courts of Denmark and Sweden, Birger Christensen was established in 1869 in Copenhagen. The firm is renowned for the quality of the skins it uses to create beautifully-crafted coats in both classical and fashion-led styles. As well as making to measure, Birger Christensen will alter stock models according to clients' wishes. Clients' furs stored over the summer are delivered back by chauffeur in the autumn.

Birger Christensen A/S
Østergade 38, DK-1100 Copenhagen K, Denmark
Tel: +45-33-11 55 55   Fax: +45-33-93 21 35

BLANCPAIN

Jean-Jacques Blancpain founded the world's oldest watch brand 250 years ago. Thirteen generations later the company still vows that it will never make a quartz watch - or even an ordinary mechanical one! Famed sticklers for detail, Blancpain's Jura craftsmen continue to create archetypes to this day, embodied in the brand's six contemporary masterpiece models.

Blancpain
CH-1094 Paudex, Switzerland
Tel: +41-21-796 3636   Fax: +41-21-796 3637

BLOHM & VOSS

This is the yard that built the spectacular, Luigi Sturchio-designed *Lady Moura* (which became part of Mouna Al-Ayoud's divorce settlement) and the 73m, 37-knot *Eco*. Established in 1877 and, today, part of the Thyssen group, Blohm & Voss combines the technological expertise developed in its commercial and military divisions with exceptional standards of craftsmanship. It currently has a 145m under construction.

Blohm & Voss
P.O. Box 10-07-20, D-20005 Hamburg, Germany
Tel: +49-40-31 19 13 01   Fax: +49-40-31 19 33 38

BLAKES

Blakes Hotel has achieved almost legendary status since it was opened 15 years ago by the multi-talented Anouska Hempel - one of London's undisputed style leaders. The first of London's designer/boutique hotels - radical at the time and still one of the very best of its genre - it was an immediate hit with fashion, film and music stars.

Standing discreetly on a quiet South Kensington street, it has grown from a single townhouse to incorporate 52 bedrooms and suites. Each of these has been decorated (and is constantly updated) with tremendous flair by Anouska Hempel herself - each in its own distinctive style. A fusion of styles from East and West - Russia, India, Turkey, the old Colonies and Imperial Eastern Europe - has been brilliantly employed, expressing the essence of travel in a deeply cocooning environment. Among the favourite rooms are numbers 007, 505 and 109.

Guests can close the door on the world when they come here, which explains why it remains the favoured London bolthole for international celebrities who wish to escape the glare of publicity. In the centre of the building is a 'secret' courtyard garden, while the basement is home to a lively bar. The stylish restaurant and adjoining Chinese Room are also available for private parties.

Blakes Hotel
33 Roland Gardens, London SW7 3PF, UK
Tel: +44-171-370 6701   Fax: +44-171-373 0442

BLUMEN COMPANY

The Munich branches of Versace, Gucci and Bulgari have one thing in common - flowers by Julius Linke of Blumen Company. Linke, who originally trained in tailoring and theatre design, redecorates the interior of his shop four times a year and designs gardens as a sideline. His style ranges from baroque to contemporary.

Blumen Company
Maximiliansplatz 18, D-80333 Munich, Germany
Tel: +49-89-29 16 10 55   Fax: +49-89-29 16 10 59

LA BOBADILLA

The motive behind La Bobadilla is to offer guests "intimate contact with nature, with every comfort at hand" and it succeeds admirably, as some-time guests King Juan Carlos, Jean-Michel Jarre and Jessye Norman will attest. Its 350-hectare estate comprises holm-oak forests, olive groves and almond orchards. The 'sophisticated rustic' style of the buildings is complemented by (apparently) laid back but faultless service.

Finca la Bobadilla
Apartado 144, E-18300 Loja, Granada, Spain
Tel: +34-958-32 18 61   Fax: +34-958-32 18 10

BOGNER

Bogner was highly influential in creating skiwear with a fashion bias; in the Fifties it became synonymous with stretch pants in the USA. Founder Willy Bogner was an Olympic skier who did stunts for the James Bond films. While it now makes many other sportswear ranges, its skiwear keeps Bogner among the élite.

Willy Bogner
Sankt-Veit-Straße 4, D-81673 Munich, Germany
Tel: +49-89-43 60 63 14   Fax: +49-89-43 60 64 37

BON LLOC

Swedish chefs are known for the intelligence with which they combine their own and other culinary traditions, and Bon Lloc is a fine example of this. Lunch-time delicacies include cod with shrimp, chopped egg, horseradish and mashed potato; for dinner, try the more sophisticated Clam "cappuccino" with scallop croutons.

Bon Lloc
33 Bergsgatan, Kungsholmen, 11228 Stockholm, Sweden
Tel: +46-8-650 5082   Fax: +46-8-650 5083

BOURGIGNON FLORISTS

For almost 70 years the Bourgignon family has supplied the upper echelons of Madrid society with flowers; Michael Bourgignon, who was born in Holland, started the company in 1930. His legacy lives on in the shape of two sons, who now manage the two Bourgignon shops and plant nursery.

Bourgignon Florists
Almagro 3, 28010 Madrid, Spain
Tel +34-91-319 2692   Fax +34-91-457 6351

BOIVIN CHEZ ASPREY

Since 1890 the jewellery of Boivin has inspired a glamorous clientèle and admirers will be delighted that, today, the house still designs in the spirit of René Boivin. Under the experienced eye of Sylvie Vilein, new designs are being introduced to the existing collection, there are new variations on old themes and some old favourites re-made. Each piece is alive, some with articulated movements, sliding parts or pieces which pivot to reveal precious stones set in gold, silver, rock crystal or wood. The result is an exceptional fluidity, with intricate details, making pieces which resemble precious toys.

Boivin chez Asprey
49 avenue Montaigne, 75008 Paris
Tel: +33-1-47 20 82 64   Fax: +33-1 47 20 82 62

BOLLINGER

Pinot Noir makes its presence felt in the gorgeous, structured and uncompromising flavour of Bollinger's Special Cuvée. A meal in itself, it also goes beautifully with food, its full-bodied, 'winey' character making it a perfect match for many dishes. The most recent trio of vintages (1988, '89 and '90) are all masterpieces but you are not a true Bollinger aficionado until you have tasted its Vieilles Vignes Françaises, one of the rarest of all champagnes.

Bollinger
B.P. 4, 51160 Ay, France
Tel: +33-3-26 53 33 66   Fax: +33-3-26 54 85 59

BOODLE'S

Despite the influx of the odd businessman, membership still contains a good percentage of knights and squires. Established in 1762 as a political institution, Boodle's settled into a more sedate mould, thus avoiding the scandals that dogged some of its neighbours. Beau Brummel, and later Ian Fleming, were members; a ladies' annexe was added more recently.

Boodle's
28 St James's St, London SW1A 1HJ, UK
Tel: +44-171-930 7166

BONPOINT

As a young mother in search of clothes for her own children, Marie-France Cohen set up Bonpoint 20 years ago. Now she has shops in several major fashion capitals, offering beautifully made, classic-with-a-twist children's clothes, distinguished by their imaginative colourings and fine fabrics.

Bonpoint
229 Boulevard St Germain, 75007 Paris, France
Tel: +33-1-40 62 76 20   Fax: +33-1-45 56 02 61

BREGUET

Founded in 1775 by Abraham-Louis Breguet, known as 'the father of modern watch making'

(Queen Marie-Antonette was a patron), this Swiss company is still a leader in mechanical horology. Among its recent, impressive pieces is the updated Type XX model, the most authentic pilot watch available. Originally launched in 1954 as a tribute to Louis Breguet, pioneering aviator and great, great grandson of the founder, it was supplied to the French Air Force until 1970. The new Type XX Aeronavale has all the original features, while the Type XX Transatlantique also has a date display.

Montres Breguet
CH-1344 L'Abbaye, Switzerland
Tel: +41-21-841-90 90   Fax: +41-21-841 90 84

BREIDENBACHER HOF (HOTEL)

Since opening in 1812 this grand, traditional hotel has undergone several changes of style, most recently when it was bought by George Rafael in 1988. The antiques that furnish its rooms, such as a fine marquetry 19th century writing desk, are there to be used and enjoyed. Examples of the hotel's attention to detail include its having enough umbrellas to provide one for every guest if it should rain.

Hotel Breidenbacher Hof
Heinrich-Heine-Allee 36,
D-40213 Düsseldorf, Germany
Tel: +49-21-11 30 30   Fax: +49-21-11 30 38 30

THE BREGENZ FESTIVAL

Held from late July to mid-August on the shore of Lake Constance, this open-air festival is notable for its spectacular floating stage built out over the water. Opera is the thing here, from a spectacular staging of *Porgy and Bess* to lesser-known early works - the latter performed also in the concert hall and churches.

Bregenzer Festspiel
Postfach 311, A-6901 Bregenz, Austria
Tel: +43-5574-4076

BREITLING

The popular choice for men of action and pilots, Breitling timepieces have a long association with aviation and are worn today by the world's top aerobatics teams. Leon Breitling set up his first workshop making chronographs and complex stopwatches in 1884 and the brand's ruggedly stylish designs continue to maintain those high standards.

Breitling SA

PO Box 1132, CH-2540 Crenchen, Switzerland

Tel: +41-32-654 5454   Fax: +41-32-654 54 00

BRENNER'S PARK

This 125 year-old hotel is Germany's legendary contribution to the genre of the grand health resort. Under the inspired direction of Richard Schmitz, it not only remains one of the most luxurious havens in that country but continues to update its spa facilities and treatments in line with the most advanced thinking. As one guest remarked, "If it is true that the real test of a hotel is how you get treated in its least grand room, Brenner's is flawless." Like the Hôtel du Cap and Le Bristol, Branner's Park is owned by the reclusive Oetker family.

Brenner's Park Hotel and Spa

Schillerstrasse 6, D-76530 Baden-Baden, Germany

Tel: +49-7221-9000   Fax: +49-7221-38 772

BRYAN MAYOU

Trained as a plastic surgeon at the Birmingham Medical School and at London's St. Thomas' Hospital, Mayou is secretary of the British Association of Aesthetic Plastic Surgeons. His highly respected practice specialises in face-lifts, liposuction and breast surgery. He is based at the discreet Lister Hospital in Chelsea.

Bryan Mayou

Lister Hospital, Chelsea Bridge Road,

London SW1W 8RH, UK

Tel: +44-171-824 8080   Fax: +44-171-259 9887

BRUNO CONDI

For perfect cosmetic work, this is the dentist of choice among Milan's fashion aristocracy. His skill, coupled with considerable personal style, has brought him a host of celebrity clients. For instance, Naomi Campbell turned to Condi when she broke her tooth during a recent catwalk show. But most of his patients are perfectly normal - like Giorgio Armani's mother.

Bruno Condi

via San Paolo 13, 20100 Milan, Italy

Tel: +39-02-86 13 23

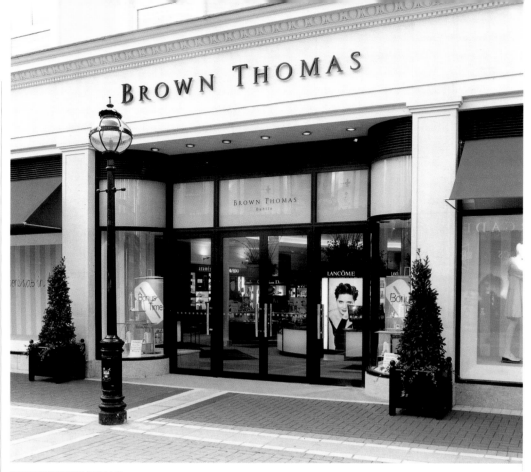

BROWN THOMAS

Canadian retail magnate Galen Weston and his elegant Irish wife, Hilary, have created Brown Thomas as their hugely successful take on the contemporary department store concept for the Irish market. If you're looking for big name designers - Dolce e Gabbana to Gucci - this is where to come. There is something for everyone, from a £20 French Connection T-shirt to a £2,000 Lainey Keogh cashmere dress. The menswear range is equally impressive, with Joseph, Nicole Farhi and Armani particularly well represented. Brown Thomas has traditionally been a strong supporter of Irish designers too: it has, for instance, recently championed up-and-coming designer Marc O'Neill.

The two-floor homeware department offers an excellent range of kitchenware, linens, china and contemporary designer furniture while, on the lower ground floor, Browns Bar is a lunchtime hot-spot for gourmet sandwiches and a glass of champagne. It is difficult to pinpoint the exact reason for Brown Thomas' success but the trick, it seems, is balancing modernism with other-worldly charm.

The company has just opened a new 'concept' store a hundred yards further up Grafton Street (BT2 is an outlet for major international designer sportswear labels in a dynamic and visually remarkable space) and has also launched Brown Thomas in Cork.

Brown Thomas

Grafton Street, Dublin 2, Ireland

Tel +353-1-605 66 66 Fax +353-1-679 52 60

Patrick Street, Cork, Ireland

Tel: +353-21-27 67 71   Fax: +353-21-27 47 92

BROOKS'S

Founded in 1764, Brooks's was described by Sir George Trevellyan as "the most famous political club that will ever have existed in London." This distinguished institution boasts up to eight generations of some families as members and, during 1998's Countryside March, allowed ladies into its main rooms for the first time ever.

Brooks's

St James's Street, London SW1A 1LN, UK

Tel: +44-171-493 4411

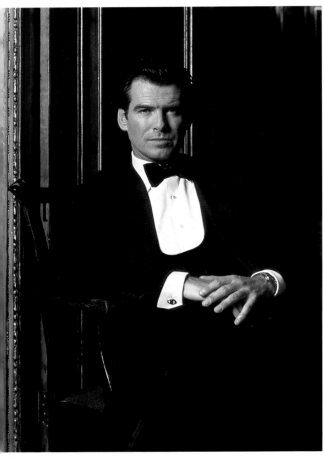

BRIONI

Established for more than 50 years at the same address on the via Barberini in Rome, Brioni is growing, under the leadership of Umberto Angeloni (grandson-in-law of co-founder Nazareno Fonticoli), into a major global brand. As well as famously dressing Pierce Brosnan as James Bond, Brioni is also responsible for the statesmanlike appearance of UN Secretary General Kofi Annan and the immaculate formal garb of conductor Riccardo Muti.

Brioni Roman Style,
via Barberini 50, 00187 Rome, Italy
Tel: +39-6-485 877   Fax: +39-6-487 3301

BÜHLERHÖHE SCHLOSSHOTEL and IMPERIAL RESTAURANT

Built as a convalescent home for officers of the Imperial Prussian Army, this castle is an elegant and deeply peaceful retreat, with 18 hectares of grounds, views over the Rhine valley and endless outdoor activities. Spa treatments range from the state-of-the-art to the simply pampering (rose-petal baths, milk-and-honey body wraps). The hotel's Imperial Restaurant is a gourmet destination in its own right.

Bühlerhöhe Schlosshotel
Schwarzwaldhochstrasse 1,
D-77815 Bühl/Baden-Baden, Germany
Tel: +49-7226-550   Fax: +49-7226-55 777

BUCARO

Renowned for the both its friendly and highly personalised service and its highly creative approach, which embraces both the traditional and modern idioms, the team at Bucaro is much in demand among Madrid's elite. Its floral decorations grace numerous embassies in the capital as well as the most glamorous parties.

Bucaro
Capitán Haya 26, 28020 Madrid, Spain
Tel: +34-91-556 4221   Fax: +34-91-556 4540

BUCHERER

With 18 shops in Switzerland and its own factory, which produces over 100,000 watches a year, Bucherer is the country's leading watch and jewellery retailer. A family-owned business, founded in 1888 and now run by Jörg Bucherer, it is also the largest Rolex retailer in Europe.

Bucherer
45 rue du Rhone, CH-1204 Geneva, Switzerland
Tel: +41-22-319 6266   Fax: +41-22-369 7000

BUEREHIESEL (RESTAURANT)

This building in the Orangerie Park is straight out of a Grimms' fairy tale - gabled, timbered and bedecked in flowers - and, in the first-floor dining room, you are surrounded by the leaves of the great plane trees. Antoine Westermann is justly celebrated for his light and modern interpretation of Alsace cuisine, with dishes like *Poulet de Bresse cuit comme un Baeckeoffe.*

Restaurant Buerehiesel
4 Parc de l'Orangerie, 67000 Strasbourg, France
Tel: +33-3-88 45 56 65   Fax: +33-3-88 61 32 00

BRUNO LAFOURCADE

"We live in the 18th century," states Bruno Lafourcade, master restorer of Provençal properties, with an air of regality. The vision of this self-educated architect/builder-cum-decorator is so assured that within ten months he can transform a dilapidated barn into a palatial *bastide* with every detail as good as, or even better than, the original. Meanwhile, his wife Dominique, a talented landscape gardener, will be redesigning the grounds with rows of lavender, cypresses, purple irises and other plants that are a match for the feisty Mistral.

Bruno Lafourcade
10 boulevard Victor Hugo, 13210 St-Rémy de Provence, France
Telephone: +33-4-90 92 10 14   Fax: +33-4-90 92 49 72

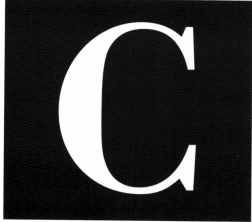

BULGARI

Since its signature antique coin jewellery and distinctive watches became favourites of the international style leaders in the late 1970s, Bulgari's influence on contemporary jewellery design has been enormous. Many of Bulgari's key design elements - generous volumes, rounded forms and a highly imaginative mixing of coloured stones, both precious and semi-precious - have become the standard vocabulary of contemporary jewellery design.

The Bulgari style is also expressed in the purity and simplicity of line seen in its silverware: centrepieces, tea services and desk accessories among them, as well as its wittily expensive versions of utilitarian objects, such as a tennis ball cannister in solid silver. Moving further into the accessories line during the 1990s, Bulgari introduced fragrance, followed by leather goods, ties, scarves and eyewear.

Paolo Bulgari remains Chairman and director of design today, while his brother, New York based Nicola - an acknowledged expert on antique silver and ancient coins - is Co-Chairman. However, it is

their nephew, Francesco Trapani, who has masterminded Bulgari's rise to become the third largest jeweller in the world (see '100 Leading Europeans' feature). Nevertheless, despite its size, Bulgari has never lost the feeling of 'soul' which comes of being a family company.

Bulgari Spa
Lungo Tevere Marzio 11,
00186 Rome, Italy
Tel: +39-06-68 81 01
Fax: +39-06-68 81 04 00

EL BULLI

Chef Ferran Adria and manager Juli Soler run an exceptional establishment, with cuisine perfectly matched to its setting in a pretty little cove, with a terrace over the sea (guests can even arrive by boat). The cooking is rooted in the Mediterranean tradition but is ingeniously creative: Black olive madeleines, Caramelised quail eggs, Tomato and watermelon consommé, Cod mousse with onion preserve, Rock mussels with garlic broth, and Langoustines with boletus mushrooms.

El Bulli
Cala Montjol, 17480 Roses, Gerona, Spain
Tel: +34-972-15 04 57   Fax: +34-972-15 07 17

C&C / PIERO CASTELLINI

A fourth-generation member of a textile industry family, Castellini works in a modern, though traditionally-inspired idiom, strongly influenced by the Tuscan rustic style. His sense of colour is wonderful; rich ochres, tempered with deep reds and greens abound. Together with his cousin, Emanuele, he has a shop in the heart of Milan, which offers a wide selection of fabrics, furnishings and decorative accessories, all displayed in imaginative room sets.

C&C / Piero Castellini
via della Spiga 50, 20121 Milan, Italy
Tel: +39-02-78 02 57   Fax: +39-02-78 05 01

CALA DI VOLPE

The shiny set continues to flock to this village-style resort, built around a private marina, a secluded step down the coast from the now tourist-choked Porto Cervo. The lovely, seemingly artless rooms, most with their own terraces, are in fact beautifully thought out, with exposed beams, rough, whitewashed stone walls and simple, Sardinian-styled furnishings.

Hotel Cala di Volpe
07020 Porto Cervo, Costa Smeralda, Sardinia, Italy
Tel: +39-0789-97 61 11 Fax: +39-0789-97 66 17

CAMPER & NICHOLSONS

Established in 1782, Camper & Nicholsons' services cover the entire, complex process of yacht ownership. The brokerage division encompasses New Construction; a Yacht Management and Technical Services division takes care of maintenance and operations and the Charter Management division helps owners to maximise income through marketing the yacht for charter.

Camper & Nicholsons
25 Bruton Street, London W1X 7DB, UK
Tel: +44-171-491 2950
Fax: +44-171-629 2068

CAMPILLO DE SAN JUAN

Madrid's élite has patronised this private sporting estate, just outside the capital, since 1971. The region's mountainous terrain provides excellent opportunities to hunt wild deer, boar and partridge. The menu in the estate's restaurant, naturally, emphasises game dishes. Other facilities on offer include horse riding and tennis.

Campillo de San Juan
Paseo de Moet 7, 28008 Madrid, Spain
Tel: +34-91-549 1862   Fax: +34-91-543 9332

THE CAPITAL HOTEL

Small but perfectly formed, David and Margaret Levin's place is a gem - truly a grand hotel in miniature. A liveried doorman greets you, a fire burns in the hearth and uncommonly courteous staff escort you to beautifully appointed rooms and suites. The small restaurant, winningly decorated by Nina Campbell, has earned a Michelin star for Philip Britten's outstanding cooking.

The Capital Hotel
22 Basil Street, Knightsbridge,
London SW3 1AT, UK
Tel: +44-171-589 5171   Fax: +44-171-225 0011

LE CAPRICE

Home from home for many of London's glitterati, Chris Corbin and Jeremy King's restaurant has established a flawless formula - often imitated, rarely equalled - for clubbish bonhomie at sensible prices. Service (led by Angelo and Jesus) is affectionate and efficient, the food perfectly pitched (its fishcakes are a famous cure-all) and the décor modern but (probably as it should be) unremarkable.

Le Caprice
Arlington House, Arlington Street,
London SW1A 1RT, UK
Tel: +44-171-629 2239

CARACENI

Discreet to the point of impenetrability, Caraceni draws a veil of silence over the élite clientele which patronises its bespoke tailoring service. The company is less reticent about its achievements, however, justifiably boasting that it makes some of the best men's clothes in the world. Silvio Berlusconi is reputedly a satisfied customer.

A. Caraceni
via Fatebenefratelli 16, 20121 Milan, Italy
Tel: +39-02-655 1972   Fax: +39-02-29 00 33 74

CARITA

The late Rosy and Marie Carita's legendary beauty salon, founded in 1947, has never seemed slicker. Sophia Loren and Catherine

CARTIER

Now the world's largest jewellery company, Cartier has been tremendously influential ever since it was founded in Paris in 1847 by Louis-François Cartier. From the days when the Empress Eugénie was its patron, its creativity has made it the toast of the élite. King Edward VII described Cartier as the "Jeweller of Kings, King of Jewellers." The house's clients over the years have ranged in style from The Duchess of Windsor to Elton John and Paul McCartney.

Conjuring up each epoch's *zeitgeist*, Cartier has interpreted everything from Art Deco and Oriental art to aviation in its quest for inspiration and, reflecting its success in doing so, vintage Cartier jewellery continues to increase in value.

High jewellery remains Cartier's forte (one of the most jaw-droppingly beautiful pieces made by any jeweller in the past year is its necklace comprising a huge, polished emerald teardrop suspended from a rope of perfect South Sea pearls). However, the more accessible 'Must de Cartier' (comprising clocks and watches, pens, lighters, eyewear, leather goods, fragrance and accessories) was launched in 1973, introducing the concept - since adopted by many of its competitors - of a 'diffusion' line. Other Cartier landmarks include the introduction of the bracelet watch in 1888.

Cartier
13 rue de la Paix, 75002 Paris, France
Tel: +33-1-49 26 17 00

Deneuve were regulars in its early days and the place still attracts international celebrities, especially following its facelift two years ago by Yves Benoit. New hair, body and skin treatments have been developed and masseur Ronald Crooks is regarded by many as the best in Paris.

Carita
11 rue du Faubourg Saint Honoré,
75007 Paris, France
Tel: +33-1-44 94 11 11
Fax: +33-1--44 34 11 25

CARLTON HOBBS

Carlton Hobbs has a well-deserved reputation for exciting discoveries, recently showing a Louis XVI panelled room previously in the JP Morgan collection, an Egyptian throne based on a design illustrated in Denon's Description of Egypt, and a pair of Adam bookcases made for Middleton Park, the Fifth Earl of Jersey's great Oxfordshire house.

Carlton Hobbs
46 Pimlico Road, London SW1W 8LP, UK
Tel: +44-171-730 3640   Fax +44-171-730 6080

CARRE DES FEUILLANTS

Situated between Place Vendôme and the Tuileries Gardens, the Carré des Feuillants is every boulevardier's dream. Mondaine guests dine in what was once a convent, enjoying a salivatory frisson at the positive sinfulness of Gascon chef Alain Dutournier's flamboyant culinary *tours des force*.

Carré des Feuillants
14 rue de Castiglione, 75001 Paris, France
Tel: +33-1-42 86 82 82   Fax: +33-1-42 86 07 71

CAZENOVE & LOYD SAFARIS

Many travel agents organise safaris in Africa but, if you wish to discover the real spirit of the continent - and enjoy great comfort at the same time, this company stands out. It takes clients to the most remote corners of sub-Saharan Africa with guides whose love and knowledge of the country will be a revelation.

Among the trips offered is one by private plane across the desert landscape of Namibia; ace pilot Bertus Schoeman flits through the sea mists along the Skeleton Coast while flocks of flamingoes fly alongside. Alternatively, Cazenove & Loyd can take you into the Central Kalahari, where you will camp out, tracking game with one of the few remaining Bushmen and learning how they live. Tailor-made journeys to the Okavango Delta, canoe trips along the Lower Zambezi and walks in Tanzania's rarely-visited Selous are other options.

But perhaps the most romantic and sybaritic of all is an old-style mobile tented safari (the word 'safari' is Swahili for 'journey'). The tents have four-poster beds, swathed in mosquito netting, and canvas bath tubs and showers, while the mess tent has Persian rugs on the floor, silver and crystal on the table and an old gramophone to provide suitably evocative music.

Cazenove & Loyd Safaris
3 Alice Court, 116 Putney Bridge Road, London SW15 2NQ, UK
Tel: +44-181-875 9666   Fax: +44-181-875 9444

CASA DE DIEGO

For fans of fans, like Karl Lagerfeld, this is the ultimate source. Ignore the frightfully kitsch 'holiday souvenir' numbers, in favour of finely carved sandalwood or simple cotton models. Real connoisseurs, though, go for the 19th century (and earlier) collectors' fans in tortoiseshell, mother-of-pearl and ivory.

Casa de Diego
Puerta del Sol 12, 28008 Madrid, Spain
Tel: +34-91-435 5144 Fax: +34-91-522 6643

CASINO DE DIVONNE

Situated a few kilometres over the French border, the tables of the Belle Epoque Casino de Divonne are a smart destination for Genevans in search of the high life. Opened in 1954 and now, under the aegis of Jean-Claude Aaron, ranked first in France, it is one of the few casinos to have renewed the playing of traditional games.

Casino de Divonne
avenue des Thermes, 01220 Divonne-les-Bains, France
Tel: +33-4-50 40 34 34   Fax: +33-4-50 40 34 23

CASINO DI VENEZIA

Italy's most elegant casino may not be particularly exclusive but the building itself is truly magnificent and worth a visit in its own right. Constructed in the 15th century, the palazzo has been sensitively updated, without sacrificing any of its precious Baroque stateliness. The Cuori d'Oro (gilt leather) room is particularly enchanting.

Casino Municipale di Venezia
Cannaregio 2040, 30121 Venice, Italy
Tel +39-041-529 7111   Fax +39-041-529 7132

EL CASTANO

Owned and run by Eduardo Araoz Cazatur, this remarkable property outside Toledo used to belong to celebrated hunter Ricardo Menem and his partner Juan Antonio Conde. It is home to a staggering variety of high-quality big game, including red stag, fallow deer, moufflon sheep, boar and several more species. Eduardo can also arrange ibex and chamois hunting nearby.

El Castaño
Edouardo Araoz Cazatur,
Jose Abascal 55, 28003 Madrid, Spain
Tel: +34-91-422 3775   Fax: +34-91-442 8643

CASTEL THALASSO

Perched on the spectacular coast of Belle-Ile-en-Mer, Castel Thalasso offers breathtaking views and bracing ocean air. This small, discreet and beautifully run institute is the place to come for weight loss and anti-stress treatments for both men and women. The *jambes lourdes* treatment is brilliant, although, to really get the best out of the spa, a six day course (with four seaweed and mud treatments a day) is recommended. Most clients stay at Claire et Jean-Louis Gourny's delightful Castel Clara next door.

Castel Thalasso
Goulphar, Belle-Ile-en-Mer,
56360 Bangor, France
Tel: +33-2-97 31 80 15   Fax: +33-2-97 31 51 69

CASTELLO DEL SOLE

This 18th century manor was transformed in 1942 into an exquisite hotel, now run with panache by Bruno Kilchenmann. Its 20-acre grounds, complete with private beach on Lake Maggiore, make it a delightfully secluded retreat. Chef Othnar Asthlegel's menu is an inventive combination of French and Italian influences.

Castello del Sole
via Muraccio 142, CH-6612 Ascona, Switzerland
Tel: +41-91-791 0202   Fax:+41-91-792 1118

Cartier

Nouvelle Vague rings
Yellow gold or white gold.

Cartier: 175/176 New Bond Street, London W1, Telephone: 0171-493 6962, 188 Sloane Street, London SW1, Telephone: 0171-235 9023, The Fine Jewellery Room and The International Room of Luxury at Harrods, Telephone: 0171-730 1234, Heathrow Terminal 4, Telephone: 0181-745 6724.

CERAMICA SANTA ANA

Rudolf Nureyev, Leonard Bernstein, Gary Cooper and Anthony Quinn have all bought *azulejos* (the colourful, glazed Andalusian tiles, introduced to the Iberian peninsula by the Moors) from this smart little shop, which was established in 1870. Santa Ana will happily undertake private commissions - and not necessarily as grand as that it undertook for Mar-A-Lago, Marjorie Merriweather Post's Palm Beach retreat.

Cerámica Santa Ana
Calle San Jorge 31, 41010 Seville, Spain.
Tel/Fax: +34-95 433 3990

CERCLE INTERALLIE

For *bon chic bon genre* Parisians there is no place more reassuring than this conservative club, founded in 1917. Membership is near-impossible to obtain but those fortunate enough to attend its lavish balls will encounter many of France's most distinguished aristocrats. In more practical terms, the club's gymnastic classes and extravagant buffet lunches are first-rate.

Cercle Interallié
33 rue du Faubourg Saint Honoré,
75008 Paris, France
Tel: +33-1-42 65 96 00

CERRO HERRERA

Close to the ravishing hill-town of Rhonda, Cerro Herrera is a dramatic destination for those (including Claus von Bulow and members of the Rolling Stones) in search of seclusion and comfort. Blessed with sweeping views as far as Gibraltar and the mountains of Africa, this Andalucian-style residence, complete with Moorish courtyard and fountain, is set in a stunning 11-acre garden.

Cerro Herrera, Andalucia, Spain
c/o Earth, 2 Durand Gardens, London SW9 0PP, UK
Tel: +44-171-793 9993   Fax: +44-171-793 9994

CERRUTI 1881

Nino Cerruti's fluidly elegant clothes are a Hollywood favourite, on screen and off. His suits helped to define Richard Gere's character in *Pretty Woman*, and that of Jeremy Irons in *Reversal of Fortune*, and his womenswear is favoured by Winona Ryder and Sigourney Weaver. A select few Cerruti clients have their suits made to measure in Paris by ultra-discreet maestro tailor Luigi Laudicina.

Cerruti 1881
3 Place de la Madeleine, 75008 Paris, France
Tel: +33-1-53 30 18 81

CERTOSA DI MAGGIANO (HOTEL)

In this former Carthusian monastery where St. Bruno's disciples gathered for meditation in the 14th century, today's epicureans meet to enjoy both the Tuscan cuisine and the comforts of the cosily fitted out rooms. Anna Recordati and Margherita Grossi run it with considerable charm, their feminine touch evident in myriad tiny details.

Hotel Certosa di Maggiano
Strada di Certosa 82, 53100 Siena, Italy
Tel: +39-0577-28 81 80   Fax: +39-0577-28 81 89

CHALET BRAMES

The ultimate in ski-hideaway luxury, Chalet Brames has been decorated with exquisite taste in the traditional alpine style by its French owner. Among its features are two elegant dining rooms and drawing rooms, a private driveway with electronic gates to ensure added privacy and security, an outdoor jacuzzi and a huge terrace with spectacular south-facing views towards Mont Vallon. As if this isn't enough to ensure your comfort, the staff includes two chefs, a ski-guide and a chauffeur for the chalet's own 4x4 vehicle. At the heart of over 600km of pistes and magical powder skiing, Chalet Brames is discreetly tucked away, yet only a short distance from

Meribel's village centre.

Chalet Brames, Méribel, France
c/o Villas and Apartments Abroad,
420 Madison Ave, New York, NY 10017, USA
Tel: +1-212-759 1025   Fax: +1-212-755 8316

CHALET DU MONT D'ARBOIS

Nadine de Rothschild owns this charming mountain lodge in Haute-Savoie. Set above Megève, it is an idyllic, intimate retreat in winter or summer. Accommodation is smart, the cuisine is classical yet innovative, the cellar understandably superb, service is discreet yet highly efficient and the rooms are bursting with character.

Chalet du Mont D'Arbois
447 chemin de la Rocaille, 74120 Megève, France
Tel: +33-4-50 21 25 03   Fax: +33-4-50 21 24 79

CHAMPNEYS

Under the aegis of Managing Director, Viscount Thurso, Champney's recent £7.5 million facelift has made it one of Europe's finest health resorts. Note the word 'resort' rather than spa, for Champneys believes in achieving well-being through pampering, not suffering, as evidenced by its superb menus and its recommendation of fine wine as a positive health benefit. Over 100 treatments, including complementary therapies, are on offer at this former Rothschild mansion.

Champneys
Wigginton, Tring, Hertfordshire, HP23 6HY, UK
Tel: +44-1442-29 11 11   Fax: +44-1442-29 10 01

CHANEL

Possibly the greatest fashion house of the 20th century, first under the seminally influential Coco and latterly under Karl Lagerfeld. From the moment that he arrived at the moribund couture house in 1983, Lagerfeld set to work creating a new and more vibrant image, which he has evolved, sometimes subtley, occasionally quite radically, in keeping with the mood of the times.

Chanel
29 rue Cambon, 75008 Paris, France
Tel: +33-1-42 86 28 00   Fax: +33-1-47 03 43 61

CHANEL HAUTE JOAILLERIE

The House of Chanel has crowned its recent achievements by reintroducing a spectacular precious jewellery collection, made to designs first created by Coco Chanel in 1932, with the addition of some new designs. Themes include starry diamond comets, pearl-studded quiltings, onyx or opal camellias and semi-precious Byzantine-style settings.

Chanel Haute Joaillerie
42 avenue Montaigne, 75008 Paris, France
Tel: +33-1-40 70 12 33   Fax: +33-1-47 20 25 42

CHARLES GORDON-WATSON

The subject of a 1997 BBC documentary, *The Big Deal*, bloodstock agent Charlie Gordon-Watson deals with many of the best known British owners, notably the Lloyd Webbers and Chris Wright of Chrysalis Records fame, as well as Prince Fahd Salman. Consistently among the top five yearling buyers, his classic winners include *Desert Prince* and *Culture Vulture*. He comes from a horse-loving family; his sister, Mary, is a leading three-day eventer.

Charles Gordon-Watson
Fairholt House, 2 Pont Street, London
SW1X 9EL, UK
Tel: +44-171-838 9747   Fax: +44-171-838 9767

CHARVET

The vibrant tie stands facing you as you enter this famous store give it the air of a bazaar but, once on the second floor, you couldn't be in more soothing surroundings to buy a made-to-measure shirt. Only one person works on each shirt, which takes 30 days to complete. Mark Birley and Jean-Louis Dumas-Hermès are clients.

Charvet
28 Place Vendôme, 75001 Paris, France
Tel: +33-1-42 60 30 70

CHÂTEAU DE BAGNOLS

Lady Hamlyn has described her restoration of this sublime 13th century château as a labour of love. The painstaking craftsmanship is evident in the majestic Grand Salon, with its beautiful wall paintings and elaborate Renaissance fireplace, one of the most important in France.

In the regal Salle des Gardes dining room, guests feast on robust charcuterie, river fish and excellent cheeses. Most impressive, though, are the bedrooms, particularly the tower room, with its 15th century trompe l'oeil ceiling imitating a tent, and the former 17th century chapel.

Château de Bagnols
69620 Bagnols-en-Beaujolais, France
Tel: +33-4-74 71 40 00   Fax:+33-4-74 71 40 49

CHÂTEAU DE BONMONT

This private 18-hole golf course - offering some of the finest golf in Switzerland and a favourite hangout for Geneva's élite - was designed by British architect Don Harradine. The terrace of a 12th century Cistercian Abbey overlooks the greens while the clubhouse, an 18th century mansion, has nine luxuriously appointed guest rooms, a fitness centre and many other sports facilities.

Château de Bonmont
CH-1275 Cheserex, Switzerland
Tel: +41-22-369 2129   Fax: +41-22-369 3412

CHATEAU DE LOCGUENOLE

Owned and run by the de la Sablière family, this 19th century château and 18th century manor are set in 250 acres of splendid parkland on the edge of a bay, complete with boathouse. The château's interior is resplendent with wood panelling, historic tapestries and magnificent chandeliers. Chef Philippe Peudenier's menu pays tribute to local produce and seafood.

Château de Locguénolé
Route de Port-Louis, 56700 Hennebont, France
Tel: +33-2-97 76 29 04   Fax: +33-2-97 76 82 35

CHATEAU DE VAULT DE LUGNY

This white, 16th century château is one of the more seductive hotels in France, as both its wealthy Parisian and discerning foreign guests attest. Cone-shaped evergreens section off squares of immaculately kept lawn, setting the scene for the drama - or romance - within, where formal, courteous staff will pamper you in decadent surroundings.

Château de Vault de Lugny,
89200 Avallon, France
Tel: +33-3-86 34 07 86   Fax: +33-3-86 34 16 36

CHAUMET

Founded in 1780, Chaumet is one of the world's oldest jewellery houses, with an impressive pedigree dating back to its days as court jewellers to Napoleon. Chairman Pierre Haquet has updated the company's image, with movers and shak-

ers such as footballer David Ginola and actress Ines Sastre promoting the latest lines of jewellery and watches.

Chaumet
12 Place Vendome, 75001 Paris, France
Tel: +33-1-44 77 24 00   Fax: +33-1-42 60 41 44

CHATEAU SAINT-MARTIN

Konrad Adenauer described Château St Martin, just up the hill from St-Paul-de-Vence, as "the antechamber to paradise" and it seems pointless to try to better his description. Originally the castle of the Knights Templar, it really is special - as guests Tom Cruise and Nicole Kidman would doubtless confirm.

Château St Martin
Avenue des Templiers, 06140 Vence, France
Tel +33-4-93 58 02 02   Fax +33-4-93 24 08 91

CHECCHINO DAL 1887

When Checchino was founded, this area of Rome was the city's abbatoir. True to its origins, the restaurant became expert in cooking with offal - so much so that it has a Michelin star. Politicians, noblemen and gourmets flock to its panelled dining room, not only for the vitals but also for superlative cheeses and one of the best cellars in the country.

Checchino dal 1887
via Monte Testaccio 30, 00153 Rome, Italy
Tel: +39-06-574 6318

CHELTENHAM LADIES' COLLEGE

This strongly academic, traditional girls' boarding school - established in 1852 on a huge, purpose-built campus with the most marvellous facilities - turns out charming and confident young ladies, who are 'destined to have a career'. Strong also in sports and music, its careers department is excellent. About 20 per cent of the pupils come from abroad.

Cheltenham Ladies' College
Cheltenham, Gloucestershire GL50 3EP, UK
Tel: +44-1242-52 06 91   Fax: +44-1242-22 78 82

CHESTER JONES

After more than 20 years at Colefax and Fowler, where he became Managing Director, Chester Jones set up his own design practice. Trained as an architect, Jones focuses on decorating but will happily act in the former capacity when required. His firm has just completed a spectacular project in Barbados.

Chester Jones Studio
240 Battersea Park Road, London SW11 4NG,UK
Tel: +44-171-498 2717   Fax: +44-171-498 7312

CHEVAL BLANC (CHATEAU)

Distinguished from the other Saint-Emilions by its 60 per cent cabernet-franc content (most are merlot-dominated), Château Cheval Blanc is, quite simply, the best of its appellation. Mellow, complex and delicate, it shows certain similarities to Pomerol, on the border of which it stands. The 35-hectare domaine has been in the hands of the Fourcaud-Laussac family for 150 years. Drink the 1985 vintage for the millennium.

Château Cheval Blanc
33330 Saint-Emilion, France
Tel: +33-5-57 55 55 55   Fax: +33-5-57 55 55 50

CHEZ NICO AT 90 PARK LANE

Chez Nico at 90 Park Lane is high rollers' heaven - sublime, classically-based French cooking from a three-star Michelin chef in a lofty grand room. Service doesn't get much better than this and, if you really want to spoil your friends in style, book the private room for 20.

Chez Nico at 90 Park Lane
90 Park Lane, London W1A 3AA, UK
Tel: +44-171-409 1290

LA CHIUSA

This family-run restaurant is housed in an old stone farmhouse. Here, Dania and Umberto Lucherini are virtually self-sufficient, producing their own meat, vegetables and olive oils and baking their bread in the original wood-burning oven. Window tables in the large and simply decorated room provide ravishing views of the Tuscan hills.

La Chiusa
via della Madonnina 88,
53040 Montefollonico, Italy
Tel: +39-0577-66 96 68   Fax: +39-0577-66 95 93

CHLOÉ

Kate Moss and the hippest girls in town are wearing Chloé, a label enjoying a renaissance under Stella McCartney, who has con-

CHEWTON GLEN

Martin and Brigitte Skan's Hampshire gem feels more like a large family home than an hotel. The Skans' wide-ranging travels (visiting dozens of the world's best hotels and restaurants) are reflected in both the myriad small luxuries they provide and their passionate attention to detail.

Set in a tranquil landscape of gardens and woodlands, a 20-minute walk from the coast, Chewton Glen is beautifully decorated - though never chi-chi; service, from a notably charming staff, orchestrated by the ever-present Managing Director Peter Crome, is impeccable, indeed almost telepathic - though wonderfully discreet. In short, this is the blueprint for a country house hotel. Small wonder that it was rated No.1 in Europe in *Condé Nast Traveller's* 1998 readers' poll, and is also the only privately owned Five Red Star Hotel in Britain. Nevertheless, over 70 per cent of first-time visitors come by word-of-mouth recommendation.

Chewton Glen is a superb place for rejuvenating and relaxing. Most of the individually decorated 33 bedrooms and 19 suites have balconies or terraces overlooking the beautifully-kept grounds. The spa, centred around a magnificent classically-designed indoor pool, offers a vast range of health and beauty treatments and, for the more energetic, Chewton Glen has both indoor and outdoor tennis courts and its own 9-hole Par 3 golf course.

Pierre Chevillard's menu in the Michelin-starred restaurant is based on local produce and seafood and the wine cellar has over 500 different bins chosen by Mark Walter, Chewton Glen's sommelier, who has been selected to represent Britain in the world sommelier competition.

Chewton Glen - 'The Hotel, Health and Country Club'
Christchurch Road, New Milton, Hampshire BH25 6QS, UK
Tel: +44-1425-27 53 41   Fax: +44-1425-27 23 10
Email: reservations@chewtonglen.com

founded critics by rewarding her employers with an upturn in sales. While perhaps not the best-made in their price range, the clothes are ravishingly pretty: will-o'-the-wisp silk skirts, corset bodices and antiquarian lawn blouses.

Chloé

54-56 rue du Faubourg St Honore,
75008 Paris, France
Tel: +33-1-44 94 33 33   Fax: +33-1-47 42 60 50

CHRISTIAN DIOR

Possibly not since Christian Dior launched his New Look in 1947 has the fashion house had such a cohesive style. Head designer John Galliano's creations are the stuff of fantasy, inspired by a pell-mell of past couturiers and suited to night-time glamour. What does all this have to do with the legendary couturier? Think of both as guardians of sensuality and the female form.

Christian Dior

30 avenue Montaigne, 75008 Paris, France
Tel: +33-1-40 73 54 44   Fax: +33-1-40 72 00 60

CHRISTIAN LACROIX

It seems extraordinary to think that (with the backing of Bernard Arnault) Christian Lacroix established his couture house only in 1987, so firmly is it up there with The Greats. Lacroix's background - Arles, with its bullfights and bright sun - is clearly reflected in his style, which mixes fabrics, patterns, colours and embroidery with great aplomb and daring.

Christian Lacroix

73 rue du Faubourg Saint-Honoré, 75008 Paris, France
Tel: +33-1-42 68 79 00 Fax: +33-1-42 68 00 12

CHOPARD

Is it a watch? Is it a jewel? Of all its world-famous watches, Chopard's 'Happy Diamonds' model (designed in 1976 by Ronald Kurowski) is the timepiece of choice amongst the young Riviera set.

Quality and creativity are the hallmarks of Chopard, the watchmaker-jeweller which produces this little beauty. Founded in 1860 by Louis-Ulysse Chopard, the firm was sold by his grandson, Paul-André, to the Scheufele family in the 1960s. It remains very much a Scheufele family affair, with Karl and Karin Scheufele at the helm and their children, Karl-Friedrich and Caroline as vice-presidents.

The firm's structure emphasises self-sufficiency. Making almost everything in-house gives it, in Karl Scheufele's words, "a high degree of flexibility and discretion" and enables it to "transform ideas into reality almost immediately." This is important for such a strongly design-led firm, which receives up to 600 orders each year for unique pieces. The most expensive to date, the $25 million Chopardissimo took over 2000 hours of work to produce.

Underlining its commitment to craftsmanship and technology, Chopard produced, in 1995, a calibre, which enabled it to return to its watch-making roots as a 'manufacture', the coveted title bestowed only on those firms which produce every single part of their watches.

Chopard Genève

8 rue du Veyrot, CH-1217 Geneva-Meyrin, Switzerland
Tel:+41-22-719 3131   Fax: +41-22-719 3135

Chopard Boutiques: Athens, Baden-Baden, Cannes, Florence, Istanbul, London, Marbella, Moscow, Munich, Paris, Vienna, and the Far East

CHRISTIAN LIAIGRE

"Minimalism with warmth" is how American designer Marc Jacobs describes the work of Christian Liaigre, who furnished Jacobs' first store in New York. His sofas and chairs are almost monastic in their simplicity of line, while exotic woods, soft leather and generous proportions give pieces a hint of luxury. Designers Valentino and Adolfo Dominguez are also fans.

Christian Liaigre

42 rue du Bac, 75007 Paris, France
Tel: +33-1-53 63 33 66
Fax: +33-1-53 63 33 63

CHRISTIAN TORTU

Having become obsessed with flowers as a young child, Christian Tortu translated that love into what has become an über-chic business. Since he set up his shop in 1979, his often radical stylistic approach has made him first port of call for the kings of the Paris couture (Dior, Chanel and Valentino among them).

Christian Tortu

6 carrefour de l'Odeon, 75006 Paris, France
Tel: +33-1-43 26 02 56
Fax: +33-1-43 29 71 99

CHRISTIAN LOUBOUTIN

Work experience with Chanel, YSL and Charles Jourdan prepared Paris' society shoemaker Christian Louboutin to go it alone in 1990 with a shop of his own, followed by another in London seven years later. His ultra-feminine shoes, with their trademark red soles, are often compared to the great Roger Vivier's.

Christian Louboutin

19 rue Jean-Jacques Rousseau,
75001 Paris, France
Tel: +33-1-42 36 05 31   Fax: +33-1-42 36 08 56

CHRISTIAN STEIN

Founded by Christian Stein in 1966, this top-flight gallery, which specialises in contemporary Italian and international artists, has included Gilbert & George, Luciano Fabro, Jannis Kounnellis, Claes Oldenburg, Antoni Tàpies, Giulio Paolini and Thomas Schutte among those exhibited.

Christian Stein

corso Monforte 23, 20122 Milan, Italy
Tel: +39-02-66 98 24 44
Fax: +39-02-76 00 71 14

CHRISTOFLE

One of the few French luxury goods companies still owned and managed by members of its founding family, Christofle was the favoured supplier of *haute orfèvrerie* to the royal court in the early 19th century. However, it was the purchase, in 1842, of the patents for electrolytic plating that heralded the company's expansion. Today, Christofle provides not only silver but also tableware in porcelain, crystal, rare woods and Chinese lacquer.

Christofle

9 rue Royale, 75008 Paris, France
Tel: +33-1-49 33 43 00   Fax: +33-1-49 33 43 84

CHRISTOPHE ROBIN

This hair colourist to the catwalk contingent is utterly charming, yet his perfectionist approach means that clients must be inordinately patient when waiting for an appointment in his jewel-box of a salon. The reward is worth it; his heady-smelling potions soothe frayed nerves, and the colour, which blends perfectly with your skin tone, lasts twice as long as normal.

Christophe Robin

7 rue du Mont Thabor, 75001 Paris, France
Tel: +33-1-42 60 99 15   Fax: +33-1-42 60 99 14

CHRISTOPHER GIBBS

This super-discreet dealer, who has been in the business for 40 years, refuses to be drawn about celebrated clients (and friends) such as John Paul Getty and Mick Jagger, who come to him, in particular, for first class 17th and 18th-century furniture. He lives in a beautiful 'mini-stately' home in Oxfordshire.

Christopher Gibbs Ltd.

3 Dove Walk, Pimlico Road, London SW1W 8PH, UK
Tel: +44-171-439 4557   Fax: +44-171-730 84 20

CHRISTIE'S

Ever since its first auction, on 5th December 1766, Christie's has maintained a pre-eminent position in the world's art market. An early coup came when the founder, James Christie, valued and negotiated the sale of Sir Robert Walpole's collection of paintings to Catherine the Great of Russia in 1778. These works of art now hang in St Petersburg's Hermitage Museum. A string of distinguished sales quickly followed, including those of Madame du Barry's jewellery and the works of artist Sir Joshua Reynolds. By the mid-19th century, Christie's had become the leader in country house sales; in 1848, its sale of the contents of Stowe, the Duke of Buckingham's stately home, lasted for 40 days.

The first work of art to sell for over £1 million, Velazquez's *Portrait of Juan de Pareja*, was sold by Christie's in 1970 for £2.31 million while, in 1990, van Gogh's *Portrait of Dr Gachet*, sold for $82.5 million at Christie's in New York, the highest price ever paid for a work of art at auction. Today Christie's sales cover artworks from pictures and furniture to ceramics and Asian art, teddy bears, celebrity memorabilia and wine. It has over 100 offices in 39 countries in Europe, the Americas and the Pacific Rim.

Christie's

8 King Street, St James's, London W1Y 6QT, UK
Tel: +44-171-839 9060   Fax: +44-171-839 1611

CIPRIANI (HOTEL)

What you miss in authentic Venetian atmosphere you make up for in calm and space in this awesomely luxurious island outpost, presided over by the brilliant Natale Rusconi. The ravishing gardens contain the only swimming pool (salt water) and tennis court in Venice, as well as a private dock. Wake to the sound of seagulls and bells, either in the grand, main building or the charming 15th century Palazzo Vendramin. Most discreet, however, are the five suites in the newly-restored, 16th century Palazzetto Nani Barbaro, which come with their own butler. The Palazzetto has a new restaurant, too. Called Cips, it floats on a terrace with a grandstand view of St Mark's Square.

Hotel Cipriani & Palazzo Vendramin

Giudecca 10, 30133 Venice, Italy

Tel: +39-041-520 7744   Fax: +39-041-520 3930

CIPRIANI COOKERY SCHOOL

The Cipriani's cookery courses where, every year, a star from the culinary world gives classes in Italian cookery to students who stay at the Cipriani, have become as renowned as the great hotel itself. In the belief that understanding the broader cultural picture is essential to an appreciation of cuisine, trips and excursions are an integral part of the course.

Cipriani Cookery School

Giudecca 10, 30133 Venice, Italy

Tel: +39-041-520 7744   Fax: +39-041-520 3930

CIRENCESTER PARK POLO CLUB

England's oldest polo club, Cirencester was established in 1894 on the Earl of Bathurst's ravishing Gloucestershire estate. The delight of this club is its low-key atmosphere, despite having its share of glamorous sponsored days each season. Lord Vestey and his brother, Mark, are both past club Chairmen and Prince Charles (this is his 'local') and the Sultan of Brunei make regular appearances.

Cirencester Park Polo Club

Cirencester Park, Gloucestershire GL7 2BU, UK

Tel: +44-1285-65 32 25   Fax: +44-1285-65 50 03

CLAIRE BATAILLE & PAUL IBENS

In partnership since 1968, Claire Bataille and Paul Ibens candidly admit to a deep dislike of Postmodernism, favouring, instead, the sober and functional style of Bauhaus and Le Corbusier and the beautiful perspectives of the baroque. Regarding themselves more as architects than decorators, they stress the importance of purity - and of natural light and good space distribution. "Only after that do we start to think about adding a little poetry." explains

CHRISTOPHER FOLEY

Christopher Foley is the most discreet of dealers. He works privately for what he describes as the "off-piste collector" and, though he rarely buys at auction, he has nevertheless amassed a large number of first-class British paintings, both from private collections and institutions. Several hundred pictures are in store at all times and other dealers often turn to him for stock. Clients come by word of mouth and include many stylish international collectors. Top-quality 18th century portraits and sporting pictures are Foley's speciality; his greatest love is the work of George Stubbs. He also handles Reynolds, Constable and Turner, among others, and has sold to the National Portrait Gallery, London and to the Mellon Collection at Yale. A major contributor to the *MacMillan Dictionary of Art*, on the subject of English Painting, Foley also advises on acceptance in lieu of tax for the Museums and Galleries Commission.

Christopher Foley

Tel/fax:+44-171-373 3130

By appointment only

Claire Bataille. Their timeless and "neutral" environments can be found in numerous commercial projects and in private houses from the Philippines to Turkey, Austria to New Mexico.

Claire Bataille & Paul Ibens

Vekestraat 13 Bus 14, 2000 Antwerp, Belgium

Tel: +32-3-231 3593   Fax: +32-3-213 8639

CLAIREFONTAINE

Since 1984 Clairefontaine has been a favoured watering-hole of the bankers and political leaders who gather in Luxembourg. In his two discreetly luxurious, Louis XIV-style dining rooms, chef-proprietor Tony Tintinger serves seasonally-inspired fare, including innovative fish dishes (he personally recommends his *Suprême de turbot à la crème du champagne et perles de caviar*) and excellent game.

Clairefontaine

Place de Clairefontaine 9,

L-1334 Luxembourg City, Luxembourg

Tel: +352-46 22 11   Fax: +352-47 08 21

THE CLARENCE

The Clarence, which was bought - and substantially upgraded - by two members of the rock band U2, is a truly original place. A second home to Dublin's new Bohemian élite, it guarantees guests a unique experience of the city - in the penthouse, for instance, you can wallow in an outdoor hot tub as you gaze out over the city skyline. And the Tea Rooms, presided over by chef Michael Martin, is one of

the most elegant restaurants in Dublin.

The Clarence
6-8 Wellington Quay, Dublin 2, Ireland
Tel: +353-1-670 9000 Fax: +353-1-670 7800

HOTEL CLARIS

Behind its 19th century façade lies an über-chic bastion of sophisticated, contemporary aesthetics. Friendly staff and eclectic artworks (including a museum of Egyptian antiquities) lend it real character, while the 20 duplex suites are bound to impress. The roof terrace has an open air swimming pool and a view to write home about.

Hotel Claris
Pauy Claris 150, 08009 Barcelona, Spain
Tel: +34-3-487 6262   Fax: +34-3-215 7970

CLAUDIA GIAN FERRARI ARTE CONTEMPORANEA

Claudia Gian Ferrari ran her father's gallery of 20th century Italian art before setting up her own business in 1990 to promote contemporary Italian and international artists – these include Sean Scully, Martin Maloney, David Salle and José Maria Sicilia. She has drawn many new Italian collectors to buy contemporary art.

Claudia Gian Ferrari
Arte Contemporanea
via Brera 30, 20121 Milan, Italy
Tel: +39-02-86 46 16 90   Fax: +39-02-80 10 19

CLINIQUE LA PRAIRIE

Famous for its cellular rejuvenation injections (said to arrest the ageing process and revitalise the body), La Prairie offers a great deal more besides, cocooning you in well-being and gentle comfort. Come here to lose weight or have plastic surgery, to repair shattered nerves or an exhausted body. There is a state-of-the-art hospital on site, a gym, personal trainers, countless beauty treatments and a wonderfully calming swimming pool. The whole point of La Prairie is to unwind and feel rejuvenated - to breathe in the sweet, alpine air, eat the delicious, healthy food and sleep soundly and untroubled.

Clinique La Prairie
CH-1815 Clarens-Montreux, Switzerland
Tel: +41-21-989 3311   Fax: +41-21-989 3333

CLIVEDEN

Formerly home of the Astors and now a hotel, this house holds many delights on the grand scale, including a ratio of four staff to each bedroom. The restaurant is decorated with gilded panelling from Mme de Pompadour's

CHRISTOPHER HODSOLL

Well known for his idiosyncratic taste - a sort of English country house grandeur seen through a quirky, 18th century connoisseur's eye - Christopher Hodsoll worked for many years with the great Geoffrey Bennison. He has continued Bennison's tradition of boldly luxurious but slightly faded aristocratic taste but has added his own enthusiasms, such as his love of architectural furniture. His shop contains a rich mixture of handsome English 18th and 19th century furniture, including tables, chairs, mirrors and bookcases, both classical and gothic in style, with the odd marble bust of a Roman worthy and over-scaled oriental porcelain. The window displays are always remarkable and it is not surprising to discover that the Hodsoll client list includes many well known figures who appreciate and respect his taste and connoisseurship.

Like his late mentor, Hodsoll himself is increasingly turning his hand from simply dealing in antiques to decorating, having recently completed a splendid townhouse in Belgravia, a large country house in Virginia for an industrialist, and an apartment in New York for a film producer. In partnership with Lulu Lytle, Hodsoll recently formed a design company called Soane, producing perfectly-scaled furniture, lamps and accessories, all with a classical inspiration.

Christopher Hodsoll
89-91 Pimlico Road, London SW1W 8PH, UK
Tel: +44-171-730 3370 Fax: +44-171-730 1516

Château d'Asnières and Nancy Astor's old bedroom now forms part of a suite, with a large private terrace overlooking the parterre and vast grounds beyond.

Cliveden
Taplow, Berkshire SL6 0FJ, UK
Tel: +44-1628-66 85 61
Fax: +44-1628-66 18 37

CLONGOWES WOOD COLLEGE

James Joyce was six and a half, or "half past six", as he put it himself, when he arrived as a pupil at Clongowes in 1888. The school, set in splendid woodlands, has changed since; it is very forward-thinking but still retains its distinctive Jesuit ethos. A major building programme is currently underway to provide even better amenities for the next millennium.

Clongowes Wood College
Naas, Co. Kildare, Ireland
Tel: +353-45-86 82 02   Fax: +353-45-86 10 42

CLUB 55

For twenty years, Club 55 has been the only smart beach restaurant in St Tropez. This is thanks to Patrice de Colmont, a real charmer, whose outwardly laid-back manner belies a steely determination never to let standards drop. There is nowhere better to enjoy a lunch of faultlessly grilled, fresh-from-the-boat sardines, an excellent bottle of rosé and a post-prandial cigar. Beyond fashion, '55' shows just how good perfect simplicity can be.

Club 55
Plage de Pampelonne, boulevard Patch,
83350 Ramatuelle, France
Tel: +33-4-94 79 80 14

CLUB DE CAMPO
Don't bother trying to get a tee-time here at the weekends; as home club to Madrid's smart set (and with the biggest membership of any golf club in Spain), it is invariably swamped. Javier Arana, designer of El Saler, has done a fine job here, on the edge of the Spanish capital, too.

Club de Campo
Villa deMadrid, Carretera de Castilla Km2,
E-28040 Madrid, Spain
Tel: +34-91-357 2132   Fax: +34-91-307 0629

COLEFAX AND FOWLER - WENDY NICHOLLS
Despite being joint head (with Vivien Greenock) of the decoration division of Colefax and Fowler, Wendy Nicholls' name is hardly known to outsiders. That's thanks to her legendary discretion about clients so private and so grand that they wouldn't dream of appearing even in *Architectural Digest*. However, they do include the Goulandris family, Paul McCartney, Sir Anthony and Lady Bamford and, currently, Tommy Hilfiger. Although steeped in Colefax's English sensibility, Nicholls' own taste is for a more contemporary simplicity.

Colefax and Fowler - Wendy Nicholls
39 Brook Street, London W1Y 2JE, London, UK
Tel: +44-171-493 2331   Fax: +44-171-355 4037

COLLEGE DU LEMAN
The pupils of this internationally recognised and accredited boarding and day school, in the small town of Versoix, enjoy a beautiful campus of 20 acres and the close attention of considerate teachers at a ratio of one to ten. The school's dual academic programme enables pupils to study in French or English and they also have the option of summer school.

Collège du Léman
74 Rue de Sauverny, CH-1290 Versoix-Geneva,
Switzerland
Tel: +41-22-755 2555   Fax: +41-22-755 1993

COLLETT ZARZYCKI
Anthony Collett and André Zarzycki specialise in residential architecture, interior design and decoration. As one of the few practices applying this multi-disciplinary approach to projects, it has attracted high-profile clients all over the world - including Lord Palumbo, Conrad Black and Lord Archer. Best known for working within the traditions of classical architecture, the firm's philosophy is one of continuous evolution and innovation.

Collett Zarzycki
Fernhead Studios, 2B Fernhead Road,
London W9 3ET, UK
Tel: +44-181-969 6967   Fax: +44-181-960 6480

COLNAGHI
Paul Colnaghi founded this business in 1760 and was invited to hang the Royal Collection soon after. Today the gallery is best known for Old Master paintings and drawings. Colnaghi worked with art historian Bernard Berenson to create major American private collections and, in 1930, formed a syndicate to purchase paintings from the Hermitage

CLARIDGE'S
Regarded by many as the finest hotel in London, Claridge's epitomises the standards which, over the last century, have made the Savoy Group synonymous with excellence. Its sympathetic restoration perfectly illustrates Group Managing Director Ramón Pajares' determination to "simultaneously bring our guests the benefits of modern technology whilst remaining true to the heritage and traditions of the Group."

More than any hotel in the British capital, Claridge's truly is a seamless blend of past, present and future. For example, new technology has made possible many discreet extras to add to the dozens of small luxuries: bathroom stair risers which light up at night, fax machines hidden behind closed doors on sliding shelves and room service which arrives exactly when asked for (a result of two new service lifts - the fastest in Europe).

The sixth floor used to house the servants and maids of the potentates and dignitaries who used Claridge's as their London home. Now, however, it has been completely re-designed to incorporate the beautifully-decorated Olympus Health and Beauty Suite, with state-of-the-art exercise machines and treatment rooms, together with a self-contained suite of private dining rooms. And, if you simply have to stay in London's smartest suite, look no further than the art-deco Brook Penthouse which comes with the services of a private butler.

Claridge's
Brook Street, Mayfair, London W1A 2JQ, UK
Tel: +44-171-629 8860   Fax: +44-171-499 2210
Email: info@claridges.co.uk

(the bulk of which were bought by Andrew Mellon and given to Washington's National Gallery of Art). Gallery director is Florentine Gian Luca Barolin who, besides being a notable expert in drawings, has successfully stream-lined the company over the last two years.

Colnaghi
15 Old Bond Street, London W1X 4JL, UK
Tel: +44-171-491 7408   Fax: +44-171-491 8851

COMME CHEZ SOI

This glorious restaurant, which has been in the Wynants family since 1926, is decorated with burnt caramel-coloured mahogany in the Art Nouveau style of Victor Horta. A giant among Belgium's chefs, Pierre Wynants numbers ethereal sea-urchin soup and terrific autumnal game dishes among his menu high points. Delicious coffees, the result of Wynant's own careful blending of beans, add a final touch of perfection.

Comme Chez Soi
23 Place Rouppe, 1000 Brussels, Belgium
Tel: +32-2-512 2921

COMTE ARMAND (DOMAINE DU)

Owned by the Armand family and directed by Québécois Pascal Marchand, this 10-hectare domaine is dedicated to the big Volnay and Pommard reds. Low yields and careful vinification make the Pommard, Clos des Epeneaux (the 1989 is the one to drink this year), a perfect example of pinot noir. Demand for the 40,000 bottles produced each year makes it hard to find on sale.

Domaine du Comte Armand
Place de l'Eglise, 21630 Pommard, France
Tel: +33-3-80 24 70 50   Fax: +33-3-80 21 65 07

COMTE GEORGES DE VOGÜE (DOMAINE)

The de Ladoucette family's characteristically dense and silky reds have brought this domaine considerable celebrity. The estate comprises only grands crus, among them 75 per cent of the musigny in cultivation and, unusually, almost half a hectare of musigny blanc - a wine which owes its fortunes to the British, who rate it as highly as they do Montrachet. The estate is right back on form, following the installation of new management in 1986 and its Musigny 1990 is highly recommended for 1999.

Domaine Comte George de Vogüe
rue Sainte Barbe,
21220 Chambolle-Musigny, France
Tel: +33-3-80 62 86 25   Fax: +33-3-80 62 82 38

COMTES LAFON (DOMAINE DES)

For many fans there is no better Mersault; Dominique Lafon's limited production (especially of his concentrated and unctuous Mersault premier cru and Montrachet), coupled with low grape yields and exceptional wine-making skills, make for high quality with prices to match. Lafon's grandfather founded the Paulée de Mersault - the lunch where all the Mersault producers assemble during the sales at the Hospice de Beaune, each bringing his own wine. Go for the Meursault-Genevrières 1990 this year.

Domaine des Comtes Lafon
Clos de la Barre, 21190 Meursault, France
Tel: +33-3-80 21 22 17   Fax: +33-3-80 21 61 64

CONNOLLY

Famously dubbed the 'Gap for millionaires', Connolly stocks indispensable basics of ineffable quality. Family-owned since 1878, the company had already supplied the upholstery for every Rolls Royce ever made, along with Concorde and the Houses of Parliament, when it moved into retailing two years ago. Its collection of beautifully designed clothing, accessories and *objets*, themed around the company's motoring heritage, has come as a revelation to style aficionados. Ross Lovegrove's elegant luggage collection is resonant of the touring sports cars of 40 years ago, combining the finest leather with burr walnut frames and polished aluminium fittings. Accessories range from a leather-clad touring espresso machine to the world's finest tool kit. Clothes are dreamy - Connolly's suede car-coats, six-ply cashmere sweaters and distinctive driving shoes (made by the factory which originally patented the design and first popularised by Gianni Agnelli in the Fifties) are currently the uniform for transatlantic lotus-eaters.

Connolly
32 Grosvenor Crescent Mews,
London SW1X 7EX, UK
Tel: +44-171-235 3883   Fax: +44-171-235 3838

CORVIGLIA

Two years after taking over from his father, Hartly in 1992, the hugely popular Retho Mathis remodelled his clutch of four restaurants, perched at almost 2500 metres above sea-level on the ski slopes overlooking St Moritz. As expected, the town's jet-setters all flock here - notably to La Marmite and The Brasserie, for *flânerie*, serious gossip and Retho's Engadine cooking.

Corviglia
7500 St. Moritz, Switzerland
Tel: +41-81-833 6355   Fax: +41-81-833 8581

COOLMORE

Without question Europe's No.1 stud, John Magnier's Coolmore - set up initially in partnership with Robert Sangster - operates on the principle of globalisation, its County Tipperary headquarters supplemented by properties in America and Australia. The progeny of Coolmore's stallions consistently produce classic Group One and Group Two

winners (see John Magnier profile in '100 Leading Europeans').

Coolmore Stud
Feathard, Co. Tipperary, Ireland
Tel: +353-52-31 298   Fax: +353-52-31 382

CONTROL RISKS

This consultancy advises individuals and companies worldwide on how to reduce the impact on their activities of political instability, social and technological change, terrorism, fraud and crime. Majority-owned by its employees, the company is retained exclusively by Lloyds of London underwriters, Cassidy Davis Hiscox, to provide priority crisis response to insured clients.

Control Risks Group
83 Victoria Street, London SW1H OHW, UK
Tel: +44-171-222 1552 Fax: +44-171-222 2296

COS D'ESTOURNEL (CHATEAU)

This world-renowned estate, owned by the Prats family, has a superb, elevated location on gravelly soil, which results in a dense, complex and harmonious 'super second' cru (of which the 1990 will be ready for drinking this year). The extraordinary château, with its bell tower and Pagoda-style roofs, is a legacy of M. d'Estournel's travels throughout India and Asia, while the splendid front gate, brought back from Zanzibar, is evidence of the Prats family's own travels.

Château Cos d'Estournel
33180 Saint-Estèphe, France
Tel: +33-5-56 73 15 50
Fax: +33-5-56 59 72 59

COUTTS & CO.

One of Britain's oldest private banks, Coutts is, today, the private banking arm of the Natwest Group. The bank describes its approach as "more holistic" than that of a traditional merchant bank, building a strategy around each client to grow the assets. Herschel Post, Chief Executive since 1995, is recognised as the architect of this new approach.

Coutts & Company
40 The Strand, London WC2R OQS, UK
Tel: +44-171-753 1000

COWDRAY PARK POLO CLUB

This is the real aficionados' polo club and the atmosphere is pure country-house polo. The late Lord Cowdray was almost solely responsible for the post-war revival of the game in England and the club stands on his

THE CONNAUGHT

How many hotels still have a moratorium on in-house advertising because "it would detract from the feeling of living in a particularly fine club"? Very few. But then, the ultra-discreet Connaught has long been a bastion of civilised values. The hotel, which celebrated its centenary in 1997, is one of the most distinctive and distinguished establishments in London.

Here is a hotel which oozes character from every pore, a place where nothing is done in half measures. For instance, General Manager, Duncan Palmer, proudly reveals that, instead of installing conventional mini-bars, the hotel has recently equipped each guest room with an elegant drinks tray - which is serviced by a butler, not once

but twice a day. Touches like these are typical of a hotel which prides itself on providing impeccable service in truly refined surroundings. In this context it hardly seems surprising that so many of the hotel's guests are regulars (as are the aristocrats and blue-chip businessmen and lawyers who patronise its oak-panelled bar, Restaurant and Grill). They come to The Connaught because they know exactly what to expect - not least, a notably friendly and personal welcome. Unlike so many hotels which claim to offer unparalleled comfort, the Connaught really does delight... every time.

The Connaught
Carlos Place, Mayfair, London W1Y 6AL, UK
Tel: +44-171-499 7070   Fax: +44-171-495 3262
Email: info@the-connaught.co.uk

17,000-acre estate, overlooked by the dramatic ruins of the castle.

The Gold Cup - as the final of the British Open, the most important match of the English season - naturally attracts a glossy social crowd; however, insiders know that the best high-goal games of the season usually take place on the preceding Thursday, during the semi-final. Brook Johnson is based here, as is superstar Adolfo Cambiasso (a 10-goal player before he could drive a car).

Cowdray Park Polo Club
Cowdray Estate Office, Midhurst,
West Sussex GU29 0AQ, UK
Tel: +44-1730-81 32 57   Fax: +44-1730-81 73 14

COYS

Coys' collection of beautiful motors is enough to bring tears to the eyes of even the least mechanically-minded. W. E. Coy founded the company in 1919 to service the motoring needs of Kensington residents and was the first to use petrol pumps. The car showroom was introduced after WWII and is now internationally renowned as a source of fine classic cars.

Coys of Kensington
2-4 Queens Gate Mews, London SW7 5QG, UK
Tel: +44-171-584 7444
Fax: +44-171-584 2733

LES CRAYERES

Gérard Boyer offers over 150 champagnes to accompany his exquisite cuisine. The titles of his dishes, such as *Le filet de Saint Pierre poêlé, une crème de chou-fleur, quelques légumes dans leur jus acidulé, un cromesqui à l'ail confit et persil plat*, are Proustian in their complexity. Retire after dinner to the stately home-style of one of the hotel's 19 rooms; number 16, with its huge terrace overlooking the tranquil, seven-hectare park, is among the best.

Les Crayères
64 boulevard Henry Vasnier,
5110 Reims, France
Tel: +33-3-26 82 80 80   Fax: +33-2-26 82 6552

CREDIT SUISSE HOTTINGUER

Hottinguer joined forces with Credit Suisse at the beginning of 1998 to create Credit Suisse Hottinguer. The new institution has gone to great lengths to ensure that the standards which Hottinguer's private banking customers had taken for granted would not now be jeopardised. Despite the merger, then, Hottinguer looks set to retain its status as one of the better private banking operations in Europe.

Credit Suisse Hottinguer,
38 rue de Provence, 75009 Paris, France
Tel: +33-1-49 70 58 00   Fax: +33-1-49 70 58 80

CRIQUETTE HEAD

A member of France's top racing dynasty (her father is the legendary Alec - now retired from training but still an active owner and breeder - and her brother jockey-turned-trainer Freddy), Criquette Head has won classics in both France and England since taking over her father's yard about 12 years ago. Her easygoing style belies a thorough professionalism - clearly appreciated by such owners as Sheikh Al-Maktoum and the Wertheimer family.

Criquette Head
32 avenue du Général Leclerc,
60500 Chantilly, France
Tel: +33-3-44 57 01 01 Fax: +33-3-44 58 53 33

CRISTINA CASTANER

The espadrille has taken on a glamorous edge thanks to the Castañer family, who have been making these casual classics for generations. Isabel Castañer, who was invited by Yves Saint Laurent to make embroidered designs for his shows, has been followed by her daughter, Cristina, who opened this boutique and has added Donna Karan, Manolo Blahnik and Inès de la Fressange to her client list.

Cristina Castañer
Mestre Nickolau 23, 08021 Barcelona, Spain
Tel: +34-93-414 2428

CROCKFORDS

The oldest private gaming club in the world, Crockfords was first established in 1828. Several changes of address later, it arrived, in 1983, at its present home, a magnificent Robert Adam house, whose beautiful plasterwork and panelling are offset by ravishing flower arrangements. Members are a mix of aristocrats and international high rollers.

Crockfords, London, UK
At the time of writing, British law prohibits the publication of contact details for British casinos. The law is currently under review.

CRISTALLERIES SAINT LOUIS

When Saint Louis was made *verrerie royale* to Louis XV in 1767, the patron saint's name replaced that of Munzthal, which dated back to 1586. Today, under the ownership of Hermès, Saint Louis' classic designs - richly coloured or decorated with precious-metal filigree - are being supplemented by ultra-modern styling, as in the edgy 'Cosmos' range.

Cristalleries Saint Louis
13 rue Royale, 75008 Paris, France
Tel: +33-1-40 17 01 74   Fax: +33-1-42 44 13 88

CVM

Although still only six years old, Baron Riedesel zu Eisenbach's company has built up a distinguished reputation as a wine importer and retailer.   Mansard Baillet, Chapuy, Volleraux and Riesner are champagnes supplied from family-run vineyards that CVM retains for its up-market clientele. Also worth procuring are the red and white Bordeaux, Château de Prieur.

CVM
Rimloser Straße 67,
D-36341 Lauterbach, Germany
Tel: +49-6641-185 20   Fax: +49-6641-185 50

DA GIACOMO

This decidedly relaxed restaurant is generally packed with the who's who of Milan's media and fashion circles. The Renzo Mongiardino decor includes alabaster chandeliers, offset by pretty, green-painted wood panelling. The cooking changes with the seasons; follow a melt-in-the-mouth caper pizza with baked sea bass with olives or eggs with black truffles.

Da Giacomo
via Pasquale Sottocorno 6, 20100 Milan, Italy
Tel: +39-02-76 02 33 13

DA GUIDO

Lilia Alciati's agnolotti are rightly in demand; she has been perfecting the recipe for 35 years. This two-star Michelin eaterie also benefits from her husband Guido's magnificent 45,000-bottle wine list. With glorious white truffles and game in winter, and exquisite zucchini flowers in summer, it is one of Italy's finest restaurants for authentic regional cooking.

Da Guido
Piazza Umberto I 27, Castigliole d'Asti, Italy
Tel: +39-0141-96 60 12   Fax: +39-0141-96 60 12

DAI DAVIES

This affable, Welsh-born plastic and cosmetic surgeon trained at Bart's and is held in the highest esteem both by his patients and his colleagues. A specialist in noses, breasts and facial surgery.

D.M. Davies FRCS
55 Harley Street, London W1N 1DD, UK
Tel: +44-171-631 3927   Fax: +44-171-636 6573

DAL PESCATORE

Opened in 1920 by Antonio Santini's grandparents, Dal Pescatore enjoys a ravishing setting on the banks of the River Oglio. Regional - and religiously seasonal - Italian cooking is given an imaginative interpretation by Nadia, Italy's greatest woman chef. Her risotto with

saffron and fried artichokes (available only in winter) is heavenly.

Restaurant Dal Pescatore
Loc Runate 17, Canneto, 46013 Mantova, Italy
Tel: +39-0376-72 30 01   Fax: +39-0376-70 304

DALI THEATRE-MUSEUM

The Dalì Theatre Museum is the largest surrealist object in the world. Salvador Dalì himself said of it: "Where, if not in my own city, should the most extravagant and solid examples of my art remain?" He created his own ambience for the display of works that trace his artistic development; highlights include a plaster cast of the artist's own backside.

Dalì Theatre-Museum
Plaça Gala-Salvador Dalì 5,
17600 Figueras, Spain
Tel: +34-972-51 18 00

DALLOYAU

A sublime caterer, traiteur and pâtissier with its own tearoom, Dalloyau is situated in the heart of Saint-Germain, where it was founded in 1802. Its skill in making cakes, chocolates

and ice cream has been handed down from generation to generation and, today, the whole operation runs under the expert eye of manageress Nadine Bernarde.

Dalloyau
99-101 rue du Faubourg Saint Honoré,
75008 Paris, France
Tel: +33-1-42 99 90 00

DAN PEARSON

Youthful garden designer Dan Pearson trained in England, India and Jerusalem before embarking on an original and distinguished career. Having made people rethink conventional English gardening, through his bold use of form and colour, he is now a cult figure among the horticultural fraternity. Milestone commissions include designs for Priscilla Carluccio, Liz Tilberis and Violante Visconti.

Dan Pearson
80c Battersea Rise, London SW11 1EH, UK
Tel/Fax: +44-171-924 2518

DANIEL KATZ LTD

The purchase of a French 19th century bronze animal triggered Daniel Katz's passion for bronzes from the 18th century to the Renaissance. He opened his gallery in 1996, staging bi-annual exhibitions, and has the knack of turning up rare and beautiful objects. In 1981 he discovered Giambologna's marble Bathsheba - carved in the mid-1560s and lost since 1632 - in a Swedish country house.

Daniel Katz Ltd
59 Jermyn Street, London SW1Y 6LX, UK
Tel: +44-171-493 0688   Fax: +44-171-499 7493

DANIEL MALINGUE

In 1998 Daniel Malingue celebrated his 35th year in business with what he calls his "musée imaginaire", an impressive catalogue of his finest pieces, including Cézanne's *Rideau à fleurs et Fruits*, Picasso's *L'homme à la Clarinette*, Renoir, Monet, Seurat, and Bonnard. Malingue says, "Impressionist Masters and 20th century art have been my focus and perhaps I have neglected contemporary art. The next generation will take the gallery in a new direction and I expect that the masters of the future will be part of it."

Galerie Daniel Malingue
26 avenue Matignon, 75008 Paris, France
Tel: +33-1-42 66 60 33   Fax: +33-1-42 66 03 80

DAUVISSAT (DOMAINE)

The plumply elegant and concentrated, barrel-aged wines from this great chablis label express, from the outset, the subtleties of the *terroir* from which they come. Would-be new clients for Dauvissat's beautifully made wines must, with little hope of success, join a waiting list. The wine to drink in 1999: Chablis Grand Cru les Preuses, 1990.

Domaine Dauvissat
8 rue Emile Zola, 89800 Chablis, France
Tel: +33-3-86 42 11 58

DAVID CHIPPERFIELD

Time is running out if you would like a David Chipperfield-designed house. Having won the redesign of Berlin's Neues Nuseum (pitching against Frank Gehry), Chipperfield has hit the international big time, although he had already practically invented the 'shop as shrine' concept in the late 80s, with his wood, slate and stone creations. Chipperfield's work is characterised by cool, clean lines, big volumes and set-square geometry and each project is tailored to its site.

David Chipperfield
1A Cobham Mews, London NW1 9SB, UK
Tel: +44-171 267 9422   Fax 44-171 267 9347

DAVID LODER

David Loder, who comes from a long and gentlemanly line of racing owners and breeders, has become Newmarket's most successful young trainer. Originally installed by brothers Charles & Edward St. George at Sefton Lodge in Newmarket, he has quickly become a favourite with Sheik Mohammed, who has hired him to uproot from Newmarket to France to train, exclusively for him, a string of 140 two year-olds at the former Evry racecourse. Tall and prematurely bald, Loder does not seek popularity and is considered to be very ambitious and single-minded.

David Loder
Graham Lodge, Bird Cage Walk,
Newmarket, Suffolk CB8 0NE, UK
Tel: +44-1638-66 22 33 Fax: +44-1638-66 55 96
(until December 1998)

DAVID MLINARIC

Probably the most respected interior designer in England, David Mlinaric's measured opulence has found favour with clients ranging from Lord Rothschild and Mick Jagger, to the David Kochs and Christopher and Pia Getty. Mlinaric is renowned for his cerebral approach, faultless taste and love of architecture ("I let the decoration answer the architecture," he has said.) He believes that it takes years to do a big house properly and, unusually among designers of his calibre, Mlinaric encourages his clients to buy things for themselves, thus making the process more personal.

Mlinaric, Henry & Zervudachi Ltd
38 Bourne Street, London SW1W 8JA, UK
Tel: +44-171- 730 9072 Fax: +44-171-823 4756

DAVIDE HALEVIM

Davide Halevim saved for two years to buy his first carpet. Now his Milan shop, which opened in 1977, has been supplemented by four more, in Porto Cervo, Cortina d'Ampezzo, Capri and Monaco, specialising in carpets dating as far back as the 14th century. Why in resorts? Because, Halevim maintains, only when free of the pressures of daily urban life can one truly appreciate such things of beauty.

Davide Halevim
via Borgospesso 5,
20100 Milan, Italy
Tel: +39-02-76 00 22 92   Fax: +39-02-78 43 28

DAVIDOFF OF LONDON

Edward Sahakian is a name familiar to epicureans all over the world who beat a path to his door in London. The wood-panelled shop over which he presides exudes the warm scent of the fine Dominican tobacco from which Davidoff makes its cigars (having moved production from Cuba in the late 1980s to safeguard quality).

Davidoff of London
35 St James's Street, London SW1A 1HD, UK
Tel: +44-171-930 3079   Fax: +44-171-930 5887

DE GRISOGNO

Having been popular in the 1930s, black diamonds lost favour with jewellers, due to their rarity and extreme brittleness. However, Fawaz Gruosi has launched a stunning collection of jewels, which combines these naturally jet-black stones with silky pearls and richly glowing emeralds and rubies.

In all of his work, Gruosi's style is characterised by a dash of Mediterranean drama and, often, a touch of whimsy (he has, after all, designed a portable telephone studded with 240 black diamonds - available by special order only).

de Grisogno
108 rue de Rhône,
CH-1204 Geneva,
Switzerland
Tel: +41-22-317 1080   Fax: +41-22-317 1088

DE LADOUCETTE

Baron Patrick de Ladoucette is passionate about his wines. Start him talking about them and you are guaranteed endless conversation. From his fairy-tale Château du Nozet, complete with its turrets and spires, he produces a superb Pouilly Fumé, Baron de L. It is a wonderfully refined and elegant expression of Sauvignon Blanc at its best.

de Ladoucette
Château du Nozet,
58150 Pouilly-sur-Loire, France
Tel/Fax: +33-3-86 39 18 33

DE CRILLON (HÔTEL)

The apogee of French *savoir-faire* in architecture, *arts de la table* and service is found at the

Crillon. Commissioned by Louis XV in 1758, the imposing building was designed by Jacques-Ange Gabriel, a fittingly celestial name for such a luxurious establishment. The Taittinger-owned hotel has always been a home from home for world leaders and celebrities. Although its sumptuous Les Ambassadeurs restaurant lost brilliant chef Christian Constant in 1998, Dominique Bouchet has taken up the baton with unwavering confidence, retaining its two Michelin stars.

Hôtel de Crillon
10 Place de la Concorde,
75008 Paris, France
Tel: +33-1-44 71 15 01   Fax: +33-1-44 71 15 02

DELAMAIN

Delamain's lack of a high public profile in no way means lack of quality. It is evocative of discreet good taste, a fact reflected in the cognac itself. Where others are robust and forceful, Delamain is refined and stylish - and none more so than its limited-edition, Très Vieille Réserve de la Famille. This is superlative cognac, unblended and dating back to before World War II. Its fruity character is allied to a delightfully complex, though never heavy, palate.

Delamain
BP 13, 16100 Garnac, France
Tel: +33-5-45 81 08 24   Fax: +33-5-45 81 70 87

DE LAMERIE

Although established for only 10 years, this firm's exquisite bone china and silverware is as finely detailed as the 18th century originals

upon which it is modelled. All silverware is produced with 22-carat rolled gold, using the partial gilding system and master craftsmen carry out the hand painting, raised-paste and enamelling work on the china. De Lamerie also undertakes private commissions.

De Lamerie
9A Winsor End, Beaconsfield,
Buckinghamshire HP9 2JJ, UK
Tel: +44-1494-68 04 88   Fax: +44-1494-68 09 00

DELBRÜCK AND CO.

Founded in 1712, Delbrück acted as financial advisors to Frederick the Great. But, unlike many once-great private banks, it has embraced the modern age with robust confidence. Focusing its resources on family-run, middle class companies has resulted in an 8 per cent rise in the volume of business undertaken last year. Private clients and institutional investors are also focal points of current strategy and a growing number of clients are taking advantage of the bank's asset management services.

Delbrück & Co.
Rankestraße 13, D-10789 Berlin, Germany
Tel: +49-30-88 46 10   Fax: +49-30-88 46 12 22

DERMOT WELD

The only Northern Hemisphere trainer to have sent a horse to Australia and won the Melbourne Cup first time (with *Vintage Crop*) and the only European trainer to win a leg of the American Triple Crown, tennis-mad Dermot Weld originally trained as a veterinary surgeon. Tony O'Reilly, Michael Smurfit, Walter Hafner and Prince Fahd Salman are among those whose horses he trains at his picturesque Rosewell yard, adjoining The Curragh.

Dermot Weld
Rosewell House, Curragh,
Co. Kildare, Ireland
Tel: +353-45-44 12 73   Fax: +353-45-44 11 19

IL DESCO

This cosy restaurant, housed in a 14th century building in Verona's historic quarter, has become the 'home' restaurant for Verona locals, who love chef-proprietor Elia Rizzo's reinterpretation of traditional Veronese cooking (classic pumpkin risotto is invigorated with bitters, for instance). Rafaele Righetti oversees the cellar of 750 Italian and French wines.

Il Desco
via Diestro San Sebastiano 7,
37121 Verona, Italy
Tel: +39-04-559 5358   Fax: +39-04-559 0236

DEUTSCHE PRIVATE BANKING

Deutsche Bank, one of the world's leading financial institutions, with AAA ratings accorded to its short, medium and long-term obligations by Standard & Poor's. The focus of private banking at Deutsche Bank is on co-ordinating the client's financial circumstances within a coherent framework. In structuring client finances, the bank spans from cash management and insurance-related products, through to managed portfolios. It is worth noting that tax and legal advice are not part of the bank's remit.

Deutsche Bank AG
Lefebvre Court, Lefebvre Street,
St. Peter Port, Guernsey GY1 6LR,
Channel Islands, UK
Tel: +44-1481-70 20 60   Fax: +44-1481-70 20 61

DEV BASRA

Basra is a famously social cosmetic surgeon who, when not working on real bodies, spends his time sculpting figures out of bronze; his surgery is full of them. Renowned for his work on eyes, Basra is also a leading exponent of chemical peeling, a service which he offers free after a face-lift.

Dev Basra
111 Harley Street, London W1N 1DG, UK
Tel: +44-171-486 8055   Fax: +44-171-486 2417

DIAM'S

As the supplier of bodyguards and security services to the stars of the Cannes Film Festival, and scores of the international heavyweights who reside in Monaco and on the Côte d'Azur, DIAM'S is the undisputed leader in its field in the South of France.

DIAM'S
37 rue d'Antibes, 06400 Cannes, France
Tel: +33-4-93 38 48 00   Fax: +33-4-92 98 44 72

DIDIER AARON & CIE

This gallery is best known for 18th century French furniture - Didier Aaron's focus when he took over the gallery founded by his moth-

er in 1923. The third generation, Madame Aaron's grandson, Hervé, recently joined the firm. Didier Aaron offers furniture, paintings, drawings and works of art in galleries in Paris, housed in a lavish *hôtel particulier*, London and New York.

Didier Aaron & Cie
118 rue du Faubourg Saint-Honoré,
75008 Paris, France
Tel: +33-1-47 42 47 34   Fax: +33-1-42 66 24 17

DOM RUINART

Champagne connoisseurs savour this marque for its full body, lingering aftertaste and bouquet, considering it one of the best special

champagne cuvées. Dom Thierry Ruinart, a Benedictine priest, watched his friend Dom Pérignon experiment with 'the wine that sparkles'. He confided the secret to his nephew Nicolas Ruinart who, in 1729, founded the first champagne house. Dom Ruinart's Blanc de Blancs Vintage, made entirely of *grand cru* Chardonnay grapes, is superb - in particular the 1976 and 1986. The rich and complex Rosé 1986 is a must, too. Finally, look out for the house's special cuvée for the millennium. Dom Ruinart's president, Roland de Calonne, is already chuckling with pride at its quality.

Champagne Ruinart
4 rue de Crayères, 5110 Reims, France
Tel: +33-3-26 77 51 51   Fax: +33-3-26 82 88 43

DIPTYQUE

Many modern. scented candles are a disappointment but here you'll find ones that magically reflect the names on their black-and-white labels. Choose from the likes of New Mown Hay, Blackcurrant Leaves and Waxed Wood. Bottles of eau de toilette have equally evocative titles.

Diptyque
34 boulevard Saint Germain, 75007 Paris, France
Tel: +33-1-43 26 45 27   Fax: +33-1-43 54 27 01

DISCOUNT BANK AND TRUST COMPANY

The Discount Bank and Trust Company was established in Geneva in 1952. Its main activity is asset management for individuals and blue chip institutions. The bank is well represented in major financial centres, employing 471 people around the world. Occasionally short term credits are granted to clients, based on solid acceptable guarantees, and at customary margins. Generally the group only deals in derivative financial instruments for risk management or to satisfy clients' requirements but, apart from this, it does not act as a market maker in securities.

Discount Bank and Trust Company
Quai de l'Ile 3, CH-1204 Geneva, Switzerland
Tel: +41-22-705 3111   Fax: +41-22-310 1703

DOLCE & GABBANA

This dynamic duo has made a name for itself putting a sexy twist on traditional Italian costume - notably corsets, little black widow dresses and lacy mantillas - and sending them down the runway with cleavages spilling and wasp-waists nipped for maximum oomph. As Demi Moore, Isabella Rossellini and Madonna can attest, these are 'result' dresses.

Dolce & Gabbana
via Santa Cecilia 7, 20122 Milan, Italy
Tel: +39-02-76 01 32 32   Fax: +39-02-76 02 06 00

DOMAINE DE SPERONE

The 136-hectare *Domaine* of Sperone is one of the most prestigious and innovative residential estates constructed in Europe in recent years. Seduced by the area's rugged beauty, Guy and Jacques Dewez decided to develop an exclusive estate in collaboration with the French architects GEA. 30 years later, its Californian-style houses are perfectly integrated into the surrounding *maquis*; several of the most beautiful are available for private rental.

Domaine de Sperone
SO.GE. Immobilière Sperone, Domaine
de Sperone, 20169 Bonifacio, Corsica, France
Tel: +33-4-95-73 13 69   Fax: +33-4-95-73 06 97

DOMAINE DE SOUVILLY

Boar-hunting and deer-stalking of the highest order are available on Comte Jean de Béarn's 700-hectare estate in Normandy. The Domaine de Souvilly has eight days' shooting available each year, from November through January, for 16 rifles on each day. Guests are wined and dined in some style - not least because the charming owner is a scion of the Roederer champagne dynasty.

Domaine de Souvilly
Bémécourt, 27160 Breteuil-sur-Iton, France
Tel: +33-2-32 29 70 54   Fax: +33-2-32 35 25 39

DOMAINE DES HAUTS DE LOIRE

Hidden deep in a park and reflected in a lake, this ivy-covered château was built as a hunting lodge in the 1860s by the Comte de Rostaing. Today Pierre-Alain and Marie-Noëlle Bonnigal cosset those who have learned, by word of mouth, about its sublime service, sensational food and calmly civilised ambience.

Domaine des Hauts de Loire
Route de Herbault, 41150 Onzain, France
Tel: +33-02-54 20 72 57   Fax: +33-02-54 20 77 32

DOMAINE DU ROYAL CLUB EVIAN

Despite its inclusion on the Women's PGA Tour, the golf here is not world class - although it will test you (especially the dog-leg 7th). The real joy is its position above Lake Geneva with a backdrop of the Alps, the greenest fairways you are ever likely to see and the purest air to relax you. The two hotels on site are pure pleasure-domes, whether you are de-stressing in the spa or dining in the flagship restaurants.

Domaine du Royal Club Evian
BP 8, 74502 Evian, Cedex, France
Tel: +33-4-50 26 85 00   Fax: +33-4-50 75 61 00

DON ALFONSO 1890

A jewel of the Amalfi coast, Livia and Alfonso Iaccarino's heavenly restaurant is the fruit of a century of family tradition. Once you've negotiated the tortuous highway, this is a perfect pit-stop. Prized San Marzano tomatoes are the basis of the divine pasta sauce, wild garlic enlivens tender fried fish and tangy lemons infuse a sorbet.

Don Alfonso 1890
Corso Sant'Agata 11,
80064 Sant'Agata Sui Due Golfi, Italy
Tel: +39-081-878 0026

DOUGLAS H. HARRISON

Harley Street wizard Douglas Harrison's skill with the scalpel has earned him many admirers for his facial work, abdominal reductions and breast augmentations. However, he is equally respected for his work in non-cosmetic fields, such as facial palsy, hand reconstructions and microsurgery.

Douglas H. Harrison FRCS
33 Harmont House, 20 Harley Street,
London W1N 1AA, UK
Tel: +44-171-935 6184   Fax: +44-171 436 1178

DREI HUSAREN

Established in 1933 and now run by Uwe Kohl, the 'Three Hussars' is one of Vienna's best-loved restaurants; a must for concertgoers, it remains open well into the evening. Its traditional Austrian specialities include Sweetbreads with dumplings and Calf's brain with spinach and mustard sauce. The atmosphere is one of subdued luxury.

Drei Husaren
Weihburggaße 4,
A-1010 Vienna, Austria
Tel: +43-1-512 109 20   Fax: +43-1-512 109 18

DROMOLAND CASTLE

Dromoland is the ancestral home of the O'Brien family, direct descendents of Brian Boru, the 10th century High King of Ireland. Set in 400 acres of wooded parkland, with 17th century gardens originally laid out by André le Nôtre, its sporting diversions include

THE DORCHESTER

It has been said that "calling The Dorchester a hotel is rather like calling champagne a fizzy drink" - and with good reason. A landmark since the Thirties, this stately Grade II listed building overlooking Hyde Park has consistently remained in fashion. In the late Eighties The Dorchester underwent a major two-year renovation programme, restoring the hotel to its former glory.

The result is a brilliant blend of comfort and tradition, bringing together the best of the past and the present. The designers commissioned work from artists which complemented or re-worked original features. Oliver Ford's elaborately patterned carpets on the bedroom floors, for instance, were re-made, while a Lalique-style glass screen by Clifford Rainey in the health club pays homage to the art deco era when The Dorchester was built. Perhaps the most praised

piece of restoration work was on the Oliver Messel Suite and the Penthouse and Pavilion rooms, originally decorated by the stage designer in 1953. The grand public rooms, too, site of the most lavish balls and state banquets this century, have all been restored to their former splendour.

The Dorchester's impressive roster of celebrity guests includes, among many others, Elizabeth Taylor, Madonna and Nelson Mandela.

The Dorchester Hotel
Park Lane, London W1A 2HJ, UK
Tel: +44-171-629 8888   Fax: +44-171-409 0114

a private 18-hole golf course, trout fishing on its own lough and shooting.
Dromoland Castle
Newmarket-on-Fergus,
Co. Clare, Ireland
Tel: +353-61-36 81 44   Fax: +353-61-36 33 55

DROTTNINGHOLMS SLOTTSTEATER

The 18th century Drottningholm Court Theatre, in the grounds of the Swedish Royal Family's summer palace, is so perfectly pre-served that, as you walk out after a performance and watch the mist rising seductively from the lake, you feel yourself transported back in time. Fittingly, the summer season specialises in revivals of operas from the 18th century and earlier, with gloriously authentic costumes and fireworks. The best way to arrive is by steamer from Stockholm.
Drottningholms Slottsteater
Box 27050, 10251 Stockholm, Sweden
Tel: +46-8-660 8225
Fax: +46-8-665 1473

DRUIDS GLEN

Couched between the Wicklow Hills and the Irish Sea, Druids Glen is one of the finest parkland golf courses in Europe. This 400-acre inland course was designed by Tom Craddock and Pat Ruddy, respecting the graceful maturity of the original estate and its wildlife, and earning the praise of Seve Ballesteros, among others. It has staged the Murphy's Irish Open for the past three years.
Druids Glen Golf Club
Newtownmountkennedy, Co Wicklow, Ireland
Tel: +353-1-287 3600   Fax: +353-1-287 3699

DUBERNET

This grand *traiteur* has excellent goose and duck foie gras produced in the town of Saint-Sever in Acquitaine, where the company was founded in 1863. Its impressive selection of preserves includes rich cassoulet, duck and beef tongue in Madeira sauce, all presented in Dubernet's trademark white porcelain dishes and jars.
Boutique Dubernet
2 rue Augereau, 75007 Paris, France
Tel/Fax: +33-1-45 55 50 71

DUCRU-BEAUCAILLOU (CHATEAU)

Created at the end of the 17th century and bought by the *négociant* Nathaniel Johnson on behalf of the Ducru-Ravez family in 1866, this 50-hectare *domaine* has been owned by the Borie family since 1929. It is centred around a pretty Carthusian monastery, with a magnificent park that extends to the banks of the Gironde. The best of this full, well-balanced and extremely elegant super second cru to drink in 1999 is (if you can't get hold of the great 1970) the 1982.
Château Ducru-Beaucaillou
33250 Saint-Julien-Beychevelle, France
Tel: +33-5-56 59 05 20   Fax: +33-5-56 59 27 37

DULWICH PICTURE GALLERY

Britain's oldest public art gallery, purpose-built by Sir John Soane, has inspired architects on both sides of the Atlantic. Stroll in uncrowded bliss to view 17th- and 18th-century masterworks by Poussin, Rubens, Van Dyck, Watteau, Hogarth, Gainsborough, Reynolds and Rembrandt (his *Jacob de Gheyn* has been stolen and returned four times). Fund-raising efforts attract the great and the good with Hilary Clinton and Cherie Blair joint-patrons of a recent exhibition.
Dulwich Picture Gallery
College Road, Dulwich Village,
London SE21 7AD, UK
Tel: +44-181-693 5254   Fax: +44-181-693 0923
Closed from January 1999 - May 2000
for restoration.

DUNDAS CASTLE

This imposing crenellated house near Edinburgh, built in 1818, is now the family home of Sir Jack and Lady Stewart-Clark, who make it available for private rental. It stands in a beautiful park, with extensive lawns, rhododendron-lined drives, high crags and a lovely loch, which is a haven for wildlife.

Dundas Castle, South Queensferry, Scotland

c/o Blandings, The Barn, Musgrave Farm, Horningsea Road, Fen Ditton, Cambs. CB5 8SZ, UK
Tel: +44-1223-29 34 44   Fax: +44-1223-29 28 88

E. GUTZWILLER & CIE

Since its founding in 1886, this private bank has developed its expertise in a number of areas centred around portfolio management. Asset allocation and investment vehicles are carefully tailored to each client's needs. Many seek global, balanced portfolios and the bank is renowned for its rigorous selection of investment vehicles and funds with outstanding performance records. Subsidiary activities include custody services and handling stock and bond transactions both nationally and in all leading foreign markets.

E. Gutzwiller & Cie

Kaufhausgaße 7, CH-4051 Basel, Switzerland
Tel: +41-61-205 2100   Fax: +41-61-205 2101

ECOLE ACTIVE BILINGUE

Founded in 1954, the EAB was the first school to devote itself to bilingualism in Paris and is a role model for language teaching today. Pupils are taught English from the age of three, by Anglophone teachers, while simultaneously learning French. From eight they can study either German or Spanish and, later, Italian. The school is very popular with a mobile population of diplomats and international business executives, due to its flexible syllabus and excellent teaching standards and, increasingly, with French parents who prefer their children to have an in-depth international education.

Ecole Active Bilingue

117 boulevard Malesherbes,
75008 Paris, France
Tel: +33-1-45 63 62 22   Fax:+33-1-45 63 30 73

L'ECOLE ALSACIENNE

This private school, which has its roots in a famous college founded in Strasbourg in the 16th century, is committed to giving its pupils a well-rounded, liberal education. It clearly appeals to parents with a socialist bent, as many French cabinet ministers' children are pupils. The curriculum is particularly strong on languages, with English taught from primary school. Situated in a secluded Left Bank street, it is about to be given a facelift by avant-garde architect Jean-Michel Wilmotte.

L'Ecole Alsacienne

109 rue Notre-Dame des Champs,
75006 Paris, France
Tel: +33-1-44 32 04 70

EFG PRIVATE BANK

Owned by Latsis family interests, EFG Bank Group has more than 1.7 billion Swiss Francs in capital and 20 billion Swiss Francs of client

assets under administration. The bank's motto, 'Total Wealth Management', gives a clear indication of its priorities. Philip Amphlett, Head of Private Banking at its London office, explains, "While we do not want to be all things to all men, if you add up all the different parts of the banking group, we cover a very wide range of services." In practice this means that, added  to the essential qualities of security, confidentiality, accessiblity and capability, the bank tailors its services in every case to meet the unique needs of each client.

EFG Private Bank

P.O. Box 1204, Geneva, Switzerland
Tel: +41-22-319 1313   Fax: +41-22-319 1401
Also in London, Zürich, Luxembourg,
Channel Islands, Monaco and Greece

ED DUBOIS

Fanatical sailor Ed Dubois established his naval architecture practice in 1977, following the racing success of his first quarter-tonner, *Borsalino III*. Wins in the Admiral's Cup and other international regattas led to many production boat designs, as well as a growing number of large, one-off commissions for both sail and motor yachts. Currently under construction in Europe are a 45m ketch, a 37m sloop and a 46m motor yacht. Another four Dubois yachts of similar size are being built in New Zealand, Australia and the Far East.

Ed Dubois Naval Architects Ltd.

Beck Farm, Sowley, Lymington, Hampshire SO41 5SR, UK

Tel: +44-1590-62 66 96   Fax: +44-1590-62 64 58

EDMISTON & COMPANY

With many years' experience as Managing Director of one of the world's leading yacht brokerages, Nicholas Edmiston set up his own company in 1998. His philosophy of limiting his team to a small, hand-picked group of experts with specialised knowledge in each area - charter, sales, purchase and new construction - ensures an exceptionally high degree of professionalism, flexibility and personal service.

Before proposing a yacht for charter, for instance, Edmiston's brokers go to enormous lengths to determine every detail of a client's tastes and priorities, to ensure a perfect match of both destination and yacht.

The company also has great expertise in the complex business of buying and selling a yacht, particularly with regard to international law, contractual obligations, registration options and engineering considerations. Recent sales include the 204ft Feadship *The Virginian* - now available for selected charter through Edmiston.

For new builds, Edmiston has a great depth of knowledge of all phases, from design through construction to final commissioning, for both sail and motor yachts. In addition, the company's experts oversee major refits, which can be even more complicated than a new build. In order to help clients maximise their financial return on their yachts during periods when they are not using them, Edmiston will advise on and undertake management of their chartering, thus providing a fully-integrated service.

Edmiston & Company

51 Charles Street, London W1X 7PA, UK

Tel: +44-171 495 5151   Fax: +44-171 495 5150

Email: edmiston@btinternet.com

9 Avenue d'Ostende, MC 98000, Monaco

Tel: +377-93 30 54 44   Fax: +377-93 30 55 33

Email: edmiston@infonie.fr

EGG

Maureen Docherty gave up her job with Issey Miyake in order to realise her vision for this shop, which she opened in 1994 with her Indian partner Asha Sarabhi. Egg sells the partners' own designs, based on Eastern work clothes. Their purity is complemented by a collection of exquisite decorative items - and all is presented in a remarkable atmosphere of calm and seclusion.

Egg

36 Kinnerton Street, London SW1X 8ES, UK

Tel: +44-171-235 9315   Fax: +44-171-838 9705

EL SALER

El Saler's links holes are designer Javier Arana's tribute to the best British courses. At 6355 yards and par 72, this is one of Europe's most challenging, with huge greens and deceptive slopes. Given that it takes every shot in the book even to make your handicap here, particularly in a stiff breeze, Bernhard Langer's 62 in the 1984 Spanish Open is all the more impressive.

Campo de Golf El Saler

Parador Nacional "Luis Vivès", E-46012 El Saler, Valencia, Spain

Tel: +34-96-161 03 84   Fax: +34-96-162 70 16

ELEGANT RESORTS

Founded 10 years ago as an organiser of luxurious tours to the Caribbean, Elegant Resorts now offers holidays all over the world. The key to the company's success is its professionalism and honesty in describing the destinations it offers, whether for pre-packaged tours or tailor-made holidays.

Elegant Resorts

The Old Palace, Chester CH1 1RB, UK

Tel: +44-1244-35 04 08   Fax: +44-1244-89 77 70

ELENA BENARROCH

As well as being Spain's leading furrier, Elena Benarroch owns one of Madrid's smartest stores, where Loro Piana cashmere is presented alongside Santa Maria Novella perfumes and Pucci clothing. Elena Benarroch's fur collections are distinguished by their lightness and youthful styling, as well as her use of such original materials as tinted sable and shaved mink.

Elena Benarroch

José Ortega y Gasset 14, E-28006 Madrid, Spain

Tel: +34-91-435 5144   Fax: +34-91-431 4960

ELIZABETH GAGE

Goldsmith and jewellery designer Elizabeth Gage's opulent jewellery combines such stones as tourmalines, spinels and opals with enamelling, baroque pearls and ancient or unusual artefacts. The resulting pieces are one-of-a-kind bijoux, as right with a Chanel suit as with a plain cashmere sweater.

Elizabeth Gage

20 Albemarle Street, London W1X 4LB, UK

Tel: +44-171-499 2879   Fax: +44-171-499 4550

ELIE BLEU

Elie Bleu creates only some of the world's most exceptional cigar humidors but also beautiful,

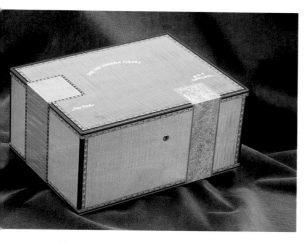

all-purpose boxes - secret keepsakes, jewellery and writing cases, even tea caddies. The company works in the tradition of the great cabinet-makers of the 18th century using the rarest, most precious and exotic woods.

Elie Bleu
8 bis rue Boissy d'Anglas, 75008 Paris, France
Tel: +33-1-47 42 12 21   Fax: +33-1-47 42 03 98

ELOUNDA BEACH

Overlooking the Gulf of Mirabello, this hotel and villa resort offers outstanding accommodation in the north-east corner of this beautiful island. Best room is the Royal Bungalow Suite, which benefits from its own indoor and outdoor pools. Guests are international and entertainment and sports facilities second to none.

Elounda Beach Hotel
72053 Elounda, Crete
Tel: +30-841-41 412   Fax: +30-841-41 373

EMILIO MAZZOLI

Emilio Mazzoli founded this gallery in 1977 to exhibit cutting-edge artists and was the first in Europe to promote the work of Basquiat, with a solo show in 1981. Other artists include Enzo Cucchi, Luciano Fabro, Jannis Kounellis and exponents of the Transavanguardia movement. The gallery often invites outside curators to organise exhibitions and continues to introduce new faces to the Italian public.

Emilio Mazzoli
via Nazario Sauro 62, 41100 Modena, Italy
Tel: +39-059-24 34 55   Fax: +39-059-21 49 80

EMMA SERGEANT

A distinguished portrait painter with a traditional English painterly style, Emma Sergeant won the National Portrait Gallery Competition in 1981. Her portrait of The Duke of York was exhibited at the Gallery in 1994 and, in 1995-'96, she accompanied the Prince of Wales on tour as official artist. Portrait commissions range from Imran Kahn to Red Crow, Chief of the Sioux Indians.

Emma Sergeant
c/o Gordon Cooke, The Fine Art Society plc,
148 New Bond Street, London W1Y 0JT, UK
Tel: +44-171-629 5116   Fax +44-171-491 9454

EMMANUEL BABLED E LIA DI GREGORIO

Make an appointment to view the exclusive designs created by Emmanuel Babled for the Japanese store Idée. Furniture inspired by the Hale-Bopp Comet sits alongside glass vases from Venetian maestro Livio Serena and free-form ceramics in his loft showroom. Lia di Gregorio's jewellery, favoured by Milan's avant garde, is made to order.

Emmanual Babled e Lia di Gregorio
via Segantini 71, 20143 Milan, Italy
Tel: +39-02-58 11 11 19

ENOTECA LA FORTEZZA

Perched in this fortified southern Tuscan hill-town, Enoteca la Fortezza belongs to the commune but is run under licence, with great flair, by Signor Pianigiani. He specialises not only in wine (including, naturally, first class Brunello di Montalcino) but also such regional treats as grappa, olive oil, honey, salami and cheeses.

Enoteca la Fortezza
Piazzale Fortezza,
53024 Montalcino (Si), Italy
Tel/Fax: +39-0577-84 92 11

ENOTECA PINCHIORRI

Chef Annie Feolde's inspired interpretation of Tuscan cooking is once more delighting diners at Enoteca Pinchiorri. This wonderful Florentine restaurant, housed in a Renaissance palazzo between the Uffizi and the Duomo, has re-opened after the heartbreaking fire last year that destroyed many of its vintage wines. However, as 150,000 bottles remain, most clients won't notice the difference.

Enoteca Pinchiorri
via Ghibellina 87, 50122 Florence, Italy
Tel: +39-055-24 27 77

ENOTECA TRIMANI

A business that began as a simple wine merchants in 1821 now has 45,000 listings – including international and fortified wines, champagnes, food delicacies, coffees and teas. It has a delightfully old-world interior featuring a Bagnoreggio basalt floor and a Carrara marble counter, worn down over the years by the passing back and forth of bottles.

Enoteca Trimani
via Goito 20, 00185 Rome, Italy
Tel: +39-06-446 9661

EMILE GARCIN

If you are looking for a blissful *mas* or *bastide* in the celebrity-encrusted countryside of Provence you need consult only Emile Garcin, for all of his properties are the home of your dreams, or at least their locations are. As Garcin's son Emmanuel says, "You can change a house to make it beautiful, but not its setting." When selling a property, the impeccably turned-out Garcin, a native of Saint-Rémy-de-Provence, first ponders whether the locals could live with the prospective buyer. "Provençal people are outwardly open and charming but, to really get to know them, you have to take time to

listen. Most people wishing to buy property here live in cities, where contact with neighbours is only superficial." His daughter Natalie, who runs the Paris branch of the firm, should have expert knowledge of this. Then again, as her properties are in the heart of St Germain des Près, with its village-like atmosphere, perhaps her clients are civilised enough.

Emile Garcin
8 boulevard Mirabeau,
13210 Saint-Rémy-de-Provence, France
Tel: +33-4-90 92 01 58   Fax: +33-4-90 92 39 57

Natalie Garcin
5 rue de l'Université, 75007 Paris, France
Tel: +33-1-42 61 73 38   Fax: +33-4-42 61 75 48

EMILIO LAVEZZARI

A board-certified dermatologist, Dr. Lavezzari originally qualified in medicine at the University of Pavia. For the last 20 years, however, he has dedicated himself to perfecting the art of hair restoration, using the 'auto-transplant' technique pioneered by Professor Norman Orentreich in New York, with whom he worked for some time.

Working in his chic office in the heart of Milan, Lavezzari can, under local anaesthetic and completely painlessly, transplant up to 6000 hairs in two to three hours. Clients greatly appreciate Lavezzari's discretion, as well as his skill, and they love his 'bedside manner', too. Gentle, warm and affable, he has an infectious passion for his craft.

Lavezzari takes great care with his pre-treatment consultations and, in order to give clients a clear understanding of what to expect, uses advanced computer graphics to create an accurate

picture of the results with treatment (and the likely prognosis if they forgo it) beforehand. He achieves the remarkably natural appearance of his transplants by using microscopic grafts - often only one or two hairs at a time - and by varying his technique, according to the way a client's hair grows naturally.

Dr. Emilio Lavezzari
via Montenapoleone 16, 20121 Milan, Italy
Tel: +39-02-79 69 36   Fax: +39-02-76 01 24 93

EPONYMO

Clients of this shop, housed in a grand Thirties building, are treated with the utmost civility - seated and served coffee, while making their choice from such designers as Lacroix, Romeo Gigli, Calvin Klein and Alberta Ferretti.

Eponymo
33 Solonos Street, 10680 Kolonaki,
Athens, Greece
Tel: +30-1-362 9906

ERIK'S GONDOLA

Erik Lallerstedt's resourceful interpretations of classical Swedish cooking (such as Baked cod

and corned beef with sweetbreads) have made him the most celebrated chef in Stockholm. Originally based in a single, eponymous restaurant in the Old Town, he has built up a mini-empire of three restaurants. However, having sold the original premises, Lallerstedt himself will be based at the new Erik's Gondola from January 1999. His admirers, who include none less than the Swedish King, will follow him there in droves.

Erik's Gondola
Staatsgäden 6,
11523 Stockholm, Sweden
Tel: +46-8-661 7090

EMMANUEL MOATTI

Installed opposite the Elysée Palace, which swarms with gendarmes, Emmanuel Moatti's gallery certainly has plenty of security. Which is just as well, given the fabulous Old Masters he has on offer. The stature of his oils and drawings is such that 40 per cent of Moatti's

sales are to museums. Moreover, he specialises in paintings with unusually striking images, so you'll be transfixed not simply by the quality of his collection but also by its persistent originality.

Emmanuel Moatti
20 rue de l'Elysée,
75008 Paris, France
Tel: +33-1-44 51 67 67   Fax: +33-1-44 57 67 68
Email: e.moatti@sillage.com

ENDTENFANG

Fürstenhof Celle, which was built by an Italian baron in 1670, is now owned by the Grafen Hardenberg family. In the Endtenfang (it translates roughly as 'duck catching') restaurant, opened in the early 1970s, Chef Hans Sobotka has, for 11 years, been creating classical French cooking, which has repeatedly been cited as among the best in Germany.

Endtenfang
Fürstenhof Celle, Hannoversche Straße 55/56,
D-29221 Celle, Niedersachsen, Germany
Tel: +49-5141-20 10   Fax: +49-5141-20 11 20

ENOTECA RONCHI

Maria Luisa Ronchi is the great, great granddaughter of the first Ronchi to run this excellent wine shop. Having become Europe's first

qualified female sommelier in 1969, her love of the noble grape is evident in everything she does. Tell her your star sign, for instance, and she'll tell you which wines you should be drinking. A gregarious, refreshingly outspoken authority on the subject, she - and the wine she sells you - will amuse you enormously.

Enoteca Ronchi
via San Vincenzo 12, 20123 Milan, Italy
Tel: +39-02-89 40 26 27   Fax: +39-02-58 10 35 59

ENGEL & VOLKERS
With offices in 10 German cities, Engel and Volkers is one of that country's leading estate agencies; however, its development into new markets is what really distinguishes it from its peers. It has established a significant presence on Mallorca and, with new offices due to open shortly in Britain and Spain, looks set to become a major player in the pan-European market.

Engel & Volkers
Stadthausebrücke 5, D-20355 Hamburg, Germany
Tel: +49-40-36 13 10   Fax: +49-40-36 13 12 22

ERMENEGILDO ZEGNA
In 1910, at the age of 20, Ermenegildo Zegna took over his father's small family business, making high quality menswear fabrics. Now, still family-run, this is the only fashion house to make everything itself, from the raw materials to the finished garment, sold in its own stores worldwide.

Ermenegildo Zegna
via Forcella 5, 20144 Milan, Italy
Tel: +39-02-58 10 37 87   Fax: +39-02-58 10 39 01

ERSEL
Making full use of the Giubergia family's 60 years of experience, from the start of its professional activity in 1936 to the establishment, in 1984, of the first Italian unit trust company, Ersel is probably the only Italian private bank qualified to claim equal footing with the American-based institutions that dominate the sector in Italy. Today Ersel holds a unique position in portfolio management, thanks to its history, structure, independence and professional competence.

Ersel
via Roma 255, 10123 Turin, Italy
Tel: +390-11-552 0111   Fax: +390-11-552 0257

ESKENAZI
Giuseppe Eskenazi's arrival London, in 1960, transformed the Oriental art scene. Specialising in early Chinese art, Japanese netsuke and lacquer, he deals in only the finest examples, displaying and cataloguing them to museum standards. When he opened his new, architect-designed 3,000 square foot gallery in 1993, Eskenazi was offered over £10 million for it by a major collector, who was so impressed that he wanted it as a museum for his own collection.

Eskenazi Ltd.
10 Clifford Street,
London W1X 1RB, UK
Tel: +44-171-493 5464
Fax: +44-171-499 3136

ESPACE HENRI CHENOT
Henri Chenot has been awarded an honorary doctorate of science for his Energy Detoxicating Diet, a regime favoured by sportsmen and around 50,000 patients. It is just one of the fantastically revitalising options available at his Espace bodycare and Health Centre, which Henri oversees with his wife, Dominique, and a team of doctors.

Espace Henri Chenot
2 Via Cavour, 39012 Merano, Italy
Tel: +39-0473-21 13 00   Fax: +39-0473-23 41 81

L'ESPERANCE
The charismatic, cigar-smoking Marc Meneau taught himself to cook in an effort to garner favour with his prospective father-in-law. Thirty-odd years of happy marriage to Françoise (who runs the front-of-house with considerable aplomb) and three Michelin stars later, his efforts have clearly paid off.

Born and raised here on the western fringe of Burgundy, Meneau has invented his own, richly sensual style of cooking based on the flavours of the region. His signature *Cromesquis* of foie gras is one of the world's true 'died-and-went-to-heaven' experiences.

L'Espérance
89450 St-Père-sous-Vézelay, France
Tel: +33-3-86 33 39 10   Fax: +33-3-86 33 26 15

ETON
This institution, for which the phrase 'old boys' network' might have been coined, endows its pupils with the advantage of mixing with the children of the great and the good - and, by

definition, their successors. Despite its social kudos, the school has maintained its impressive academic status for centuries and provides an enviable all-round education for a generation of future achievers.

Eton College
Windsor, Berkshire SL4 6DB, UK
Tel: +44-1753-67 12 49   Fax: +44-1753-67 12 48

ETRO

Appropriately, for a firm which began as family of specialist fabric makers, the richness of Etro's textiles transport you to a world of heightened exoticism, from jewel-coloured silks embroidered with the company's hallmark paisley to flowered scarves that might have come from a Dutch still life. These fabrics are now used to create men's and women's clothing and a home collection, as well as sublime accessories.

Etro
3 via Spartaco, 20135 Milan, Italy
Tel: +39-02-55 02 01   Fax: +39-02-54 10 83 66

ETUDE TAJAN

This independent auction house stages approximately 150 sales per annum, sending 100,000 catalogues world-wide from its Paris base. Rare stamps, antique dolls, fine wine, Old Masters and contemperary art are catered for in 12 separate departments. The company has other European offices in Monaco and Milan.

Etude Tajan
37 rue des Mathurins, 75008 Paris, France
Tel: +33-1-53 30 30 30   Fax: +33-1-53 30 30 31

FABRIZIO APOLLONI

Founded in 1926 by Maurizio Apolloni, this gallery is now run by his son Fabrizio. Specialising in Italian paintings, drawings and sculptures from the 16th to the 19th century, the gallery has sold works to the Galleria Nazionale d'Arte Antica and the Palazzo Braschi in Rome, as well as the Fondazione Magnani Rocca in Parma.

Fabrizio Apolloni
via del Babuino 132/134, 00187 Rome, Italy
Tel: +39-06-36 00 22 16   Fax: +39-06-36 00 22 17

FALKENSTEIN

A Harry Colt classic, the par-71 Falkenstein was inaugurated in 1906. The German Open and the original German Senior Players Championship have taken place here. The course is both beautiful and challenging, with natural obstacles such as forest and heath making for narrow fairways. Club President Nikolaus Schües' vote for the most difficult hole, due to the positioning of the two bunkers, combined with a wave-shaped green, is the 17th.

Falkenstein
In De Bargen 59, D-22387 Hamburg, Germany
Tel: +49-40-812 177   Fax: +49-40-817 315

FALSLED KRO

This idyllic haven in the midst of beautiful Danish countryside is home to talented chef Jean-Louis Lieffroy, whose creations include *Aiglefin fumé au caviar d'Aubergine* and *Pigeon en pot-au-feu à la Scandinave*. With his partner, Sven Gronlykke, Mr Lieffroy has created a calm, simply decorated space that is warmly recommended as much for its ambience as for its cuisine.

Falsled Kro,
Assensvej 513, Falsled DK-5642,
Millinge, Denmark
Tel: +45-062-68 11 11   Fax: +45-062-68 11 62

FARAONE

Luscious jewellery of the old school defines this traditional, originally Florentine jeweller. Rivulets of diamonds make up necklaces and bracelets, some offset by baroque pearls, others with pendant sapphires or rainbow-hued semi-precious stones. The richer pieces are complemented by a designer watch range and modern silverware from Tiffany, which now owns the company.

Faraone
via Montenapoleone 7/A, 20121 Milan, Italy
Tel: +39-02-76 01 36 56   Fax: +39-02-78 41 70

FARMACIA DI SANTA MARIA NOVELLA

Established by Dominican Friars in 1612, the Officina Profumo-Farmaceutica di Santa Maria Novella was originally the monastery's sanatorium. Run by four generations of the same family since 1866, it still uses many of

the original recipes for its glorious, pampering range of colognes, unguents and creams - all based on top-quality natural herbs and fats and produced by hand. Having gazed to contentment at the ravishing frescoed salesroom, ask to see the private chapel - its frescoes untouched by restorers since they were painted in the 15th century.

Farmacia di Santa Maria Novella
via della Scala 16, 50123 Florence, Italy
Tel: +39-055-230 2649   Fax: +39-055-28 86 58

FARNESE

From ancient Roman to 18th-century baroque, impeccable reproductions of ceramics and frescoes are Farnese's speciality. Owners, Mr and Mrs Di Donato, also offer an unparalleled range of terracotta, marble and stone flooring, all expertly aged. Repairs are undertaken, too, and the grander the scale the better: Mr Di Donato is currently restoring the floors of the Kremlin.

Farnese
47 rue de Berri, 75008 Paris, France
Tel: +33-1-45 63 22 05

FEADSHIP

Established in 1949, Feadship owes much of its success to the attention that it paid to the American market in its early years. This three member consortium, comprising De Vogt International Ship Design and Engineering and two family-owned shipyards, De Vries and Van Lent, builds ocean-going motor yachts, which are renowned for both their reliability and their exceptional quality.

Feadship Holland
Aerdenhoutsduinweg 1, P.O.Box 70,
2110 AB Aerdenhout, The Netherlands
Tel: +31-23-524 7000   Fax: +31-23-524 8639

FEAU

If you are occasionally fascinated by a glimpse of a superb townhouse behind the great heavy doors of a building - accessible only by keying in the code - in Paris' sixth arrondissement, the chances are that Philippe Chevalier, the director of Féau, can tell you all about it. Associated with Christie's, the auctioneers, this estate agent handles some of the most sumptuous properties in the neighbourhood.

Féau
21 rue Bonaparte, 75006 Paris, France
Tel: +33-1-44 07 30 00   Fax: +33-1-44 07 31 15

FELDAFING

Standing in the middle of a landscaped park beside Lake Starnberg, this 18-hole golf course has just reopened after a three-year renovation. The view of the lake and the Alps is what makes it so special and membership of the club is ultra-exclusive. Many of the members live in Munich but have homes in neighbouring villages like Possenhofen and Tutzing.

Golf Club Feldafing
Tutzingerstrasse 15, D-82340 Feldafing,
Germany
Tel: +49-8157-93 340   Fax: +49-8157-93 34 99

FEINKOST KÄFER

The Käfer family is a legend in its own lunchtime in Munich, running the chic-yet-*gemütlich* Käfer-Schänke restaurant, the wondrous delicatessen Feinkost Käfer and a catering business that holds 50 parties a week for socialites, celebrities and visiting royalty. This is the gourmet headquarters for Bavarian society, who count father and son Gerd and Michael Käfer as "one of us".

Feinkost Käfer GmbH
73 Prinzregentstrasse, D-81675 Munich, Germany
Tel: +49-89-41 681   Fax: +49-89-416 8207

FELIX MARCILHAC

A world-class expert on René Lalique, this gallery owner and collector spent 11 years writing the definitive work on the master glassmaker. A great admirer of Emile Galle, Marcilhac was instrumental in popularising the revival of Art Nouveau and Art Deco. He lives in a Paris suburb, alongside his exquisite private collection.

Felix Marcilhac
rue Bonaparte 8, 75007 Paris, France
Tel: +33-1-43 26 47 36

FENDI

Established in 1925 and now run by five sisters, the Fendi label has always been coveted by style leaders. Among those sporting its inimitable style are Lee Radzwill, Barbra Streisand, Glenn Close, Catherine Deneuve, Sophia Loren and Luciano Pavarotti, as well as members of the British Royal Family.

Fendi
via Cornelia 498, 00166 Rome, Italy
Tel: +39-06-61 41 01   Fax: +39-06-624 6838

LES FERMES DE MARIE

Wild flowers, gargantuan log fires and antique books set the scene at Jean-Louis and Jocelyne Sibuet's very private hotel - in fact a beautifully restored hamlet of farms - set in a two-and-a-half-acre park on the outskirts of Megève. The ambience is utterly relaxed - a great attraction to guests such as Tom Cruise and Nicole Kidman.

Les Fermes de Marie
Chemin de Riante Colline,
74120 Megève, France
Tel +33-4-50 93 03 10   Fax: +33-4-50 93 09 84

FERNANDO BUSTAMENTE

Fernando Díaz de Bustamente owns what is generally regarded as the premier partridge shoot in Spain. Guests are housed in a magnificent medieval castle, which was restored by a member of the Witney clan. The food and wine provided by Fernando are of the highest levels but your pockets do not need to be deep.

Many sportsmen believe great Spanish partridge shooting to be on a par with grouse. However, a big bag day in Scotland would be a small day in Spain. For shooters who are used to Britain, the form in Spain is dramatically different. Poaching is *de rigueur*; indeed, it is considered more fun to shoot your neighbour's bird than your own. Occasionally a Spaniard in the next butt will shoot a bird after you have already killed it. If you yell over "Why did you shoot my bird, it was dead", the most common reply is "Dead birds don't fly".

Fernando Díaz de Bustamente
Ulloa 10, 184 Torremocha, Cacéras, Spain
Tel: +34-927-19 01 30   Fax: +34-927-19 01 29

FESTIVAL DE LA MUSIQUE BAROQUE DE BEAUNE

During July Beaune welcomes a host of top-grade conductors and performers, in town for a celebration of 18th-century greats like Handel and Bach. Here, in the heart of Burgundy, affluent Parisians and discerning music lovers converge for a month-long feast of music, food and very fine wine. Kader Hassissi has been the man behind the festival for 17 years.

Festival de la Musique Baroque de Beaune
rue de l'Hôtel-Dieu, 21200 Beaune, France
Tel: +33-3-80 26 21 30

FINOLLO (E.)

Daniela Finollo is the designer at this celebrated Genoa shirtmaker, which has scarcely changed since its establishment in 1899. Although the staff were allowed to dispense with formal wear some years ago, the original wood panelling is still in place, the welcome is still that uniquely Genose brand of slightly aloof courtesy and, most importantly, the standards of craftsmanship are as high as ever.

E. Finollo
via Roma 38R, 16121 Genoa, Italy
Tel: +39-010-56 20 73   Fax: +39-010-54 327

FERRAGAMO

Ferragamo is a proudly independent family company which, in the past five years, has tripled its business, adding silk and leather accessories and clothing to its core shoe business. The company first found fame when Salvatore Ferragamo, a poor Neapolitan immigrant, went to seek his fortune in Hollywood in 1914 and found it by making shoes for Mary Pickford and Rudolph Valentino.

Salvatore Ferragamo Italia Spa
via dei Tornabuoni 2, 50123 Florence, Italy
Tel: +39-055-33 601   Fax: +39-055-336 0215

FIORERIA BAGNI

The flower market in Pescia provides much of the raw material for Fioreria Bagni, which has been run by the same family since it was founded 50 years ago. As well as supplying ravishing mixed bouquets, it specialises in elaborate arrangements for weddings and parties in the surrounding churches and villas.

Fioreria Bagni
via del Giglio 16, 50053 Empoli, Italy
Tel: +39-0571-73 770

FISCHERZUNFT

The River Rhine rushes through the town of Schaffhausen, dropping 25 metres in the process, and forms the impressive backdrop to this restaurant. Virtuoso chef André Jaeger trained in Hong Kong and his East-West fusion cooking (Foie gras with sesame or Tea-smoked baby chicken with kimchi) is a feast for all senses.

Rheinhotel Fischerzunft
8 Rheinquai,
CH-8202 Schaffhausen, Switzerland
Tel: +41-52-625 3281   Fax: +41-52-624 3285

FLEURIOT

Situated in Geneva's old town, the Millo family's shop has been supplying flowers to *le tout Genève* since it was founded by Charles Fleuriot in 1920. Their rich bouquets are traditionally styled and the quality of both the flowers and the service are superb. This is a great source for wonderful orchids and bonsai, too.

Fleuriot
26 rue de la Correterie,
CH-1204 Geneva, Switzerland
Tel: +41-22-310 3655   Fax: +41-22-310 2072

LES FLEURS DU CHATELAIN

For the past six years France (nobody uses her surname) has done the flowers for the best private parties in Brussels - and for the likes of Calvin Klein, Porsche and the EU. The monochromatic interior of her shop sets off the brilliant display of colours to perfection but it is the scent that will knock you off your feet.

Les Fleurs du Chatelain
39 Place du Châtelain,
1050 Brussels, Belgium
Tel/Fax: +32-2-537 1369

FLIPOT

In a modest 200-year-old house 50km from Turin, Walter and Gisella Eynard run this atmospheric restaurant with adjoining guest rooms. The couple are renowned for their intelligent cuisine and for their cookbook *Supa Barbetta*, both based on ingredients from the surrounding Valdese mountains and recipes handed down by word of mouth, yet incorporating elements from French, German, Russian and Persian traditions. The Lavender and chocolate mousse is a must.

Restaurant Flipot
Corso Gramsci 17, Torre Pellice 10066, Italy
Tel: +39-0121-91 236

FMR

Franco Maria Ricci is justly celebrated for his cult magazine and the beautiful art books that he publishes. That he boldly chose a Renaissance palace in Naples' *centro storico* as the location for his newest shop, is evidence of how quickly that area is developing.

FMR
via Benetto Croce 38, 80133 Naples, Italy
Tel: +39-081-551 9009

FOGAL

Swiss company, Fogal, has cornered the market in Europe's most desirable hosiery, cannily promoted by an advertising campaign worthy of a pin-up calender. The high prices are well worth it for the sheerest of deniers, the sexiest lace-top stockings and the most covetable cashmere tights.

Fogal
20 Claridenstraße, Postfach 5028,
CH 8022 Zürich, Switzerland
Tel: +41-1-205 8585 Fax: +41-1-205 8586

FONDATION BEYELER

The Hildy and Ernst Beyeler collection developed parallel to the Beyeler Gallery over the course of 50 years. The gallery's first exhibition took place in the 1940s and soon gained an international reputation, becoming a meeting place for leading modern artists such as Picasso. Early on, the Beyelers started accumulating works that they could not or did not want to sell and these form the Beyeler collection, which opened in October 1997 in a stunning red porphyry building designed by Renzo Piano. The collection consists of around 160 works by 33 artists and provides an extensive overview of classical modern art.

Fondation Beyeler
Baselstraße 77, CH-4125 Riehen, Switzerland
Tel: +41-61-645 9700 Fax: +41-61-645 9719

FPD SAVILLS

Founded in 1855 by Alfred Savill, as a firm of chartered surveyors, Savills has grown into one of Britain's most prestigious real estate firms, dealing in prime London and country homes, as well as agricultural and sporting estates. Savills joined forces, in 1998, with Hong Kong-based First Pacific Davies, with the aim of becoming a global player.

FPD Savills
1 Berkeley Street, London W1X 5AA, UK
Tel: +44-171-499 8644 Fax: +44-171-495 3773

FOUR SEASONS MILAN (HOTEL)

A dramatically reborn 15th-century monastery, the intimate Four Seasons is just steps from Milan's couture houses and finan-

cial district. The decent Lombardy cuisine at La Veranda (abuzz with ladies who lunch) ensures its popularity. But the real delights are the glassed-in cloister and frescoed lobby and the excellent, indulgent concierges.

Four Seasons Hotel, Milan
via Gesù 8, 20121 Milan, Italy
Tel +39-02-77 088 Fax +39-02-77 08 50 07

FRANCK MULLER

From his headquarters in a turn-of-the-century manor, Franck Muller has been designing and producing some of the world's most sought-after watches since 1991. Aesthetically pleasing as well as being works of technical genius, Muller's instantly recogniseable timepieces are offset by straps of gold or crocodile, as well as fashionably-hued satin and lizard for ladies.

Franck Muller
22 route de Malagny,
CH-1284 Genthod, Switzerland
Tel: +41-22-959 8888 Fax: +41-22-959 8883

FRANCO BOMPIERI

With more than 55 years' of clippings swept from beneath his salon chair, Franco Bompieri is the barber of choice among Milan's most elegant men. The heads of Marcello Mastroianni, Luchino Visconti and even Giacomo Puccini have all received his attention. With Bompieri's talent an open secret, good luck getting an appointment!

Franco Bompieri at Antica Barbieria Colla
via Morone 3, 20100 Milan, Italy
Tel: +39-02-87 43 12

FRANCO CURLETTO

For the past ten years, this enterprising stylist, who takes his inspiration from the catwalks, has been promoting himself and his salon tirelessly. It has paid off, making Franco Curletto not only the hairdresser of choice among the elegant wives of Turin's industrial emperors but a name known to practically every style-conscious Italian.

Franco Curletto
corso Ferrucci 34A, 10138 Turin, Italy
Tel: +39-011-433 6000 Fax: +39-011-434 6080

FRANCO DELL'ORTO

When Milan's fashion aristocracy feel the need for some green space, they call in Franco dell'Orto; several of his gardens have been used as a backdrop for fashion shoots. His projects include a private sculpture park outside Milan and a woodland terrace for artist Guido Somarein in the city centre. He was obviously destined for his profession, since his surname translates as 'of the garden'.

Franco dell'Orto
via Ausonia 9/A, Milan, Italy
Tel: +39-02-89 40 12 32 Fax: +39-02-58 01 14 58

FRETTE

What have the Borghese family, Claridges and The Pope got in common? They all go to Frette for their bed linens. This most Italian of companies (actually founded in Grenoble, France, in 1860 by Edmund Frette) was already celebrated internationally by the turn of the century for its use of the finest fabrics and its exquisite craftsmanship.

Frette
via Montenapoleone 21, 20122 Milan, Italy
Tel/Fax: +39-02-76 00 37 91

FRANÇOIS-JOSEPH GRAF

François-Joseph Graf's classical training (he spent three years working under the chief architect at the Château de Versailles) and sumptuous personal taste are in huge demand from those wishing to join Pierre Bergé and the Henry Kravises on his client list. Taking a couturier's approach to decorating, he often employs jewel colours - mixing, as Bergé has said, "rigeur with fantasy". Graf's work can be seen in public at Avignon's Hôtel de la Mirande and at L'Ambroisie restaurant in Paris.

François-Joseph Graf
Ariodante, 17 rue de Lille, 75007 Paris, France
Tel: +33-1-42 61 39 39   Fax: +33-1-42 61 40 45

FRANCOIS LEAGE

This is one of the least showy of the major Paris antique dealers but M. Léage's collection of 18th-century French furniture and objets d'art is among the best in the city. Not surprisingly it attracts major art institutions worldwide, including the Getty Museum. Service is discreet, yet exemplary in its thoroughness.

François Léage
178 rue du Faubourg St Honoré,
75008 Paris, France
Tel: +33-1-45 63 43 46   Fax: +33-1-42 56 46 30

FRANKONIA JAGD

Over the past 90 years, Frankonia Jagd has grown from a tiny family business into Germany's most prestigious address for top-quality outdoor kit.

With 14 shops throughout Germany, Frankonia is not only *the* source for hunting and shooting clothes and accessories, it is also the most significant shotgun retailer in the country.

Frankonia Jagd
Randersackerer Straße 3-5,
97064 Würzburg, Germany
Tel: +49-931-80 00 70 Fax: +49-931-800 0710

S. FRANSES

Established in 1909, this is Europe's leading gallery for European and Asian tapestries and carpets dating from the 15th century.

These beautiful and historically important objects are all meticulously recorded in the world's largest tapestry and carpet research archive, also located at the gallery.

S. Franses
80 Jermyn Street,
London SW1Y 6JD, UK
Tel: +44-171-976 1234
Fax: +44-171-930 8451

FRIEDRICH

Run by brothers Stephan and Christophe Friedrich since 1977, this leading jeweller was established in 1947 by their father, Karl. All of the house's exquisite creations are manufactured in its Frankfurt *atelier*. The firm has won 30 important prizes for its designs, including the prestigious Diamonds International Award.

Friedrich GMBH
Goethestraße 9, D-60313 Frankfurt, Germany
Tel: +49-69-28 41 41 Fax: +49-69-28 41 22

GABHAN O'KEEFFE

London-based South African/Irish interior designer Gabhan O'Keeffe makes Christian Lacroix look positively minimalist. He has taken the international decorating world by storm, producing extravagant designs for some of the world's most discerning - and affluent - men and women. His work invariably provokes strong responses. His recent refurbishment of Parisian *grande dame* São Schlumberger's house, for instance, was the talk of the city for months. Yet O'Keeffe's flamboyant style continues to attract such clients as Isabelle Goldsmith, Princess Gloria von Thurn und Taxis, Nan Kempner and British Paymaster General, Geoffrey Robinson. If you want to follow suit, the ground rules are simple: you must be good fun, extremely brave and very, very rich (O'Keeffe's partner George Warrington has admitted that most of the fabrics he uses cost £1,000 a yard). If you meet these criteria, join the queue; he's booked up for the next four years.

Gabhan O'Keeffe
3 Kinnerton Place South,
London SW1X 8EH, UK
Tel: +44-171-259 5658   Fax: +44-171-259 5614

GAJA

Among Italian wine-makers, Angelo Gaja stands in the highest rank. Producing a range of traditional and modern styles from his base in Piedmont, Gaja has a magician's touch. His chardonnay is wonderful, but the real treats are his single vineyard barbarescos, which cry out for the finest Italian food and a Verdi aria ringing in the background.

Angelo Gaja
Via Torino 36B,
12050 Barbaresco, Cuneo, Italy
Tel: +39-0173-63 52 55   Fax: +39-0173-63 52 56

GALLERIA NELLA LONGARI

Galleria Nella Longari is a treasure hunter's delight; packed to the brim with delightful curiosities and magnificent antiques. For stylish 19th-century Italian furniture with seriously impressive provenances this is the place to come. But whatever you do, leave butter-fingered children at home. There are many less expensive museums!

Galleria Nella Longari
via Bigli 15, 20121 Milan, Italy
Tel: +39-02-79 42 87   Fax: +39-02-78 03 22

GALERIE BRACHOT

Mr Brachot, a world-class expert on Magritte, also deals with works by Paul Delvaux and Marcel Broodthaers. His gallery, founded in 1915, currently handles just one artist, Panamarenko, and is considered the 'North Sea Depot' of the artist's works. The Brachots participate every year in the Basel Art Fair and Art Brussels.

Galerie Christiane and Isy Brachot
Rue Villa Hermosa 8, 1000 Brussels, Belgium
Tel: +32-2-511 05 25   Fax: +32-2-514 33 35

GALERIE CARLO ORSI

Founded by Alessandro Orsi in 1950, this stunning gallery, which has sold paintings to the Sforza Castle Museum in Milan, has been directed by his son, Carlo, for 20 years. He specialises in old master paintings, sculpture and works of art from the 15th to 18th centuries, and previous exhibitions have included Pietro Longhi in 1993, and Italy and the Grand Tour in 1997.

Galerie Carlo Orsi
via Bagutta 14, 20121 Milan, Italy
Tel: +39-02-76 00 22 14   Fax: +39-02-76 00 40 19

GALERIE GMURZYNSKA

Galerie Gmurzynska, founded in 1965, is Cologne's most respected private gallery specialising in classical modern art and the Russian avant garde. Constructivism, Bauhaus, and de Stijl all get a look in. In the last couple of years the gallery has hosted exhibitions of work by Picasso, Mirò and Yves Klein. The gallery has a twin sister in Zug, Switzerland.

Galerie Gmurzynska
Goethestraße 65A, D-50968 Cologne, Germany
Tel: +49-221-37 64 40   Fax: +49-221-37 87 30

GALERIE KARSTEN GREVE

Having begun dealing in 1969, Karsten Greve has been based since 1980 in the intimately-scaled pre-war house of Aenne Abels, in the shadow of Cologne Cathedral, presenting post-war avant garde artists of international renown. A second gallery, housed in a modern building on Albertusstraße, was opened in 1992. Its sober and spacious interior provides excellent conditions for showing larger-scale sculpture in particular.

Galerie Karsten Greve
Wallrafplatz 3, D-50667 Cologne, Germany
Tel: +49-221-257 8737   Fax: +49-221-258 0479

GALERIE LAHUMIERE

German-born Anne Lahumière has worked with French artists all her life, becoming President of the Comité des Galeries d'Art in 1993. The gallery specialises in art from 1917 to the present day; clients include both museums and private clients. Lahumière acts as both collector and dealer; "When we acquire pieces we always think of its place in our collection - a great guarantee for our clients."

Galerie Lahumière
17 rue du Parc Royal, 75003 Paris, France
Tel: +33-1-42 77 27 72   Fax: +33-1-42 77 27 78

GALERIE MAX HETZLER

Max Hetzler is one of Germany's leading contemporary art dealers, representing - among others - Jeff Koons, Thomas Struth and Gerhard Merz. After founding his gallery in Stuttgart in 1974, he caused a stir by moving to Berlin twenty years later - but has proved to be a pioneer in whose footsteps many have followed.

Galerie Max Hetzler
Zimmerstraße 89, D-10117 Berlin, Germany
Tel: +49-30-229 2437 Fax: +49-30-229 2417

GALERIE NEOTU

This gallery is tailor-made for collectors of avant-garde art looking for furniture to go with their Schnabels and Basquiats. Owners Pierre Staudenmeyer and Gérard Dalmon will not complete a sale if they feel a piece isn't right for a potential buyer. A word of warning: do not touch, as this smacks of consumerism rather than art appreciation.

Galerie Neotu
25 rue du Renard, 75004 Paris, France
Tel: +33-1-42 78 96 97   Fax: +33-1-42 78 26 27

GALERIE ROBERT SCHMIT

Founded in 1929 by Jean Schmit, this gallery specialises in 19th- and 20th-century masters. It has sold, among other pictures, a Fantin-Latour to the Metropolitan Museum of Art, a Seurat to the Musée d'Orsay, a Géricault to the National Gallery in Washington. Its private clients include Mr and Mrs Paul Mellon, Alice Tully and William Koch.

Galerie Schmit
396 rue Saint-Honoré, 75001 Paris, France
Tel: +33-1-42 60 36 36   Fax: +33-1-49 27 97 16

GALERIE SEGOURA
Maurice Segoura is much admired by, among other people, his good friend Hubert de Givenchy, the president of Christie's France. His gallery, in a *hôtel particulier*, decorated by François-Joseph Graf, is an Aladdin's cave of masterpieces ranging from 18th-century bronzes and Gobelin tapestries, to Chinese lacquer-work and exquisite examples of Boulle marquetry.

Galerie Segoura
14 Place François Ier, 75008 Paris, France
Tel: +33-1-42 89 20 20   Fax: +33-1-42 89 64 13

GALLERIA D'ARTE MARESCALCHI
In 1991 Halo Spagna took over this gallery, which was founded in 1973 by his father-in-law. Specialising in figurative art of the 19th and 20th centuries, he deals in Picasso, Chagall, Magritte, Renoir, Monet and Sisley, as well as the Italians, Di Chirico and Morandi. Dott. Spagna is especially proud of a surrealist exhibition which the gallery mounted, featuring the greatest works of Magritte, Mirò and Dalì.

Galleria d'arte Marescalchi
via Mascarella 116/B, 40126 Bologna, Italy
Tel: +39-051-24 03 68   Fax: +39-051-25 13 41

GALLERIA BORGHESE
Long closed for restoration, the Borghese's splendid collection has recently been re-opened. The Villa dei Borghese was built in the early 15th century for Cardinal Scipione Borghese, who acquired numerous works of art - a tradition his family continued. The collection includes countless sculptural masterpieces as well as paintings such as Raphael's *Sacred and Profane Love* and Giovanni Bellini's *Madonna and Child*.

Galleria Borghese
Piazzale Scipione Borghese 5, 00197 Rome, Italy
Tel: +39-06-854 8577

GALLERIA KRUGIER
Jan Krugier is an authority on European 18th- and 19th-century Masters, but his gallery also stocks a comprehensive selection of contemporary painters from all over the world. Krugier has a gallery in New York, where the exhibition 'From Ingres to Picasso' has been running for most of the decade.

Galleria Krugier
29-31 Grande Rue,
CH-1204 Geneva, Switzerland
Tel: +41-22-310 5719   Fax: +41-22-310 5712

GALERIE THOMAS
A leading exponent of German Expressionism and Classical Modern Art, the Galerie Thomas has for the last 30 years enjoyed a worldwide reputation. It has held major exhibitions of works from the group 'Der Blaue Reiter' by such artists as Wassily Kandinsky, Alexej Jawlensky and Gabriele Münter, as well as works of the group, 'Die Brücke', which includes Karl Schmidt-Rotluff, Ernst Ludwig Kirchner, Otto Mueller and Emil Nolde. One-man exhibitions by such artists as Max Beckmann, Pablo Picasso, Edvard Munch and Fernando Botero have also been held over the years. Galerie Thomas has participated for many years in the most important art fairs, including Cologne, Basel, Paris and Maastricht.

Galerie Thomas
Maximilianstraße 25, D-80539 Munich, Germany
Tel: +49-89-22 27 41   Fax: +49-89-29 14 04

IL GAMBERO ROSSO
The homely and unpretentious Il Gambero Rosso overlooks the sea in the little port of San Vicenzo. Fulvio Pierangelini has developed an original cuisine from simple seafood, a mixture of traditional Italian and Japanese. There is invariably a brace of Japanese chefs learning their trade here, which is a tribute to Pierangelini's achievements. Try *Passatina di cocci con gamberi* - sublime!

Il Gambero Rosso
Piazza della Vittoria 13, San Vicenzo,
52027 Livorno, Italy
Tel: +39-0565-70 10 21   Fax: +39-0565-70 45 42

THE GARRICK CLUB
Named after the famous actor manager, David Garrick, this is one of London's more famous gentlemens' clubs. Today its members still come from the theatrical world as well as from the legal, media and literary professions.

The Garrick Club
15 Garrick Street, London WC2E 9AY, UK
Tel: +44-171-395 4100

GASTHOF POST
In 1937 the Moosbrugger family purchased a former Imperial post house and turned it into this idyllic, family-run inn. The Post's 39 bedrooms are beautifully restored and decorated with painted wooden clocks and antiques. Fanatical skiers and discreet celebrities alike return year after year to be cosseted by the charming Kristl Moosbrugger and her son Florian.

Gasthof Post Lech
A-6764 Lech-am-Arlberg, Austria
Tel: +43-5583-22 060   Fax: +43-5583-22 06 23

GASTINE RENETTE
When this legendary gunsmith opened just off the Champs Elysées in 1813, the area was an oasis of calm - except for the occasional loud bang coming from the nearby Bois de Boulogne. In fact, it was unheard of to fight a duel without first visiting this well-placed canoneer. Famed worldwide for duelling pistols, it also makes exquisite hunting rifles and supplies all the accompanying kit for a shoot.

Gastine Renette
39 avenue Franklin D. Roosevelt,
75016 Paris, France
Tel: +33-1-43 59 77 74   Fax: +33-1-42 56 21 11

LE GAVROCHE
Set to capitalise on the return of 'proper' haute cuisine to fashionable palates, Le Gavroche was the first restaurant in Britain to be awarded a

Michelin star. Marco Pierre White and Gordon Ramsay both trained here. High priests in the form of manager Silvano Giraldin and chef Michel (son of Albert) Roux Jr rule a roost recently said to have generated London's most expensive restaurant bill ever. The set lunch is, however, a great gastronomic bargain.

Le Gavroche
43 Upper Brook Street, London W1Y 1PF, UK
Tel: +44-171-408 0881   Fax: +44-171-409 0939

GELOT

Wearers of French fedoras, such as Donald Sutherland and Anthony Quinn, depend on this legendary shop, which produces the hat in an infinite variety of shapes, using 100 different shades of Italian and English felt. François Mitterrand was a regular customer, though in more hat-conscious times the variety of M. Gelot's designs attracted all types.

Gelot
15 rue du Faubourg Saint Honoré,
75008 Paris, France
Tel: +33-1-44 71 31 61

GENEVA LIMOUSINE

For the best chauffeur-driven limousines in Switzerland, this Geneva based company is difficult to beat. Its director, Philippe Menoud, has more than 14 years of experience, plus the cars and drivers to suit the most demanding clients.

Geneva Limousine
3 rue du Levant, CH-1201 Geneva, Switzerland
Tel: +41-22-908 3880   Fax: +41-22-908 3890

GEORGES BLANC

Half-timbered and flower-bedecked, the welcoming exterior of Georges Blanc's inn is a taste of things to come. Georges Blanc, who learned to cook at the knee of his legendary grandmother, Elisa, is a great French traditionalist.

Georges Blanc
Place du Marché, 01540 Vonnas, France
Tel: +33-4-74 50 90 90   Fax: +33-4-74 50 08 80

GIAN ENZO SPERONE

For the last 40 years, Gian Enzo Sperone has been enthusiastically promoting American contemporary art and European and Italian artists who are influenced by American currents. In 1964 he opened his gallery in Turin with works by Lichtenstein, Rauschenberg and Rosenquist and, following his move to Rome in 1971, he continues to display the likes of Julian Schnabel, Tom Sachs, Mimmo Paladino and Alighiero Boetti.

Gian Enzo Sperone
via di Pallacorda 15, 00186 Rome, Italy
Tel: +39-06-689 3525   Fax: +39-06-689 3527

GIANLUCA CAMPIGLIO

Gianluca Campiglio was a martial arts instructor before he trained as a plastic surgeon, reflecting his all-round awareness of the body's potential. He has a distinguished academic career to his credit, and today works at the Niguarda Hospital in Milan doing a limited amount of cosmetic surgery in addition to regular medical procedures.

Gianluca Campiglio
via Dezza 48, 20144 Milan, Italy
Tel: +39-02-48 59 34 00   Fax: +39-02-48 59 35 19

GIANNI VERSACE

While best known for the overtly sexy, drop-dead glamour favoured by his legions of Hollywood fans, the late Gianni Versace was a master of draping and cutting, often designing 'live' on models to create supremely elegant, pared-down and deeply feminine clothes. Versace's own lifestyle matched that of his celebrity clients and friends; the princely style of his houses is reflected in his hugely successful Home collection. Gianni's generosity was legendary; as well as hosting magnificent parties, he regularly sent vast bunches of flowers to fashion editors and favourite clients alike, a tradition perpetuated by his charismatic sister, Donatella.

Having taken over the design helm since her brother's murder in 1997, Donatella (whom Gianni had regarded as his chief

muse) is successfully carrying forward her late brother's philosophy. Their brother, Santo, continues to be the business brain behind the empire.

Gianni Versace SpA
via della Spiga 25, 20121 Milan, Italy
Tel: +39-02-76 09 31   Fax: +39-02-76 00 26 35

W & H GIDDEN

The Duke of Wellington rode into battle against Napoleon on a Gidden saddle in 1815 and the company has continued to supply them, along with bridles, harnesses and riding clothes, to top horse people ever since. Official saddler to the British Olympic team, Gidden has fulfilled private commissions ranging from racing silks for camel jockeys to pack saddles for camera crews.

W & H Gidden
15d Clifford Street, London W1X 1RF, UK
Tel: +44-171-734 2788   Fax: +44-171-494 2388

GIDLEIGH PARK

Where do you start when you write about Gidleigh Park - a blissful interpretation of the English country dream, created in 1977 by Americans Paul and Kay Henderson and continually perfected ever since? Is it the Michelin-starred food, the exceptional quality of the wine-

GIANNI CAMPAGNA

"A tailor's first talent is his eye," declares Gianni Campagna. "I always start with a person's face; I recognise immediately the clothes that will suit him." As a child in Sicily, Campagna spent

his days in the local tailors and his evenings in the cinema; this conditioned his enduring passions, fashion and the movies. Today, stars like Jack Nicholson, Pierce Brosnan, Roger Moore, Charlton Heston, Sharon Stone....as well as high flyers like Ronald Perelman and Henry Kravis beat a path to the door of this diminutive, genial and occasionally volcanic man, clamouring for his flawless cutting and peerless choice of fabrics: vicuña, cashmere and super 150 wools, always lined with pure silk. Each suit is individually designed, then cut by Gianni Campagna in person and sewn by a single tailor.

Now joined by his sons, Angelo and Andrea, Gianni Campagna's limited production of custom-made suits (the only ones that are still completely made by hand), make him the most sought-after tailor by the world's élite.

Campagna & C.
Piazza San Babila 5, 20122 Milan, Italy
Tel: +39-2-76 02 23 60   Fax: +39-2-76 00 41 03
NB: new address from spring 1999: via Palestro 24 (corner of corso Venezia), 20122 Milan, Italy

list, or is it the setting - 45 acres of woodland and lawns, herb beds, water gardens and terraces, nestled in an idyllic valley of the North Teign river?

Gidleigh Park
Chagford, Devon, TQ13 8HH, UK
Tel: +44-1647-43 23 67   Fax: +44-1647-43 25 74

GIORGIO ARMANI

One of the most influential designers of the late 20th century, Giorgio Armani inspired a complete re-think of feminine style when he introduced his unstructured, menswear-influenced women's collection in the mid-70s. His menswear has, in turn, been equally influential. Armani's premium collection carries the 'White Label', his main-line collection the 'Black Label'.

Giorgio Armani SpA
via Borgonuovo 11, 20121 Milan, Italy
Tel: +39-02-72 31 81   Fax: +39-02-72 31 84 50

GIOVANNI PRATESI

Giovanni Pratesi, who lives in a former Medici villa outside Florence (where he makes his own wine and olive oil), founded his eponymous gallery in 1976. Specialising in baroque sculpture and painting, he often sells to museums and his photographic archive of 17th-century Florentine sculpture was so complete that it became the basis of a scholarly book in three volumes, *Repertorio della scultura fiorentina del '600 e '700*. Pratesi is president of the Italian Antique Dealers' Association.

Giovanni Pratesi
via Maggio 13R, 50125 Florence, Italy
Tel: +39-055-239 6568   Fax: +39-055-211 096

GIRASOL

Joachim Koerper has won endless accolades from food critics and gourmets alike since set-

ting up Girasol with his wife, Victoria, in an elegant villa just outside Moraira. His French-inspired cooking includes such signature dishes as *Rougets de roche aux pois-mange-tout et sauce crustaces* and a remarkable Carpaccio of pineapple with Jamaican chillies.

Girasol
Moraira-Calpe, E-03724 Moraira, Alicante, Spain
Tel: +34-96-574 4373   Fax: +34-96-649 0545

GISELE CROES

A leading specialist in early Chinese art, Gisèle Croës lived in Peking for two years, developing her knowledge by travelling throughout China. Having made her first purchases in the dark boutiques of erudite antique dealers there, she established her gallery in 1976, in a classical Brussels townhouse, with a stunning interior designed by Marc Corbiau.

Gisèle Croës Gallery
Boulevard de Waterloo b-1,
1000 Brussels, Belgium
Tel: +32-2-511 82 16   Fax: +32-2-514 04 19

GIULIANO BUGIALLI

In 1973 Giuliano Bugialli founded Cooking in Florence, the first school of its kind in Italy and still certainly one of the best. Already a recognised author and authority on Italian regional cuisine, Giuliano seeks out an additional area each year in which to specialise. That he markets his courses through a New York office is clear indication of his popularity with American clients.

Giuliano Bugialli, Cooking in Florence
c/o 60 Suttton Place South 1KS, New York, NY 10022, USA
Tel: +1-212-813 9552   Fax: +1-212-486 5518

GILLES SAINT GILLES

Interior architect Gilles Saint Gilles has had

no formal training in the discipline; rather, he learned his trade by working with artisans. When he undertakes projects abroad (he has designed several palaces in the Middle East, for example) he takes his hand-picked team of craftsmen with him. His work reflects his love of height, space and light and his rich, yet serene colour schemes echo the marble, stone, wood and terracotta which he loves so much.

Gilles Saint Gilles

53 avenue Montaigne,
75008 Paris, France
Tel: +33-1-42 25 59 95   Fax: +33-1-43 59 77 56

GIVENCHY

Alexander McQueen's creations have become gradually more docile since the rebel couturier moved into this illustrious fashion house in 1997. His designs are more focused and almost wearable, having lost none of their innovative quality. McQueen has the potential to do wonders for the company, founded in 1952 by the masterful Hubert de Givenchy, if he smoothes down those rough edges.

Givenchy

3 avenue George V,
75008 Paris, France
Tel: +33-1-44 31 50 00   Fax: +33-1-47 20 44 96

GLENEAGLES

Set in an 830-acre estate at the foot of the Scottish Highlands, this resort hotel is equipped with three 18-hole championship golf courses, a renowned shooting school and equestrian centre, as well as tennis, swimming and spa facilities. A staff of over 500 ensures a high degree of personal service.

The Gleneagles Hotel

Auchterarder,
Perthshire PH3 1NF, Scotland , UK
Tel: +44-1764-66 22 31   Fax: +44-1764-66 21 34

GLYNDEBOURNE

Now firmly established as an essential part of the English summer Season, the Glyndebourne Festival Opera was founded in 1943 by Audrey and John Christie. Around 5,500 members divide up the ticket spoils before the general public hears even a whisper of this prestigious venue's fine operas and the world-class artists who perform them. As well as enjoying a feast of music, the chosen ones can revel in the company of fellow opera-lovers in evening dress picnicking in the grounds during the interval.

Glyndebourne

Nr Lewes, East Sussex, BN8 5UU, UK
Tel: +44-1273-81 38 13

GLIN CASTLE

Set in a 500-acre estate on the banks of the River Shannon in Co Limerick, Glin Castle has been the seat of the Knights of Glin since the 13th century. Times have changed somewhat since the 24th knight built the present castle in the 1780s. Now the 29th Knight of Glin and his wife, Madam FitzGerald, live in one wing and let guests and visitors have the run of the main house, providing what must be one of the world's most glorious private country-house accommodations.

The castle is more fairy tale than dungeons and draughts. Its beautifully decorated reception rooms contain a marvellous collection of Irish 18th-century mahogany furniture and fine plaster-work. The long windows of the drawing room and library look out over the croquet lawn; the unique 'flying' staircase is lit by a Venetian window and looks onto the formal garden. All of the bedrooms have ravishing views - either onto the River Shannon or the gardens.

The grounds are a delight. A large walled garden supplies vegetables for the kitchen, while hens and bees provide fresh eggs and honey for breakfast. Guests may stay at the castle for dinner, overnight and for breakfast. Alternatively, you can hire the whole castle, fully staffed, for your own house party.

Glin Castle

Glin, Co Limerick, Ireland
Tel: +353-68-34 173   Fax: +353-68-34 364

GOFF'S BLOODSTOCK SALES

Established in 1866, Goff's is the premier bloodstock auction house in Ireland and is distinguished from its European peers by its international outlook, pro-active marketing and slick presentation. It has sold most of the great Irish horses, including *Arkle*, *Red Rum*, *Snurge* and, more recently, *Tony Bin* and *Kooyonga*. Its shareholders include the Aga Khan, Walter Hafner's Moyglare Stud and Tony Smurfit.

Goff's Bloodstock Sales

Kill, Co. Kildare, Ireland
Tel: +353-45-88 66 00   Fax: +353-45-87 71 19

GOLDENER HIRSCH

Just a few steps away from Mozart's birthplace this charming 15th-century inn is the best place to stay in Salzburg, not least during the Music Festival. Situated right in the heart of the Baroque city, the rooms are beautifully decorated its restaurant is one of the finest in Salzburg and host Count Walderdorff's welcome is as warm as they come.

Hotel Goldener Hirsch

Getreidegaße 37,
A-5020 Salzburg, Austria
Tel: +43-662-80 840   Fax: +43-662-84 33 49

GOLF CLUB BIELLA

Designed in 1958 by John Morrison, Biella has been voted the top Italian course for the last 11 years in succession. Situated in the middle of a forest, Biella is long and very technical - but almost entirely natural, carved out of a rocky landscape created in the Ice Age by glaciers. As Morrison himself said, "If God wanted a round of golf, he would feel at home here."

Golf Club Biella

Valcarozza, Magano, 13888 Biella, Italy

Tel: +39-015-67 91 71   Fax: +39-015-67 92 76

GOLF CLUB ROMA

Founded in 1908 by the British community living in Rome, the club is the oldest in Italy. Renowned for the unique view of the Aqueduct of Appio Claudio from the 4th hole and for its challenging water hazards, the club attracts Rome's most discreet movers and shakers. Apparently Sylvester Stallone was refused entry unless he left his bodyguards behind.

Golf Club Roma

via Appia, 00178 Rome, Italy

Tel: +39-06-78 61 29   Fax: +39-06-78 34 62 19

GOLF DE CANNES-MOUGINS

In an area swarming with smart golf clubs the 18-hole Golf de Cannes-Mougins is the smartest. Just outside the picture-perfect village of Mougins, it is where matinee idols like Bruce Willis and Clint Eastwood rub shoulders with sports stars like Boris Becker and Richard Krajicek. The undulating course begins with a blisteringly difficult 1st hole.

Golf de Cannes-Mougins

175 route d'Antibes, 06250 Mougins, France

Tel: +33-4-93 75 79 13   Fax: +33-4-93 75 27 60

GOLF DE CHANTILLY

A long course on heavy soil, this Tom Simpson-designed championship course requires some strength and stamina - as well as considerable courage at the 15th (or 17th, depending on which of two configurations you are playing), whose green is guarded by a ravine. If you blow your tee shot, console yourself with the lovely view of the clubhouse in the distance. This is where members of Chantilly's racing aristocracy come during their time off.

Golf de Chantilly

Allée de la Menagerie, 60500 Chantilly, France

Tel: +33-3-44 57 04 43   Fax: +33-3-44 57 26 54

GOLF DE MORFONTAINE

While it doesn't touch the nearby Chantilly club for social cachet, this course, designed by Tom Simpson in 1927, is rated higher for golf by many more discerning players. A beautiful heathland course, it begins with a punishing first three, includes a couple of difficult par-4s and has some greens "worthy of Augusta", according to one enthusiast.

Golf de Morfontaine

60128 Morfontaine, France

Tel: +33-3-44 54 68 27   Fax: +33-3-44 54 60 57

GONZALEZ BYASS

Founded in 1835 by Manuel Maria Gonzalez Angel, the world's largest producer of sherry is still family owned. Best-known for its excellent fino, Tio Pepe, the firm also produces magnificent olorosos. Its Apostoles is utterly dry, nutty, creamy and intense - about as far removed as possible from the confected brown unction normally associated with this term.

Gonzalez Byass S.A

Manuel Maria Gonzalez 12,

11403 Jerez de la Frontera, Spain

Tel: +34-956-35 70 00 Fax: +34-956-35 70 44

GLOBAL ASSET MANAGEMENT

The Global Asset Management group of companies was formed in 1983 by Gilbert de Botton and now manages over $14 billion on behalf of high ne-worth individuals, institutions and direct investors.

In the belief that no single organisation can attract the best fund managers in all sectors and asset classes, de Botton pioneered the multi-manager approach to achieve superior, risk-adjusted returns. Client portfolios are managed by a blend of in-house and external talent and each is tailored to achieve capital preservation and growth in line with clients' risk parameters, liquidity needs and tax considerations.

GAM's asset allocation strategy flows from an objective assessment of world markets; operating from 12 offices world-wide, it has no natural domestic bias and, thus, no investment bias. It actively manages currency exposure according to client requirements.

The frequency and quantity of client reporting is tailored to suit the needs and wishes of individuals. GAM's capabilities include reporting via the Internet in a secure manner for those wishing to have 24-hour electronic access to portfolio data. In addition to its portfolio management service, GAM offers mutual funds, run by both in-house and external managers, some of which are not otherwise easily available to the investing public.

Global Asset Management Ltd

12 St. James's Place, London SW1A 1NX, UK

Tel: +44-171-493 9990   Fax: +44-171-493 0715

Internet: www.gam.com   Email: info@gam.com

GORDON RAMSAY

Controversial talent Gordon Ramsay received universal praise for his robustly-flavoured cooking at Aubergine, though less enthusiasm for his *enfant-terrible* ways with guests. Nevertheless, having opened his first independently-owned restaurant in the autumn of 1998, the waiting list for his tables in this simple, yet sophisticated new location is as long as ever.

Gordon Ramsay
68 Royal Hospital Road, London SW3 4HP, UK
Tel: +44-171-352 4441

GORDONSTOUN SCHOOL

Gordonstoun is perhaps most famous as the school which moulded the Prince of Wales. But that obscures the fact that it is a superb breeding ground for the real world too. Although it is a young school (founded by German educationalist Dr. Kurt Hahn in 1934) it has an ethereal, old world atmosphere, magnificent buildings and a fourth-generation headmaster.

Gordonstoun School
Elgin, Moray 1V30 2RF, Scotland
Tel: +44-1343-83 78 07   Fax: +44-1343-83 78 08

THE GOULANDRIS MUSEUM OF CYCLADIC ART

Although specialising in ancient Cycladic art and sculpture, the permanent display in this private museum appears extraordinarily modern. The mix of old and new continues on the top floor which is where a number of contemporary exhibitions are held.

The Goulandris Museum of Cycladic Art
4 Neofytou Douka Street, Kolonaki,
10674 Athens, Greece
Tel: +30-1-722 8321/722 8323   Fax: +30-1-723 9382

GRAFF

Jeweller to the mega-rich, Laurence Graff possesses an awe-inspiring vault of superb multi-carat diamonds, many of them in 'fancy' colours. Having risen from humble beginnings as a jeweller's apprentice aged 15, Graff's buying power today is acknowledged to have a significant influence on the world market for important stones.

Graff
6-7 New Bond Street, London, W1Y 9PE, UK
Tel: +44-171-584 8571   Fax: +44-171-581 3415

GRAND CASINO DE MONTE-CARLO

Nothing beats losing your shirt at this grand and gilded establishment - unless it is winning a small fortune in one if its opulent Salles Privées. Those who wish to improve their chances make a pilgrimage first to the Hôtel de Paris, across the street, to touch the hoof of the bronze horse which stands in the lobby.

Grand Casino de Monte-Carlo
MC 98000, Monaco
Tel: +377-92 16 21 21

GRAND HOTEL DU LION D'OR

With its stylish bedrooms replete with old-world charm, pretty courtyard and panelled dining room illuminated by candles and gleaming silverware, the Grand Hôtel du Lion d'Or is an enviable destination - a Renaissance manor that fulfils all the promise of its welcome. Delicious Loire wines and Didier Clément's brilliant cuisine complete the experience.

Grand Hôtel du Lion d'Or
69 rue Georges Clemenceau,
41200 Romorantin-Lanthenay, France
Tel: +33-2-54 94 15 15   Fax: +33-2-54 88 24 87

GRAND HOTEL EUROPE

The Grand Hotel Europe is one of the best hotels in Russia. This St. Petersburg gem is situated just off Nevskiy Prospekt, within walking distance of the Hermitage. With five restaurants including a caviar bar and a fully equipped business centre, it is certainly leagues ahead of any other hotel in the city. Now restored to its former art-deco glory it offers charm, elegance and sophistication.

Grand Hotel Europe
Nevskiy Prospekt, Mikhailovskaya Ulitsa 1, 191011
St. Petersburg, Russia
Tel: +7-812-329 6000   Fax: +7-812-329 6001

GRAND HOTEL PARK GSTAAD

Set on a sunny hill just outside the town, Dr Jean Nussbaumer's five-star hotel, which opened in 1990, looks set to provide formidable opposition for the well-established Gstaad Palace. It finds favour with currency kingpin George Soros, as well as a host of European blue-bloods who flock to the Gstaad Polo tournament, sponsored by the hotel every August.

Grand Hotel Park
CH-3780 Gstaad, Switzerland
Tel: +41-33-748 9800   Fax: +41-33-748 9808

GRAND HOTEL STOCKHOLM

The Grand Hotel is a Stockholm institution - traditional, luxurious and defiantly elegant. For a hundred years visiting statesmen and celebrities have plotted, perused and partied in its gilt-edged lobbies and lavishly furnished suites. All 285 rooms are individually furnished and most of them have waterfront views. Hotel guests are offered complimentary use of the nearby Sturebadet health spa.

Grand Hotel
Blasieholmshamnen 8, Stockholm 10327, Sweden
Tel: +46-8-679 3500   Fax: +46-8-611 8686

LE GRAND VEFOUR

Le Grand Véfour is one of the oldest and most grandly seductive of French restaurants - the names of Victor Hugo, Colette and André Malraux are all carved into copper plaques on the banquettes. Although it is every inch an institution, it is also a living, breathing space which remains as popular as ever. Traditional French favourites mingle with new classics on a menu which also boasts a magnificent cheese board.

Le Grand Véfour
17 rue de Beaujolais, 75001 Paris, France
Tel: +33-1-42 96 56 27   Fax: +33-1-42 86 80 71

GRITTI PALACE (HOTEL)

Built in the 16th century for the Doge Andrea Gritti, this magnificent palace - which commands a prime position on the Grand Canal - was transformed into a hotel in the 1950s. The Palace's long history has seen kings and cardinals, actresses and statesman staying in its grand, antique-laden suites.

Hotel Gritti Palace
Campo Santa Maria del Giglio 2467,
30124 Venice, Italy
Tel: +39-041-79 46 11   Fax: +39-041-520 0942

GUALTIERO MARCHESI

Culinary supremo and great innovator Gualtiero Marchesi, rated one of the top 15 chefs in the world, was the first Italian to be awarded three Michelin stars. Understandably, his countryside restaurant is a top-flight destination for Milanese movers and shakers pining for his delicious *raviolo aperto*. Sleepy diners can check into his cosy adjoining hotel, Albereta.

Gualtiero Marchesi Restaurant
via Vittorio Emanuele 11, 25030 Erbusco, Italy
Tel: +39-030-776 0562   Fax: +39-030-776 0379

GUARDS POLO CLUB

As the Regimental club, with 10 pitches set in the middle of Windsor Great Park, Guards is the most 'establishment' of all polo clubs. High-goal polo is played throughout the season (from May until the end of July) and, while the Queen's Cup, in June, and the Cartier Tournament, at the end of the season, are the social highlights, the regular Sundays are when you will find The Queen here, in relaxed mode, as often as not watching her eldest son play.

The Guards Polo Club

Smith's Lawn, Windsor Great Park, Egham,
Surrey TW20 OHP, UK

Tel: +44-1784-43 42 12   Fax: +44-1784-47 13 36

GUERLAIN

Despite Guerlain's introduction of new scents and increasingly sophisticated skin-care products over

the years, its flagship store and the Beauty Institute upstairs look much as they have for the last 60 years. The sumptuous decor by Jean-Michel Franck and Christian Bérard is still there - as, indeed, are the Giacometti appliqués. The building was recently classified as an historical monument by the French Ministry of Culture.

Guerlain

68 avenue des Champs-Elysées, 75008 Paris, France
Tel: +33-1-41 27 31 00   Fax: +33-1-41 27 31 07

GUCCI

Phoenix-like, Gucci has risen from the ashes of family dissention and design torpor, to re-invent itself under the aegis of design guru Tom Ford. A noted perfectionist, Ford oversees every aspect of the company's image from the clothes collections and accessories to the minutiae of the

THE GROSVENOR HOUSE ART & ANTIQUES FAIR

A highlight of the British social Season, this fair enjoys the patronage of H.M. Queen Elizabeth The Queen Mother. The diversity and quality of the works of art on offer attracts connoisseurs, collectors and museum curators from all over the world; all of the £300 million worth of exhibits on display each year are for sale. It also attracts the movers and shakers of international society to its Charity Gala Evening. Visitors in 1998 included Princess Caroline of Monaco and Prince Ernst-August of Hanover, Ivana Trump, Princess Firyal of Jordan and the Duke and Duchess of Marlborough. As Thomas Woodham-Smith of leading furniture dealer, Mallett, explains, "Although the Fair appeals to the smart set, its beauty is that it is very discreet; while people buy on the first night, they also come back quietly throughout the Fair."

Exhibitors include specialists of international renown, drawn from the entire spectrum of fine art and antiques, ensuring an unparalleled variety and calibre of works for sale. In 1994 the Fair dropped all datelines, meaning that 20th century works of art could be shown alongside antiques. This was the first event of its kind to institute the strict vetting of every item shown; quality and authenticity rather than age or price are the criteria for each exhibit.

The Grosvenor House Art & Antiques Fair

Grosvenor House, Park Lane, London W1A 3AA, UK
Tel: +44-171-495-8743   Fax: +44-171-495 8747
Annually: 9-15 June 1999

shops' fittings. The effect has been little short of miraculous, making Gucci once more the outfitter of choice for discerning It-girls.

Gucci

11 Via Tornabuoni, 50123 Florence, Italy
Tel: +39-055-75 921   Fax: +39-055-75 72 74

GUILLERMO DE OSMA

Though this gallery exhibits paintings, sculptures and works on paper from the 18th to the 20th centuries, it is most remarkable for its dedication to the avant-garde of Spain. Guillermo de Osma used to work as an expert for Sotheby's, hence his continuing interest in research. Among his many discoveries is the extraordinary *Nu Feminin* (1928) by Salvador Dalì, previously part of the collection of Paul Eluard.

Guillermo de Osma

Claudio Coello 4, 28001 Madrid, Spain
Tel: +43-91-435 5936   Fax: +43-91-431 3175

GUINEVERE

Decorators, both amateur and professional, adore this shop (established 35 years ago by French-born Geneviève Weaver and now run by her two personable sons, Kevin and Marc), finding inspiration in its collection of treasures.

Unlike some dealers who specialise in only one period or style, Guinevere happily puts together antiques of various colours and textures, from different periods and countries, in a series of magical room sets: here, a biscuit barrel or a tortoiseshell tea caddy is mixed with an elegant Louis XVI console; there an art-deco silver mounted decanter stands alongside a chinese Han dynasty soldier.

Mirrors add to the sense of space - and the sense of discovery. Look into a fine gilded French 18th century one and see reflected an exquisite paisley shawl draped over an elegant daybed or gaze into a full-length shagreen mirror and see a shelf stocked with crocodile handbags or Anglo-Indian turned ivory *objets*.

While every item is of excellent quality, at Guinevere the aesthetic counts for far more than the intrinsic value of any one piece. Yet everything is done with such stylistic aplomb that the disparate items look as though they were all made for each other.

Guinevere Antiques
574 - 580 Kings Road, London SW6 2DY, UK
Tel: +44-171-736 2917   Fax: +44-171-736 8267

GUY ARMAGNOL

Although French-based, bloodstock agent Guy Armagnol has strong American connections and is frequently seen on the West Coast, particularly at Hollywood Park and Santa Anita, Le Dôme, where he is a regular. Among the many spectacular deals of this stylish *bon viveur*'s 30-year career, the most outstanding was his 1996 purchase, at Newmarket, of the $3m *Lunar Wells* for an American owner.

Armagnol's client list also includes several leading French and Saudi owners.

Guy Armagnol
8 rue Sedillot, 75007 Paris, France
Tel: +33-1-44 18 72 32 Fax: +33-1-44 18 72 34

GUY LAROCHE

After eight years with Geoffrey Beene, the 37-year-old Israeli-American designer Alber Elbaz, took the helm at Guy Laroche, updating the conservative house with deftly revised versions of Laroche's signature design details. So successful was he that he caught the eye of Pierre Bergé, who has lured him away to design Yves Saint Laurent's ready-to-wear. Elbaz' not-to-be-missed final collection for Guy Laroche is Spring 1999. His successor has yet to be appointed at the time of writing.

Guy Laroche
28-30 rue du Faubourg St Honoré,
75008 Paris, France
Tel: +33-1-40 69 68 00   Fax: +33-1-40 69 69 16

GUY SAVOY

With its creamy dining room of well-spaced, damask-clad tables, elegance is the hallmark of this top Paris restaurant. Superlatives are frequently used to describe virtuoso chef Guy Savoy, who served an apprenticeship with the *"grand maître"* Troisgros. His signature dishes, including *Terrine de pamplemousse, sauce au thé*, are complemented by a marvellous cellar.

Guy Savoy
18 rue Troyon, 75017 Paris, France
Tel: +33-1-43 80 40 61   Fax: +33-1-46 22 43 09

HACIENDA DE SAN RAFAEL

This traditional cortijo has been transformed by its owners, Tim and Kuky Reid, from a tumbledown olive mill into a welcoming, elegant home. Surrounded by gardens and vast tracts of agricultural land, it is a peaceful and very private retreat. Those who have rented the property rave as much

about Kuky's hospitality and attention to detail (she will be as visible or invisible as you wish) as about her cooking.

Hacienda de San Rafael, near Seville, Spain
c/o The Kiozka Collection,
Trinifold House, London W1R 1AG, UK
Tel: +44-171-292 9149   Fax: +44-171-292 9424

HAMBURGER POLO CLUB

Founded in 1898 and located in the ultra-smart residential area of Flottbeck, this club introduced polo to Germany. Medium and low-goal polo is played throughout the summer, punctuated by two high-goal tournaments: the German Championship in May and the Derby Cup - a key event in Hamburg's social calendar - in August. Coffee magnate Albert Darboven, a player for 35 years, is based here and

visiting stars include Howard Hipwood, Andrea Viviani and Marco di Paolo.

Hamburger Polo Club
Jerichstraße 26, D-22609 Hamburg, Germany
Tel: +49-40-82 06 81   Fax: +49-40-82 06 89

HAMILTON OSBORNE KING

Estate agents, auctioneers and valuers, Hamilton Osborne King has had its finger on the pulse of the Irish property market for over 50 years. Aidan O'Hogan and his team deal in the cream of Hibernian house sales, both city and country (along with commercial transactions and fine art auctions) and have an impressive roster of international clients.

Hamilton Osborne King
32 Molesworth St, Dublin 2, Ireland
Tel: +353-1-618 1300   Fax: +353-1-676 7066

HARBOUR CLUB

A favoured haunt of Milan's bankers, lawyers and fashion crowd, this club boasts 10 indoor and 10 outdoor (clay) tennis courts. Other facilities include an ultra-modern gym and indoor squash courts. The club's first-rate restaurant serves light and healthy Italian classics.

Harbour Club
via Cascina Bellaria 19, 20153 Milan, Italy
Tel: +39-02-45 28 61

HARDENBERG CONCEPT

Some of the most star-studded events, both in Berlin and throughout Germany, have been planned and executed by Countess Hardenberg and her talented team. They seek out unusual locations, give advice in drawing together guest lists (the Countess gives her clients access to some of the most influential members of German society), develop special ideas for the event and take care of every tiny detail of its organisation.

Hardenberg Concept
Burgenderstraße 5, D-14129 Berlin, Germany
Tel: +49-30-803 8846   Fax: +49-30-803 6163

HAREL

The last bastion of the hand-made classic court shoe, Harel has Parisian women swooning over its quality and scintillating range of colours - from pistachio green through lemon yellow to burnt orange. As for the stratospheric prices, the company's advertisement puts these perfectly in perspective, saying, "Only a woman would understand."

Harel
8 avenue Montaigne, 75008 Paris, France
Tel: +33-1-47 23 83 03   Fax: +33-1-43 54 16 16

HARRODS

Probably the most famous department store in the world, Harrods offers five floors of shopping heaven. The Food Halls are justifiably famous, not only for their fine displays but for the extraordinary variety and quality of products on offer, and other highlights include the Fine Jewellery department (Bulgari, Van Cleef & Arpels, Tiffany and Theo Fennell are among the names to be found here) and the first floor Designer Room. The only real drawback for serious shoppers is that its fame has made it a major tourist attraction.

Harrods Ltd
Knightsbridge, London SW1X 7XL, UK
Tel: +44-171-730 1234   Fax: +44-171-581 0470

HARROW

Founded in 1572, Harrow has traditionally been an 'establishment' boarding school in the truest sense of the word. Pupils came from grand families and were almost destined to end up in the corridors of power (Winston Churchill, Lord Palmerston and King Hussein of Jordan among them). Has all that changed? Not really, although there are now more pupils from abroad than ever. Incidentally, Elmfields is still *the house* to get your son and heir into.

Harrow School
Harrow-on-the-Hill, Middlesex HA1 3HW, UK
Tel: +44-181-42 22 196   Fax: +44-181-42 33 112

HARRY'S BAR

A supremely refined outpost of Mark Birley's empire, this private club is simply *the* place to lunch for members passing through town and any locals lucky enough to belong. Its perfectly wrought food might be Venetian but the ambience is strictly Mayfair - much in keeping with the urbane crowd: a hybrid of Almanach de Gotha and Fortune 500 folk. (See the profile of Mark Birley elsewhere in this book.)

Harry's Bar
26 South Audley Street, London W1Y 5DJ, UK
Tel: +44-171-408 0844

HARVEY NICHOLS

'Harvey Nicks', owned since 1991 by Hong Kong entrepreneur Dickson Poon, is every bit as much the party-girl's pit-stop as the soignée housewife's stand-by. Second to none for retail therapy, it stocks the best selection of clothes on the planet, eminently suitable things for the home, and delicious comestibles on the Fifth Floor, all in beautifully designed packaging.

Harvey Nichols
109-125 Knightsbridge, London SW1X 7RJ, UK
Tel: +44-171-235 5000   Fax: +44-171-259 6084

THE HAVANA CLUB

Having shaken off their somewhat stuffy image, cigars are now bought by young men (and, increasingly, women), not simply to celebrate important occasions but, rather, as a reflection of their appreciation of the finer things in life. It was this renaissance of cigar smoking amongst the young and upwardly mobile which led to the establishment, in 1995, of The Havana Club.

Here, cigar lovers convene to sample Cuban, Dominican and Honduran favourites, including Davidoff & Valdrych, Cohiba Esplendido and the Upmann Sir Winston, while lounging on deep leather sofas and enjoying a game of backgammon. Indeed, this sleek haven with its polished wood floors, panelled walls and potted orchids is rather like a Nineties version of the 'smoking divans' of the Victorian era. The Havana Club is also a great source of hard-to-find cigars, such as the Monte Cristo No. 2.

Manager of the club, Neil Millington, spent two years before it opened trawling the world for the finest objects, such as customised humidors, cigar boxes and lighters, to complement the fine collection of cigars. The Havana Club also organises regular cigar and wine-tasting dinners for its clients, in the adjoining private club, Monte's.

The Havana Club
165 Sloane Street, London SW1X 9QB, UK
Tel: +44-171-245 0890   Fax: +44-171-245 0895

HASSLER (HOTEL)

Still run by the Swiss Wirth family after more than a hundred years, the Hassler - a masterpiece of quiet elegance - belongs to a great European tradition of grand family-run hotels. Yet it belongs indisputably to Rome. Perched at the top of the Spanish Steps, it commands sweeping views over the city's rooftops. Perhaps incongruously, the hotel lists free bicycles among its services. Some may find this tempting. But in Rome, cycling seems to be a form of transport in which only priests dare to indulge.

Hotel Hassler Villa Medici
Trinità dei Monti 6, 00187 Rome, Italy
Tel: +39-06-69 93 40   Fax: +39-06-678 9991

HATFIELDS

Since 1834 when John Hatfield reframed all the royal miniatures at Windsor and Buckingham Palace, the company has been conserving the most complex and demanding items of furniture, including marquetry and Boulle, and recasting and chasing bronze mounts so that they are indistinguishable from the originals. Pieces which have received Hatfields' attention include the rococo commode by Channon that made £1 million at Christie's and the Badminton Cabinet.

Hatfields
42 St Michael's Street, London W2 1QP, UK
Tel: +44-171-723 8265   Fax: +44-171-706 4562

HAUT-BRION (CHATEAU)

Classified first growth in the 1855 appellation, this renowned château, located in the suburbs of Bordeaux, produces famously elegant, thoroughbred wines - the equal of the finest from the broader Médoc region. Its current

American owner, Clarence Dillon (formerly finance minister in the JFK administration), follows other illustrious proprietors, among them the de Pontac family and Talleyrand. Choose the 1982 or 1985 red for drinking this year.

Château Haut-Brion
133 avenue Jean Jaurès, 33602 Pessac, France
Tel: +33-5-56 00 29 30   Fax: +33-5-56 98 75 14

HAWELKA

The spirit of the writers and philosophers who used to gather here before the First World War still hovers over this Viennese café and the waiters - who treat the regulars like family - seem always to have been here, too. Loyal Viennese come here every morning to read the papers over coffee and *Buchteln* (little yeast-cakes filled with plum jam) and, in the afternoon, for Frau Hawelka's excellent *Kügelhupf*.

Hawelka
Dorotheergaße 6, A-1010 Vienna, Austria
Tel: +43-1-512 8230

HAYWARD

Having made his name during the genuinely cool Britannia days of the swinging Sixties, when he was the darling of David Bailey, Michael Caine and Terence Stamp (who have all remained his close friends), Doug Hayward now numbers aristocrats, financiers and media tycoons among his clients. They come for this modest and charming man's carefully-made bespoke suits, which bear his unmistakable, yet elusive, stamp of individuality.

Hayward
95 Mount Street, London W1Y 5HG, UK
Tel/Fax: +44-171-499 5574

HELLY NAHMAD GALLERY

Like the Wildenstein family, the Nahmads are famous for the great works of art they are

rumoured to have in store. In 1998 Helly Nahmad, Courtauld Institute alumnus and third-generation art dealer, opened London's largest gallery. It holds three exhibitions a year of museum-quality works from the 19th and 20th centuries, some from the Nahmads' fabled store in the Geneva free-port.

Helly Nahmad Gallery
2 Cork Street, London W1X 1PB, UK
Tel: +44-171-494 3200   Fax: +44-171-494 3355

HEMMERLE

Originally a jewellery and military medals specialist supplying Bavarian dignitaries, Hemmerle remains in family hands. Third-generation artistic director, Stefan Hemmerle, takes the

inspiration for his jewellery designs from sources as diverse as the Bauhaus and flora and fauna. The service here is famously courteous, thanks - in part, at least - to the Hemmerles' seemingly telepathic ability to remember clients' names.

Hemmerle
14 Maximilanstrasse,
D-80539 Munich, Germany
Tel: +49-89-242 2600   Fax: +49-89-24 22 60 40

HENNESSY

That something so quintessentially French as cognac should have so distinctively Irish a name as Hennessy is due to Richard Hennessy, originally from Co. Cork, who joined the Irish Brigade of King Louis XV's army. In 1765 he founded the eponymous firm, still run by his direct descendants. In 1996 his memory was marked by the launch of 'Richard Hennessy', a cognac so subtle and sublime that to taste it is to get a glimpse of heaven on earth.

Hennessy
8 rue de Lichonne, 16101 Cognac, France
Tel: +33-5-45 35 72 72   Fax: +33-5-45 35 79 79

HENRY CECIL

Undoubtedly the top English trainer, in both achievement and reputation, Cecil has the feel for his horses and an uncanny knack of sending them out race-fit and ready to win first time. Few years go by without his training a classic winner. For owners such as Lord Howard de Walden and Wafic Said, he trains about 200 horses - and knows each of them personally. Amazingly modest - diffident almost - Cecil has horses in the blood; his stepfather was royal trainer Sir Cecil Boyd-Rochford and his first wife, Julie, was the daughter of legendary trainer Sir Noel Murless.

Henry Cecil
Warren Place, Newmarket, Suffolk CB8 8QQ, UK
Tel: +44-1638-66 21 92   Fax: +44-1638-66 90 05

HEREND

For over 170 years this company's fine porcelain has been hand made in a factory in its

HOLLAND & HOLLAND

Founded in 1835, Holland & Holland rapidly established a reputation for exquisite craftsmanship and products of the highest quality. Over the years this very British company has expanded beyond its traditional core business of making sporting guns and now offers a broad range of luxury goods, including clothing, accessories and decorative items.

Its elegant shops are heaven for those who wish to buy into the country sports lifestyle: antiques and pictures jostle with crystal, jewellery, shoes, luggage and handbags (including hand-stitched bridle leather, luxuriant suede and specially treated flax, unique to Holland & Holland). Its chic, country-inspired fashion collections for both men and women are characterised by an easy elegance, masterly tailoring and fine fabrics; styling details clearly reflect the company's rich sporting heritage.

In addition, Holland & Holland's Sport & Travel Department offers first class tailor-made adventure travel programmes and shooting trips to far-flung destinations, including Africa and South America.

Holland & Holland
31-33 Bruton Street, London W1X 8JS, UK
Tel: +44-171-499 4411   Fax: +44-171-499 4544

namesake town in Hungary. It was here that the Austro-Hungarian aristocracy (and the likes of Queen Victoria and King Victor Emanuele) bought their porcelain, and sent it to be repaired. In addition to producing a full range of dinner-ware, Herend is equally celebrated for its collectible ornamental figures, sculptures and vases.

Herend
H-8440 Herend, Hungary
Tel: +36-88-26 11 44   Fax: +36-88-26 15 18

HERMES

This family-owned company has made an almost seamless transition from being harness-makers to purveyors of an ever-growing range of *art de vivre* luxury goods, with an increasing emphasis on fashion. The Hermès Museum, which can be visited by appointment, is full of quirky, equine-related paraphernalia, which Hermès designers use for inspiration.

Hermès
24 rue du Faubourg St Honoré, 75008 Paris, France
Tel: +33-1-40 17 47 17 Fax: +33-1-40-17-47-09

HERVE LEGER

Currently regarded as the 'king of cling', Léger's bandage-wrapped goddess gowns define the body, uplifting and shaping curves to perfection. Strong meat for the less-than-slender, they are nevertheless beloved by sylphs - Viscountess Linley has one in every colour. Turning his hand to swimwear, Léger

HOTEL DU CAP - EDEN ROC

A-List celebrities such as Clint Eastwood, Madonna, Sean Connery, the Aga Khan and any Hollywood film producer worth his credits rub shoulders with the cream of Europe's business aristocracy, including assorted Agnellis, Lord Hanson and Sir Anthony Bamford, at the Hôtel du Cap, one of the world's most expensive - but undeniably magnificent - hotels. Here, these luminaries arrive by yacht, either to stay or simply to partake of lunch, and the parade of the world's most elegant women makes the Hôtel

du Cap very special indeed. The white neo-classical building stands sentinel over a 30-acre enclave. Its marble entrance salon is one of the smartest places in Europe in which to sip a glass of champagne before dinner. The best suites are built right on the water at Eden Roc - and well worth the extra money. The heated sea-water swim-

ming pool is the most glamorous on the Côte d'Azur - an invitation to lunch overlooking the pool is hugely prized. Other leisure facilities include a state-of-the-art fitness centre and five championship clay tennis courts. Owned by the Oetker family, the Hôtel du Cap runs like clockwork thanks to the wonderfully professional staff that work under the brilliant Jean-Claude Irondelle. Honoured by the late President Mitterand with the Legion d'Honneur for his services to French tourism, Jean-Claude has, just possibly, become an even bigger star than his guests. Be warned, however - the Hôtel du Cap is 'cream of Hollywood' territory and unless you're the biggest name star or film producer, you can forget about a reservation during the Cannes Film Festival.

Hôtel du Cap - Eden Roc
Boulevard Kennedy, Cap D'Antibes, France
Tel: +33-4-93 61 39 01   Fax: +33-4-93 67 76 04

produces Hollywood-honed bathing suits with all the chic of a fully turned-out outfit.

Hervé Léger
9-11 rue du Roule, 75001 Paris, France
Tel: +33-1-40 41 98 40   Fax: +33-1-40 41 98 40

HERMITAGE (HOTEL)

During the Grand Prix the Hermitage's rooms overlooking the port offer one of the best views in the Principality. Some may disagree, of course, but it offers marginally better service, in more elegant surroundings and a more discreet location, than the landmark Hôtel de Paris. The lobby, for instance, is a stunning baroque confection; the only thing missing is people (occupancy is never as high as the hotel deserves).

Hôtel Hermitage
Square Beaumarchais, MC 98000 Monaco
Tel: +377-92-16 40 00 Fax: +377-92-16 38 52

HERZOG ANTON ULRICH-MUSEUM

Germany's first museum when it opened in 1754, its collections offer insight into the taste of Duke Anton Ulrich two hundred years ago. Highlights include a self-portrait by Giorgione and works by Rubens, Rembrandt, Vermeer, Cranach and Holbein the Younger. The museum also has a comprehensive collection of drawings and prints, antiquities and the decorative arts.

Herzog Anton Ulrich-Museum
Museumstrasse 1, D-38100 Braunschweig, Germany
Tel: +49-531-484 2400

C. HOARE & CO.

The last of the old-established private deposit banks remaining in England, C. Hoare & Co. offers customers current and deposit account facilities, in addition to a wide range of other services. The Managing Partners are all direct descendants of the founder; they own the entire share capital and, unusually in present times, these shares carry unlimited liability. Among the special benefits offered is the knowledge that Partners are in attendance every day and thus can take immediate decisions on urgent matters.

C. Hoare & Co.
37 Fleet Street, London EC4P 4DQ, UK
Tel: +44-171-353 4522   Fax: +44-171-353 4521

HOLGER STEWEN

Holger Stewen's antiques shop, which he established 25 years ago, has evolved into a highly successful decorating business, with two large shops - in Hamburg and Mallorca. Stewen's private commissions include a country house for Jil Sander, an apartment for Count Von Bismarck, and Elb Florenz, a luxurious small hotel in Dresden.

Holger Stewen
Hohe Bleichen 23, D-20354 Hamburg, Germany
Tel: +49-40-34 84 70   Fax: +49-40-348 4727

HOLWICK & WEMMERGIL

These twin estates, which are owned by Lord Strathmore and have been leased for the past seven years by Tom Cowie, are widely regarded as the world's top grouse moors. Last year produced a total bag of 9543 brace and, under Sir Tom's astute management, there is optimism that the 1934 record of 13,500 brace may be broken - a remarkable effort. A suitcase full of cash will help if you want to join the lines here.

Holwick & Wemmergil
H&W Sporting Estates, Broadwood Hall, Lanchester, Co. Durham, DH7 0TD, UK
Tel: +44-1207-52 96 63   Fax: +44-1207-52 95 39

HOME

Thomas Niederste-Werbeck, Art Director of *Architectur & Wohnen* has applied his creative talents to this decorating-cum-florist shop, which he owns in partnership with Günter Haluszczak. Their imaginative and well-chosen decorative accessories are as noteworthy as the very special bouquets of flowers that they make up for Hamburg's style elite.

Home
An Der Alster 72, D-20099 Hamburg, Germany
Tel: +49-40-234 34 84   Fax: +49-40-280 38 45

HORCHER

First established in Berlin, Horcher was a favourite haunt of the Nazi grandees during the Third Reich. When things became a little tricky there, Horcher fled - with Franco's help - to Madrid. He did not leave so much as a napkin behind and here, overlooking the Parque del Buen Retiro, you can still enjoy excellent, traditional game dishes, using the original silver and china but now surrounded by Spanish grandees.

Horcher
Alfonso XII 6, Madrid, Spain
Tel: +34-91-522 0731

HUBLOT

Sleek and remarkably elegant, Hublot wristwatches have a timeless quality, yet with a resolutely modern edge - a style to which many other watchmakers can merely aspire.

When Carlo Crocco launched Hublot, at the 1980 Basle Watch Fair, his then radical design - based on the classic yacht porthole (*hublot* in French) and combining finely brushed gold with a simple, black rubber strap - caused a sensation. Since then, the understated design has been taken up by such style leaders as Giorgio Armani and Princess Caroline of Monaco (who has called it her "favourite watch") and sophisticates like King Juan Carlos of Spain and King Carl Gustav of Sweden, whose relaxed and discreet style it perfectly echoes.

The apparent simplicity of Hublot's watches belies the exceptional level of craftsmanship required to produce them; making the case alone requires 180 separate operations by hand. Through working closely with MDM Genève's design team, the initial Hublot model has been expanded into a complete family of styles with more complex features and functions, a choice of finishes (brushed or polished stainless steel or gold) and the occasional issue of limited editions.

Hublot
MDM Genève, 44 route de Divonne, CH-1260 Nyon, Switzerland
Tel: +41-22-362 1970   Fax: +41-22-362 1617

HOSTAL DE LA GAVINA

This aristocratic hacienda, which overlooks the Costa Brava's two finest beaches, is decorated with Gobelins tapestries, exquisite wood panelling and fine antiques and pictures. To complement such distinguished surroundings the cuisine, in which seafood and other local produce feature heavily, is exquisite and the cellar first class.

Hostal de la Gavina

Plaza de la Rosaleda, E-17248 S'Agaro, Spain
Tel: +34-972-32 11 00   Fax: +34-972-32 15 73

HOTEL ARTS

The 1992 Olympics changed Barcelona forever and this sleek hotel by the port - with its 33-storey tower by US architects Skidmore, Owings and Merrill - dominates the new skyline. Book well ahead to stay in The Club, on the three uppermost floors, and enjoy breathtaking views and a one-to-one staff/guest ratio.

Hotel Arts

Carrer de la Marina 19-21, E-08005 Barcelona, Spain
Tel: +34-93-221 1000   Fax: +34-93-221 1070

HOTEL COSTES

The fashion and movie set love this über-chic hotel in the first arrondissement. Why? The décor is exceedingly smart and the gym as good as the one at The Ritz, its snooty rival. The restaurant is filled with super-cool ladies who lunch, and the opulent reception room is great for watching the *beau monde* do its thing.

Hôtel Costes

239 rue Saint-Honoré, 75001 Paris, France
Tel: +33-1-42 44 50 00   Fax: +33-1-42 44 50 01

HOTEL D'ANGLETERRE

This palatial hotel has pampered many distinguished guests since it was established over 150 years ago, including Hans Christian Anderson, Alfred Hitchcock (who filmed a scene from *Torn Curtain* here) and Michael Jackson. The rooms, decorated in French style, have a *dégagé* elegance and the hallways remain as grand as when ladies in crinolines passed down them.

Hôtel D'Angleterre

Kongens Nytorv 34, 1021 Copenhagen K, Denmark
Tel: +45-33-12 00 95   Fax: +45-33-12 11 18

HOTEL DE PARIS

A traditional 'Grand' hotel built in 1863, the Hôtel de Paris and, in particular, its bar (under the watchful eye of head barman, Louis) has become a home away from home for jetsetters and bejewelled *grandes dames*. Slap bang in the

HUMEWOOD CASTLE

Humewood was built in the late 19th century as an "occasional resort in the summer or shooting season." Now it has been magnificently restored by its charismatic owner, Renata Coleman.

In recent years Humewood has become regarded as one of Ireland's finer duck shoots. (The Shooting Times is, for the first time, leaving England for its annual weekend of corporate entertaining, foregoing partridge or pheasant in England for duck here). This year Humewood is even better with the establishment of two additional lakes.

The outstanding gamekeeper and shoot manager have devised techniques that can keep birds in the air, circling over the guns, for up to 45 minutes. While the first few days of the season can produce very large bags, a typical day at Humewood yields 400 ducks, give or take a few, and the quality of these birds rivals some of the tallest pheasant shoots.

Humewood is also a sporting estate which boasts a polo field, an event course, fine Sporting Clay and Fitasc courses, as well as one of only two ZZ Bird (Helice) fields in the British Isles. While there are pheasant at Humewood, they are not spectacular and, to correct this shortcoming, Humewood has acquired a superb tall pheasant shoot 20 minutes from the castle.

Humewood Castle

Kiltegan, County Wicklow, Ireland
Tel: +353-508-73 215   Fax: +353-508-73 382

middle of town, it provides a luxurious refuge from the tourists outside. The harbourside suites are particularly smart and Alain Ducasse's Louis XV restaurant is truly world class.

Hôtel de Paris

Place du Casino, Monte Carlo, MC 98000 Monaco
Tel: +377-92-16 30 00   Fax: +377 92 16 38 50

HOTEL EDEN

During the 1960s the Hotel Eden was a key place for the jet set to live out *la dolce vita*. Reopened in 1994 after massive renovation, it now attracts new generation stars such as Tom Cruise and Naomi Campbell. Chef Enrico

Derflingher was the personal chef of TRH, the Prince and the late Princess of Wales.

Hôtel Eden

via Ludovisi 49, 00187 Rome, Italy
Tel: +39-06-47 81 21   Fax: +39-06-482 1584

HOTEL STADT HAMBURG

This gem of a hotel, favoured by discreet Europeans (including many escapees from its namesake city), is run with great style by Bernd Knochenhauer. Set on the romantic North Atlantic island of Sylt, with its miles of fine sand beaches, it is a supremely comfortable retreat - decorated in charming country style and always filled with flowers. The menu here is, not surprisingly, based on the freshest imaginable seafood.

Hotel Stadt Hamburg
Strandstraße 2, D-25980Westerland/Sylt,
Germany
Tel: +49-4651-85 80   Fax: +49-4651-85 82 20

THE HOUGHTON CLUB

Most of the world's top fisheries owe their greatness, at least in part, to their remoteness. It is therefore all the more remarkable that the Test, one of the birthplaces of fly fishing, is barely a two hour drive from London. The story of the Test, its fabled waters and large, selective trout is largely a history of the Houghton Club and its keepers. As a lad, Mick Lunn, now third generation keeper for Houghton, attended to General Eisenhower, who fished here while planning D-Day.

The Houghton Club
The Grosvenor Hotel, Stockbridge,
Hampshire SO2O 6EU, UK
Tel: +44-1264-81 06 06   Fax: +44-1264-81 07 47

HUNTSMAN

The excellent quality of Huntsman's traditionally-styled bespoke suits is matched only by its level of service. Established in 1849, its tailors today will travel to the US and Europe to take orders and fittings and Huntsman also offers a valeting and repair service to ensure that clothing remains in top condition.

H. Huntsman & Sons Ltd.
11 Savile Row, London W1X 2PS, UK
Tel: +44-171-734 7441   Fax: +44-171-287 2937

THE HURLINGHAM CLUB

This is like a country club in the heart of London, centred around a magnificent Georgian house and spread over 50 acres along the River Thames. If you wish to enjoy its tennis courts (grass and indoors), its croquet grounds, its cricket pitch and its two swimming pools (one indoors and one in the grounds) you'd best befriend an existing member; the waiting list is *very* long.

The Hurlingham Club
Ranelagh Gardens, London SW6 3PR, UK
Tel: +44-171-736 8411

ILIAS LALAOUNIS

Fourth-generation Greek goldsmith, Ilias Lalaounis, made his name with classically-inspired jewellery, much of it gem-studded, using the motifs and symbols of ancient civilisations. The pieces are at once bold yet decorative - perfect for offsetting simple winter tailor-

ing or a sleek summer wardrobe. His four daughters now run the business.

Ilias Lalaounis
6 Panepistimiou Avenue, 10671 Athens, Greece
Tel: +30-1-361 1371   Fax: +30-1-365 4798

IM PALAIS SCHWARZENBERG (HOTEL)

From its marble and gilt entrance hall to its vast gardens, this baroque summer palace is one of the most idyllic places to stay in any capital city. Naturally, it caters well to Vienna's two delights - opera and cakes - with a concierge to obtain tickets, staff to care for your gowns, and a log fire in the Kaminzimmer beside which to indulge in hot chocolate and cakes.

Hotel im Palais Schwarzenberg
Schwarzenbergplatz 9, A-1030 Vienna, Austria
Tel: +43-1-798 4515   Fax: +43-1-798 4714

IM SCHIFFCHEN

There has been a restaurant at this address since 1793 but, since their arrival in 1977, Jean-Claude Bourgueil and his wife, Janine, have (despite two arson attacks over the years) made it one of Germany's finest - much appreciated by an elegant crowd of industrialists, art lovers, media barons and politicians. The stunning simplicity of Bourgueil's cooking is echoed by his insistence on serving it up on plain white china.

Im Schiffchen
Kaierswerther Market 9, D-40489 Düsseldorf,
Germany
Tel: +49-02-11 40 10 50   Fax: +49-02-40 36 67

IMPERIAL (HOTEL)

Established in 1873 by Emperor Franz Joseph I as the hotel of the Imperial court, this Renaissance-style former palace is still Austria's official hotel for state visits. Stay in a suite and a butler/valet will not only attend to your rooms, but will accompany you on shopping or sightseeing trips. Gustav Mahler, Oscar Wilde, Luciano Pavarotti, Alfred Hitchcock and Walt Disney have all done so.

Hotel Imperial
Kärntner Ring 16, A-1015 Vienna, Austria
Tel: +43-1-50 11 00   Fax: +43-1-50 11 04 10

INES DE LA FRESSANGE

For a *bon chic, bon genre*, look with a youthful accent, go no further. This doll's house of a shop is filled with impeccably-made shirts and pants, skirts and jackets in natural fabrics, as well as charmingly decorated plates, elegant leather bags and rows of suede shoes in sunshine colours - all styled by Karl Lagerfeld's former muse. The Provençal ambience works perfectly; in few other boutiques on the avenue Montaigne are staff so relaxed and inclined to let you browse.

Inès de la Fressange
14 avenue Montaigne, 75008 Paris, France
Tel: +33-1-47 23 08 94 Fax: +33-1-47 23 05 54

L'INFANZIA

Italy's smartest families recruit their nannies from this excellent school. As well as receiving comprehensive instruction in nutrition and child psychology, pupils here undergo training in music and gymnastics, with the aim of providing a balanced lifestyle for their future charges.

L'Infanzia
viale Lario 16, 220159 Milan, Italy
Tel/Fax: +39-02-69 00 22 01

INVERLOCHY CASTLE

"I never saw a lovelier or a more romantic spot," declared Queen Victoria when she stayed at Inverlochy Castle in 1870. Nestling among the mountains and surrounded by 500 acres of private grounds, the castle faces its own loch. Inverlochy has only 17 bedrooms but 50 staff, managed by Michael Leonard, whose exceptional charm dazzles all comers. The other talking point is the kitchen, now under the supervision of Raymond Blanc-trained Simon Haigh.

Inverlochy Castle Hotel
Torlundy, Fort William, Inverness-Shire PH33 6SN, Scotland, UK
Tel: +44-1397-70 21 77   Fax: +44-1397-70 29 53

INPERSAU

Most of the drivers who work for Jean-Baptiste and Antoine Aubrun's chauffeur-hire company are bilingual and all are, naturally, trained in security. The biggest plus of all is that Inpersau will, if you wish, customise your car - providing, for example, a special hi-fi system with a stock of your favourite CDs.

Inpersau
51 rue de St. Lazare, 75009 Paris, France
Tel: +33-1-53 19 00 66   Fax: +33-1-53 19 00 88

L' INSTITUT DE THALASSOTHERAPIE HELIANTHAL

This is one of the most progressive health centres in Europe. Its courses of six to nine days' duration, all based on sea water therapy, emphasise stress management and the detoxifying and re-balancing of the entire system. One course is tailored to new mothers (it even offers special facilities for their babies) and another, l'Ecole du Dos specialises in the re-education of posture.

L' Institut de Thalassothérapie Hélianthal
Place M. Ravel 469, 64504 St-Jean-de-Luz, France
Tel: +33-5-59 51 51 51   Fax: +33-5-59 51 51 54

INSTITUT MATIS PRESTIGE

One of the most reputed beauty institutes in Paris, Matis offers 50 different treatments, including 19 facial treatments for women and two for men, all with delicious, natural fruit and flower aromas. Matis' ultimate pampering comprises three treatments at once from three different beauticians. Its indispensable powders are favoured by actresses, due to their resilience under spotlights and in hot climates.

Institut Matis Prestige
22 rue des Capucines, 75002 Paris, France
Tel: +33-1-42 86 07 19

IPCA

As well as running one of the most highly-regarded cookery schools in Europe, IPCA publishes the glossy monthly *La Cucina Italiana*. With a huge range of courses on offer the school caters for both the complete novice and the skilled professional. Silvio Berlusconi's daughter was a recent student.

IPCA (Istituto per la promozione della cultura Alimentare)
Piazza Aspromonte 15, 20137 Milan, Italy
Tel: +39-02-266 4907   Fax: +39-02-266 5555

IWC

This Swiss company was founded in 1868 by an American watchmaker, Florentine Ariosto Jones, who introduced new machines and production processes to Switzerland and so established the firm's reputation for solidly made, high-precision timepieces. A succession of milestone models, including the first wristwatch-size Grande Complication in 1990, has ensured its cult status.

IWC
The International Watch Company
15 Baumgartenstraße, CH-8201 Schaffhausen, Switzerland
Tel: +41-52-635 6533   Fax: +41-52-635 6505

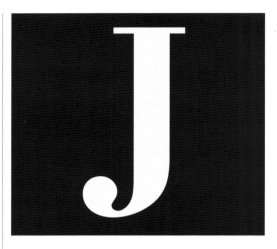

J.P. TOD'S

J.P. Tod's desirable moccasins, originally created as driving shoes, have been nicknamed "Concorde slippers" because so many of the jet-set wear them.

Tod's addicts who can bear the three-month wait get them made up to order, selecting the type of material, colour and stitching, to create a totally unique pair, made in the firm's workshops near Ancona.

J.P. Tod's
via della Spiga 22, 20121 Milan, Italy
Tel: +39-02-76 00 24 23

J.P.B. SECURITY

This is a priceless address for anyone who feels in need of protection while in France. The company is particularly adept at looking after super-models during the fashion collections and regularly sends its men (and women) on assignment throughout France.

J.P.B. Security
135 Emile Beaufils,
93100 Montreuil-sous-Bois, France
Tel: +33-1-48 70 49 10 Fax: +33-1-48 57 58 44

JACQUES GARCIA

Nothing fazes this visionary interior decorator, whether he is working on a new residence for the Sultan of Brunei or a Parisian tearoom. Although his inspiration comes from the 17th- and 18th century, he is a master at mixing styles. "Why reconstitute a precise period when homes were never like this?" he asks.

Garcia takes pleasure in using furnishings and paintings that have been passed down through generations to create a richly comfortable ambience.

Jacques Garcia
212 rue de Rivoli,
75001 Paris, France
Tel: +33-1-42 97 48 70 Fax:+33-1-42 97 48 10

JACK BARCLAY LIMITED

Jack Barclay was born in the year 1900 and by the age of 23 he had successfully established the business which, 72 years later, is the world's largest retailer of Rolls Royce and Bentley motor cars. In 1929 the Society press dubbed him "the finest luxury motorcar salesman in the trade". Although there is no longer a Barclay at the helm, the company's Mayfair showroom is staffed by a hugely experienced team of salesmen - with over 90 years at the company between them. The Service department is equally capable, dealing with over 300 Rolls-Royce and Bentley motor cars every month. The company has also added chauffeur hire

to its portfolio, an aspect of the business which has taken off in the last couple of years, much by word of mouth, due to the first class quality of both cars and drivers. Jack Barclay looks set to retain its position at the very top of the luxury car trade.

Jack Barclay Limited
18 Berkeley Square, London W1X 6AE, UK
Tel +44-171-629 7444   Fax +44-171-629 8258

JACQUES GRANGE

A superstar interior decorator in France for many years (Yves Saint Laurent was a major client), Grange has been taking things easy in the South of France for some time - although he has produced a range of furniture in the interim. However, private commissions are beckoning again; Aerin Lauder has asked him to design her apartment in New York.

Jacques Grange
118 rue du Faubourg St Honoré,
75008 Paris, France
Tel: +33-1-47 42 47 34

JACQUES KUGEL ANTIQUAIRES

When Jacques Kugel died in 1985 his sons Nicolas and Alexis took over the helm of this gallery on rue Saint-Honoré. Its three floors house precious collections of gold and silver from the Renaissance to the early 20th century, along with paintings, furniture and *objets d'art* in ivory, amber, rock crystal and delicate marquetry.

Jacques Kugel Antiquaires
279 rue St Honoré, 75008 Paris, France
Tel: +33-1-42 60 86 23   Fax: +33-1-42 61 06 72

JACQUES MENDEL FOURRURES

If you haven't worn your beautiful quality but out-dated fur for years, Jacques Mendel is the man for you. A fifth-generation furrier, he is simply brilliant at transforming old classics into chic modern staples.

Jacques Mendel Fourrures
396 rue St Honoré, 75001 Paris, France
Tel: +33-1-42 61 75 77   Fax: +33-1-426 0694

JACQUES PERRIN

Jacques Perrin, who specialises in 18th-century pieces and Boulle, has been described as having "perfect American millionaire taste", and the lifestyle to go with it. He is, for example, a member of the Racing Club de France, the Cercle de l'Union Interalliée and the golf club de Saint-Nom-la-Bretêche and his honours include the Legion d'Honneur. Monsieur Perrin's important discoveries include one of the few clock cases by 18th-century cabinet maker Latz, and a rare console table attributed to Charles le Brun.

Jacques Perrin,
98 rue du Faubourg St Honoré,
75008 Paris, France
Tel: +33-1-42 65 01 38   Fax: +33-1-49 24 04 08

JAEGER-LECOULTRE

Deeply fashionable to lovers of crests and monograms, Jaeger LeCoultre's enduringly desirable Reverso watch presents an ideal opportunity for personalisation when its back is turned. The company also produces the aptly named Master Control range, as well as numerous Haute Joaillerie timepieces for discerning members of the jet-set.

Jaeger LeCoultre
8 rue de la Golisse, CH-1347 Le Sentier,
Geneva, Switzerland
Tel: +41-218-45 02 02   Fax: +41-218-45 15 50

JAMES PURDEY & SONS

Recently acquired by the Vendôme group, illustrious gunsmith Purdey has served six generations of the British royal family since George III. Based at purpose-built Audley House, Purdey's guns and rifles - all made to measure - are still handcrafted in the firm's own factory. Aficionados favour the unique hammerless ejector mechanism and the balance of the guns, each of which take 700-800 man-hours to make. When you visit the shop, ask to see the memorabilia-packed Long Room, which remains virtually unchanged since it was built in 1881.

James Purdey & Sons Ltd.
Audley House, 57-58 South Audley Street,
London W1Y 6ED, UK
Tel: +44-171-499 1801   Fax: +44-171-355 3297

JANE CHURCHILL

Since selling her eponymous fabric and wallpaper business to Colefax & Fowler, Jane Spencer-Churchill, one of the most celebrated exponents of the 'Traditional English' interior, has wrestled with an identity crisis. She is Jane Churchill, decorator, but she is no longer *that* Jane Churchill. In a 30 year career she has designed everything from epic country houses to the inside of a Rolls Royce. Her eclectic client list includes HRH The Prince of Wales, Robert and Susan Sangster and Bill Wyman.

Jane Churchill Interiors Ltd.
81 Pimlico Road, London SW1W 8PH, UK
Tel: +44-171-730 8564   Fax: +44-171-823 6421

JANET REGER

Since Janet Reger first unleashed her little bits of frothy lace and ribbon on to a grateful British womanhood in 1967, she has reflected the mood of the times in her range of underwear. Jerry Hall, Kate Moss, Madonna and Joan Collins all adore her daring colour combinations and luxurious fabrics.

Janet Reger
2 Beauchamp Place, London SW3 1NG, UK
Tel: +44-171-584 9360

LE JARDIN DES SENS

Visitors rhapsodise about the inventive cuisine of twin brothers, Jacques and Laurent Pourcel, which pays tribute to a glorious repertoire of Mediterranean tastes and the market produce of the Languedoc region. The modern, glass-fronted dining room, overlooking a lovely garden, is a setting worthy of their Truffle soup and Baby squid stuffed with ratatouille and lobster. Olivier Chateau runs the excellent cellar.

Le Jardin des Sens
11 avenue Saint-Lazare,
34000 Montpellier, France
Tel: +33-4-67 79 63 38   Fax: +33-4-67 72 13 05

JEAN BARDET/CHATEAU BELMONT

Three ducks stand guard over the entrance to Château Belmont. At the cocktail hour the owner's elegant wife, Sophie Bardet, comes out to feed them meticulously prepared sponge-cakes. A minor detail - but it illustrates the service that you can expect here. Jean Bardet - renowned for his sense of humour - holds sway both in the kitchen and in his fabulous *potager*. Dishes such as the sublime *Aumonière de légumes du potager de Jean Bardet* are the result.

Jean Bardet / Château Belmont
57 rue Groison, 37100 Tours, France
Tel: +33-2-47 41 41 11   Fax: +33-2-47 51 68 72

JEAN-LUC FIGUERAS

Jean-Luc Figueras is a man of sufficient style to have chosen the former studio of Cristobal Balenciaga as his restaurant. His inventive Mediterranean menu includes Sea bass with cod tripe and the house speciality is *butifarra nera* (blood sausage). Figueras' wife, Sandra, charms all comers out front.

Jean-Luc Figueras
Santa Teresa 10, E-08012 Barcelona, Spain
Tel: +34-91-415 2877

JESURUM

In 1870 Venetian Michelangelo Jesurum took over an antiquated textile workshop and began making the wonderfully refined household linens that the company still produces today. Tablecloths, bed linen and other household necessities come in the finest linens and cottons, many decorated with hand-made lace. Colours range from subtle, un-dyed neutrals to show-stopping brights.

Jesurum
Venezia Mercerie de Capitello 4856,
30124 Venice, Italy
Tel: +39-041-520 6177   Fax: +39-041-520 6085

JIL SANDER

Once upon a time she was a well-kept secret, but now Barbra Streisand, Winoner Ryder and Holly Hunter count among Jil Sander's legions of fans. Her sleek, minimalist vision, executed in the finest fabrics available to man, have gained her almost iconic status among those who prefer their luxuries to be discreet.

Jil Sander
32 Osterfeldstraße, 22529 Hamburg, Germany
Tel: +49-40-55 30 20   Fax: +49-40-553 3034

JO HANSFORD

Jo Hansford has built up a formidable international reputation as a hair colourist – so much so that she has been dubbed "Best tinter on the planet" by American *Vogue*. She numbers among the clients at her Mayfair salon Kate Winslett, Melanie Griffiths and Camilla Parker-Bowles.

Jo Hansford
19 Mount Street, London W1Y 5RA, UK
Tel: +44-171-495 7774   Fax: +44-171-495 7747

JOCKEY

If the walls of this Madrid institution could speak, there would be many riveting tales told of the scandal and intrigue that come with having received countless celebrities and statesmen at its tables. Established by

Clodoaldo Cortès in 1945, its elegant and classical cuisine is equally renowned. Don't miss the heavenly Mandarin soufflé crêpe.

Jockey
Amador de los Rios 6, E- 28010 Madrid, Spain
Tel/Fax: +34-91-319 24 35

LE JOCKEY CLUB

One of the last refuges of the French nobility, this is where they can lunch, dine or simply escape the hoi polloi. For impoverished thoroughbreds, the simple pleasure of hearing a white-jacketed waiter announce, "Monsieur le Comte est servi" is reason enough to come here. One cardinal sin for potential members is lying about their origins; Valéry Giscard d'Estaing was blackballed, not because he isn't a real aristocrat but because he refused to drop the 'd' in his name when he presented himself for election.

Le Jockey Club
2 rue Rabelais, 75008 Paris, France
Tel: +33-1-43 59 85 63

JOHN BOWEN

John Bowen is a plastic surgeon whose approach is straightforward and conservative, and whose manners are charmingly old-school. His aim is to improve the general appearance of the face, through traditional surgical methods, without necessarily making it look a great deal younger. He also offers a range of other treatments, including lip augmentations.

John Bowen
Flat 1, 30 Harley Street, London W1N 1AB, UK
Tel: +44-171-636 0955

JOHN ESKENAZI

Johnny Eskenazi is Giuseppe Eskenazi's cousin and London's other important dealer in Oriental art. He joined the family business in Milan in 1977 - concentrating on Chinese, Japanese and Indian art, as well as early carpets and textiles - and moved to London in 1994. His gallery is known for its outstanding Asian discoveries; clients include the Metropolitan Museum in New York, London's V & A and the Musée Guimet in Paris.

John Eskenazi Ltd
15 Old Bond Street, London W1X 4JL, UK
Tel: +44-171-409 3001   Fax: +44-171-629 2146

JOHN FRIEDA

When Meg Ryan or Nicole Kidman comes to London, this man helps them to maintain their star looks. Having trained with the great Leonard of Mayfair, Frieda set up on his own in 1979. Kick-started by his popularity as a session stylist for *Vogue*, he became - as he remains

JOHN HOBBS

Walk into a discreet mews amongst Pimlico Road's smart antique shops and you will encounter the dramatic facade of this gallery, with its huge, black-painted broken pediment. It belongs to a man who is commonly acknowledged to have one of the most discerning eyes in the trade. Hubert de Givenchy perhaps summed him up best, when he spoke of Hobbs' "sense of fantasy and good taste; there is never a hint of preciousness in his choice of objects".

Entering the shop is like stepping inside a magic box that keeps expanding to reveal endless surprises. For here lies a whole landscape of exquisite furniture, sculpture, mirrors, lamps and curios, which Hobbs has collected from all over the world.

John Hobbs Ltd
107A Pimlico Road, London SW1W 8PH, UK
Tel: +44-171-730 8369   Fax: +44-171-730 0437
Website: www.johnhobbs.co.uk

today - a favourite among rock stars and royalty. Frieda was the first British hairdresser to launch a signature product line, again with phenomenal success; his Frizz-Ease Serum is currently the biggest-selling hair product in America.

John Frieda
4 Aldford Street, London W1Y 5PU, UK
Tel: +44-171-245 0033   Fax: +44-171-235 1345

JOHN GALLIANO

Since his 1996 move to Dior gave him greater financial stability, Galliano has given free rein, in his own-label collection, to his sense of drama and love of fashion history. "It is imperative to study the masters," he says. "Only by understanding the past can one create something modern and enduring." The results enthral such clients as Diana Ross, Nicole Kidman and Mouna Al-Ayoub.

John Galliano
Tel: +33-1-55 25 11 11 (for stockists only)

JOHN GOSDEN

Best known as Sheikh Mohamed's trainer, Gosden won the 1997 Epsom Derby with *Benny The Dip*. Sheikh Mohamed lured him back from a successful training career in Los Angeles to install him in the late Lord Derby's stables. Although the Sheikh is his main owner, Gosden is able to take on others and is likely to broaden his base. He is also one of Sheikh Mohamed's most trusted advisors and, being extremely well-educated and well-read, is an eloquent speaker.

John Gosden
Stanley House Stables, Bury Road,
Newmarket, Suffolk CB8 7BT, UK
Tel: +44-1638-66 99 44   Fax: +44-1638-66 99 22

JOHN LOBB

One doesn't go to Lobb's club-like shop simply to buy shoes, but to have have one's feet measured and recorded and made into a cast that will become the pattern for the most divinely comfortable footwear. His creations are amongst the most prized, not least because the production of just one of these shoes requires the skill of no less than six skilled craftsmen.

John Lobb
9 St James's Street,
London SW1A 1EF, UK
Tel: +44-171-930 3664   Fax: +44-171-930 2811

JOHN MERTON

This portrait painter's meticulously depicted subjects include Diana, Princess of Wales, painted in 1988, The Queen as Head of the Order of Merit and the Duchess of Buccleuch, the only painting since 1918 to receive a Royal Academy Triple A award.

He developed a passion for Renaissance art at Eton and Oxford, and uses an updated version of the Renaissance technique, egg tempura on gesso.

John Merton MBE
Pound House, Oare,
Near Marlborough, Wiltshire SN8 4JA, UK
Tel: +44-1672-63 539

JOHN OXX

Having first trained as a vet, John Oxx worked as an assistant to his father (also called John Oxx) before setting up on his own in 1979. Quiet and self-effacing - though a great wit - Oxx trains for Sheikh Mohammed, The Aga Khan and the Maktoums at his Currabeg yard. His filly, *Ridgewood Pearl*, won the Cartier Horse of the Year Award in 1995 and was the highest rated miler in the same year, having also won the Breeders Cup mile.

John Oxx
Creeve Currabeg, Curragh, Co. Kildare, Ireland
Tel: +353-45-52 13 10   Fax: +353-45-52 22 36

JOHN PAWSON

Although John Pawson never completed his formal training as an architect, his influence on modern architecture and interior design is enormous. While traditionalists loathe his asceticism, Pawson has become the high priest of minimalism and the darling of contemporary style leaders (including Calvin Klein, whose New York store is a Pawson masterpiece). Pawson's book, *Minimum*, is the definitive work on the subject.

John Pawson
Unit B, 70-78 York Way, London N1 9AG, UK
Enquiries to: Fax: +44-171-837 4949

JOHN STEFANIDIS

Since starting his practice in 1967, Alexandria-born and Oxford-educated John Stefanidis has influenced a whole generation of interior designers. His work is characterised by a lack of artifice, a fastidious - though imperceptible - attention to detail, a love of texture and a certain grand simplicity, all infused with a Mediterranean spirit of colour and light.

John Stefanidis
7 Friese Green, Chelsea Manor Street,
London SW3 3TW, UK
Tel: +44-171-351 7511   Fax: +44-171-352 9460

JOHN TAYLOR INTERNATIONAL

In 1864 John Taylor, who knew the grand Riviera estates from his work as a gardener there, set up shop as a property consultant. His bright idea has grown into a substantial multi-national concern (now owned by Monaco property barons, Pastor), with offices in London, Barcelona and all over the Côte D'Azur. The company buys and sells blue-chip properties on behalf of heads of state, celebrities and seriously wealthy individuals.

John Taylor International
55 La Croisette, 06400 Cannes, France
Tel: +33-4-93 38 00 66   Fax: +33-4-93 39 13 65

JUSTERINI & BROOKS

Justerini & Brooks has two specialist outlets, one in London and another in Edinburgh, selling a wide range of wines and spirits to private and corporate customers. Royal Warrant holders for eight successive monarchs, the company was founded by Giacomo Justerini in 1749. The company goes to great lengths to offer the best selection possible and it currently lists over 1,200 wines from nearly 30 major wine-producing areas.

Its very detailed brochure gives helpful explanations of grape varieties. For those partial to Pinot Noir, for instance, it recommends the wines of Scotchmans Hill and Dry River, two of the best names in the southern hemisphere for this variety. J&B's extensive and award-winning range of over 300 clarets remains the heart of its list and, if a particular wine is unavailable, the recently established Broking department will make every effort to source it. Alternatively, if customers are holding larger stocks of fine wine than they require, J&B would be delighted to sell these on their behalf. The major wines of the Rheingau and Mosel are well represented, as the company believes that the Riesling grape has a consistent, exciting exuberance.

As well as the regular wine tastings that it has been organising since Charles Dickens' day, Justerini & Brooks also arranges private tastings, on request.

Justerini & Brooks Ltd
61 St James's Street, London SW1A 1LZ, UK
Tel: +44-171-493 8721 Fax: +44-171-499 4653
45 George Street, Edinburgh EH2 2HT, UK
Tel: +44-131-226 4202 Fax: +44-131-225 2351

JOHN WONNACOTT

The work of one of Britain's foremost living portrait painters hangs in galleries all around the world. His most celebrated sitter of late was former Prime Minister, John Major, painted in 1997 and now in the National Portrait Gallery. Major was so delighted with the portrait that he ordered a copy for himself.

John Wonnacott
c/o Thomas Agnew & Sons,
43 Old Bond Street, London W1X 4BA, UK
Tel: +44-171-629 6176

JOHRI'S TALVO

An open secret among St Moritz regulars, Roland and Brigitte Jöhri's chalet on the outskirts of the town is gourmet heaven, thanks to Roland's inspired mixing of regional specialities with classical French techniques. His Duck in a salt crust with gnocchi is superb. Book well ahead for a table on the terrace on sunny days.

Jöhri's Talvo
via Gunels 15,
CH-7512 St Moritz/Champfer, Switzerland
Tel: +41-81-833 4455   Fax: +41-81-833 0569

JON BANNENBERG

A great aesthete and a talented pianist, Australian-born Jon Bannenberg is, without question, the late 20th century's most influential yacht designer. His twin beliefs - that tastes evolve according to broader social changes and that the only constraints on design possibilities are technological - enabled him to break free from the narrow traditionalism which prevailed when he began designing yachts in the 1970s. The distinctive, angled lines which he gives to his yachts have been widely imitated, though never matched. Bannenberg's mould-breaking designs run from the early *Carinthia IV*, *Galu* and *Nabila* to the recent, 96m *Limitless*.

Working closely with the Australian shipyard, Oceanfast, Bannenberg also pioneered the concept of the high-speed megayacht. That 14-year collaboration led to his joining the yard's board of directors in 1998, although he retains his independence as a designer, working with all of the world's major builders.

Jon Bannenberg
6 Burnsall Street, London SW3 3ST, UK
Tel: +44-171-352 4851 Fax: +44-171-352 8444

JOHNNY VAN HAEFTEN

Johnny van Haeften, who deals exclusively in 17th-century Dutch and Flemish paintings, runs one of Europe's most successful galleries. Yet, for ten years at Christie's he tried, without success, to get into its picture department.

He would rather sell a major painting by a minor master, than vice versa, yet paid £4.2 million for a Cuyp *Orpheus Charming the Animals*, found in a Madrid house.

Johnny van Haeften
13 Duke Street, St James's,
London SW1Y 6DB, UK
Tel: +44-171-930 3062 Fax: +44-171-839 6303

JORGEN CHRISTENSEN

The good news is that a romantic Czech castle can be bought for as little as US$75,000; the bad news is that many are wrecks, requiring as much again to be spent on renovation. Jorgen Christensen knows the market intimately and will lead you to a gem, as well as taking care of the complex red tape. If you want something special and have up to $10 million to spend, his portfolio also includes the most outstanding properties in the Republic.

Jorgen Christensen
Sorent Realitni Kancelar, Podskalska 3,
128 00 Prague 2, Czech Republic
Tel: +420-2-29 47 27 Fax: +420-2-24 92 10 50

JOSEPH

This hairdresser-turned-fashion guru has, for the last 20 years, had a seminal influence on fashion retailing in London. This extraordinary success is due to his uncanny talent for spotting the Next Big Thing - whether it is a new designer (in the Seventies he introduced Kenzo to London, in the Nineties Prada) or the way that shops will look - his pioneering work with architect Eva Jiricna in the Eighties has influenced a whole generation of retailers.

Joseph
77/79 Fulham Road, London SW3 6RE
Tel: +44-171-823 9500 Fax: +44-171-823 7534

KEMPINSKI HOTEL TASCHENBERGERPALAIS

This grand hotel, restored in the mid-1990s with the help of the original construction plans, is a delightful combination of baroque façades and modern interior design. Exceptionally well-trained staff lend the Taschenbergpalais the unmistakable feeling that someone at the top knows the difference between the modern notion of service and good old-fashioned hospitality.

Kempinski Hotel Taschenbergpalais
Taschenberg 3, D-01067 Dresden, Germany
Tel: +49-351-491 20 Fax: +49-351-491 28 12

KENNEMER GOLF & COUNTRY CLUB

Outside the British Isles, this is probably the finest links course in Europe. A round here in the wind off the North Sea will take you back in time and give you a taste for real golf. Wonderfully traditional, the Harry Holt-designed course is complemented by the old-fashioned charm of the thatched-roof club house. Huge dunes defy Holland's reputation for being flat and featureless.

Kennemer Golf and Country Club
P.O Box 85, 2040 AB Zandvoort, Netherlands
Tel: +31-23-571 2836 Fax: +31-23-571 9520

KENNETH TURNER

An auspicious introduction to Lady Pulbrook and Miss Gould in the Sixties launched floral decorator Kenneth Turner's professional career, which earned him the Prince of Wales' Royal Warrant in 1996, and a client list that has included Lauren Bacall and Jackie Onassis. His originality and bold style have had a seminal influence on the art.

Kenneth Turner
18 Sleaford Street, London SW8 5AB, UK
Tel: +44-171-978 2939 Fax: +44-171-978 2940

KILGOUR FRENCH STANBURY

You don't usually think of Savile Row tailors as having edge but, beyond this traditional shop entrance you will find a modern studio furnished by Philippe Starck and Matthew Hilton. And it's not just the interior that has changed; to complement its bespoke business, Kilgour has introduced a made-to-measure line to give younger clients a 'soft' introduction to bespoke, as well as a ready-to-wear collection of modern classics.

Kilgour French Stanbury
8 Savile Row, London W1X 1AF, UK
Tel: +44-171-734 6905

KITON

Ciro Paone, founder of Kiton, sometimes stops at the local market on the way to work, to choose the vegetables which the chef at his factory will use to prepare lunch. Such perfectionism is reflected in the quality of the clothing that his team of 180 tailors turns out. Kiton (the name derives from the ancient Greek tunic, *chiton*) is one of the few companies still to make its suits - now for women as well as men - almost entirely by hand.

Kiton
Ciro Paone SpA, viale delle Industriale, 80022 Arzano, Naples, Italy
Tel: +39-81-573 3174   Fax: +39-81-731 8617

KNIGHT FRANK INTERNATIONAL

This property consultancy, established in 1896, now has offices in nine European countries. The historic deals brokered by Knight Frank include the sales of Stonehenge, Chartwell (to Sir Winston Churchill) and the All-England Tennis Club, Wimbledon. In 1994 Knight Frank listed London's most expensive house, at £25 million, and it handled the recent sale of Luton Hoo.

Knight Frank International
20 Hanover Square, London W1R OAX, UK
Tel: +44-171-629 8171   Fax: +44-171-493 4114

KNIZE & Co.

Ever since the Empress Elizabeth bought her riding clothes here in 1856, a virtual who's who of international society has passed through the doors of this ultra 'establishment' shop. Its classically styled, custom-made and ready-to-wear clothing and accessories are a miracle of cut and quality.

Knize & Co.
Graben 13, A-1010 Vienna, Austria
Tel: +43-1-512 21 19   Fax: +43-1-512 21 19 25

KONRAD O. BERNHEIMER

Germany's leading address for Old Master paintings (including Dutch, Flemish, Italian and German paintings from the 16th to 19th centuries), this gallery, with a second office in London, also specialises in high-quality Chinese porcelain. Mr Bernheimer's great-grandfather, who was appointed Purveyor to the Royal Bavarian Court of Ludwig II, founded the gallery in 1864.

Konrad O. Bernheimer Kunsthandel
Promenadeplatz 13, D-80333 Munich, Germany
Tel: +49-89-22 66 72   Fax: +49-89-22 60 37

KORSO BEI DER OPER

Reinhardt Gerer is the culinary genius behind the success of this chic restaurant, located in the Bristol hotel. It serves up classical Austrian fare with idiosyncratic flair and the wine list, overseen by sommelier Christian Zach, is first-rate. A favourite haunt of Vienna's glossy opera-goers.

Korso bei der Oper
Mahlerstraße 2, A-1010 Vienna, Austria
Tel: +43-1-51 51 65 46   Fax: +43-1-51 51 65 50

KPM

Frederick the Great was a devotee of 'white gold', or porcelain, so it is entirely appropriate that he gave the Königliche Porzellan Manufaktur its name and symbol - the royal blue sceptre. Revered by collectors and

THE KILDARE HOTEL & COUNTRY CLUB

Centred around a grand, French-style 1830s house built by the Barton family (who had founded the Château Barton winery in 1725), this 350-acre estate was bought in 1987 by industrialist Dr. Michael Smurfit. He has lavished a fortune on landscaping, on rebuilding an entire wing of the house (demolished in the 1930s) and on embellishing one of the sitting rooms with the world's finest private collection of Jack B. Yeats' paintings, to make it one of Europe's loveliest retreats. The setting is idyllic, with the river Liffey (teeming with trout and salmon) sweeping in a broad arc around the lawns.

The K Club is a world-class resort, with superb cuisine, an Arnold Palmer-designed golf course (upon which Dublin's burgeoning millionaire class comes out to play and home to the Smurfit European Open), tennis courts, gym, pool and spa treatments, croquet lawns, clay pigeon shooting, riding, fishing, even an archery range (where you are taught by Jim Conroy, who made the arrows for Mel Gibson's *Braveheart*).

The special magic, however, comes from its being Irish. There is none of the *sotto voce* pretentiousness here that you may encounter in similarly luxurious surroundings elsewhere; come back from shooting in your wellies and it's quite OK to walk into the front hall before changing into your shoes. The staff are genuinely friendly and fantastically eager to please.

The Kildare Hotel & Country Club
Straffan, Co. Kildare, Ireland
Tel: +353-1-601 7200   Fax: +353-1-601 7299
Email: golf@kclub.ie   hotel@kclub.ie

experts, KPM's exquisitely formed, flawless porcelain pieces are still shaped and painted by hand, as they were in the king's day.

KPM - Königliche Porzellan Manufaktur
Wegelystraße 1, D-10623 Berlin, Germany
Tel: +49-30-39 00 92 15   Fax: +49-30-39 00 92 06

KRAEMER & CIE

Situated in an elegant townhouse overlooking the Parc Monceau, this family-run company offers nothing but the choicest pieces of 17th- and 18th-century furniture and art. Indeed, its discreet service, depth of knowledge and exacting eye make it one of the most emulated antique dealers in Paris. Reclusive superstars, such as Michael Jackson, heavyweight art connoisseurs and museum curators patronise this temple to French craftsmanship.

Kraemer & Cie
43 rue Monceau, 75008 Paris, France
Tel: +33-1-45 63 24 46   Fax: + 33-1-45 63 24 46

KRONBERG

Situated just outside Frankfurt, this is Germany's most prestigious and elegant golf club; it belongs to the Hesse family and is where the city's banking and business czars come to play. While it is fiendishly difficult to become a member, you will certainly get a round if you stay at the adjoining Schlosshotel Kronberg.

Kronberg Golf Club
Hainstraße 25, D-61476 Kronberg, Germany
Tel: +49-6173-70 101   Fax: +49-6173-701 267

KRONENHALLE

A favourite of Frederico Fellini and other artistic luminaries, this legendary restaurant serves simple, traditional Swiss dishes, such as liver-dumpling soup. Its late propreitress was the formidable Hulda Zumsteg; her beady-eyed portrait presides over the dining room alongside works by former customers, Picasso, Braque and Mirò.

Kronenhalle
Rämistrasse 4, CH-8001 Zürich, Switzerland
Tel: +41-1-251 0256

KRUG

With its hand-crafted refinement and multi-dimensional flavour, Krug sits easily at the top of the champagne pecking order. The magisterial Grand Cuvée provides one of the world's great drinking experiences. Rarities include Clos du Mesnil, a 100 per cent chardonnay champagne, first produced in 1979 from the walled *clos* in Le Mesnil-sur-Oger, and the delicately pale Krug Rosé, from 1983. Each is a masterpiece of its kind.

Krug
5 rue Cocuebert, 51100 Reims, France
Tel: +33-3-26 84 44 20   Fax: +33-3-26 84 44 49

THE LADY APSLEY SCHOOL FOR BUTLERS & DOMESTIC AGENCY

The guiding principles at this establishment are loyalty, trustworthiness and discretion. Run from a private manor house, the school turns out 60

new butlers a year, all expertly coached by Michael Shaw, who trained at Buckingham Palace. Of course the duties of a butler have evolved considerably since Jeeves's day; they are expected not only to serve their employers with the greatest aplomb, exactitude and discretion but also to be computer literate and possess first-class administrative and social skills. Within a year of its being established, the school and domestic agency have already placed butlers and other members of domestic staff with prominent families in Britain and internationally.

The Lady Apsley School for Butlers and Domestic Agency
Bathurst Estate Office, Cirencester Park, Gloucestershire GL7 2BT, UK
Tel: +44-1285-88 52 83   Fax: +44-1285-65 62 91

LA PERLA

777 Madison Avenue, New York
Tel: 212-570 0050

LA PERLA

178 Bal Harbour, Miami
Tel: 305-864 2070

LADUREE

If the 'industrialisation' of croissant-making has jaded your appetite for this *petit déjeuner* staple, Ladurée's creations might just reconvert you. This bastion of French pâtisserie also makes excellent macaroons and Tarte Tatin. Then again, you needn't come here just for tea; French diplomats, returning to Paris on vacation, are tempted by its dining room's comforting and classic fare.

Ladurée
16 rue Royale, 75008 Paris, France
Tel: +33-1-42 60 21 79

LAFITE-ROTHSCHILD (CHATEAU)

These wines have graced the tables of Richelieu, Louis XV and Madame de Pompadour and the château's list of successive owners is equally prestigious, from the de Ségur family to the Rothschilds (currently Eric de Rothschild). Their wine is delicate, elegant and beautifully perfumed; its power comes cloaked in the silkiest of textures. Do whatever it takes to get your hands on the 1961 Lafite; failing that, the 1985 is coming right on song.

Château Lafite-Rothschild
33250 Pauillac, France
Tel: +33-5-56 73 18 18   Fax: +33-5-56 59 26 83

LALIQUE

At the turn of the century, René Lalique made his name as a maker of jewellery and of handbags crafted out of silk and metal, while on the way to becoming a leader of the Art Nouveau and, subsequently Art Deco movements. It is this design iconography which continues to give Lalique's crystal its unmistakable identity, whether applied to small collectibles (boxes, the animal series, scent bottles) or major pieces which are made to private commission.

Lalique's collections for 1998 followed four

LA PERLA

Most modern women would concur that La Perla is not only top of their wish list but that it has changed the face of contemporary underwear. La Perla's starting point was that underwear is not only functional but is an integral part of fashion; unlike other clothing, though, it offers women the opportunity to satisfy their own wish for self-gratification and to express their seductive qualities. The result is sensual lingerie in highly original colour combinations, embellished with fine embroidery and lace (the latter made in Calais on rare Leavers looms).

Founded in Bologna (for centuries the home of Europe's best corsetry makers) by Ada Masotti as a little couture atelier, La Perla now has several flagship stores worldwide and is run under the chairmanship of her son Alberto. Combining tradition with high technology (hand embroiderers next to computers), the company has extended its expertise to swimwear, pret-à-porter and couture, all of which echo its signature fluid fabrics and body-conscious styling. As well as its seasonal production, La Perla makes highly coveted limited and numbered editions of certain styles.

La Perla
via Montenapoleone 1, 20121 Milan, Italy
Tel: +39-02-76 00 04 60   Fax:+39-02-76 00 24 73
Flagship stores in: Bologna, Florence, Rome, Paris and Barcelona

themes, including the Art Nouveau and Love. In the same year the company returned to René Lalique's roots by launching a collection of handbags in lambskin and lamb suede, all of which are embellished with a gilt-and-crystal clasp. Quite apart from their aesthetic value, the company's products are worth investing in - period Lalique grows in value every year.

Lalique
11 rue Royale, 75008 Paris, France
Tel: +33-1-53 05 12 12   Fax: +33-1-42 65 59 06
Also at: 201 Sloane Street, London SW1X 9QX, UK
Tel: +44-171-245 9090   Fax: +44-171-235 3337

LAGAVULIN

This is one of the truly great malt whiskies. Remember to say "Lagga-voolin" when you order it and to sit down when you drink it. Prepare to be overwhelmed. This malt does not creep up on you softly, rather it announces itself in stentorian tones. The colour is a lovely amber, the nose is full and rich, and the flavour is deeply satisfying and complex.

Lagavulin
United Distillers, Landmark House,
Hammersmith Bridge Road, London W6 9DP, UK
Tel: +44-181-846 8040   Fax: +44-181-235 2400

LAGERFELD GALLERY

Truly a Renaissance man, Karl Lagerfeld is, at once, fashion designer, gifted photographer, quadrilingual bibliophile and an art collector of some note. These interests are all represented in this Left Bank store-cum-gallery. Books and works by various artists (including Lagerfeld's own photographs) are on the main floor, while the lower floor houses his eponymous clothing collection.

Lagerfeld Gallery
40 rue de Seine, 70075 Paris, France
Tel: +33-1-55 42 75 50 Fax: +33-1-40 46 05 95

LAGUIOLE

These beautifully crafted knives were originally made by shepherds in the mountains of the Auvergne, the best examples coming from the town that they are named after. The blades are perfectly balanced and the beautifully sculpted handles are made in a variety of woods or horn. Just holding one is an experience in itself.

La Maison du Laguiole
2 Place de la Patte d'Oie, 12210 Laguiole, France
Tel: +33-5-65 48 44 22   Fax: +33-5-65 44 35 59

LAMELOISE

A 15th-century house in a pretty square has been the site of the Lameloise family's restaurant and hotel for over a century. The food owes much to Burgundy's culinary tradition. One particularly well-travelled gourmet was reduced to "tears of joy" by his *Ravioli d'escargots de Bourgogne dans leurs bouillon d'ail doux*.

Lameloise
36 Place d'Armes, 71150 Chagny, France
Tel: +33-3-85 87 08 85   Fax: +33-3-85 87 03 57

LANCASTER (HOTEL)

The brains behind the stylish Hôtel Montalembert, Grace Leo Andrieu has proved

her impeccable taste once again with the restoration of The Lancaster, a mansion house sumptuously decorated in the Thirties by Emile Wolf. Andrieu has cleverly blended his collection of antiques with French contemporary furniture, fine paintings - particularly those by Félix Ziem - and Oriental touches, as in the patio garden. The hotel's marvellous intimacy is especially due to Leo Andrieu's philosophy that "we are like a club for the guests. Someone who is paying over 2000 francs a night should be the focus of everything that we do". One manifestation of this: the Lancaster's restaurant is reserved exclusively for hotel guests.

Hôtel Lancaster
7 rue de Berri, Champs-Elysées,
75008 Paris, France
Tel: +33-1-40 76 40 76   Fax: +33-1-40 76 40 00

LANDHAUS SCHERRER

Panelled, well-furnished and hung with attractive artwork, this is a fine addition to Hamburg's roster of dining places. It lies on the north bank of the River Elbe and is home to chef Heinz Wehmann, who uses Northern German recipes as the basis for a menu that is complemented by excellent wines and rarefied cigars.

Landhaus Scherrer
130 Elbchaussee, D-22763 Hamburg, Germany
Tel: +49-40-880 1325   Fax: +49-40-880 6260

A. LANGE & SOHNE

The most distinguished name in German watch-making, A. Lange & Söhne, has returned to centre-stage some 50 years after its factories were destroyed in World War II. Walter Lange, the founder's great grandson, has revived Saxony's horological tradition by re-launching the family company and its elegant watches have rapidly become a badge of style for the cognoscenti.

A. Lange & Söhne
Altenberger Straße 15,
D-01768 Glashütte, Germany
Tel: +49-35053-48 541   Fax: +49-35053-48 544

LANVIN

The name Lanvin conjures up an image of silk-lined salons and the faint trace of a 1950s' scent. As the label's gifted new designer, 32 year-old Cristina Ortiz, describes it, a typical Lanvin woman is "feminine but not frilly". Formerly design director for Prada Donna, she is bringing the house right up to the minute, "prioritising comfort and purity in fabrics, cuts and colours".

Lanvin
11-22 rue du Faubourg Saint Honoré,
75008 Paris, France
Tel: +33-1-44 71 33 33   Fax: +33-1-44 71 31 76

CHATEAU LATOUR

This is the daddy of all clarets: sumptuous, full-bodied and oozing power and class. You either like it or not but, if not, you are missing

out on one of the world's greatest wines. Latour 1945 remains the all-time great but the 1970 comes a good second and the 1982 will be ready to drink for the millennium. Financier François Pinault bought the celebrated château from British media conglomerate, Pearson, in 1993.

Château Latour
33250 Pauillac, France
Tel: +33-5-56 73 19 80   Fax: +33-5-56 33 19 81

THE LANESBOROUGH

When a hotel describes itself as "London's foremost address for discriminating travellers" you cannot help suspecting that this is merely hype, for there are a dozen hotels that would make such a claim.

But The Lanesborough, named after a grand country house that once stood on this prime location at Hyde Park Corner, really has a lot going for it: 49 richly decorated bedrooms and 46 suites, each more luxurious than the last; one of the city's most fashionable bars, with an exceptional range of cigars and vintage cognacs; five Private Dining rooms (each individually decorated in Regency style); The Conservatory restaurant - casually refined with cuisine to match; 21st-century technology and (of course) a beautifully equipped fitness studio and discreet, full-service business centre.

However, many guests' abiding impression is not of the building itself - a meticulously restored, early 19th-century white stucco-fronted masterpiece - but of the graceful, traditional service offered by the staff, under the inspired direction of Geoffrey Gelardi. This is a hotel where everyone knows your name and nothing is too much to ask - not even complimentary 24-hour butler service or personalised note paper waiting in your room when you arrive.

The Lanesborough
Hyde Park Corner, London SW1X 7TA, UK
Tel: +44-171-259 5599 Fax: +44-171-259 5606

LAUDA EXECUTIVE SERVICE

Motor racing legend Niki Lauda founded his eponymous airline in 1979 and, in 1994, began a private charter service with a Learjet and a Challenger 601. Both are available for short-haul journeys at short notice. Rock star Phil Collins used the Learjet for city-hopping on his recent European tour.

Lauda Executive Service
P.O. Box 56, 5 World Trade Centre, Stock,
A-1300 Vienna Airport, Austria
Tel: +43-1-70 07 82 20 ext. 5678
Fax: +43-1-70 07 56 28

LAURENT-PERRIER

The Grand Siècle cuvée of this illustrious champagne house, founded in 1812, is its finest wine.

The 1990 vintage shows an added complexity, with a slightly spicy bouquet. The finesse of the blending process and the infinite care taken in ageing the wines ensure the continuing prominence of this champagne house.

Laurent-Perrier
Avenue de Champagne,
51150 Tours-sur-Marne, France
Tel: +33-3-26 58 91 22   Fax: +33-3-26 58 77 29

LE LAUSANNE PALACE HOTEL

Over 70 million Swiss francs have been spent on renovating this grand old lady, which boasts sublime views over Lake Geneva and the Alps. Discretion, luxury and immaculate service are the trademark features - hardly surprising, given the fact that the General Manager is Jean-Jacques Gauer, scion of the legendary clan of hoteliers and Chairman of Leading Hotels of the World.

Le Lausanne Palace Hotel
Grand-Chêne 7-9, CH-1002 Lausanne,
Switzerland
Tel: +41-21-331 31 31   Fax: +41-21 323 25 71

LE CACHEMIRIEN

The intricately embroidered shawl on a dark wood chair and the neatly layered scarves in vivid sorbet shades make entering this bou-

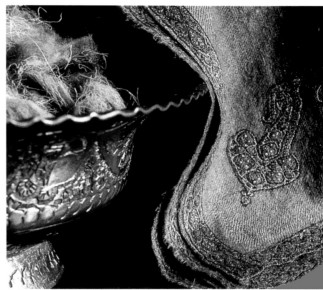

tique like walking into a Vuillard painting. Rosenda Arcioni Meer's cashmere products, woven in the Himalayas following traditions dating back to the 16th century, are works of art in themselves; a patterned pashmina shawl, always spun by women and embroidered by men, takes four years to complete. The simplicity of each piece belies the elaborate rituals involved in its creation, but, once you have wrapped one around your neck, its lightness and softness make you realise why Rosenda Meer has no need of jewels. Italian by birth and a designer by training, she became devoted to preserving and developing cashmere-making traditions when her Kashmiri husband gave her a pashmina shawl as a wedding present.

Le Cachemirien
12 rue de l'Echaudé, 75006 Paris, France
Tel: +33-1-43 29 93 82

J.F. LAZARTIGUE

Jean-François Lazartigue has succeeded in making the science of trichology seem almost glamorous. His technicians are charming, well-trained and very fast - and he makes excellent products to use at home. The private *cabines* at the Paris flagship each boast a personal telephone and a closet - with a lock for one's fur.

J.F. Lazartigue
5 rue du Faubourg St-Honoré,
75008 Paris, France
Tel: +33-1-42 65 29 24   Fax: +33-1-47 11 19 10

LE COUP / GERHARD MEIR

Gerhard Meir shot to prominence, in the mid-80s, as hairdresser to Princess Gloria von Thurn und Taxis. Since then Gabriele Henkel, Cindy Crawford and Claudia Schiffer have also become clients. Yet Meir retains a refreshingly egalitarian attitude. When asked how one gets an appointment, he says, simply, "Just give us a ring". Although Meir himself claims to be discreet, his salons in Munich, Berlin and Hamburg are hotbeds of gossip - especially before big social events, when everyone who's anyone is there.

Le Coup / Gerhard Meir
Theatinerstraße 23, 80333 Munich, Germany
Tel: +49-89-22 23 27

LEFLAIVE (DOMAINE)

These are grandiose wines - rich, powerful and elegant - made by an exceptional wine maker, Pierre Morey. The finest white Burgundies, the Montrachets from the estate of Anne-Claude Leflaive have been called "the wine of the angels" and are selected by many as their 'desert island' wine. Due to demand, they are hard to find but seek out the 1989 Chevalier-Montrachet for the millennium.

Domaine Leflaive
Place des Marronniers,
21190 Puligny-Montrachet, France
Tel: +33-3-80 21 30 13   Fax: +33-3-80 21 39 67

LEIXLIP HOUSE

This gem of a hotel in the village of Leixlip, eight miles from the centre of Dublin, is housed in a handsome Georgian building. It is quietly furnished with many pieces of antique furniture and its restaurant serves modern Irish cuisine - freshly baked bread and locally caught fish and game are among the highlights.

Leixlip House
Captain's Hill, Leixlip,
Co. Kildare, Ireland
Tel: +353-1-624 2268   Fax: +353-1-624 4177

LEMAIRE

Robert de Niro beats a path to Guy Pihan's door when he arrives in Paris. Why? Because Pihan is Director of the finest cigar shop in Paris. Established at the turn of the century, it now exports cigars all over the world.

Lemaire
59 avenue Victor Hugo, 75116 Paris, France
Tel: +33-1-45 00 75 63   Fax: +33-1-45 01 70 65

LENOTRE

A small pastry shop near Deauville, opened by Gaston Lenôtre in 1947, was the foundation on which he built a catering empire which now includes shops in all of the smartest areas of Paris and two restaurants (Le Pré Catalan and Le Pavillon Elysée). This temple of classical French gastronomy is where the *haute-bourgeoisie* comes when planning a party and, on Sunday afternoons, *grandes dames* queue around the block for its exquisite cakes and pastries.

Lenôtre
48 avenue Victor Hugo, 75116 Paris, France
Tel: +33-1-45 02 21 21   Fax: +33-1-45 00 34 64

THE LEFEVRE GALLERY

In 1897 Alex Reid shared an apartment in Paris for nine months with Vincent van Gogh, who painted three portraits of him. Having met all the Impressionist painters, Reid bought many of their pictures and sent them back to his art-dealer father in Glasgow, who sold them to such collectors as Burrell, Cargill and Maitland. The Reid Gallery moved to London and, in 1926, amalgamated with a French dealer, Ernest Lefevre, who already had a successful business there. The Lefevre Gallery, as it became known, has held many distinguished exhibitions, including the first London showings of such painters as Seurat (1926), Dégas (1928), Modigliani (1929), Francis Bacon (1945), Lucien Freud (1946) and Balthus (1952).

Today the gallery, under the directorship of Desmond Corcoran (partner 1964) and Martin Summers (partner 1967) maintains the tradition of exhibiting fine Impressionists and early 20th-century paintings but has added a second, modern gallery on the first floor, to deal with post-war British and contemporary art. The gallery has sold paintings to many private collectors around the world, such as Stavros Niarchos and Walter Annenberg and to many great museums.

The Lefevre Gallery (Alex Reid & Lefevre Ltd)
30 Bruton Street, London W1X 8JD, UK
Tel: +44-171-493 1572   Fax : +44-171-499 9088

LEOVILLE LAS CASES (CHATEAU)

Michel et Jean-Hubert Delon's estate is, unusually for the Médoc, surrounded by a huge stone wall; it is entered through a magnificent iron gate, decorated with a recumbent lion. In Bordeaux parlance, Léoville-Lascases is a 'super second', one of the *second crus classés* whose quality and price, in fact, exceed the 1855 classification. The 1996 is particularly good example of this solid, powerful and distinguished wine and the 1985 will be ready to drink this year.

Château Léoville Las Cases
33250 Saint-Julien-Beychevelle, France
Tel: +33-5-56 73 25 26   Fax: +33-5-56 59 18 33

LEROY (DOMAINE)

From the absurdly small yields of this estate, Lalou Bize-Leroy produces the most extraordinary Côtes de Nuits and Côte de Beaune: concentrated, highly perfumed, complex and very elegant. The huge demand for the 90,000 bottles of this nectar produced each year maintains its astronomically high prices. To drink for the millennium, do your utmost to get your hands on a bottle of 1989 Clos Vougeot.

Domaine Leroy
rue du Pont Boillot, 21190 Auxey-Duresses, France
Tel: +33-3-80 21 10   Fax: +33-3-80 21 63 81

LINLEY

Devotees of modern and antique furniture alike are drawn to David Linley's exquisite pieces. Timeless styling and the use of a rich variety of woods are his hallmark, whether he is working on a major private commission (Elton John and Mona Al-Ayoub are among his clients) or a simple decorative accessory. Unique pieces, such as a drum table made from ebonised sycamore with inlays of rhodium-plated silver or a scroll bench in sycamore with ebony roundels, sit in his shop alongside

his new collection of chairs and tables, which are aimed at a less rarified market (his supremely elegant wooden accessories, from walnut fruit bowls to Grecian column pencil pots, having already proved a huge hit). Clearly, the fact that Viscount Linley is nephew of The Queen has proved far less important than his innate talent and emphasis on creating pieces of enduring quality.

Linley Furniture
60 Pimlico Road, London SW1 8LP, UK
Tel: +44-171-730 7300   Fax: +44-171-730 8869

LODEN FREY

Young royals in exile favour the Loden, as do the cosmopolitan, expatriate denizens of Kensington and the Upper East Side. The funny thing about the coat is that it is so traditional it is practically anti-fashion - and therein lies its charm and enduring popularity amongst Europe's more aristocratic clans. The company was founded by Johann Georg Frey in 1842 and is situated in the centre of Munich, commanding a fine view of the city's landmark church - the Frauenkirche. The store is not dissimilar to Saks or Harrods in that it has five floors of sophisticated and cutting-edge fashion designers ranging from Versace and Dolce & Gabbana for women, to Brioni and Ermengildo Zegna for men. Aside from its famous *Lodenmantel* (available in grey and brown as well as green) which was worn by King Maximilian of Bavaria as long ago as 1850, the store also stocks a wide range of traditional dress, or *Tracht*, which forms the backbone of German country apparel. Folkloric and *Trachten* items, such as hand-painted or printed tablecloths and bedspreads, may also be bought at Loden Frey's Wallach store which is situated close by.

Loden Frey
Maffeistraße 7-9, D-80333 Munich, Germany
Tel: +49-89-21 03 90   Fax: +49-89-21 03 92 50   Website: www.loden-frey.com

LINSLERHOF

Linslerhof combines relaxed country living, complete with shooting, riding and other sports, with the utmost pampering. This 800 year-old farm, owned by the von Boch family, used to be a hunting retreat for the Emperor Barbarossa. At its renowned shooting school, pupils learn on Europe's most modern range, housed underground.

Linslerhof
D-66802 Uberherrn, Germany
Tel: +49-6836-8070   Fax: +49-6836-80 717

LE LION D'OR

When they want spectacular food for a very special party - whether a dinner for four or a gala for 800 - Geneva's smartest hostesses call upon the catering services of Thomas Bryne and Gilles Dupont. Their beautifully presented dishes emphasise seasonal products and Mediterranean flavours and the quality is guaranteed by the fact that they also happen to own the Michelin-starred restaurant of the same name.

L'Auberge du Lion D'Or
Place Pierre Gautier 5,
CH-1223 Cologny, Switzerland
Tel: +41-22-736 44 32   Fax: +41-22-786 74 62

LISMORE CASTLE

With an average catch of 525 salmon per season for the last six years, this stretch of almost two miles on the Blackwater River offers some of Europe's most glorious fishing. Creature comforts are well taken care of too: a cricket pavilion is set up on the river bank to provide lunch and, in the evening, a splendid dinner is served in the lodge.

Lismore Castle
Careysville Lodge, Careysville,
Fermoy, Co. Cork, Ireland
Tel: +353-58-54288   Fax: +353-58-54896

THE LISSON GALLERY

Lisson Gallery artists have won the Turner Prize, Britain's most influential award for young artists, more times than those from any other dealer. Established 30 years ago by Nicholas Logsdail, the gallery's speciality is contemporary minimalist sculpture, though the emergence of 'Brit Pack' artists means that film and video are also now well represented.

The Lisson Gallery
52-54 Bell Street, London NW1 5DA, UK
Tel: +44-171-724 2739 Fax: +44-171-724 7124

LOCANDA DELL'AMOROSA

This exquisite 14th-century *borgo*, presided over by the charming Carlo Citterio, nestles in the Sienese hills. The buildings, sensitively transformed into a hotel, stand around a Renaissance square: there's an old manor house, vaulted stables, church, an original tower and ancient farm buildings. Beyond are vineyards, pastures and a large park-garden.

Locanda dell'Amorosa,
53048 Sinalunga, Siena, Italy
Tel: +39-0577-67 94 97 Fax: +39-0577-63 20 01

LOCK'S

With over 300 years of tradition, James Lock & Co is a family business deliciously redolent of another age. Here, like the Prince of Wales and the Duke of Edinburgh, you will find a gentleman's hat for every occasion - ready-made or bespoke - as well as a new country clothing and accessories range, much of it in Lock's Teflon-coated house tweed.

James Lock & Co.
6 St James's Street, London SW1A 1EF, UK
Tel: +44-171-930 8874   Fax: +44-171-976 1908

LODEN PLANKL

Traditional Tyrolean clothing - especially the loden - is the hallmark of this long-established Viennese shop. Run by the John family for several generations, the business now keeps the city's élite in classic hunting coats and Alpine headgear.

Loden Plankl
Michaelerplatz 6, A-1010 Vienna, Austria
Tel: +43-1-533 8032   Fax: +43-1-535 4920

LOEWE

One of this year's hottest designers, Narciso Rodriguez, has been given the task of taking Loewe (originally a Spanish leather-goods company and now based in Paris as part of the LVMH empire) into the millennium. He has given a new twist to luxurious materials such as mink, cashmere and shearling and done marvellous things with contrasting textures.

Loewe
54 avenue Montagne, 75008 Paris, France
Tel: +33-1-44 20 84 24   Fax: +33-1-44 20 84 98

LOMBARD ODIER

All good private banks provide comprehensive and highly competent portfolio management for high-net worth individuals. The distinction between the outstanding ones and those which are merely good is that the former boast superb staff and provide an exceptionally high level of service. Lombard Odier is a perfect example. Each new account holder is assigned a personal 'adviser', who is available to take instructions and provide advice on a daily basis.

Lombard Odier
11 rue de la Corraterie,
CH-1204 Geneva, Switzerland
Tel: +41-22-709 2111   Fax: +41-22-709 2199

LOPEZ DE ARAGON (FELIX)

Of all the antique dealers in Spain, Felix Lopez de Aragon is perhaps the most forward-looking. Working with his sons, Gonzalo and Diego, he keeps track of the latest scientific advances, in order to illuminate his study of the Medieval and Renaissance treasures that pass through his hands. Lopez' passion for antiques was inspired early in life, by his father's collection of Medieval goldsmiths' work.

Felix Lopez de Aragon
Jorge Juan 9E, 28001 Madrid, Spain
Tel: +34-91-576 0012   Fax: +34-91-576 0012

G. LORENZI

This lovely old-fashioned shop opened in 1929 when the Lorenzis, a family of blade grinders, arrived in Milan from Trentino. Scarcely changed since then, it stocks a huge range of cutlery, scissors, shaving equipment and smokers' accessories, made of wood, horn, leather, copper and brass - all of superb quality.

G. Lorenzi
via Montenapoleone 9,
20121 Milan, Italy
Tel: +39-02-760 22848   Fax: +39-02-760 03390

LORETTA CAPONI

Housed in a suite of frescoed rooms in the Palazzo Aldobrandini, Loretta Caponi and her daughter Lucia preside over this fabled lingerie and linen emporium, stacked to the gills with bright white and pastel-hued bedclothes, silk underwear, childrenswear, towels and tablecovers. Visitors may glimpse embroiderers at work in the adjoining workshops.

Loretta Caponi
Piazza Antinori, 4r 50123 Florence, Italy
Tel: +39-055-21 36 68   Fax: +39-055-29 31 18

LORNA WING

Lorna Wing has become one of Britain's most sought-after caterers and party planners thanks to her fabulously inventive food, which ranges from Asian to Mediterranean, chic to rustic, and classic to contemporary. Her company organises every style and size of party, from the tiny and intimate to the grand and glamorous; its client list reads like a who's who of the fashion, music and art worlds, as well as royalty and blue-chip companies.

Lorna Wing Ltd.
Studio 21, The Talina Centre,
Bagleys Lane, London SW6 2BW, UK
Tel: +44-171–731 5105   Fax: +44-171-731 7957

LORO PIANA

The cashmere and vicuña shawls, scarves and throws produced by this family-owned company are, quite simply, the best - not only for their superb quality but also for their subtle colourings. The company is expanding its product lines and, at the end of 1998, opens its first-ever shop in Milan.

Lanificio Loro Piana
Corso Rolandi 10,
13017 Quarona, Italy
Tel: +39-0163-20 111   Fax: +39-0163-43 00 99

LOUIS ROEDERER

Although they would never admit it openly, the heads of several other great champagne houses consider Roederer's Cristal to be the finest of its genre. The name itself dates from the time when the champagne house supplied Nicholas II of Russia; determined to impress the Tsar, the cellar-master decided to present the champagne in crystal bottles. This champagne is full-bodied and powerful; Cristal Rosé 1982 and Cristal 1979 are sublime - and continue to improve with age.

Louis Roederer
21 boulevard Lundy,
51100 Reims, France
Tel: +33-3-26 40 42 11   Fax: +33-3-26 61 40 35

LOUIS BENECH

Benech's classically inspired gardens, characterised by rich plantings, seem to float against the surrounding landscape. One of France's foremost designers (responsible for the restoration of Paris' Jardin des Tuileries) this modest and charming man continues to describe himself simply as "a gardener", which is how his career began. By re-thinking the formal garden, Benech is equally at home with the formal setting of a grand château or with the rustic simplicity of a Normandy *manoir*.

Louis Benech
175 avenue Victor Hugo, 75016 Paris, France
Tel: +33-1-44 05 00 21   Fax: +33-1-44 05 95 65

LOUIS VUITTON

Perhaps the most heavily marketed of all today's luxury brands, Louis Vuitton's eponymous firm has come a long way since 1834, when he came to Paris as an apprentice trunk-packer at the court of the Empress Eugénie. The house's eagerly awaited womenswear collection by American designer Marc Jacobs (which debuted for summer 1998), with its neutral colours and utilitarian style (albeit in deeply luxurious fabrics), is an elegant backdrop to Vuitton's tempting accessories.

Louis Vuitton
101 avenue Champs Elysées, 75008 Paris, France
Tel: +33-1-45 62 47 00   Fax: +33-1-45 62 90 43

LE LOUIS XV

The richness of this fabulous Empire room is complemented perfectly by Alain Ducasse's celebrated signature dishes, such as Ravioli with foie gras and truffles. This demi-god among chefs insists on the simplicity of his cooking, based on the purest ingredients. This is 'millionaire simple' - but even the awesome bill cannot ruin the suspicion that you, as the diner, come out on top.

Restaurant Le Louis XV
Hôtel de Paris, Place du Casino, MC 98000, Monaco
Tel: +377-92 16 30 01   Fax: +377-92 16 38 49

LUCIANO BARBERA

This is the name of the clothing line, introduced in 1969, of Carlo Barbera & C., a distinguished, family-owned company which produces fabrics for Chanel, Hermès and Versace amongst others. Most of the 400,000 metres it produces each year are woven from the finest cashmere and Australian merino.

Carlo Barbera & C.
via Dogliette 2, 13051 Biella, Italy
Tel: +39-015-28 689   Fax: +39-015-22 597

LUCIEN PELLAT-FINET

Beloved of 'Voguettes' on both sides of the Channel, cashmere maestro Lucien Pellat-Finet has been in the fashion business for almost 30 years but has established his name only in the last five. As the maker of Europe's most seductive and luxurious knitwear in beautifully thought-out styles and colours, his wares are instantly recognisable to the cognoscenti.

Lucien Pellat-Finet
222 rue de Rivoli, 75001 Paris, France
Tel: +33-1-42 60 74 37   Fax: +33-1-42 60 31 18

LUCKNAM PARK

This Palladian mansion (built in 1720) is set in 500 acres of leafy Wiltshire parkland. Sumptuously decorated and immaculately staffed, Lucknam is remarkably serene, as both Donatella Versace and Luciano Pavarotti would attest (they have both stayed in the Coral Suite). Chef Paul Collins' Modern English cuisine is first-rate.

Lucknam Park
Colerne, Wiltshire SN14 8AZ, UK
Tel: +44-1225-74 27 77   Fax: +44-1225-74 35 36

LUIGI BOCCHI

Don't be fooled by the Baroque flourishes on Luigi Bocchi's business card; his flower shop is built to his own ultra-modern design. From the warm Tuscan terracotta paving and the central fountain - rather like a small grotto - made of Travertino stone, to the skylight prisms, Mr Bocchi has thought out everything with the utmost care to show off the displays to their best advantage - and what displays! Much in demand for weddings and grand parties, Mr Bocchi's style is characterised by originality and a modernistic simplicity; he uses exotic flowers and foliage to great effect.

Luigi Bocchi
corso Vittorio Emanuele 136, 00186 Rome, Italy
Tel: +39-06-68 89 09 31   Fax: +39-06-68 89 25 79

LUIS ELVIRA

From an incomparable spot (his gallery is on the slopes of the mountain overlooking the Mediterranean near the Oropesa Castle), Luis

Elvira has successfully projected himself on an international level. These days, people from all over the world refer to him when looking for the finest examples of Medieval, Roman, Gothic and Renaissance works.

Luis Elvira
Ramon y Cajal 1, 12594 Oroposa del Mar,
Castellon, Spain
Tel: +34-96-431 0751 Fax: +34-96-431 2091

LUIGI BORRELLI

With Luigi Borrelli's shirts you get what you pay for. What you pay is anything up to $400 for a bespoke model and what you get is a masterpiece of Neapolitan artistry. Borrelli's signature fit is key and so is the use of the finest Italian fabrics. However, it is the hand-stitching, which creates fluidity and 'give' that really makes the quality and comfort.

Luigi Borrelli
viale dei Platani 29,
80040 S. Sebastiano al Vesuvio, Naples, Italy
Tel: +39-081-771 2941 Fax: +39-081-771 8222

LURSSEN YACHTS

Friedrich and Peter Lürssen are the fourth generation to head up this family-owned company, which has a formidable reputation for its state-

of-the-art technological expertise in the construction of large, custom-built motor and sailing yachts.

Lürssen prides itself on offering excellent value for money; yachts are constructed in self-contained sections, each honed, moulded and finished to a certain point and then assembled in a single unit, thus saving time and labour, as well as ensuring maximum flexibility and superior craftsmanship. The company's in-house design group also plays a crucial role in the construction process; it collaborates closely with owners and independent designers to achieve the most stylish and practical solutions for both exteriors and interiors. Celebrated Lürssen craft include the 96m Jon Bannenberg *Limitless*, the 40.5m Holland/Freivokh *Twirlybird*.

Lürssen Yachts
Friedrich-Klippert-Strasse 1,
D-28759 Bremen, Germany
Tel: +49-421 66 04 166   Fax: +49-421 66 04 170

LUTTRELLSTOWN CASTLE

Just 15 minutes' drive from Dublin, this romantic gothic revival-style mansion is set in a 560-acre walled estate in the Liffey Valley. The castle accommodates up to 28 people, and has its own golf course. The whole dreamy location can be rented privately on a daily basis or for lunch and dinner parties.

Luttrellstown Castle
Castleknock, Dublin 15, Ireland
Tel: +353-1-808 9988   Fax: +353-1-808 9989

THE MACALLAN

It is only in the last 30 years that The Macallan has established its near-legendary reputation. Epithets such as "broad", "full" and "satisfying" are regularly used to describe its uniquely rich flavour. The 25 year-old is outstanding. Deep amber in colour, it has a hint of sweetness to its flavour, which softens the great underlying power, yielding a malt of wondrous complexity.

The Macallan
Highland Distillers plc.,
West Kinfaunn,
Perthshire PH2 7XZ, Scotland
Tel: +44-1738-44 00 00   Fax: +44-1738-62 81 67

IL MAESTRO DI CASA

This is the company if, like Louis Vuitton, Gucci or Calvin Klein and the cream of Milanese society, you wish to locate a splendid venue and organise top-flight social or business events. Tailor-made menus, impeccably professional staff, stunning flowers and exclusive place-settings set exactly the right tone.

Il Maestro di Casa
via Udine 85,
20010 Canegrate (Mi), Italy
Tel: +39-0331-41 13 40   Fax: +39-0331-41 13 41

MAGGIO MUSICALE FIORENTINO

The 2,000-seater Teatro Comunale is the nucleus of the Festival of Florence - the city in which the first opera was created at the end of the 16th century. The Maggio Musicale was founded by Vittorio Gui in 1933, and over the years has been graced by the world's top conductors, directors and set designers; not to mention the greatest singers of the age - Maria Callas made her debut here.

Maggio Musicale Fiorentino
Biglietteria Teatro Comunale, Corso Italia 16,
50123 Florence, Italy
Tel: +39-055-21 11 58 / 21 35 35
Fax: +39-055-277 9410

MAGGS BROS

The doyen of London's (and possibly the world's) antiquarian book dealers, John Maggs is the fourth-generation head of this family firm. Based in a haunted Georgian house in Mayfair, Maggs' is a marvellously old-fashioned treasure-trove of rare volumes, manuscripts and precious bindings. You don't come here merely to buy a book, so much as to sit down over a pot of tea with Mr Maggs and be inspired; he is a delight - discreet and modest, with a dry wit and a burning passion for his work.

Maggs Bros
50 Berkeley Square,
London W1X 6EL, UK
Tel: +44-171-493 7160   Fax: +44-171-499 2007

MAISON BLANCHE GRAND BAIN

As well as the life-enhancing alpine air, guests of the Hôtel Maison Blanche and Grand Bain

enjoy first-rate treatments at its adjoining Alpentherme spa. There are two indoor and outdoor thermal pools, a sports pool and a grotto pool heated to 40°C. Beauty, fitness, medical care and special diets are all catered for in great style.

Hôtel Maison Blanche Grand Bain
Loeche-les-Bains,
CH-3954 Leukerbad, Switzerland
Tel: +41-27-470 5161   Fax: +41-27-470 34 74

LES MAISONS DE BRICOURT and RICHEUX HOTEL

Olivier and Jane Roellinger have created three lovely retreats overlooking the bay of Mont Saint-Michel. You can choose between the cottage simplicity of Les Rimains, overlooking the Cancale oyster beds, the 18th-century *malouinière* (Roellinger's childhood home), which

houses his marvellous Maisons de Bricourt restaurant, and the turreted Victorian Hôtel Richeux on the cliff-top nearby.

Les Masions de Bricourt
1 rue Duguesclin, 35260 Cancale, France
Tel: +33-2-99 89 64 76   Fax: +33-2-99 89 88 47

MAKE-UP FOR EVER

While working as a make-up artist, former sculptress Dany Sanz decided to create a range of products, following her own ideas and the requirements of her fellow professionals. The fruits of that labour - over 1800 items - are sold at this store, which she opened in 1985. She also organises classes and workshops for budding professionals and keen amateurs.

Make-Up For Ever
5 rue de la Boétie, 75008 Paris, France
Tel: +33-1-44 51 68 80   Fax: +33-1-44 51 68 81

MALLETT

Founded in 1865, Mallet has grown to such an extent that, seven years ago, it went public. The Bond Street section specialises in English furniture and glass (John Smith, its glass expert, is a world authority on the subject), while Bourdon House deals in unusual, decorative items. The latter is an appropriate setting for Mallet's quirkier pieces; the last Duke to live here had a well-known liaison with Coco Chanel.

Mallet of Bond Street
141 New Bond Street, London W1Y OBS, UK
Tel: +44-171-499 7411 Fax: +44-171-495 3179

Mallet at Bourdon House
2 Davies Street, London W1Y 1LJ, UK
Tel: +44-171-629 2444 Fax: +44-171-499 2670

MANGANI

Mangani's transformation from a tiny, family-run porcelain studio into a business which, today, employs 50 highly skilled artisans, is due to a quirk of fate: a director of Tiffany's happened to see a coffee-cup, tracked down its maker and ordered over 1000 pieces. Mangani's exquisitely fine reproductions of 18th-century works of art are complemented by a collection of contemporary shapes, colours and finishes, all produced entirely by hand.

Mangani Srl
20 via P. Arentino, Settinello,
50040 Florence, Italy
Tel: +39-055-882 5132   Fax: +39-055-887 3258

LE MANOIR "INTER SCALDES"

There's something very English about this sublime 12-bedroom manor house hotel, which, surprisingly, was once a military police bar-

racks. Perhaps it is the beautiful rose gardens. Or is it the thatched roof of the main building? In any case, Kees and Maartje Boudeling's manoir is supremely comfortable and their restaurant is rightly celebrated for its outstanding seafood.

Le Manoir "Inter Scaldes"
Zandweg 2, NL-4416 NA Kruiningen Yerseke,
The Netherlands
Tel: +31-113-38 17 53   Fax: +31-113-38 17 63

LE MANOIR AUX QUAT'SAISONS

Completely self taught, the intense and sometimes iconoclastic Raymond Blanc is a chef whose cooking defies categorisation but invariably provokes plaudits. As one restaurant critic put it: "Lucky are those of us who have experienced this exceptional man's art". Others simply cannot understand why the 'Michelin Man' continues to withhold a third star. The manoir itself feels more English than French: a rambling Cotswold house with croquet lawns and rose beds, deep armchairs and the lingering suggestion of an old-fashioned house party.

Le Manoir aux Quat' Saisons
Church Road, Great Milton,
Oxfordshire OX44 7PD, UK
Tel: +44-1844-27 88 81   Fax: +44-1844-27 88 47

MANOLO BLAHNIK

Vibrant colours and exquisitely crafted high heels are the hallmarks of Manolo Blahnik's creations, which have been adored by *Vogue* editors and international ladies who lunch for 30 years. Now Blahnik has added a range of shoes for men; the trademark colours are there but Blahnik emphasises their classic cut and style. "Men's shoes aren't meant to be fashionable," he insists.

Manolo Blahnik
49-51 Old Church Street, London SW3 5BS, UK
Tel: +44-171-352 3863

MANUEL CANOVAS

It is almost 30 years since textile designer Manuel Canovas revolutionised interior decoration with his joyful colour schemes and pan-global eclecticism. But nowadays he is equally celebrated for his pretty fashion and home accessories. His deliciously scented candles are an absolute must-buy.

Manuel Canovas
7 rue de Furstenberg, 75006 Paris, France
Tel: +33-1-43 25 75 98   Fax: +33-1-45 04 04 83

MARCO DATRINO & CO

Founded 50 years ago by Marco's father Carlo, this gallery specialises in Northern Italian antiques, works of art and furniture. In 1993, it bought part of the collection amassed by the House of Savoy; from this, a Giulio Monteverde cradle in bronze, silver and gold was sold to the Galleria Nazionale d'Arte Moderna in Rome.

Marco Datrino & Co
Via Balbo 34, 10010 Torre Canavese, Italy
Tel: +39-0124-50 10 71   Fax: +39-0124-50 11 17

CHATEAU MARGAUX

Corinne Mentzelopoulos presides over this magnificent château, designed by the architect Louis Combe. Established at the beginning of the 18th century (and the only *cru classé* to carry the name of an appellation in its own right) its dense, complex and extremely elegant wines quickly gained a reputation as one of Bordeaux's best clarets. Ernest Hemingway was, famously, so impressed that he named a daughter after the château. Margaux 1990 will be ready for drinking in 1999.

Château Margaux
33460 Margaux, France
Tel: +33-5-57 88 83 83   Fax: +33-5-57 88 31 32

MARINA B

Marina B, daughter of Constantine Bulgari, a co-founder of the Bulgari jewellery empire, started her own design company in Geneva after her father's death in 1979. With the backing of Sheikh Ahmed H. Fitaihi since 1996, she has gained worldwide recognition for her rich artistic talent and strong, contemporary designs.

Marina B
40 rue de Rhône, CH-1204 Geneva, Switzerland
Tel: +41-22-817 0212   Fax: +41-22-817 0201

E. MARINELLA

An almost absurdly discreet little store in Naples, still decorated as it was when Eugenio Marinella founded this firm in 1914, is home to an internationally celebrated company. Subscribing to Don Eugenio's maxim that "it is the tiniest of the tiniest details that make up the elegance of the whole man", Luca di Montezemolo, Prince Charles, Presidents Bush, Gorbachev and Mitterand and Gianni Agnelli are among those who have beaten a path to Marinella's door.

Quite simply, this firm, now run by the founder's grandson, Maurizio, makes the finest ties in the world. 60 percent of them are made to measure. "A client may like his ties shorter or longer, wider, lighter or heavier than standard," explains Marinella. "He may wear a larger-than-usual knot or want his ties unlined." The one thing that you won't find is anything loud; the patterns are as discreet as the company itself.

Four times every year, Maurizio Marinella travels to England to place orders for fabrics (mostly silk twill) and work on designs. The mills produce a given pattern, in myriad subtle colour variations, for

only a 15-day period; each design is printed in a quantity sufficient for only four ties. In the words of former Italian President, Francesco Cossiga, "There is nothing to touch Marinella's fabrics."

E. Marinella
287 Riviera di Chiaia, Naples, Italy
Tel/Fax: +39-081-764 4214

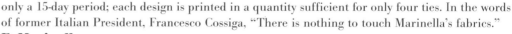

MARIA BRUNA BEAUTY WORKSHOP

After studying graphic design and psychology, Maria Bruna (widely regarded as the best in her business in Italy) realised that the beauty business was her true calling. She set up her own treatment studio in Brescia 20 years ago, later moving to a house in the *centro storico*. Her special steam treatment with aromatic and essential oils is a must; utterly relaxing to both brain and body at the same time as curing and nutrifying the skin.

Maria Bruna Beauty Workshop
Piazza Vescovato 1/C, 25125 Brescia, Italy
Tel: +39-030-45 194   Fax: +39-030-42 092

MARIA LUISA

Venezuela-born Maria Luisa, a self-confessed clothes addict, stocks the best of today's most talked-about designers, from Galliano to Gaultier. In her menswear boutique the hip designs of bright new talent Raf Simons hang alongside suits by Helmut Lang and Vivienne Westwood, while the addictive stilettos of Manolo Blahnik fill her accessories shop across the street.

Maria Luisa
2 rue Cambon, 75001 Paris, France
Tel: +33-1-47 03 96 15

MARINA BAROVIER

A member of Murano's most celebrated glassmaking family, Marina Barovier opened this gallery two years ago. It stocks the work of contemporary designers and artists, such as Lino Tagliapietra, Bale Cihailue and Bertil Vallin. Four times a year, she takes travelling exhibitions, which showcase these works, to Milan and New York.

Marina Barovier
Calizzada San Samuele, San Marco 3216,
30124 Venice, Italy
Tel: +39-041-522 6102

MARIO BUCCELLATI

One of Mario Buccellati's ancestors was the illustrious 18th-century silversmith Contardo Buccellati and the company that his descendant started in 1919 continues the tradition today. Head goldsmith Lorenzo and his wife Claudia Buccellati create exquisite jewels and *objets d'art* featuring carved or brushed gold with precious stones.

Mario Buccellati
via Montenapoleone 4,
20121 Milan, Italy
Tel: +39-02-76 00 21 53 Fax: +39-02-78 09 03

MARIO PELINO

The Pelino family still makes *confetti* (sugared almonds) using the same methods - a four day process - as it did when it began in business in 1783. These traditional sweets, which come in myriad colours (white for weddings, green for engagements, red for graduation), and shapes (oval, teardrop and spherical) are presented at every important occasion in Italian life.

Confetti Mario Pelino
via Introdacqua 55, 67039 Sulmona, Italy
Tel: +39-0864-21 00 47 Fax: +39-0864-55 203

MARIUCCIA

Mariuccia Langi may not be listed in the Milan telephone directory, but the city's smartest ladies all have her in their little black books. For the last 30 years her agency has been supplying them with blue-chip housekeepers, maids and other domestic staff.

Mariuccia
via Malpighi 3, 20129 Milan, Italy
Tel: +39-02-29 40 98 43

MARK'S CLUB

Many habitués of London's traditional clubs have forsaken the smoky rooms of St James's for the pleasures of this discreet Mayfair townhouse. The decor in Mark Birley's private dining club is comfortably English country-house, the service impeccable and the perfectly-wrought cooking is the world's finest and grandest example of English 'nursery food'. Members are discreet movers and shakers, rather than the glossy set.

Mark's Club
46 Charles Street, London W1X 7PB, UK
Tel: +44-171-499 2936

MARLBOROUGH FINE ART

Founded in 1946 by Frank Lloyd (described by *The Economist* as "the world's greatest art dealer"), this is the biggest art business in the world. It was Mark Rothko who made Marlborough famous. Then, as London's art world came into its own, the gallery staged remarkable exhibitions, including Bacon, Chadwick, Freud and Hepworth - a pace it has maintained ever since.

Marlborough Fine Art
6 Albemarle Street, London W1X 4BY, UK
Tel: +44-171-629 5161   Fax: +44-171-629 6338

MARLIES MOLLER

With her headquarters in a 1400 square-metre former palace, Hamburg hairdresser and makeup artist, Marlies Möller, is ideally situated to pamper both the city's élite and visiting celebrities. Men and women keep coming back for her specialist "dry hair" cuts. In 1996, Moller won the World Master Award of Art and Fashion in New York.

Marlies Möller
Tesdorpfstraße 20, D-20148 Hamburg, Germany
Tel: +49-40-444 0040   Fax: +49-40-45 36 42

MARNI

Consuela Castiglioni's combination of beautiful fabrics and colours and attention to detail give her clothes a feeling of great quality - luxury even - at a moderate price. With no formal training, Castiglioni (whose husband is President of Giwi Furs) launched her first collection under the Marni name in 1991 at the age of 37.

Marni
via Sismondi 70,
20133 Milan, Italy
Tel: +39-02-74 81 91   Fax: +39-02-70 10 19 77

MARQUIS D'ANGERVILLE (DOMAINE DU)

This *domaine* stands on one of the best parcels of land in Volnay and its old vines and light yields result in fine, complex and beautifully perfumed wines of great class and longevity. During the 1930s, the grandfather of present owner, Jacques d'Aerville, was one of the first in Burgundy to bottle wines on the estate (previously it was sold in barrels). Volnay Clos des Ducs 1990 will make great drinking this year.

Domaine du Marquis D'Angerville
21190 Volnay, France
Tel: +33-3-80 21 61 75 Fax: +33-3-80 21 65 07

MARTIN MARGIELA

The Garbo of the fashion world, Belgian Martin Margiela shies away from media attention, believing that his clothes should speak for themselves. Although renowned as an iconoclast when designing under his own name, Margiela nonetheless sealed a pact with the establishment when he produced his first ready-to-wear collection for Hermès in March 1998.

Martin Margiela
2bis Passage Ruelle,
75018 Paris, France
Tel: +33-1-44 89 65 20 Fax: +33-1-44 89 65 29

MARTIN PIPE

Martin Pipe, the son of a bookmaker, is a record-breaking trainer of steeplechasers and hurdlers, although he also dabbles in the flat. The object of much jealousy, he trains literally hundreds of winners a season, never minding how small the prize money is. However, he is focusing more and more on the big races and did extremely well at Cheltenham in 1997, having won the previous year's Grand National with *Minnehoma*. Based in Somerset, Pipe makes much use of his helicopter and mobile telephone.

Martin Pipe
Pond House, Nicholashayne,
Wellington, Somerset TA21 9QY, UK
Tel: +44-1884-84 07 15 Fax: +44-1884-84 13 43

MAS DE TORRENT

This beautifully restored 18th-century farmhouse, imbued with old-fashioned Catalan charm, is favoured both by weary Spanish urbanites (Princess Cristina and President Arnaz have both stayed) and affluent Northern Europeans in search of discreet luxury and an element of privacy (the 20 bungalows are perfect for sybaritic hermits).

Mas de Torrent
E-17123 Torrent,
Girona, Spain
Tel: +34-972-30 32 92   Fax: +34-972-30 11 50

MAURITSHUIS

This 17th-century Dutch Classicist-style palace holds the oldest national collection in The Netherlands and includes world-famous paintings by the likes of Rembrandt, Frans Hals, Rubens and Van Dyck.
It was recently host to a phenomenally successful exhibition of the work of Vermeer, which brought many of the artist's paintings together for the first time.

Mauritshuis
Koret Vijverberg 8, 2513 AB Den Haag,
The Netherlands
Tel: +31-70-302 3456

THE MERRION

In the heart of Dublin four Georgian houses have been converted into a discreet hotel - so discreet, in fact, that as you enter the door of the Main House, you are faced not with a reception desk but with the sort of entrance hall you would expect to find in an elegant townhouse: a black and white marble floor, a fireplace, some good paintings.

Everything about the hotel seems designed for relaxation. Peat fires burn year-round in the drawing room grates, scenting the air. The peaceful, half-acre courtyard has been landscaped with

classically-inspired gardens. The Tethra Spa offers deeply pampering ESP'A treatments and its elegant 18m infinity pool has ozone-treated water. The staff, too, under the direction of the affable Peter McCann, are friendly and low-key - though scrupulously professional.

The decoration of some bedrooms may seem slightly restrained but the simple style and muted colours are, in fact, authentically Georgian; great pains were taken to ensure its historical accuracy. However, if you admire richly decorated plaster-work, ask for a room in the old wing, where one of the houses was the home of Lord Mornington, father of the 1st Duke of Wellington.

The Merrion
21-24 Upper Merrion Street, Dublin 2, Ireland
Tel: +353-1-603 0600   Fax: +353-1-603 0700

METRO BUSINESS AVIATION

The leading executive jet handling agent in the United Kingdom, Metro has facilities at three London airports. Its sister company, Air Harrods, offers a world-wide charter broking service, with an extensive portfolio of both fixed-wing aircraft and helicopters.

Metro Business Aviation
Southern Perimeter Road, Heathrow Airport,
Hounslow, Middlesex, TW6 3AE, UK
Tel: +44-181-585 7004   Fax: +44-181-585 7007

SIR MICHAEL STOUTE

Sir Michael has been a spectacular success on the international scene for over 20 years, as well as winning two Derbys for the Aga Khan - notably with the great *Shergar* in 1981. Significant though his racing achievements have been, his 1998 knighthood was, somewhat bizarrely, awarded for services to tourism in Barbados, his native country. Stoute's principal owners include the Aga Khan (again, after a hiatus of several years), Lord Weinstock and members of the Maktoum family.

Sir Michael Stoute
Freemason Lodge, Bury Road, Newmarket,
Suffolk CB8 7BT, UK
Tel: +44-1638-66 38 0   Fax: +44-1638-66 72 76

MICHEL BRAS

The impressive modern architecture of Michel Bras' eponymous restaurant takes full advantage of its eyrie-like position on a plateau, overlooking the glorious Aubrac countryside. As breathtaking as the view from the floor-to-ceiling windows, however, are dishes such as *Pièce de boeuf de l'Aubrac*, scented with local herbs.

Michel Bras
Route de l'Aubrac, 12210 Laguiole, France
Tel: +33-5-65 44 32 24   Fax: +33-5-65 48 47 02

MICHELE REICHENBACH

As hard-working as she is elegant and sociable, Michèle Reichenbach established her event planning and PR company in 1989. Her enviable client list includes Piaget, Chopard and Vacheron Constantin. With unsurpassed connections in the worlds of politics, the arts and show-business, Reichenbach is equally renowned for her network of celebrity and social contacts. Having begun with Geneva-based projects, she is increasingly in demand - even beyond the Swiss borders - for her imaginative and beautifully executed events.

Michèle Reichenbach & Associés
3 rue Bellot, CH-1207 Geneva, Switzerland
Tel: +41-22-789 52 52   Fax: +41-22-78 95 45

MIDLETON VERY RARE

If you like your whiskey rugged and robust, Midleton Very Rare is probably not for you. But, if you are charmed by the idea of a silky smooth initial flavour followed by a touch of sweetness and finishing with a hint of spice, you would be foolish to pass it by. Savour it with a good book or good company.

Midleton Very Rare
Irish Distillers Ltd., Bow Street Distillery,
Smithfield, Dublin 7, Ireland
Tel: +353-1-872 5566   Fax: +353-1-872 3109

LES MILLE FEUILLES

A profusion of roses fills this heavenly shop, which has an enormous selection of unusual varieties. There are country roses in abundance - as well as rarer examples, such as Paul Ricard, a luminous beige colour with a heavy scent, and the stunning blue rose, Mamy Bleu.

Mille Feuilles
2 rue Rambuteau, 75003 Paris, France
Tel: +33-1-42 78 32 93   Fax: +33-1-42 78 17 90

MILLESIMES

For those who need their fix of Bordeaux grand crus or top class Burgundies while in the rosé-drenched Midi, Millésimes is a precious find. Its awesome selection includes 1945 to 1995 vintages from the very best estates in the two regions. As for Provençal wines, it recommends the domaines of Trevallon and Rouge Garance.

Millésimes
Verger d'Entreprises de la Capelette,
13520 Maussane, France
Tel: +33-4-90 54 49 45   Fax: +33-4-90 54 49 44

MILLFIELD SENIOR SCHOOL

The broad mix of pupils at this top-flight boarding school (children of celebrities and powerful Third World families among them) may help to explain the eclectic array of subjects on offer - Hindi and Norwegian among them. Millfield's academic record is sound, sports and the Arts outstanding; recreational facilities include a television studio and a polo school.

Millfield Senior School
Buckleigh Road, Somerset BA16 OYD, UK
Tel: +44-1458-44 22 91

MIRIAM PONZI INVESTIGATIONS

Miriam Ponzi's father established this highly regarded investigative agency 50 years ago. It is now a leader in its field, employing over 50 full-time detectives. Most of Ponzi's agency is for large corporate outfits but the real growth sector is 'the lipstick issue' - i.e. determining whether one half of a couple is faithful or not.

Miriam Ponzi Investigations
Via Veneto 116, Postcode 00187 TBA, Rome, Italy
Tel: +39-06-487 0007   Fax: +39-06-48 80 590

LE MEURICE

Situated within the archways of the rue de Rivoli,

opposite the Tuileries Gardens, this palatial hotel retains its aura of grandeur. Indeed, plans are underway to make the Meurice even more sumptuous, now that it is part of the Audley Group. The decoration of the hotel, though, with its gilded plasterwork and 18th-century furnishings, is not its only claim to fame. In the 1920s the Meurice was known for its literary salon which attracted writers such as Andre Gide and François Mauriac. The hotel carries on this tradition by setting aside its salons for the judging of the annual Prix Novembre literary award. Music is also an integral part of the hotel's life, with a lyrical dinner held every two months, at which talented opera singers perform the classics, reflected in the restaurant's antique bevelled mirrors. As for the rooms, all 152 are spacious, soundproofed and filled with antique furnish-

ings. There are also 28 stunning suites, the largest having 100 metres of floor space. For over 160 years the Meurice has played host to kings and politicians, sultans and princesses; as the new owners breathe fresh life into this Parisian *grande dame*, they will feel more at home here than ever.

Hotel Le Meurice
228 rue de Rivoli, 75001 Paris, France
Tel: +33-1-44 58 10 10   Fax: +33-1-44 58 10 17

MOET ET CHANDON

It is surprising how many people do not readily associate Moët et Chandon with its flagship vintage, Dom Pérignon; first marketed in 1936, 'DP' (as insiders call it) is now the world's number one prestige cuvée. Cleverly named after the monk who is credited with inventing the champagne process, it is renowned for both the soft texture contributed by its tiny bubbles and the superb balance of flavours. Its rosé is always superb, though rarely available.

Moët et Chandon
4 rue de Crayeres, 51100 Reims, France
Tel: +33-3-26 77 51 51   Fax: +33-3-26 82 88 43

MOLLAND

The pretty Devon village of Molland nestles in a valley at the heart of this 2,500-acre private pheasant shoot. The terrain is ideal for both partridge and pheasant, with mature woodlands, streams and grassy open slopes, presenting challenging birds, both high over the valleys or fast through the trees.

Molland, near Tiverton, Devon, UK
c/o Holland & Holland, 31-33 Bruton Street,
London W1X 8JS, UK
Tel: +44-171-499 4411   Fax: +44-171-491 4544

MONOGRAMMED LINEN SHOP

Anne Singer designs most of the traditionally-inspired linens that are sold at this treasure trove in Walton Street. As well as a stock of exquisite towels, dressing gowns and children's clothes, private

commissions - such as a special tablecloth for a wedding or christening - are happily undertaken.

Monogrammed Linen Shop
168-170 Walton Street,
London SW3 2JL, UK
Tel: +44-171-589 4033   Fax: +44-171-823 7745

MONT BLANC

Mont Blanc was originally a cult-status pen patronised by style-brokers and those in the know about real quality. However, with the Vendôme group's financial muscle behind it, the marque today is world famous, having expanded into writing items, leather goods, eyewear, watches and a variety of accessories.

Montblanc
100 Hellgrundweg,
D-22525 Hamburg, Germany
Tel: +49-40-84 00 10   Fax: +49-40-84 00 13 50

MONT CERVIN (HOTEL)

Zermatt's best hotel, built in 1852, stands right in the centre of this charming, car-free village. Its many comforts are greatly enhanced by the exceptional friendliness and competence of the staff. Many rooms have breathtaking views of the Matterhorn; make a point of requesting one, as it adds enormously to the experience.

Hôtel Mont Cervin
CH-3920 Zermatt, Switzerland
Tel: +41-27-966 8888   Fax: +41-27-967 2878

MONTALEMBERT (HOTEL)

This Left Bank haven is a perfect antidote to the gilt and grand manners beloved of so many of the best Paris hotels. Built in 1926, it was transformed a few years ago, by Grace Leo Andrieu, to create an uncluttered - though beautifully decorated - contemporary environment, enhanced by the refreshingly easy (yet relentlessly professional) manner of the staff.

Hôtel Montalembert
3 rue de Montalembert, 75007 Paris, France
Tel: +33-1-45 49 68 68   Fax: +33-1-45 49 69 49

MONTE CARLO BEACH CLUB

This is the apogee of Mediterranean beach life. The waiting list for the front-row cabanas is years long and, when they do change hands, it is for thousands. It is where nannies and bodyguards pace beside the Olympic-sized pool, keeping an eye on the children - whose fathers are busy playing backgammon and whose elegantly bejewelled mothers are tanning themselves to a perfect shade of golden brown (the few wearing bikini tops are probably American). There is a restaurant by the pool but the better choice is La Vigie, perched out on the rocks; this is where the younger Grimaldis come for family lunches.

Monte Carlo Beach Club
avenue Princess Grace,
MC 98000 Monaco
Tel: +33-4-93 28 66 66   Fax: +33-4-93 78 14 18

MONTROSE (CHATEAU)

This is an old-style claret, stern and demanding. Not for this giant of Saint Emilion the easy charms of soft fruit and mild tannins. To be cellared for years, when it is finally ready for the table it will hold its own with the finest. Best drinking this year is the 1982 - an honourable exception to the rocky patch which the château experienced in the early Eighties. Montrose 1988 is just about ready, too.

Château Montrose
33180 Saint-Estèphe, France
Tel: +33-5-56 59 30 12   Fax: +33-5-56 59 38 48

MOSER

While the gilded, baroque style of much of this crystal may not be to everybody's taste, it is justly celebrated for its extraordinary clarity. It is unique among crystal for containing no lead, its complex chemical make-up being responsible for its brilliance (optimum in the elegant, simpler pieces). Moser's grand store is a symphony of varnished wood, engraved Doric columns and dripping chandeliers.

Moser
Na Príkope 12, Prague 1, Czech Republic
Tel: +420-2-24 21 12 93   Fax: +420-2-24 22 86 86

MOSHAMMER

Rudolf Moshammer is Munich's most colourful and outrageous celebrity. Swanning around town in his white Rolls Royce, or cavorting with his clients in the swish boutique at the centre of his empire, Moshammer is every inch the modern eccentric. The clothes that he sells are wildly expensive but beautifully made.

Moshammer
Maximilianstrasse 14, D-80357 Munich, Germany
Tel: +49-89-22 69 24

MOTSCH

Since 1887, gentlemen from all over the world have come here to have hats reblocked, repaired or made to their specifications. Though these legendary *chapeaux* now share the shop floor with scarves from Hermès, who took over the store some years ago, Motsch nevertheless remains an unmissable piece of French heritage.

Motsch
42 avenue George V, 75008 Paris, France
Tel: +33-1-47 23 79 22

MOULIE

Specialising in camellias, this flower shop is filled with wonderfully exotic, attention-grabbing plants. The adjoining shop has a good selection of 19th-century urns and other garden ornaments. However, Mr Moulié is nostalgic for the days when the offices of French *Vogue* were next door, which brought streams of top models sauntering past every day.

Moulié
8 place du Palais Bourbon,
75007 Paris, France
Tel: +33-1-45 51 78 43   Fax ; +33-1-45 50 45 54

MOUNT JULIET

This is a big, modern test of a golf course, with beautifully conditioned fairways that meander through huge stands of oak, lime and beech trees. That Nick Faldo and Bernhard Langer have both won Irish Opens here shows its calibre. The mansion hotel, built by the Earl of Carrick, is a fine place, too.

Mount Juliet
Thomastown, Co. Kilkenny, Ireland
Tel: +353-56-24 455   Fax: +353-56-24 522

MOUSSAIEFF

Despite their unprepossessing shop in London's Hilton Hotel and their publicity-shy ways, Palestinian-born Sam and Alisa Moussaieff are reckoned to be among the four most powerful buyers of important stones in the world. The spectacular, traditionally-styled pieces that appear in the shop window pale into insignificance beside some of the private commissions undertaken by this ultra-discreet firm.

Moussaieff
Hilton Hotel, Park Lane,
London W1Y 4BE, UK
Tel: +44-171-408 0487

MUNICH OPERA FESTIVAL

Local heroes, including Wagner and Strauss, feature prominently on the menu at this annual festival, held for the duration of July, in Germany's most social city. Performances for 1999 include Verdi's *Aida* and Mozart's *The Marriage of Figaro* presented at the Nationaltheater, a suitably iconic venue.

Munich Opera Festival
Bayerische Staatsoper,
Maximilianstrasse 11,
D-8000 Munich, Germany
Tel: +49-89-21 85 01   Fax: +49-89-21 85 11 33

MURDOCH

In order to do one's shopping on the avenue Montaigne in style, a call to this limousine service is all that is required. Chauffeurs, all of whom are security-trained, dress in civilian clothes or full livery, according to the client's preference.

Murdoch
182 boulevard Pereire, 75017 Paris, France
Tel: +33-1-53 81 14 20   Fax: +33-1-40 68 75 62

MOUTON-ROTHSCHILD (CHATEAU)

This is the name that Baron Nathaniel de

Rothschild gave to Château Brane-Mouton when he acquired it in 1853. It was promoted to *premier cru* in 1973, thanks to the tireless efforts of Baron Philippe. A born innovator, Baron Philippe introduced the now widespread practice of château bottling. His daughter, Philippine, a former actress, now runs the *domaine*, continuing her father's practice of commissioning a major artist (the roster includes Balthus, Miró, Vasarely, Bacon and Braque) to design each year's label. Although it is overshadowed by the celebrated 1961 vintage, 1962 is also first-rate.

Château Mouton-Rothschild
33250 Pauillac, France
Tel: +33-5-56 73 20 20   Fax ; +33-5-56 73 20 44

MURIEL GRATEAU

At first glance Muriel Grateau's showroom looks like an art gallery but, on closer inspection, it is elegant tableware and delicate linens - in pure shapes and subtle colours - which line the shelves of this pristine space. Grateau, who previously worked for Genny and Ermenegildo

Zegna, has an impressive client list, which includes Catherine Deneuve, Donna Karan and Calvin Klein.

Muriel Grateau
37 rue de Beaune, 75007 Paris, France
Tel: +33-1-40 20 42 82

MUSEE CARNAVALET
This important collection illustrates the rise of Paris from pre-history to the early 20th century. It is located in the heart of the Marais in an imposing 16th-century *hôtel particulier*. The great staircase, with mural paintings by Brunetti, and reconstructed interiors from 18th-century mansions are especially impressive.

Musée Carnavalet
22 rue de Sévigné, 75003 Paris, France
Tel: +33-1-42 72 21 13

MUSEE COGNACQ-JAY
Devoted to the 18th century and inaugurated in 1929, this museum was started by Ernest Cognacq, businessman, philanthropist, collector and founder of the Magasins de la Samaritaine. It is an intimate museum that reflects his wide range of interests, providing a 'lived-in' atmosphere in which to view fine paintings, furniture and Sèvres porcelain.

Musée Cognacq-Jay
8 rue Elzévir, 75003 Paris, France
Tel: +33-1-40 27 07 21

MUSEE DE LA CHASSE ET DE LA NATURE
The castle at Gien, approached by stepped alleys and rebuilt in 1484 by Anne de Beaujeau, provided shelter for Anne of Austria, young Louis XIV and Mazarin during the Fronde (1652). Since 1952, however, it has housed a hunting museum that includes early 17th-century tapestries and an impressive array of hunting horns and trophies.

Musée de la Chasse et de la Nature
60 rue des Archives, 75003 Paris, France
Tel: +33-1-42 72 86 43 Fax: +33-1-42 77 45 70

MUSEE DES ARTS FORAINS
An extraordinary collection of European fairground art is at the disposal of the happy few who are able to rent Jean-Paul Favand's magical museum for the evening. Better still, the Belle Epoque carousels and shooting galleries, some decorated by leading artists of the day such as Toulouse-Lautrec, are in perfect working order.

Musée des Arts Forains
53 avenue des Terroirs de France,
75012 Paris, France
Tel: +33-1-43 40 16 22

MUSEE EPHRUSSI-DE-ROTHSCHILD
The Villa Ephrussi was built by Béatrice de Rothschild on Cap Ferrat and today presents visitors with a pink Belle Epoque palace filled with 5,000 treasures as well as a themed garden of delights. It is a rare gem on the Côte d'Azur - a relic of the golden age of the Riviera set and their memorable *beaux gestes*.

Musée Ephrussi-de-Rothschild
06230 Saint-Jean-Cap-Ferrat, France
Tel: +33-4-93 01 45 90   Fax: +33-4-93 01 31 10

MUSEE GUSTAVE MOREAU
The atmospheric studio of Gustave Moreau holds the 18,000 paintings and drawings that the symbolist artist left to the state. A stunning spiral staircase leads to the upper floor where, in addition to Degas' 1876 *Portrait of the Artist*, Moreau's water-colours are exhibited in rotation and his drawings viewed in cases with moveable panels.

Musée Gustave Moreau
14 rue de la Rochefoucauld,
75009 Paris, France
Tel: +33-1-48 74 38 50

MUSEE JACQUEMART-ANDRÉ
This museum contains a remarkable collection of French 18th-century and Italian art in a superb setting (restored in 1996) with a delightful *salon du thé* in the former dining room, complete with Tiepelo fresco. The house was built in 1870 by Edouard André, who married the painter Nélie Jacquemart in 1881. She donated their collection to the Institut de France in 1912.

Musée Jacquemart-André
158 Boulevard Haussman, 75008 Paris, France
Tel: +33-1-42 89 04 91

MUSEE PICASSO
Picasso's collection - comprising his own work and that of the artists he admired - was received by the State in lieu of death duties and is a delight for lovers of contemporary art. Works are arranged chronologically to show Picasso's development from 1894 to 1972 and include his haunting Blue Period self portrait (1901), preparatory works for *Les Demoiselles d'Avignon* and, of course, portraits of the women in his life.

Musée Picasso
5 rue de Thorigny, 75003 Paris, France
Tel: +33-1-42 71 25 21

NATASHA
For those who are less fussy about their food than about the company they keep, this restaurant will fascinate. The faces of such celebrities as Mick Jagger, Giorgio Armani, Sean Penn and Naomi Campbell light up the rather subdued interior. The marvellous loft apartments in this street used to house some of Montparnasse's most famous artists.

Natasha
17 bis rue Campagne Premier,
75014 Paris, France
Tel: +33-1-43 20 79 27

THE NATIONAL GALLERY OF SCOTLAND
The gallery's flamboyant director, Tim Clifford, recently acquired one of Britain's most famous works of art, Canova's *The Three Graces*, which it now shares with the Victoria & Albert Museum. Housed in a spectacular temple in the centre of Edinburgh, the Gallery also owns outstanding works by Van Dyck, Tiepolo, El Greco, Bernini, Raphael, Titian, Rembrandt and Poussin, as well as many Scottish paintings.

The National Gallery of Scotland
The Mound, Belford Road,
Edinburgh EH2 2EL, Scotland
Tel: +44-131-624 6200   Fax: +44-131-220 0917

NAUTOR'S SWAN
Every vessel leaving this shipyard, just below the Arctic Circle, has a four-hundred-year heritage of craftsmanship instilled in its bows. The company, established in 1966 by Pekka Koskenkyla, is now run by Luciano Scarmuccia (ex-Perini Navi). Having built an unassailable reputation for semi-custom sailing yachts of 40-60 ft, Swan is, this year, constructing the first of a new line of 112ft craft.

Nautor's Swan
Oy Nautor Ab, P.O. Box 10,
Fin-68601, Pietarsaari, Finland
Tel: +358-6-760 1111   Fax: +358-6-766 7364

THE NATIONAL GALLERY OF IRELAND

The National Gallery of Ireland houses the collection of historic Irish art, and an impressive array of European Old Master paintings from the 14th to the 20th centuries. Great artists like Caravaggio, Poussin, Vermeer and Gainsborough are all represented.

Located on Merrion Square, Dublin's finest example of Georgian architecture, the National Gallery is contained within a series of buildings, which were reopened after an extensive refurbishment in 1996. The gallery will be further enlarged with a new 4,000 sq. metre extension on Clare Street, due to open in the year 2000.

Interest in modern Irish art is at an all-time high at the moment, with the country's booming economy producing a whole new class of culture-vulture. Jack B. Yeats, the current darling of the auction room, is particularly well-represented in the Gallery's collection. A special Yeats museum devoted to the creative genius of the Yeats family will open in Spring 1999. Other notable Irish artists, such as Hone, Orpen, Lavery and Osborne are also afforded ample space.

Under the supervision of Director Raymond Keaveney, the National Gallery of Ireland looks set to retain its prestigious reputation among the finest European art galleries.

The National Gallery of Ireland
Merrion Square (West), Dublin 2, Ireland
Tel: +353-1-661 5133   Fax: +353-1-661 5372
http://www.nationalgallery.ie

LA NAVA

Devotees of partridge-shooting flock to the exclusive preserve of La Nava. There, on a selected number of days each year, they can enjoy some of the finest sport in Spain with birds that are wild and reared naturally. The estate is set in hauntingly beautiful countryside, and the Medem family house offers traditional accommodation and old-fashioned hospitality to guns and their guests.

La Nava (near Almuradiel)
126 Bajo, 28006 Madrid, Spain
Tel: +34-915-64 57 30   Fax: +34-915-63 49 88

NEICHEL

Among Barcelona's many excellent restaurants, Evelyn and Jean-Louis Neichel's establishment is perhaps the finest. The simple, modern room, with its polished wooden chairs and beige walls is a perfect foil for Neichel's cooking - an innovative fusion of Mediterranean ingredients with classical French techniques. His Duck with chorizo is outstanding.

Restaurant Neichel
16bis Beltran i Rozpide, E-08034 Barcelona, Spain
Tel: +34-93-203 8408   Fax: +34-93-205 6339

NELAHOZEVES CASTLE

One of the most important Renaissance buildings in Bohemia, Nelahozeves Castle is home to the Roudnice-Lobkowicz family's splendid collection, which comprises literally thousands of works of art from the Renaissance to the late 1930s. Interestingly, the exhibition presents connections between the artists, family patrons and the works which they acquired. Some State Rooms may be hired for private parties.

Nelahozeves Castle
Roundnice-Lobkowicz Foundation,
Belehradska 77, 120 00 Prague 2, Czech Republic
Tel: +420-2-21 99 41 11 Fax: +420-2-21 99 41 12

NEW & LINGWOOD

For generations, Eton schoolboys - and those who want to look like old Etonians - have been buying their shirts here. Fabrics and styles are mostly traditional and the cut and construction faultless. As with all bespoke shirt-makers, it records its customers' details so that they may order shirts from anywhere in the world. Tom Wolfe gave this firm enthusiastic endorsement in *Bonfire of the Vanities*.

New & Lingwood
53 Jermyn Street, London SW1Y 6LX, UK
Tel: +44-171-493 9621   Fax: +44-171-499 3103

NICKY CLARKE

Booking Nicky Clarke is like trying to get a table at the hottest restaurants - nigh on impossible, unless you have connections. Currently the most widely recognised hairdresser in Britain, he learned his craft at the knee of the prototype celebrity crimper, Leonard. TV appearances, a range of hair products and a bevy of famous clients like Liz Hurley and the Duchess of York only add to his kudos.

Nicky Clarke
130 Mount Street,
London W1Y 5HA, UK
Tel: +44-17-491 4700   Fax: +44-171-491 9564

NICOLA RESTAURI

Fifty years ago Guido Nicola and his wife, Maria Rosa, began restoring paintings on canvas, board and frescoes. Since then, their children have joined them, along with 50 other restorers and conservators. As well as expanding its expertise to include sculpture, works on paper, frames and ancient Egyptian artefacts, the company is one of the few conservation laboratories able, at the request of the appropriate authorities, to remove frescoes from their original site.

Nicola Restauri
Via Santa Giulia 65, 10124 Turin, Italy
Tel/Fax: +39-011-812 2780

NIEPOORT

It's worth looking beyond the big names in port to this shipper. Niepoort's vintage wines easily bear comparison with the heavyweights of the trade and its Colheitas - vintage dated tawnies - are regarded by many as the best. Even their humblest wines have great concentration and definition of flavour - a welcome attribute in a world increasingly dominated by bland and soupy offerings at this level.

Niepoort (Vinhos) S.E
rue Infente D. Henrique 39-2-Ñ,
4000 Porto,
Portugal
Tel: +35-12-200 1028   Fax: +35-12-332 0209

NIGEL BURGESS

Under the direction of Jonathan Beckett and Daniel Ponchau, this firm specialises only in yachts of over 36 metres; its limited portfolio enables it to provide a highly personalised service. Yachts available for charter include *Kingdom* (ex-*Nabila* and *Trump Princess*), which the firm has managed through three successive owners. As European representative for Amels, it has placed, on behalf of clients, orders for four yachts (of 50 to 85 metres) at the Dutch yard in the last two years.

Nigel Burgess Ltd.
16-17 Pall Mall, London SW1Y 5LU, UK
Tel: +44-171-766 4300   Fax: +44-171-766 4329

NINA CAMPBELL

Having begun her decorating career as (in her own words) "official bag carrier for John Fowler at Colefax & Fowler", Nina Campbell has become the doyenne of English decorating. Nobody does the style better - whether in a New York penthouse, a Scottish castle, a Parisian hotel or a grand London house. With her sure sense of colour and beady eye for detail, Campbell's rooms have a no-nonsense ease, as if they have been lived in for a generation or more.

Nina Campbell
7 Milner Street, London SW3 2QA, UK
Tel:+44-171-225 1011 Fax:+44-171-225 0644

NOBILIS FONTAN

Founded in 1928, this distinguished house produces beautiful wallpapers and fabrics, inspired by a rich variety of decorative arts from Italy, Britain and the Orient. Lately, Nobilis has broadened its range of merchandise; the new lines of architect-designed furniture and tableware reflect the steadiness

NOEL

Table linen purists will be in safe hands with Noël, which has been supplying household linen to the aristocracy since 1883. Practically all the range is in white or pastel shades, and the delicate embroidery appears like freshly-cut flowers on the crisp tablecloths and napkins. Given Noël's rich legacy, it is not surprising that Adeline Dieudonné has changed little within the company since she took it over in 1992. She has, however, opened a baby wear department downstairs, filled with delightful embroidered outfits. In this light, soothingly decorated area you will also find that rarity for women: simple cotton or silk night gowns.

Boutique Noël
1 avenue Pierre 1er de Serbie, Place d'Iéna, 75116 Paris, France
Tel: +33-1-40 70 14 63

and sense of grandeur that its devotees have come to expect.

Nobilis Fontan
40 rue Bonaparte, 75006 Paris, France
Tel: +33-1-43 29 21 50   Fax: +33-1-43 29 77 57

NOBU

Regulars may grumble about the noise and stratospheric prices but that doesn't stop them from flocking to the British outpost of chef Nobuyuki Matsuhisa, and sometime-partner Robert De Niro's burgeoning empire, based in the über-chic Metropolitan Hotel. The Japanese-Peruvian fusion cooking (dishes include Hamachi sashimi with jalapeños) earned Nobu a Michelin star less than a year after opening.

Nobu
19 Old Park Lane, London W1Y 4LB, UK
Tel: +44-171-447 4747   Fax: +44-171-447 4749

NORLAND NANNIES

Unique in the world, Norland has been training the best nursery nurses since 1892. Norland graduates (many of whom come from smart families themselves) are in enormous demand all over the world. While many employers allow

their Norland-trained nannies to wear civilian clothes, some consider it so prestigious to have a Norland nanny that they insist on their wearing the distinctive beige uniform.

Norland Nannies
Denford Park, Hungerford,
Berkshire RG17 0PQ, UK
Tel: +44-1488-68 22 52   Fax: +44-1488-68 52 12

NOTRE-DAME DES OISEAUX

Birds still sing in the trees which surround this top-class private Catholic school, which has encouraged individuality in its pupils for 400 years. Ten years ago the school, which covers primary to secondary level and welcomes those of all religious persuasions, became co-educational. Standards are second to none; the pass rate for the baccalauréat is 95 per cent and most go on to higher education.

Notre-Dame des Oiseaux
12 rue Michel Ange, 75016 Paris, France
Tel: +33-1-42 88 02 52   Fax: +33-1-42 88 01 92

O'SULLIVAN ANTIQUES

Chantal O'Sullivan's unerring eye for the decorative (as well as the rare) has resulted in an eclectic collection of Irish treasures from the Georgian to the Edwardian periods; furniture and chimney-pieces sit side-by-side with garden furnishings and *objets d'art*. While her client list reads like an Irish who's who, O'Sullivan's strong American following influenced her decision to open a New York shop in 1998.

O'Sullivan Antiques

43-44 Francis Street,

Dublin 8, Ireland

Tel: +353-1-454 1143   Fax: +353-1-454 1156

THE OAK ROOM

Marco Pierre White's flagship restaurant allows you to experience his signature dishes in an opulent room, hung with artwork selected by the chef himself. White, who originally trained at Le Gavroche, justly deserves the many accolades which have been heaped upon him, for his brilliantly inventive interpretation of classical French cuisine.

The Oak Room – Marco Pierre White

Le Meridien, 21 Piccadilly,

London W1V 0BH, UK

Tel: +44-171-437 0202   Fax:+44-171-437 3574

OCEANCO

The young and dynamic Monégasque, Richard Hein, who founded Oceanco in the mid-Eighties, insists that passion and commitment are the determining factors in his company's success. Growing from a small yacht design consultancy, Oceanco now owns three Dutch shipyards (with eight motor yachts currently under construction) and has a significant presence in the US market.

Oceanco

Gildo Pastor Centre, 7 Rue du Gabian,

MC98000 Monaco

Tel: +377-93-10 02 81   Fax: +377-92-05 65 99

ODILE LECOIN

This beautician's facial treatments are unique in Paris. Her speciality is skin cleansing with aluminium crystals, a system developed in Italy and gaining ground in the US. The process is not only highly effective at lifting layers of dead cells and ground-in pollution, it gives the skin a glowing transparency. Her anti-wrinkle and cellulite treatments are entirely plant-based, as are the four lotions she uses for her famous body massages. Paloma Picasso has said that discovering Lecoin's treatments was "a revelation".

Odile Lecoin

75 avenue Paul Doumer,

75016 Paris, France

Tel: +33-1-45 04 91 85

ONE ALDWYCH

London's newest five-star hotel redefines the stylistic tenets of big-city luxury, finding the perfect, contemporary balance between over-stuffed brocade and self-conscious minimalism. The brainchild of its Managing Director and co-owner Gordon Campbell Gray, One Aldwych confirms the truth of his belief that "most so-called luxury is just superfluous trappings". Real luxury, he believes, comes from simple things being done perfectly and, above all, from perfect service. The latter isn't a problem, as most of his staff have come from London's grandest five-star establishments. The former is expressed in a pared-down elegance, complemented by countless works of art, chosen for aesthetic appeal rather than intrinsic value. "I don't understand the assumption," says Campbell Gray, "that people who are paying over £200 a night won't notice if the pictures on the wall have come from a catalogue." As well as the now-requisite state-of-the-art gym and stand-alone restaurant with star chef, the 105-room hotel boasts a private cinema (equally good for film screenings and business presentations) and an 18-metre swimming pool, complete with underwater music.

One Aldwych

London, WC2B 4BZ, UK

Tel: +44-171-300 1000   Fax: +44-171-300 1001

ODIOT

This gold and silversmith, established in 1690, is one of the rare workshops still hand-crafting cutlery by traditional methods. Its detailed Compiègne design commemorates a Louis XVI hunting trip in 1776; other styles include Nemours, a Second Empire baroque model, and a Directoire design called Potocki, with mouldings of threads fastened with acanthus.

Odiot

7 place de la Madeleine, 75008 Paris, France

Tel: +33-1-42 65 00 95   Fax: +33-1-42 66 49 12

OMAS

Omas is an increasingly sought-after name among collectors of limited edition writing

implements. The Chinese government commissioned the only pen authorised to sign official documents at the Hong Kong handover from Omas; the 'Return to the Motherland' pen, already highly coveted by collectors, is detailed with a repousée dragon in silver and gold.

Omas
9 rue Auber, 75009 Paris, France
Tel: +33-1-47 42 31 42   Fax: +33-1-49 24 90 57

OPERA MUSEO STIBBERT

This museum was founded by Frederick Stibbert (1838-1906), a wealthy collector who studied at Harrow and Cambridge, fought with Garibaldi and knew Queen Victoria. Stibbert spent his life travelling and collecting arms and armour, costumes, paintings, tapestries and porcelain; the museum he bequeathed to Florence retains the flavour of its 19th-century origins.

Opera Museo Stibbert
via Stibbert 26, 50134 Florence, Italy
Tel: +39-055-48 60 49

SAL. OPPENHEIM JR. & CIE.

Simon von Oppenheim wrote to his sons, 150 years ago, "Ein Bankhaus muß Prizipien haben, sonst geht es zu Grund." (A Bank has to have Principles, otherwise it will fall). Tradition, flexibility and a sense of quality and discretion continue to be the main virtues of this bank. The bank is still in the hands of the Oppenheim and Pferdmenges families and a couple of partners including former Bundesbank President, Karl-Otto Pöhl, all of whom are personally liable. Among the bank's areas of activity, the management of private assets is considered to be one of its great strengths.

Sal. Oppenheimer Jr. & Cie
Unter Sachsenhausen 4,
D-50667 Cologne,Germany
Tel: +49-221-14 501   Fax: +49-221-145 1512

THE ORIENTAL AT THE DORCHESTER

This restaurant - an architectural and decorative *tour de force* - is a perfect foil for the Michelin-starred Cantonese cooking of Kenneth Poon and his team. The main room floats on a mezzanine above a series of private dining areas, each decorated in jewel colours, according to different Eastern styles - Thai, Chinese and Indian.

The Oriental Restaurant
The Dorchester, Park Lane,
London W1A 2HJ, UK
Tel: +44-171-629 8888

ORLIK CASTLE

Under communism, this 9,700-hectare estate was the venue of choice for the apparatchiks' shooting orgies. In those days Husak, Ceaucescu, Honneker and Brezhnev came in search of pheasant, deer, hare, wild boar, stag and roebuck; today Karel Schwarzenberg's guests are more likely to be European crowned heads. The hunting lodge retains its 19th-century exterior but, having been seized by the state after WWII, it has all the hallmarks of communist décor; the 15 bedrooms, however, are cosy. (Note: as with all things Czech, you will need an assistant who speaks Czech or German.)

Orlik Castle
c/o Czech Forestry Administration
Tel: +420-362-84 11 16

L'ORTOLAN

John Burton-Race began thinking about becoming a chef as a child in Singapore; by the age of 26 he had his first Michelin star. He asserts that "taste is of the utmost importance, rather than prettiness of presentation". Nevertheless, the peach-toned dining room and conservatory of this former Georgian country vicarage are exceedingly pretty. The tastes are to die for, too.

L'Ortolan
The Old Vicarage, Church Lane, Shinfield,
Berkshire RG2 9BY, UK
Tel: +44-1189-88 37 83   Fax: +44-1189-88 53 91

PAÇO DA GLORIA

Once the country retreat of the King of Portugal's mistress, this majestic 18th-century mansion was bought ten years ago by a Portuguese antiquarian and collector of art and vintage cars, who has filled it with rare *objets d'art*. It is set in a small wine estate, which produces its own vinho verde.

Paço da Gloria, Northern Portugal
c/o Earth, 2 Durrand Gardens,
London SW4 OPP, UK
Tel: +44-171-793 9993   Fax: +44-171-793 9994

PALACIO DE CAMPO REAL

This 13th-century palace in the centre of old Jerez has been in the hands of the same family since the early 1600s and was declared a national monument in 1990. Available for private rental, the stunning accomodation surrounds a

Moorish courtyard and fountain; the rooms are vast - many with Renaissance architectural details - and the archive room contains museum-quality documents, dating back to 1264. The two gardens are every bit as beautiful as the interior.

Palacio de Campo Real, Jerez, Spain

c/o Blandings, The Barn, Musgrave Farm,
Horningsea Road, Fen Ditton,
Cambridge CB5 8SZ, UK
Tel: +44-1223-29 34 44   Fax: +44-1223-29 28 88

PALACE HOTEL, MADRID

Commissioned by King Alfonso XIII in 1912, the Palace Hotel sits right in the heart of Madrid, between the Parliament and the Prado. Following major restoration, the hotel's combination of monumental elegance and superb service make it unquestionably Madrid's finest. Its Royal Suite is stupendously grand.

Palace Hotel

Plaza de las Cortes 7, 28014 Madrid, Spain
Tel: +34-91-360 8000   Fax: +34-91-360 8100

PALAZZO SASSO

This property, built in the 12th century, with ravishing views of the Amalfi coast, became one of the most glamorous hotels of the 1950s, playing host to Bogart, Bergman, Rosselini and Garbo. Having fallen into semi-ruin in the 1980s, it has had $20million lavished on it by a new owner. Placido Domingo was the first guest to stay and Gore Vidal is a big fan.

Palazzo Sasso

Via San Giovanni del Toro 28,
84010 Ravello, Italy
Tel: +39-89-81 81 81   Fax: +39-89-85 89 00

PAOLO OLBI

The revival of *carta marmorata*, the marbled paper originated by the Turks and the Chinese was pioneered by Paolo Olbi, although, due to its commercialisation, he no longer makes it. Today, his loyal clients (including Bianca di Savoia-Aosta) come to him for notebooks and albums covered in calf-skin inlaid with glass and silver - a local craft from the Renaissance, which he has also revived.

Paolo Olbi

Calle della Mandola 3653, 30100 San Marco,
Venice, Italy
Tel: +39-41-528 50 25   Fax: +39-41-522 40 57

PAULO PEJRONE

That a gardener of such taste and knowledge as Marella Agnelli should choose Paolo Pejrone as her collaborator speaks volumes for the designer's qualities, both creative and human. Pejrone describes the creation of gardens as a philosophical rather than a physical exercise. Indeed, he admits to having turned down projects because "the feeling was not right". Past projects do, however, include the late Sir James Goldsmith's garden in Burgundy and all of the Aga Khan's hotels.

Paolo Pejrone

via san Leonardo 1, 12036 Ravello, Italy
Tel: +39-0175-25 19 58   Fax: +39-0175-25 72 65

PAOLO TEVERINI

The hotel which houses Paolo Teverini's intimate little restaurant has been in his family since the 17th century. In the 1920s Mussolini intended to stay there but his guards, who came to check it out in advance, decided that there were too many doors to watch. Teverini's signature dishes, inspired by his region's tradition, include fresh-water prawns and wonderful Potato tortellini with black truffles.

Paolo Teverini

via del Popolo 1, 47021 Forlì,
Bagno de Romagna, Italy
Tel: +39-0543-91 12 60   Fax: +39-0543-91 10 14

PAPE CLEMENT (CHATEAU)

Described by one leading wine writer as "a model of wine-making", Château Pape Clément bears the name of the man who founded it at the end of the 13th century. Owned today by Léo Montagne (whose family bought it in 1939) and the leading *négociant* Bernard Magrez, it produces around 160,000 bottles a year of robust, concentrated and full-bodied red wines.

The 1989 Pape Clément will be spot-on for drinking in 1999.

Château Pape Clément

216 avenue du Docteur Nancel-Pénard,
33602 Pessac, France
Tel: +33-5-57 26 38 38 Fax: +33-5-57 26 38 39

PARADOR HOSTAL DE LOS REYES CATOLICOS

A refuge for pilgrims in the late 15th century, this luxurious parador is considered to be one of the oldest hotels in the world. Its remarkable architecture is a living art-history lesson, tracing the Gothic, Renaissance and Baroque and includes four beautiful cloisters. Chef Daniel Durrala cooks traditional meat and fish dishes '*a la gallega*'.

Parador Hostal de los Reyes Catolicos

Pza. do Obradoiro,
E-15705 Santiago de Compostela, Spain
Tel: +34-981-58 22 00   Fax: +34-981 56 30 94

PARIS BAR

This is the Berlin insider's place to see and be seen. Relentlessly French, it satisfies the appetites of celebrities and artists with the obligatory *steack frites*, snails and oysters. Packed to the gills during the art or film festivals; Wim Wenders and Volker Schlondorf love it. The unspoken seating code would have them placed on the left, while the *arrivistes* are always led to the back of the room.

Paris Bar

152 Kantstraße, 10623 Berlin, Germany
Tel: +49-30-313 9052

PARTRIDGE FINE ART

Four generations after Frank Partridge founded the business in 1900, Partridge remains in family hands. Its speciality is finding pairs and sets of (often museum quality) furniture; clients often approach them with specific ideas or pieces in mind. Perhaps surprisingly for such a grand firm, it is not averse to gentle bargaining, as a female client recently discovered to her delight.

Partridge Fine Art

144-6 New Bond Street, London W1Y OLY, UK
Tel: +44-171-629 0834   Fax: +44-171-629 2292

PASCAL BARY

Bary's 1997 win in the French Derby (a race that he had previously won) confirmed his place among France's top-flight trainers. He worked originally under the late François Boutin and has inherited some of his owners, notably the Niarchos family and also trains for Chryss O'Reilly and Prince Abdullah. Regarded as

PATEK PHILIPPE

At one time it was cars which were the great status symbol but these days all it takes to gain kudos is a flick of the wrist. For the price of a Porsche, Patek Philippe offers timepieces which have been perfected through almost 150 years of Swiss watchmaking know-how. Of course, the company does have more humble models - the equivalent of a Renault Clio, for instance. No car manufacturer, however, can beat Patek Philippe for attention to detail; on average, it takes a year to make a single watch, including 800 hours of quality control.

The company was established in Geneva in 1839 by Antoine Norbert de Patek, originally from Poland, who went into partnership with the Frenchman Adrien Philippe soon afterwards. Philippe was the first person to create a keyless pocket watch, inventing a method of winding and setting timepieces by the crown instead of the key. In 1932 the company was bought by the Stern family of watchmakers, who still own it today. Patek Philippe continues to produce innovative mechanical watches, specialising in those with highly sophisticated complications. What makes its models particularly sought-after is that they are produced in such small numbers: 10-15 for the super deluxe models and 1,000 for its more commercial Nautilus Aquanaut sports watch.

Patek Philippe SA
Chemin du Pont du Centenaire, CH-1228 Plan Les Ouates, Geneva, Switzerland
Tel: +41-22-884 2020   Fax: +41-22-884 2040
15 New Bond Street, London W1Y 9PF, UK
Tel: +44-171-493 8866   Fax: +44-171-629 1673
Harrods, Knightsbridge, London SW1, UK

dynamic and an absolute perfectionist, Bary has about 120 horses in training at a time.
Pascal Bary
5 Chemin des Aigles, 60500 Chantilly, France
Tel: +33-3-44 57 14 03 Fax: +33-3-44 67 20 15

PASTICCERIA MARCHESI

Operating from the same Liberty-style premises since 1824, this *pasticceria* is always packed to the rafters with chic shoppers, who come for the best coffee in town. Served in beautifully fine porcelain cups, it is perfectly complemented by feather-light pastries.
Pasticceria Marchesi
Via Santa Maria alla Porta 11a,
20100 Milan, Italy
Tel: +39-02-87 67 30

PATRICK BARBE

These days Patrick Barbe, President of the French bloodstock agents' association (A.F.C.), does 90 per cent of his business with Japan - notably with the Yoshida family, for whom he has bought 'Arc' winners *Halissyo* and *Carroll House*. An owner as well as an agent (his wife Corrinne trains their 25 horses), some of Barbe's best deals have been on his own account; he bought *Deep Root* - subsequently champion French two- year-old - for 80,000 French francs at the 1982 Deauville sales.
Patrick Barbe
Mill Cotttage, 1 chemin des Aigles,
60500 Chantilly, France
Tel: +33-3-44 58 18 55   Fax: +33-3-44 58 18 25

PATRICK GUILBAUD

This elegant restaurant is currently Dublin's most fashionable - the bright and airy room is hung with a wonderful collection of contemporary Irish art. Guilbaud (and now his head chef) cook in a 'modern classical' French style, with a nod to nouvelle cuisine, using top-quality Irish ingredients. However, while Michelin has awarded the restaurant two stars, Ireland's leading restaurant directory, *The Bridgestone Guide*, has failed to list it, much to M. Guilbaud's horror.
Restaurant Patrick Guilbaud
Merrion Hotel, Upper Merrion Street,
Dublin 2, Ireland
Tel: +353-1-676 4192

PATRICK MICHEELS (DR.)

Dr. Micheels has built a devoted following among both men and women, thanks as much to his discreet and charming 'bedside manner' as to his highly skilled use of (largely) non-invasive treatments. His specialities include the remodelling of lips, the laser treatment of facial veins, hair transplants and the treatment of wrinkles - the latter using collagen and Botox, among other state-of-the-art techniques.
Dr. Patrick Micheels
58 rue de la Terrassière,
CH-1207 Geneva, Switzerland
Tel: +41-22-735 9116   Fax: +41-22-735 1734

PAUL HEATHCOTE'S RESTAURANT

Sir Cliff Richard and Robert de Niro are among those who have sampled Paul Heathcote's modern British cooking - notably his Goosnargh duckling and Roast suckling pig - and felt that the journey to Lancashire was worth the effort. Fans forgive the fussy decor and concentrate on savouring the chef's competent treatment of local ingredients.
Paul Heathcote's Restaurant
104-6 Higher Road, Longridge,
Preston PR3 3SY, UK
Tel: +44-1772-78 49 69

PAUL OLSEN TOBAKSBLANDERI

The Danes take the blending of their pipe tobacco very seriously indeed. Paul Olsen will spend hours, if necessary, to get a blend just right for his clients and keeps the recipes of all 35,000 of them on file. His impressive selection of pipes includes many hand-carved models.
Paul Olsen Tobakblenderi
Glomonce 4, 1117 Copenhagen K, Denmark
Tel: +45-33-14 09 22 Fax: +45-33-14 09 85

PAUL SMITH

In 1970 Paul Smith opened his first shop, operating two days a week; in 1976 he first showed his collection in Paris and, today, he has 20 shops in Europe (not to mention an empire in Japan), selling both men's and women's collections. His designs, inspired by traditional British menswear, are enlivened by his off-beat fabrics and colours, which instil character and wit into every piece.

Paul Smith
Westbourne House, 122 Kensington Park Road,
London W11 2EP, UK
Tel: +44-171-727 3553   Fax: +44-171-727 3847

PECK

Founded in 1933 by Czech-born Ferenc Peck, this is the spiritual home of Milan's smartest gourmets. It stocks an enormous range of top-quality comestibles, from lobster and fresh pasta to porcini and Parmigiano and its meat section contains the most awesome selection of salamis that you will ever see, anywhere.

Peck
Via Spadari 9, 20123 Milan, Italy
Tel: +39-02-86 08 42   Fax: +39-02-86 04 08

IL PELLICANO

This delicious cliffside hideaway on Italy's Argentario coast was founded in the 1960s by two dashing lovers in search of a perfect reclusive spot. Its privacy and effortless atmosphere have made it a popular retreat for the rich and famous. Take time out to laze in the salt water pool, indulge in thalassotherapy or brave water-skiing with the house boat.

Il Pellicano
58018 Porto Ercole, Italy
Tel: +39-0564-83 38 01   Fax: +39-0564-83 34 18

LA PENDULERIE

There is only one time to arrive at this extraordinary gallery: 12 noon, when the dozens of antique clocks that fill the premises start to chime. Christophe Guérin has unearthed all kinds of fine pieces from the 17th to the 19th centuries; his partners, Stéphane Gagnon and Benoît Redsand, restore his finds - hence the melody that greets visitors.

La Pendulerie
134 rue du Faubourg Saint Honoré,
75008 Paris, France
Tel: +33-1-45 61 44 55   Fax: +33-1-45 61 44 54

PENHALIGON'S

William Henry Penhaligon, barber to Queen Victoria's court, set up shop in St James's in the 1860s to supply perfumes, toilet waters and hair pomades to the smart clientele of the neigh-bouring Turkish Baths. Its distinguished line of fragrances (including Sir Winston Churchill's favourite, *Blenheim Bouquet*) has had a loyal following ever since.

Penhaligon's
16 Burlington Arcade, Picadilly,
London W1V 9AB, UK
Tel: +44-171-629 1416

PERLE DE PRAGUE (LA)

With its all-French crew, its gifted chef, Emmanuel Ruz, and its bold violet and green interior design, this is unquestionably Prague's smartest restaurant. Ruz' Foie gras nuggets and free-range chicken in candied ginger and lemon are to die for. The prices are as dizzying as the view from its perch on top of a tower.

La Perle de Prague
Rasinovo Nabrezi 80, Prague 2, Czech Republic
Tel: +420-2-21 98 41 60   Fax: 420-2-221 98 41 79

LA PENUELA

Renting this magnificent *Cortijo*, set on a 2,500-acre estate, will give you a taste of aristocratic Spanish life in the 18th century (albeit with every modern comfort). Coachmen will take you for picnics in the countryside in the collection of antique coaches, bulls are tested in the pri-

PERINI NAVI

A combination of technical brilliance and near-perfect aesthetics put Perini Navi's sailing yachts in a class of their own. Industrialist Fabio Perini, unable to find the boat that he wanted for himself - a large sailing yacht which could be handled by one person - built his own. Since its 1984 launch, the company has added 22 yachts, up to 58m in length, to its stable.

With over 65 per cent of the world market for sailing yachts over 45m, Perini Navi's track record is truly impressive; never before has a yacht builder come so far in such a short time. The reasons for its success? In-house design has allowed Perini to implement its own systems and inventions. All the sail controls are developed and manufactured by Perini Navi, as are the masts and rigging. Exclusive Perini software monitors the performance of the yacht under sail, relaying information via satellite connections back to the builder.

Yet, rather than just to its technological breakthroughs, Perini Navi owes its fame more to the quality of its construction, the perfect finish of its lavish, yet clean-lined interiors and the sheer comfort of its yachts, which have introduced an entirely new concept of sailing vessels.

Perini Navi
via Coppino 114, 55049 Viareggio, Italy
Tel: +39-0584-38 33 84   Fax: +39-0584-42 42 00

vate bull-ring, flamenco dancers will come to perform in the flamenco gallery and, for riding, there are Pure Spanish horses, which are bred on the estate.

La Peñuela, near Jerez, Spain
c/o Blandings, The Barn, Musgrave House,
Horningsea Road, Fen Ditton,
Cambridge CB5 8SZ, England
Tel: +44-1223-29 34 44 Fax: +44-1223-29 28 88

PERRIER-JOUET

In 1962, Pierre Ernst, then director of Perrier-Jouët, decided to recreate a bottle designed by the master craftsman Gallé in 1902. Since the Belle Epoque's launch, the cuvée has been a huge success. The Belle Epoque rosé, decorated with black anemones, is a marvellous treat; and the house's Blason de France label, whose wines have a surprising, original bouquet, is also top notch.

Perrier-Jouët
11 and 26 avenue de Champagne,
51200 Epernay, France
Telephone: +33-3-26 53 38 00

PETIT FLEUR

Since opening her shop in the mid-1970s, Inge Söffker has become the florist of choice among the Hamburg bourgeoisie, as well as providing flowers to the city's smartest offices and restaurants. Her bouquets are classical, tone-on-tone arrangements, with a little touch of magic.

Petit Fleur
Zimmer Straße 38, D-22085 Hamburg, Germany
Tel/Fax: +49-40-229 7439

PETROSSIAN

This is no ordinary caviar specialist; it is an institution. In the 1920s Christian Petrossian travelled to Russia to pick out the very best caviar from the ports on the Caspian Sea. Today, the family is equally strict about quality,

not only for caviar, but for its other specialities, too, such as smoked sturgeon and Norwegian salmon and Russian salmon eggs, all beautifully presented in the boutique's signature packaging.

Petrossian
18 boulevard de la Tour Maubourg,
75007 Paris, France
Tel: +33-1-44 11 32 22 Fax: +33-1-44 11 32 25

PETRUS (CHATEAU)

Thanks to the Americans, who discovered it in the 1950s, Madame Lacoste-Loubat and Jean-Pierre Moueix's Château Petrus has become the world's most famous red wine. Its exceptionally opulent, complex and velvety quality is due to brilliant winemaker Jean-Claude Berrouet, who still ferments it in a simple concrete vat, while his Bordeaux rivals employ ever more sophisticated techniques in their quest for perfection. The 1985 Petrus is the one to drink for the millennium.

Château Petrus
Jean-Pierre Moueix,
54 quai du Prieurat, 33500 Libourne, France
Tel: +33-5-57 51 93 66 Fax: +33-5-57 51 79 79

PEVERO GOLF CLUB

Although its golfing values have earned mixed reviews (in golf designer Tom Doak's words, "They spent a fortune grading the course through the rocky terrain, but if you're off the short grass you're still on the rocks.") there is no denying that this course, designed by Robert Trent Jones and built with the Aga Khan's money, has both outstanding views and top-drawer social cachet. Particularly during the summer, blue-chip Europeans vie for tee times with international jet-setters.

Pevero Golf Club
07020 Costa Smeralda, Sardinia, Italy
Tel +39-0789-96072 Fax +39-0789-96 572

PHILIP TREACY

Philip Treacy's cutting-edge millinery has graced the catwalks of Chanel and Valentino, as well as the heads of countless society ladies at Ascot. Every Treacy hat is a work of art, thanks to his extraordinary creativity, coupled with fine craftsmanship. Look out, too, for his accessories collection, including scarves, gloves and handbags, first launched in 1997. Treacy's constant companion, a Jack Russell terrier named Mr. Pig, stands sentinel over his London shop.

Philip Treacy
69 Elizabeth Street, London SW1W 9PJ, UK
Tel: +44-171-259 9605 Fax: +44-171-824 8559

PHILIPPE MODEL

Philippe Model's hats are pounced upon at the beginning of each season by France's most elegant women; indeed, the Prix Diane race meeting might just as well be his catwalk show. A pioneer in the world of *haute couture*, Model has diversified into accessories, adding gloves, shawls and shoes (for men) to his collection. Madonna is a big fan.

Philippe Model
33 Place du Marche Saint Honoré,
75001 Paris, France
Tel: +33-1-42 96 89 02 Fax: +33-1-40 20 05 11

S J PHILLIPS

S J Phillips was founded in 1869 by the son of a silversmith, great-grandfather of the current director. The gallery, run by four members of the Norton family, has fine displays of antique and Continental silver as well as *objets de vertu*, including an outstanding collection of 17th- to 19th-century gold boxes.

S J Phillips Ltd.
139 New Bond Street,
London W1A 3DL, UK
Tel: +44-171-629 6261 Fax: +44-171-495 6180

PICHON-LONGUEVILLE COMTESSE DE LALANDE (CHATEAU)

This is one of the two châteaux which were created from the original Pichon-Longueville property in 1850. Current owner, the imposing May Eliane de Lencquesaing, is the daughter of Edouard Miailhe, who bought Pichon-Comtesse in 1925. Their high merlot content makes these elegant and fruity wines more approachable than many Pauillacs and they are even good in lesser years. While the 1986 may still be slightly too young, the 1978 is superb for drinking this year.

Château Pichon-Longueville Comtesse de Lalande
33250 Pauillac, France
Tel: +33-5-56 59 10 40 Fax: +33-5-56 59 29 78

PIERINO PENATI

A family-run restaurant in the great Italian tradition, Pierino Penati is situated in a large country house, with a garden for summer dining and a huge vegetable patch which supplies the kitchen. Penati recreates the dishes eaten by the local Brianza gentry over the centuries, giving them a modern edge. Signor Penati's wife, Tiziana, their two sons, Theo and Ronnie, and daughter, Rovena, all work together in the restaurant.

Pierino Penati
via XXIV Maggio 36, 2260 Vigano, Italy
Tel: +39-039-95 60 20 Fax: +39-039-921 1400

PIAGET

Piaget began life in 1874 in the romantically-named village of La Côte-aux-Fées in the Swiss Jura. At first a manufacturer of watch movements, Piaget began to make a name for itself as a maker of 'jewellery' watches and ultra-thin watches (its most recent movement, calibre 500P, is one of the smallest automatic movements in existence).

There are very few Swiss watchmakers today which can, like Piaget, honestly claim to be genuine manufacturers, controlling every process that contributes to the creation of a watch, including all movements, cases and bracelets. In this way Piaget guarantees absolute control over its quality.

Today Piaget is recognised for its creativity; its most famous watches include the rectangular-shaped 'Protocole', with its distinctive *guilloché* work, and its feminine counterpart, 'Miss Protocole'. This contemporary styling has been carried over into the house's 'Possession' collection of sleekly wearable jewellery. A recent introduction (pictured) is the ultra-thin, square-faced men's hand-wound mechanical watch in 18-carat white gold.

Piaget International SA
61 route de Chêne, CH-1208 Geneva, Switzerland
Tel: +41-22-707 3232   Fax: +41-22-707 3888

PIERRE CELEYRON

If you have deep pockets, Pierre Celeyron can make dreams come true that you never knew you had. He is, quite simply, *the* party planner in Paris. From designing the invitations to blowing out the candles at the successful conclusion of yet another soirée, minute details are his forte. Working throughout Europe and occasionally America, Celeyron is an artist who vows never to do the same thing twice.

Pierre Celeyron
44 avenue Gabriel, 75008 Paris, France
Tel: +33-1-42 89 58 45   Fax: +33-1-42 89 58 48

PIERRE FREY

This family-run fabric house continues to draw its inspiration primarily from French decorative arts documents of the 18th- and 19th century, although it has an ever-growing line of contemporary designs; one of its most striking recent creations is a remarkably realistic zebra-skin fabric. In addition, sheets, duvet covers and cushions all come in the signature prints.

Pierre Frey
47 rue des Petit Champs, 75001 Paris, France
Tel: +33-1-42 97 44 00   Fax: +33-1-42 97 46 00

PIERRE GAGNAIRE

Pierre Gagnaire has really found his feet since moving from St Etienne to Paris. His outstanding, cult-status dishes include *Pigeon Gauthier cuit au sautoir, aux bâtons de cannelle, cotes de blettes terre de Sienne, à la fondue de ceps*. Fellow three Michelin-starred chef, Marc Meneau, describes Gagnaire's daring combinations of up to ten flavours in a single dish as, simply, "brilliant".

Pierre Gagnaire
6 rue Balzac,
75008 Paris, France
Tel: +33-1-44 35 18 25   Fax: +33-1-44 35 18 37

PIET OUDOLF

A true plantsman (the nursery that he runs with his wife Anja is one of Europe's best) Oudolf's prior training as an architect is evident in his use of space and structure. Having led the trend to use grasses and meadow plants in borders, he combines plants to look as stunning in winter as they are in summer, offset by evergreen topiary and tightly clipped hedges. However, if you would like Oudolf to work his magic on your plot, patience is the key; he is booked up years ahead.

Piet Oudolf
Broekstraat 17, 6999 De Hummelo,
The Netherlands
Tel: +31-314-38 11 20   Fax: +31-314-38 11 99

PIGUET & CIE S.A.

One of the oldest banks in Switzerland, Banque Piguet, established in 1856, is now part of Banque Cantonale Vaudoise, the country's fourth largest banking group. Tailor-made solutions are what President Pierre Dejardin bills as the company's greatest strength and its private banking division is rightly renowned as one of Europe's finest.

Banque Piguet & Cie S.A.
Rue du Rhône 100, CH-1204, Geneva,
Switzerland
Tel: +41-22-311 27 00   Fax: +41-22-311 26 80

PININ BRAMBILLA

For 40 years Dottoressa Pinin Brambilla has specialised in restoring paintings on canvas and wood, as well as frescoes. She studied under Pellicolli and is continuing his work on da Vinci's *Last Supper*. She has also restored Giotto's *Crucifixion* and numerous paintings by Caravaggio, Tiepolo and Titian. One of the senior restorers who works and studies under Dottoressa Brambilla insists that she "would not work with any other restorer in the whole world".

Dottoressa Pinin Brambilla
via Savona 43,
20144 Milan, Italy
Tel: +39-02-423 4350   Fax: +39-02-423 4350

PIPPA POP-INS

The whimsical name of this nursery-school-cum-children's hotel belies the seriousness of Pippa Deakin's approach to child care. Her excellent staff of trained nannies give pre-schoolers the most marvellous start in life and her unique, overnight hotel service (complete with bed-time stories, cuddly toys and 'midnight' feasts) is heaven for children aged up to 12. Be in early, though, if you would like your child to join the programme of school-holiday excursions; they get booked up well in advance.

Pippa Pop-Ins
430 Fulham Road, London SW6 1DU, UK
Tel: +44-171-385 2458   Fax: +44-171-385 5706

PITRIZZA (HOTEL)

This is exactly what you want of a hotel on the Costa Smeralda. The atmosphere is easy-going, you are sufficiently protected from the masses by a private jetty and beach, there is a wonderful granite sea-water swimming pool and the rustically-styled suites are cool and bright, with rough-stone balconies looking out over the bay.

Hotel Pitrizza
07020 Porto Cervo, Sardinia, Italy
Tel: +39-0789-93 01 11   Fax: +39-0789-93 06 11

POGGIO DEI MEDICI GOLF AND COUNTRY CLUB

This elegant club is a mecca for Florence's sophisticates and the expatriates who have villas nearby. The course, designed to PGA standards, offers some treacherous holes over hilly terrain and has everything that Tuscany should have: ravishing views of the countryside, a 16th-century castle and great food and wine at the club house.

Poggio dei Medici Golf & Country Club
via S. Gavino 27, 50038 Scarperia,
Florence, Italy
Tel: +39-55-843 04 36   Fax: +39-55-843 04 39

POLO CLUB DU DOMAINE DE CHANTILLY

Since it was established three years ago, under the auspices of Patrick Guerrand-Hermès, Chantilly has become *the* polo club in France. Located on a 150-hectare farm in the heart of France's racing community (its lovely, English-style stone club-house was once a farm building), it counts the sons and wives of several leading jockeys and trainers among the members of its polo school. The Rothschild children, too, play pony polo here. Key events are the Open de Paris in the spring, the biennial Coupe Hermès in September and the medium-goal Trophée de Coquedier d'Or in July, a tournament established by Guerrand-Hermès in memory of his late son, Lionel.

Polo Club du Domaine de Chantilly
La Ferme d'Apremont, 60300 Apremont, France
Tel: +33-3-44 64 04 30   Fax: +33-3-44 64 04 32

POLO DE DEAUVILLE

August is the key time to be here, when many of the top players decamp to France at the end of the English season (Deauville, in fact, is in full 'horse mode' this month, with racing and the bloodstock sales also on). The style is relaxed, as may be expected when *le tout Paris* is on holiday.

Polo de Deauville
45 avenue Hocquart de Turlot,
14800 Deauville, France
Tel: +33-2-31 98 95 34

PLAZA ATHENEE

The publicity for this grand establishment insists that "the Plaza is not just a hotel, it's a way of life". Unlike many such self-trumpeting claims the statement is entirely accurate. Hervé Houdré, who became General Manager in 1995, is a priceless hotelier - warm, witty and wise - whose competence is confirmed by legions of grateful guests from around the globe. And his product is truly remarkable; quiet, beautiful and distinguished, it serves as an archetype for mid-size hotels throughout Europe.

Situated on the fashionable Avenue Montaigne, with its plethora of designer shops, the hotel offers elegant, comfortable accommodation and discreet service. Executive chef Eric Briffard, a disciple of Joël Robuchon, is fast acquiring a reputation as a leading light in French haute cuisine. If you have a weakness for celebrity-spotting, take tea in winter in the sumptuous Gobelins gallery or on the ivy-covered terrace in summer. You will also find famous *habitués* of the hotel crammed into the Scottish bar in the basement.

In March of 1997 the hotel was bought by the Royal family of Brunei, which has signalled its intention to completely renovate the property without detracting from its unique ambience.

Hotel Plaza Athénée
25 Avenue Montaigne, 75008 Paris, France
Tel: +33-1-53 67 66 65   Fax: +33-1-53 67 66 66

PORTHAULT

World-famous for its embroidered table linens, this rambling boutique also offers covetable crisp bed linen, towels and bathrobes. It's a shop you can walk around at leisure; don't miss the fetching negligées on the first floor and the framed letter from Forties' author Louise de Vilmorinho, describing poetically why she could not do without Porthault.

Porthault
18 avenue Montaigne, 75008 Paris, France
Tel: +33-1-47 20 75 25   Fax: +33-1-40 70 09 26

PORTMARNOCK GOLF CLUB

Portmarnock is a rugged and unforgiving links course, hewn into a stretch of land jutting out into the Irish Sea. Nature, rather than design, has moulded it into a great golfing challenge. Its famously gruelling finishing strait includes the notorious par-3 15th, rated one of the world's finest short holes. Befriend a member if you want to join the cream of Dublin society in the clubhouse.

Portmarnock Golf Club

Co. Dublin, Ireland

Tel: +353-1-846 2968 Fax: +353-1-846 2601

LA POSTA VECCHIA

John Paul Getty spent the best part of the Sixties renovating this 17th-century villa. Today, a private museum houses the objects found in the building's subterranean chambers. The museum, along with a private beach and a heliport, are just some of La Posta Vecchia's jewels. Only a 40-minute drive from Rome, it is a valued retreat for business and diplomatic meetings.

La Posta Vecchia,

Loc. Palo Laziale, 00055 Ladispoli, Italy

Tel: +39-06-994 9501 Fax: +39-06-994 9507

PRADA

This old-established family company was reinvented in the 1980s by Miuccia Prada, the politically-minded younger daughter. She brought a progressive eye to bear on the house's signature bags - and added a fashion-forward range of covetable clothes, which have been fêted by the world's press.

Prada

60-65 Galleria Vittorio Emanuele,

20121 Milan, Italy

Tel: +39-02-87 69 79 Fax: +39-02-72 00 21 85

PRAGUE SPRING FESTIVAL

In recent years The London Philharmonic, L'Orchestre de Paris and The Vienna Philharmonic have all played here but, probably, the best reason to attend is the opportunity to hear the work of Dvorak, Smetana and Janacek in such splendid venues as Prague Castle's Spanish Hall, St Vitus' Cathedral and the recently restored, Art Nouveau Obecní Dum. Devotees include Vaclav Havel and the country's aristocracy (Schwarzenbergs, Kinskys and Lobkowiczes).

The Prague Spring Festival

Box Office, Hellichova 18, 118 00 Prague 1, Czech Republic

Tel: +420-2-53 02 93 Fax: +420-2-53 60 40

POMMERY

Behind the imposing wrought-iron gates of Pommery's estate in Reims, neo-gothic and Elizabethan towers rise up around the extensive grounds. Madame Pommery's choice of architecture was apparently a tribute to her loyal British clients.

In 1858 she had inherited a small company from her husband, selling wines from the region. Soon she was buying vineyards in the finest areas of Champagne. Today Pommery has 300 hectares of vineyards, spread over an area which includes seven villages rated at 100 per cent, the highest grade in the official Champagne grape scale.

In 1874, sensing a demand for drier wines, Madame Pommery produced the first Brut champagne, Pommery Nature, which received a rapturous welcome, particularly from across the Channel. For 25 years, Prince Alain de Polignac, her great, great grandson, has been honing to perfection the champagne's distinctive style: fresh and light with a discreet bouquet and balanced body.

For Pommery president, Jean-Marie Lefevre, the estate's folly-like appearance above ground and cathedral-style atmosphere in the 18 kilometres of chalk cellars below, sum up the double identity of the estate: "unconventional and free-thinking - but also committed to preserving its great heritage". Given its superb Louise Pommery Rosé 1980, the house is doing just fine.

Pommery

5 Place du Général Gouraud, 51053 Reims, France

Tel: +33-3-26 61 62 63 Fax: +33-3-26 61 62 99

PRATESI

Now in the hands of the fourth generation of the Pratesi family, this company produces some of the world's most covetable household linens. Every two years it issues a new 'fantasy' collection to complement its classic lines; the latter can be made to order in special colours and measurements. Pratesi also makes charming baby layettes and delicious room scents.

Pratesi

via Montenapoleone 27E,

20121 Milan, Italy

Tel: +39-02-76 01 27 55 Fax: +39-02-78 35 74

PRATT'S

William Nathaniel Pratt was the seventh Duke of Beaufort's steward and the Duke's habit of dropping off at Pratt's rooming house in Park Place with friends for an informal kitchen supper led to the dining club that exists today. Under the ownership of the current Duke of Devonshire, the basement is still the nucleus of Pratt's, where the 600 or so members dine side by side. Eccentrically, all the staff are called George.

Pratt's

14 Park Place, London SW1A 1LP, UK

Tel: +44-171-493 0397

PORZELLAN-MANUFAKTUR NYMPHENBURG

Unmistakable to the cognoscenti, Nymphenburg's works are drawn from 30,000 historical archive designs, which include animal sculptures, Art Nouveau vases, Empire services and Rococo Commedia dell'Arte figures by sculptor Bustelli. Produced at a romantic villa

situated opposite the Bavarian King's summer castle, every single piece is thrown, shaped and painted by hand. Founded in 1747, the company has produced an uninterrupted succession of treasures. The craftsmanship is quite breathtaking; details are modelled free-hand and added, for instance, blossom by blossom on the lid of a tureen, or leaf by leaf on hedges and trees.

Porzellan-Manufaktur Nymphenburg
8 Nördliches Schlossrondell 8,
D-80638 Munich, Germany
Tel: +49-89-179 1970   Fax: +49-89-17 91 97 50

LES PRES ET LES SOURCES D'EUGENIE

As Catherine Deneuve and Isabelle Adjani will testify, this is a retreat second to none. The secret, it seems, is that everyone is treated as a house guest rather than a paying customer. Virtuoso chefs Christine and Michel Guérard blend exotic spices with herbs and vegetables from the garden to create their sublime *cuisine minceur*.

Les Pres et Les Sources d'Eugénie
40320 Eugénie-Les-Bains, France
Tel: +33-05-58 05 06 07   Fax: +33-05-58 51 10 10

PRINCIPE DI SAVOIA (HOTEL)

A grand palazzo with chandeliers, wood panelling and acres of marble, all expensively refurbished, this hotel is very much of the old school, with efficient service and above-par food. Its star attraction is the Presidential suite, 490 square metres of exceptional luxury, where both Sophia Loren and Woody Allen have stayed.

Hotel Principe di Savoia
Piazza del Repubblica 17, 20124 Milan, Italy
Tel: +39-02-62 301   Fax: +39-02-659 5838

PRINCIPE DE SAVOIA - CLUB 10

Ostensibly a service for guests staying in the Hotel Principe de Savoia, Club 10 also has 60 'outside' members (Diego Della Valle among them). There is, of course, a huge waiting list to join. The pool and its wraparound sun deck, with breathtaking views over Milan, is where you'll find the best bodies.

Club 10
Hotel Principe de Savoia,
Piazza del Repubblica 17,
20124 Milan, Italy
Tel: +39-02-62 301   Fax: +39-02-659 5838

PRIVATAIR

Absolutely incommunicado on the subject of

his clients, Chief of Cabin Services, Victor Grove, stops at nothing to ensure that their needs are met. Operating for over 15 years, with a security and safety record second to none, PrivatAir has its own terminal at Geneva and owns the first Boeing 737-300 available for hire on the continent.

PrivatAir
33 Chemin de l'Avanchet,
CH-1216 Cointrin-Geneva, Switzerland
Tel: +41-22-929 6750   Fax: +41-22-929 6701

PROFESSIONAL SECURITY

Electrical engineers Gianni and Roberto Fagnoni design and set up sophisticated security systems for both properties and people. The brothers have worked throughout the world and Gianni has the distinction of launching the first active anti-burglary smoke screen. Their motto, like the product, is devastating but simple: "What you cannot see, you cannot steal."

Professional Security
Via Ghibellina, 69 Florence 50122, Italy
Tel: +39-055-24 15 06   Fax: +39-055-24 15 62

PROSE

Prose's bodyguards have special police clearance, in order that they can watch over vulnerable public figures wherever they might be. They are highly trained in evasive and defensive driving, combat shooting and anti-kidnap protection techniques - some to the benchmark Israeli Army standard. At the same time, all men are regularly monitored, both medically and psychologically, to ensure peak performance.

Prose S.A.
Calle Lezama 4, 27435 Madrid, Spain
Tel: +34-91-729 1961   Fax: +34-91-631 0105

PUIFORCAT

Stepping inside this renowned silverware shop is as stimulating as visiting an art gallery. The products range from tea services and soup tureens to pitchers, napkin rings and decorative objects. The re-edited Jean Puiforcat pieces of the 1930s, with their dense, sculptural forms, are particularly beautiful. The company is now controlled by Hermès.

Puiforcat
2 avenue Matignon, 75008 Paris, France
Tel: +33-1-45 63 10 10   Fax: +33-1-42 56 27 15

PULBROOK & GOULD

London's grandest florist was founded by Lady Susan Pulbrook and Rosamund Gould over 40 years ago. The house style - exuberant, loosely arranged bouquets and country-inspired arrangements - is reminiscent of Constance Spry (where Miss Gould trained).

The shop has a marvellous stock of scented candles and small garden ornaments and Lady Pulbrook runs a very select flower school.

Pulbrook & Gould
Liscartan House, 127 Sloane Street,
London SW1X 9AS, UK
Tel: +44-171-730 0030   Fax: +44-171-730 0722

PULLMAN GALLERY
Former stockbroker Simon Khachadourian has been passionate about Art Nouveau and Art Deco since his school days. His recently opened gallery is a marvellous source of objects from the great luxury goods makers of the late 19th- and early 20th centuries. Cocktail shakers, cigar boxes, lighters, fine luggage and even Lalique car mascots are among the treasures on display.

Pullman Gallery
14 King Street, St. James's,
London SW1Y 6QU, UK
Tel: +44-171-930 9595   Fax: +44-171-930 9494

PUPI SOLARI
Upper-crust Milanese ladies beat a path to Pupi's door to dress their children in the most exquisite, hand-made classical clothes and themselves in discreetly tailored suits and beautifully crafted hats. Pupi's son, Andrea Host, reigns over a stylish menswear shop next door.

Pupi Solari
Piazza Tommaseo 2, 20145 Milan, Italy
Tel: +39-02-46 33 25 Fax: +39-02-481 9210

THE PUSHKIN MUSEUM
This museum houses the remarkable collection of Impressionist paintings which was assembled before the Revolution by Ivan Morozov and Sergei Shchukin, two wealthy Moscow merchants. There are works by all the greats: Monet, Renoir, Cézanne, Degas, Matisse and Chagall among them. Less well known but equally fascinating are the museum's vast collections of Byzantine, Gothic and Flemish art.

The Pushkin Museum of Fine Art
12 Volkhonka Ulitsa, 101000 Moscow, Russia
Tel: +7-095-203 9578

QUARTIER 206

Quartier 206 is a 27,000-square-foot shrine to style on Berlin's Friedrichstraße. Although the store opened only last year, it has already established a reputation as Germany's most cutting-edge retailer. Whether you want precious antiques, classic scents, Havana cigars or Manolo Blahnik's legendary stilettos, Quartier 206 is an aesthetes' delight masquerading as a clothes shop.

Quartier 206
Friedrichstraße 71, D-10117 Berlin, Germany
Tel: +49-30-20 94 68 00   Fax: +49-30-20 94 68 10

QUINZI E GABRIELLI
The magnificent display of seafood that greets you upon entering and the bright, aquamarine walls set the stage for the treats to come in Enrico Gabrielli's simply decorated restaurant, set in an historic building near the Parthenon.

From his kitchen, Gregorio Ramaglia produces outstandingly fresh fish dishes, including a sublime Carpaccio of sea bass and possibly the best Spaghetti with lobster that you will ever eat. Clients are a lively mix of business people, stylish Romans and international celebrities (while filming at Cinecittà, Sylvester Stallone could often be found here in the evening) and the small tables add to the buzz.

Quinzi E Gabrielli
Via delle Coppelle 5-6, 00186 Rome, Italy
Tel: +39-06-687 9389   Fax: +39-06-687 4940

RACO DE CAN FABES (EL)

Within a very short time of opening his restaurant in his family's former country home, Santi Santamaria was being hailed as one of the greats of his profession. His style is a very personal interpretation of traditional, largely Catalan, dishes, such as Cod tripe with butefarra nera and Braised vegetables with truffles and ceps. The cellar is impressively structured and Maria Angels, Santi's wife, a very welcoming hostess.

El Raco de Can Fabes
Sant Joan 6, Sant Celoni, E-08080 Barcelona, Spain
Tel: +34-93-867 28 51   Fax: +34-93-867 2851

RADI DI MONTAGNA

Six hundred years ago, this medieval hilltop settlement was abandoned after its owners led an unsuccessful rebellion against Siena. It lay untouched until an American couple, keen collectors of early Italian art, stumbled across it and fell in love with this perfectly preserved piece of Sienese history, surrounded by olive groves, woods and vineyards. But, perhaps even more breathtaking than the views which the Radi commands, are the lengths to which the owners have gone to transform the site into a luxurious place to stay. The entire hamlet can be rented as a whole or its houses rented individually.

Radi di Montagna, near Siena, Italy
c/o Villas and Apartments Abroad
420 Madison Ave, New York, NY 10017, USA
Tel: +1-212-759 1025   Fax: +1-212-755 8316

RAIMONDO BIANCHI

This gifted florist has a penchant for the unique and the original. Nature provides him with the raw materials and his humour and spontaneity make for floral arrangements that are often more *objet d'art* than bunch of flowers: a bouquet of roses surrounded by tree branches or wild flowers with nettles, for instance.

Raimondo Bianchi
via Montebello 7, Milan, Italy
Tel: +39-02-655 5108

RAVASI

Piero Castellini is just one of the top interior designers who comes to this upholsterer when he needs a precious antique restored. Gabriella Ravasi and Guido Lamperti are as happy to tackle a Bauhaus icon as they are to revive an early Renaissance sofa - always with brilliant results.

Ravasi
via Como 34, 23807 Merate, Italy
Tel: +39-039-59 93 97

RAVENEAU (DOMAINE)

You will have to join a waiting list (or find a very well-connected merchant) to buy Jean-Marie and Bernard Raveneau's full-flavoured chablis. They give equal value to the fruit and to the mineral composition of the soil from which they come, resulting in wines which gain in stature as they age (five years for *premiers crus* and ten for *grands crus*). Best drinking for 1999 is their chablis Grand Cru Valmur, 1990.

Domaine Raveneau
9 rue de Chichée, 89800 Chablis, France
Tel: +33-3-86 42 17 46   Fax: +33-3-86 42 45 55

RELAIS DE JARDIN

Possibly Rome's most romantic restaurant, this gem is hidden away in Amadeo Ottaviani's chic little Lord Byron hotel, in leafy Parioli. The décor of white lattice and chintz is complemented by masses of flowers. Luigi Sforzellini makes a plebian dish such as Beans and clams into an elegant treat and his Risotto with pheasant, asparagus and black truffles is a dream.

Relais de Jardin
Hotel Lord Byron, via G. de Notaris 5,
00197 Rome, Italy
Tel: +39-06-361 3041   Fax: +39-06-322 0405

RELILAX CLUB

Fifteen kilometres from Padua, at the foot of the Euganian Hills, the Braggion family's hotel is home to a 1,000-year-old spa and the thoroughly modern-minded Relilax Club - the oldest

RAFAEL (HOTEL)

In 1989, following an illustrious career which took him to the very top of the Regent Hotels group, George Rafael realised his dream of creating his own hotel. This Munich gem, set on a quiet street in the heart of Old Munich, is the result.

It has all the luxuries and services of a grand hotel - yet on an intimate scale. The interiors are light and contemporary, yet utterly luxurious; inlaid marble floors and fruit-wood panelling are offset by clean-lined furniture and rich fabrics. Remarkably beautiful flower arrangements add a touch of drama. One of the hotel's great glories is its bathrooms, done out in Portuguese marble; some even allow a view of the skyline while you laze in the tub. The real highlight in summer, however, is the heated infinity pool on the roof, whose water seems to spill over into the view of Munich's church spires.

Hotel Rafael
Neuturmstraße 1, D-80331 Munich, Germany
Tel: +49-89-29 09 80   Fax: +49-89-22 25 39

and largest of its kind in Italy. Take time out to enjoy over 50 treatments, in a watery paradise of grottos and baths.

Relilax Club-Hotel Terme Miramonti
Piazza Romas 19,
35036 Montegrotto Terme, Padua, Italy
Tel: +39-49-891 1755   Fax: +39-49-891 1678

REM KOOLHAAS
Described by Architectural Digest as being "perhaps the world's most astonishing architect", Rem Koolhaas creates remarkably bold and uncompromisingly modern buildings in concrete, glass and steel. His latest work to be completed is an extraordinary house in Bordeaux.

Rem Koolhaas
Office for Metropolitan Architecture,
Heer Bokelweg 149, 3032 AD Rotterdam,
The Netherlands
Tel: +31-10-243 8200   Fax: +31-10-243 8202

REMY MARTIN
To ensure the quality of its premium blends, Rémy Martin's sister company, Séguin-Moreau, supplies it with barrels, nearly all made from Limousin oak; brandies may rest in them for 30 years - or longer, for the top-of-the-range Louis XIII. It is simply delicious, with a multi-dimensional, yet beautifully integrated, flavour.

Rémy Martin
rue Société Vinicole, BP 37,
15112 Cognac Cedex, France
Tel: +33-5-45 35 76 00   Fax: +33-5-45 35 02 85

RENA LANGE

LA RESERVE DE BEAULIEU
Situated right on the water's edge between Nice and Monte Carlo, this Italian Renaissance-style villa was restored to its former pink-coated splendour in 1994 by owners Jean-Claude and Nicole Delion. This Relais & Châteaux property's 27 rooms and ten suites all have stunning sea views and combine a traditional ambience with the very best modern facilities. Whether you slip in and out of La Réserve's private port on a speedboat or spend your time relaxing by the large swimming pool which hovers above the sea, you could easily imagine yourself on the Côte d'Azur of the Thirties, when F. Scott Fitzgerald wrote in such lyrical terms about its seductive powers. Just as breathtaking as the stunning seascape is La Réserve's ornate dining room, once referred to as "the restaurant of kings and the king of restaurants". Christophe Cussac, the hotel's 43-year-old Michelin-starred chef, has devised a radiant menu which varies with the season, the fishing and the fresh market produce available. Added to that, the hotel has an impressive wine cellar presided over by the immensely knowledgeable Jean-Louis Valla. For those who feel

La Réserve de Beaulieu

up to taking in a little culture during their stay, the treasure-filled Ephrussi de Rothschild Foundation and the Villa Kerylos museum in neighbouring Cap Ferrat are well worth a visit.

La Réserve de Beaulieu
5 boulevard du General-Leclerc, 06310 Beaulieu-sur-Mer, France
Tel: +33-4-93 01 00 01 Fax: +33-4-93 01 28 99
Internet: http://www.webstore.fr/la-reserve   Email: reserve@webstore.fr

Tall and willowy, designer Renate Gunthert is married to Peter Gunthert, CEO of M. Lange & Co. Together they manufacture and market the recherché, elegant clothes worn by discerning women with the same style and outlook as Renate herself. If Coco Chanel were alive and designing in Germany, these are the kind of pieces she might have been creating.

Rena Lange
Rosenheimer Strasse 139, D-81671 Munich, Germany
Tel: +49-89-41 86 61 12   Fax: +49-89-49 18 48

RENE CAOVILLA
Self-proclaimed 'Laboratorio Artistico', shoe-maker René Caovilla makes some of the world's most sexy and feminine shoes. Each is considered a work of art; only the finest leather and silk is used, together with pearls and other decorative flourishes sourced from the best suppliers in Venice and Paris. Fans include Caroline of Monaco, Elizabeth Taylor and Ornella Muti.

René Caovilla
via Paradisi 1, 30032 Fiesso D'Artico, Venice, Italy
Tel: +39-049-980 1300   Fax: +39-049-980 1315

LA RESIDENCIA
Two manor houses, dating from the 16th- and 17th century, were converted to create this hotel. Richard Branson purchased it in 1987 and undertook major refurbishment, designed

RESIDENCE DE LA PINEDE

Away from the madding crowd, yet only a minute from the waterfront of St Tropez, this Relais & Châteaux property is like having your own private villa in the heart of this superstars' playground - yes, the town still manages to work its old magic on such celebrities as Clint Eastwood and Tom Cruise, while Brigitte Bardot has remained a relentless habituée since the Sixties.

The stately, cream-coloured property, situated in wooded grounds with its own private beach, was snapped up by Jean-Claude and Nicole Delion (owners of La Réserve de Beaulieu) while they were

on holiday in St Tropez in 1985. Since then the couple have been perfecting the hotel's most captivating qualities: luxury trappings, a peaceful ambience and attentive service. They offer 39 bedrooms and five lavish suites, all impeccably decorated and with beautiful marble bathrooms. If you eschew St Tropez' frenetic nightclubbing, the hotel's chefs, Hervé Quesnel (Michelin-starred) and Thierry Paludeto, will prepare intimate dinners for you, including such delicacies as Truffle ravioli in a wild mushroom sauce and Fresh fig tart. Afterwards, would-be yacht owners can retire onto their balcony and pretend they are on the bridge of their cruiser, gazing out onto the endlessly enchanting St Tropez peninsula.

Résidence de le Pinède
Plage de la Bouillabaise, B.P. 74, 83990 St Tropez, France
Tel: +33-4-94 55 91 00   Fax: +33-4-94 97 73 64
Internet: http://www.webstore.fr/la-pinede   Email: pinede@webstore.fr

in Mallorcan style by Axel Ball. It now boasts an art gallery, a beauty salon, two superb restaurants and 30 acres of landscaped gardens. There is also a shuttle service to the private beach.

Hotel La Residencia
Deia, 07179 Mallorca, Spain
Tel: +34-971-63 90 11   Fax: +34-971-63 93 70

RESIDENZ HEINZ WINKLER

There has been an inn at this site, at the foot of the Bavarian Alps, since 1405. Here, Heinz Winkler, who once cooked at the celebrated Tantris in Munich, produces his own delicately-wrought version of traditional German cooking in dishes such as Venison in a salt crust with celeriac mousseline. He also runs cookery classes for the fortunate few.

Residenz Heinz Winkler
1 Kirchplatz, D-83229 Aschau im Chiemgau, Germany
Tel: +49-8052-17 990   Fax: +49-8052-17 99 66

RESTAURANT DIETER MULLER

The son of hoteliers, Dieter Müller began cooking as a child and, following 17 distinguished years at the Schweizer Stuben, came here in 1992. His extensive travels are reflected in his restrained use of Asian herbs and spices and his inspired interpretation of French classics, such as Stuffed pig's trotters and Foie gras with lentils and balsamic vinegar. The glass-walled dining room opens onto lovely gardens.

Restaurant Dieter Müller
Schloßhotel Lerbach, Lerbacher Weg, D-51465 Bergisch Gladbach, Germany
Tel: +49-2202-2040   Fax: +49-2202-20 49 40

RESTAURANT GIRARDET - PHILIPPE ROCHAT

When the legendary Freddy Girardet retired a couple of years ago, he handed over the reins here to his "best pupil", the young Philippe Rochat. It's a tough act to follow but Rochat is filling the master's shoes admirably. The simply decorated room is a perfect foil for such *tours de force* as his *Chartreuse de pointes d'asperges aux morilles à la fricassée de grenouilles.*

Restaurant Girardet
1 rue d'Yverdon, CH-1023 Crissier, Switzerland
Tel: +41-21-634 05 05   Fax: +41-21-634 24 64

RHODE SCHOOL OF CUISINE

The Rhode School offers week-long spring and summer courses in two charming villas - one in Tuscany and the other on the Côte d'Azur. Professional, native chefs instruct students in the art of French and Italian (principally Tuscan) cookery. Classes are small (a maximum class of seven in France, and 15 in Italy) which makes for a real 'hands-on' experience.

Rhode School of Cuisine
c/o CBB, 25 Boulevard Hélvetique, CH-1207 Geneva, Switzerland
Tel: +41-22-736 7878   Fax: +41-22-736 7919

RICHARD COUTANCEAU

Masterpieces of Richard Coutanceau's seafood menu include *Homard breton à la coque ou en millefeuille* and *Bar de ligne roti sur sa peau croustillée au parfum de basilic et à la tomate confite.* Food is served in up-to-date surroundings (bunker-like from the outside but very comfortable within), complemented by a well-stocked cellar, which includes such rarities as a 19-year-old Pineau blanc.

Restaurant Richard Coutanceau
Plage de la Concurrence, 17000 La Rochelle, France
Tel: +33-5-46 41 48 19   Fax: +33-5-46 41 99 45

RICHARD GINORI 1735

When the Marquis Carlo Ginori started manufacturing in 1735, with the aim of creating porcelains to rival those produced in the Orient, the secret of making porcelain had been discovered in Europe (in Meissen) only 25 years before. The original Ginori designs were produced in traditional reds and blues and, by the 1740s and '50s, the tulip, cockerel and flower decorations which founded the line and still help to sustain it today, were made.

Richard Ginori 1735
via Giulio Cesare 21, 50019 Florence, Italy
Tel: +39-055-42 04 91   Fax: +39-055-420 4954

RICHARD GREEN

The son of an art dealer, Richard Green set up on his own before he was 20. Now he has three separate galleries in Mayfair and a stock of over 3,000 pictures. Green attributes his success to a passion for paintings, a good eye (he never misses a 'sleeper') and hard work. His two siblings and four children also work in the business.

Richard Green
147 New Bond Street, London W1Y 9PE, UK
Tel:+44-171-493 3939   Fax:+44-171-629 2609

LE RICHEMOND

With both the exclusivity of a private members club and the spellbinding glamour of a night at the opera (every room is decorated differently), Le Richemond has become a home-from-home for privacy-loving grandees. The whole operation is overseen by the delightful Madame Martinini, who has worked at the hotel for 30 years. Le Richemond also provides an excellent outside catering service.

Le Richemond,
Jardin Brunswick, CH-1201 Geneva,
Switzerland
Tel: +41-22-731 1400   Fax: +41-22-731 6709

RIEDEL

Wine lover George Riedel's Big Idea was stunning in its simplicity: to create glasses in top quality crystal which are actually designed to get the best from the wine that they hold. The bonus is that their pure lines are elegant in the extreme. The 'Sommelier' collection is the Rolls Royce of the range.

Riedel Crystal
Weissachstraße 28, A-6330 Kufstein, Austria
Tel: +43-53-72 64 896   Fax: +43-53-72 63 225

THE RITZ, PARIS

As Ernest Hemingway once said, "When I dream of the afterlife, the action always takes place at the Paris Ritz." Since buying this legendary (and already near-perfect) property, Mohamed Fayed has lavished a fortune on upgrading it. Perhaps the best way to spend a day at this most civilised - and civilising - establishment is to take a cookery class at the Ritz Escoffier Ecole de Gastronomie Française.

The Ritz, Paris
15 Place Vendôme, 75041 Paris,
France
Tel:+33-1-43 16 30 30   Fax: +33-1-43 16 36 68

RIVA

The hand-built wooden boats that Riva produced on the shores of Lake Iseo became a jet-set icon on the Riviera in the Fifties and Sixties - and nothing has yet equalled the grace of its classic Super Aquarama, the waterborne equivalent of a gull-wing Mercedes. Now, with new ownership (the Stellican group) and new models in development, the signs are good that Cantieri Riva will regain its former pre-eminence.

Cantieri Riva
24067 Sarnaco, Italy
Tel: +39-035-911 202   Fax: +39-035-911 059

RIVER CAFE

While Ruth Rogers' and Rose Gray's much-vaunted Tuscan-inspired food is undoubtedly superb, the River Café's other bonus is its glorious position on the bank of the Thames. The décor, however, clearly shows its origins as the staff canteen for (Ruth's husband) Richard Rogers' architectural practice. Media dons love the restaurant's al fresco informality and people-watching potential.

The River Café
Thames Wharf, Rainville Road,
London W6 9HA, UK
Tel: +44-171-381 8824

ROB VAN HELDEN

Self-taught florist Rob van Helden's first job was delivering flowers by bicycle in the Dutch village where he was born. Today he counts royalty and rock stars (notably Elton John) among his clients. His work is distinguished by strong structures and natural shapes, often incorporating fruit and vegetables or unusual containers. Van Helden's favourite flowers include lily of the valley, tuberoses, peonies and blue hyacinths.

Rob Van Helden Floral Design
Unit 8, Tun Yard, Peardon Street,
London SW8 3HT, UK
Tel: +44-171-720 6774   Fax: +44-171-720 9568

ROBBE & BERKING

The first silversmiths to introduce Northern European design to the wider world in the 1950s, Robbe & Berking is renowned for its innovative, contemporary cutlery designs. Its 'Alta' pattern, designed by Wilfreid Moll in the 1980s, is exhibited in 17 European museums. The company celebrates its 125th anniversary this year.

Robbe & Berking
Zur Bleiche 47, D-24941 Flensburg, Germany
Tel: +49-461-90 30 60   Fax: +49-461-903 0622

ROBERT CLERGERIE

Workaday elegance is the hallmark of Robert Clergerie shoes; the broad range of comfortable, well-tooled styles in leather, satin and grosgrain are favoured by discreetly fashionable ladies and gentlemen in the world's capitals. Brogues, ballet pumps and streamlined court-shoes are among the favourites of Clergerie's followers.

Robert Clergerie
5 rue du Cherche-Midi, 75006 Paris, France
Tel: +33-1-45 48 75 47

ROBERT NATAF

The doyen of French bloodstock agents, Nataf has done business for practically every name in French breeding and owning circles and is the French representative of both John Magnier and Michael Tabor. In the last 25 years, he has bought more than 50 individual Group One winners, notably *Triptych* which he bought as a yearling for the then huge price of $2.15 million for Alan Clore. At the other extreme, a 'claimer' that he picked up in 1990 for FF200,000 went on to win the French Derby three months later. Nataf is currently retained by Lebanese owner Issam Faris to disperse his entire asset of 496 horses.

Robert Nataf
Horse France, 49 avenue Pierre Grenier,
92100 Boulogne, France
Tel: +33-1-46 94 84 00   Fax: +33-1-46 94 00 14

ROBERTO (RESTAURANT)

Redoubtable octogenarian Roberto Carugati is the man behind Restaurant Roberto, a Geneva institution for 30 years and a favourite haunt of the late Edmond de Rothschild. The restaurant's classical menu reminds you just how Italian food used to taste. Regulars toast the splendid wine list, which devotes a whole booklet to whites.

Restaurant Roberto
10 rue Pierre-Fatio, CH-1204 Geneva, Switzerland
Tel: +41-22-311 8033   Fax: +41-22-311 8466

ROLAND BARTHELEMY

The foodies who beat a path to the door of this shop might have missed out on Roland Barthelemy's exceptional cheesemaking talents, as he almost became a ski teacher in his youth. However, his fantasy about owning a little cheese shop (developed during the long days of his National Service in Fontainebleau) won out, to the benefit of gastronomy in general.

Roland Barthélemy
51 rue de Grenelle,
75007 Paris, France
Tel: +33-1-42 22 82 24

ROMANEE-CONTI (DOMAINE DE LA)

The Roch and de Vilaine families' domaine has been a legend since the Prince de Conti introduced his wines to Parisian society in the 18th century. It produces only 450 cases a year of rich and complex wines of the utmost finesse and subtlety. The domaine sells directly to private clients and, despite the £500-a-bottle price tag for a good vintage, there is seldom a dissenting voice.

Domaine de la Romanée-Conti
1 rue Derrière le Four,
21700 Vosne-Romanée, France
Tel: +33-3-80 62 48 80   Fax:+33-3-80 61 05 72

RON HOLLAND DESIGN

An unassuming New Zealander with a great sense of humour and an even greater talent for designing yachts, Ron Holland has been based in Ireland since 1973. Having begun by designing fast racing boats, he identified an interest in the revival of large sailing yachts and pioneered the design of large, high performance boats with the greater interior volumes associated with motor yachts. Holland is currently working on a 187-foot ketch.

Ron Holland Design
PO Box 23, Kinsale,
Co. Cork, Ireland
Tel: +353-21-77 48 66   Fax: +353-21-77 48 08

ROSALP (HOTEL)

Small and unashamedly cosy, the Rosalp caters to a mixed crowd - mainly Europeans (including plenty of clever young Brits), although in recent years Americans have discovered this charming ski resort. Not only was owner Roland Pierroz named Chef of the Year, he has been awarded 4 toques by Gault et Millau.

Hotel Rosalp
Route de Medran, CH-1936 Verbier, Switzerland
Tel: +41-27-771 6323   Fax: +41-27-771 1059

ROSEMARY VEREY

The doyenne of English garden designers and a prolific author, Mrs Verey is a trusted adviser to Prince Charles on horticultural matters and has worked closely with him at Highgrove. She has created gardens for private clients throughout Europe, Australia and North America, in which recurring themes include *potagers*, laburnum walks and knot gardens. Shining examples of these may be seen in her own garden at Barnsley House, which is open to the public.

Rosemary Verey
Barnsley House, Cirencester,
Gloucestershire GL7 5EE, UK
Tel/Fax: +44-1285-74 02 81

LE ROSEY

Notwithstanding its glamorous image, Le Rosey, owned and run by the fourth generation of the Gudin family, has a sound academic and sporting record. However, one of the greatest privileges of attending is that pupils gain a posse of international friends-for-life. Founded in 1880 and open to girls since 1967, the school decamps every winter to Gstaad.

Institut Le Rosey
Chateau du Rosey, CH-1180, Switzerland
Tel: +41-21-822 5500   Fax: +41-21-822 5555

ROSSINI OPERA FESTIVAL

Nicknamed the "Italian Bayreuth" this festival, held in the composer's birthplace, is dedicated to the works of Rossini. World-class singers partic-
ipate and the programme is always a well-conceived mixture of well-known and rarely played works by the composer. Performances take place in the Teatro Rossini or the 'Palace of Sport', large enough to allow for some wonderful staging.

Rossini Opera Festival
via Rossini 37, 61100 Pesaro, Italy
Tel: +39-0721-30 161   Fax: +39-0721-30 979

ROTHSCHILDS BANK

The provision of private banking services could justifiably be said to be as old as the Rothschild association with finance. Through the skilful management and investment of capital, the family established a reputation which has been sustained for 200 years. Today, the corporate investment portfolios managed by one of the group's many trust companies have replaced the private accounts more typical of the 19th-century bank but the traditions of care, trust and skilful management remain unchanged.

N.M Rothschild Services Ltd.
New Court, St. Swithins Lane,
London EC4P 4DU, UK
Tel: +44-171-280 5000   Fax: +44-171-929 1643
Banque Rothschild & Cie
17 avenue Matignon, 75008 Paris, France
Tel: +33-1-40 74 40 74

ROXTON BAILEY ROBINSON

The greatest quality of Roxton Bailey Robinson, specialists in field sports and safaris, is the infectious enthusiasm and tremendous knowledge of its staff; this is not just a job for them

but a way of life. You immediately feel reassured that these people will sympathise completely with your expectations of a sporting holiday. This goes as much for the accommodation as the sport, whether saltwater fishing in Cuba, salmon fishing in Russia, shooting in Argentina or with the Masai in Kenya or safaris at Tarkuni (the largest private reserve in South Africa). Roxtons also organises days at some of the best shoots in the UK, such as Lord Lichfield's, with accommodation in the private wing of his house, Shugborough Park.

Roxton Bailey Robinson
25 High Street, Hungerford,
Berkshire RG17 0NF, UK
Tel: +44-1488-68 32 22   Fax: +44-1488-68 29 77

THE ROXBURGHE ESTATE

The River Tweed is legendary for its salmon fishing and there are few stretches finer than the two prime beats - the Upper and Lower Floors - on the Duke of Roxburghe's estate. They provide double-bank fishing for four rods each, in a mix of slack and flowing water. An added bonus of fishing here is the accommodation, in the beautifully appointed Roxburghe (formerly Sunlaws) Hotel on the estate, which has its own golf course attached. There are usually some rods available for spring fishing but, if you want to fish in the autumn, join the waiting list and prepare to be patient.

The Roxburghe Estate
Estate Office, Kelso,
Roxburghshire TD5 7SF,
Scotland
Tel: +44-1573-22 33 33   Fax: +44-1573-22 60 56

ROYAL COPENHAGEN

Although best known for its ubiquitous blue-flower range (*musselmalet*) and sometimes twee ornaments, this distinguished manufacturer produces some exquisite hand-made patterns - notably its precious and finely detailed Flora Danica, which was introduced in 1804. The flagship boutique has all of the varieties on display.

Royal Copenhagen
Amagertorv 6, 1160 Copenhagen K, Denmark
Tel: +45-33-13 71 81   Fax: +45-38-14 99 40

ROYAL COUNTY DOWN

Northern Ireland's must-play course, Royal County Down delights the eye with its majestic setting by the Irish Sea, its gorse-edged fairways (in May and June) and the backdrop of the mountains of Mourne. Its No.1 course, consistently rated among the world's top ten, owes as much to the spectacular lie of the land as to the design offices of Old Tom Morris and Donald Steel.

Royal County Down
Newcastle, Co. Down BT33 0AN,
Northern Ireland
Tel: +44-13967-23 314   Fax: +44-13967-26 281

ROYAL COUNTY OF BERKSHIRE POLO CLUB

Traditionally a sport for the land-owning classes, this is polo for the helicopter-owning classes. Created in 1985 by music-industry magnate, Bryan Morrison, the club is largely private, although a telephone call to the charming Fiona Hamilton-Andrews will usually gain you admission. The six pitches play host to a series of glamorous charity matches throughout the season and highlights include pre- and post-racing polo during Ascot Week and the high-goal Prince of Wales Trophy in May.

The Royal County of Berkshire Polo Club
North St, Winkfield, Berkshire, SL4 4TH, UK
Tel: +44-1344-89 00 61 Fax +44-1344-89 03 85

ROYAL DORNOCH

The beauty of Royal Dornoch's location, four degrees below the Arctic Circle, is that, on a mild June evening, it is possible to play golf until almost midnight. This remote beauty spot is where Donald Ross nurtured his love for the game. Ben Crenshaw once spent a week here preparing for the British Open. When he

ROYAL HUISMAN SHIPYARD

Founded in 1884 by Jan Huisman, this company has developed into one of the most cutting-edge shipyards in the world. It was one of the first to use aluminium for its racing yachts in the Sixties and built the aptly-named *Flyer* which won the Whitbread Round-the-World Race in the late Seventies. For the past two decades, the Huisman family has concentrated on producing custom-made luxury yachts from 20-65 metres for a very select clientele; the company's superb workmanship was officially recognised in 1984 when Queen Beatrix added 'Royal' to the company's name. A particularly fine example of its technological expertise is the 47-metre *Hyperion*, commissioned by Dr Jim Clark, Chairman of Netscape. Naturally enough, given its owner's business interests, this fast, elegant sloop is crammed with the latest computer gadgetry; however, the shipyard is just as capable of creating a classic yacht. Wolter Huisman, grandson of the founder, is amazed by how rapidly the company has developed. "None of the technology we use today existed when I worked with my father back in 1945," he says. Nevertheless, Royal Huisman remains very much a family concern; Wolter's wife, Ali, and three daughters, along with their husbands all work for the firm.

Royal Huisman Shipyard BV
Flevoweg 1, 8325 PA, Vollenhove, Holland
Tel: +31-527-24 31 31   Fax: +31-527-24 38 00
E-mail: yachts@royalhuisman.com

arrived at Muirfield, he was asked how he got on. "Put it this way," he said, "I nearly didn't come back."

Royal Dornoch

Golf Road, Dornoch, Sutherland IV25 3LW, Scotland

Tel: +44-1862-81 02 19   Fax: +44-1862-81 07 92

ROYAL SOCIETY OF PORTRAIT PAINTERS

Unlike the continent where portrait painting is rare, both good and bad portrait painting survives as a living art form in Britain. A diverse range of well-regarded portrait painters is available for commission via the Royal Society of Portrait Painters. The Queen is its patron and Augustus John and J. McNeill Whistler are among its past members. Current members include John Ward, Richard Foster, Susan Ryder and June Mendoza (all of whom have painted members of the Royal Family).

Royal Society of Portrait Painters

17 Carlton House Terrace, London SW1Y 5BD, UK

Tel: +44-171-930 6844   Fax: +44-171-839 7830

ROYAL TROON GOLF CLUB

Established in 1878, this club is traditional in two respects. The layout - where the front nine runs out to the far end of the course and the back nine plays into the prevailing wind all the way home - and the fact the ladies are not allowed to play on the Old Course. The most prestigious on Scotland's West Coast (Colin Montgomerie's father is Club Secretary), it is home to the doctors, solicitors and accountants of the Glasgow area. Its 8th hole, 'The Postage Stamp', famous for its tiny green, is the shortest of the Championship rota - and one of the toughest.

Royal Troon Golf Club

Troon, Ayrshire KA10 6EP, Scotland

Tel: +44-1292-31 15 55 Fax: +44-1292-31 82 04

ROYAL YACHT SQUADRON

From the outside, this is as grand as a yacht club can be (it famously blackballed Sir Thomas Lipton because he was 'in trade' and remains extremely particular about its membership to this day). However, once in, the atmosphere is relaxed and friendly; sailing is, after all, a great leveller. It sticks to tradition, however; ladies (except Princess Anne) still have to use the tradesmen's entrance.

The Royal Yacht Squadron

The Parade, Cowes, Isle of Wight PO32 6QT, UK

Tel: +44-1983-29 21 91

RUBELLI

Sumptuous, intricately worked jacquard fabrics and delicate silks and velvets in rich, Renaissance-inspired colours are the signature of this fabrics house, established by Lorenzo Rubelli in 1858. However, since Rubelli's beautiful headquarters, in the Palazzo Corner Spinelli, are not open to the public, you will have to content yourself with a visit to one of the shops.

Rubelli

San Marco 3877, 30124 Venice, Italy

Tel: +39-041-521 6411   Fax: +39-041-522 5557

THE RUSSIAN MUSEUM

Although its fame is eclipsed by that of The Hermitage, this museum houses the finest chronological exhibit (some 300,000 works) of Russian Art from the 14th century to the 1930s. The museum is housed in a palace built in 1819 for Grand Duke Michael, younger brother of Alexander I - worth seeing for its interiors alone.

The Russian Museum

Inzhenernaya ul., 4, St. Petersburg, Russia

Tel: +7-812-219 1615

S.I.R. - SERVICE D'INTERVENTION RAPIDE

S.I.R employs an élite band of private protection agents, who work efficiently within the law. Established in 1978, the firm takes full advantage of technology - recently introducing mobile security by satellite, for instance. Other specialist areas include plain-clothed or uniformed party protection, house key holding and a bleeper assistance service.

S.I.R. - Service d'Intervention Rapide

Chemin de la Crétaux, Case Postale 29, CH-1196 Gland, Switzerland

Tel: +41-22-364 4644   Fax: +41-22-364 4873

SADLER-OSTERIA DI PORTA CICCA

Claudio Sadler's light and imaginative interpretation of traditional dishes from all of Italy's regions attracts a regular stream of blue-chip lawyers industrialists and (gourmet) celebrities. Debora Masotti organises the seating plan (book early for a table in the preferred back room) and the well-chosen wine list. Happy to share his secrets, Sadler runs cookery classes and special wine-appreciation evenings and is due to have a book published at the end of 1998.

Sadler-Osteria di Porta Cicca

ripa di Porta Ticinese 51, 20143 Milan, Italy

Tel: +39-02-58 10 44 51   Fax: +39-02-58 11 23 43

SALIMBENI

Silver-enamellers Franco and Giorgio Salimbeni are descended from the illustrious family which founded Monte dei Paschi di Siena, the world's oldest bank. They followed their father and grandfather into the family business, which makes finely-crafted picture frames, boxes, clock cases and other decorative objects. The most valuable Salimbene enamels, sold by some of the world's most prestigious jewellers, incorporate crystal, precious stones and woods, ivory or jade into the designs.

Salimbeni

via dell'Olivuzzo 70/A, 50143 Florence, Italy

Tel: +39-055-71 12 96   Fax: +39-055-71 07 30

SALZBURG FESTIVAL

Steeped in Mozartian history, this charming town plays host to the most splendid of summer festivals. All the great musical names appear here - Mackeras, Rattle, Jessye Norman, José van Dam - delighting black-tie-clad audiences of well-groomed cognoscenti and international socialites. There is, however, an unspoken social pecking order; rather like Oscars night, it all depends on which parties you are invited to.

Salzburg Festival
Postfach 140, Hofstallgasse 1,
A-50610 Salzburg, Austria
Tel: +43-662-84 45 01

SAM FOGG

Sam Fogg has taken the market in medieval and Asian manuscripts and miniatures by storm since establishing his business in 1986. From his base in London he acts as a conduit for some of the world's most rare and valuable manuscripts. Even John Maggs, doyen of antiquarian book sellers, admits to being "a trifle jealous".

Sam Fogg
35 St George Street, London W1R 9FA, UK
Tel: +44-171-495 2333   Fax: +44-171-409 3326

SAMUEL MONTAGU

Now owned by the Hong Kong and Shanghai Bank, Samuel Montagu is one of the most highly regarded private banks in Europe. While many banks pride themselves on a 'personalised' service, Samuel Montagu really does offer just that, with round-the-clock access to account managers. As one client put it, "You really feel like you're doing business with an individual rather than an institution."

Samuel Montagu
10 Lower Thames Street, London EC3, UK
Tel: +44-171-260 33 44   Fax: +44-171-256 5210

SAN LORENZO

Designed by Joseph Lee and Rocky Roquemore and ranked second in continental Europe after Valderrama, San Lorenzo demands great resourcefulness and imagination. Set on coastal land near the Rio Formosa estuary, it has matured rapidly in the ten years since it was built - not least because of its exclusivity; to get a game there it's best to stay at the Dona Filipa or San Lorenzo hotel.

San Lorenzo
Quinta do Lago, P-8135 Almancil, Portugal
Tel: +351-89-39 65 22   Fax: +351-89-39 69 08

THE SAMLING AT DOVENEST

In ancient Cumbria, gatherings to share ideas, dreams and plans were known as "Samlings". At Dovenest, Roger McKechnie, who made his fortune manufacturing Phileas Fogg snack food, has created a private retreat which facilitates exactly that. Perched on the hillside overlooking the ravishingly pretty Lake Windermere, this 18th-century house (once owned by the poet Wordsworth's landlord) is surrounded by 67 acres of private wildflower meadows and woodlands; it offers a secluded haven to relax, to find inspiration or simply to have a jolly good house party. The interior - an exquisite blend of open fires and delicately lit rooms - was designed by  Amanda Rosa, who adorned it with dramatic fabrics from the likes of Ralph Lauren and Designers Guild. Gathered around the splendid oak dining table, you will enjoy deliciously fresh cooking, much of it using produce from the property's own organic gardens.

Should you wander from the house, The Samling is a great base for leisure activities: Fishing, grouse shooting, paragliding, kayaking on the Kent River, or horse-riding through the meadows. After such energetic pursuits, come home and sink into the outdoor Hot Tub for a leisurely soak as you gaze, dreamlike, over the lake below.

The Samling At Dovenest
Ambleside Road, Windermere, Cumbria LA23 1LR, UK
Tel: +44-1539-43 19 22   Fax: +44-1539-43 04 00

IL SAN PIETRO

Clinging to the cliffs outside Positano, Il San Pietro was never planned as a hotel. The late Carlo Attansi simply kept carving more and more rooms out of the rock, in order to accommodate his friends (one is numbered $8\frac{1}{2}$, in honour of Fellini). The result is quirky, magical and desperately romantic - terraces dripping with bougainvillea and roses, bathrooms wide open to the view and a private beach (with elevator service) below.

Il San Pietro
via Laurito 2, 84017 Positano, Italy
Tel: +39-089-87 54 55   Fax: +39-089-81 14 49

SANT'ANDREA IMMOBILI DI PRESTIGIO

So discreet is this property company that you cannot simply walk into its offices; all business is done by appointment only. And rightly so, for its portfolio includes some of the most beautiful apartments, villas and castles in the most sought-after locations in Italy, chosen specifically for their architectural merit or for the desirability of their address.

Sant'Andrea Immobili di Prestigio
Corso Matteotti 9, 20100 Milan, Italy
Tel: +39-02-76 02 14 85   Fax: +39-02-76 02 14 92

SANTA MARIA POLO CLUB

Once regarded by serious players as little more than 'beach polo', the standard of play here has become increasingly competitive since Enrique

Zobel established the club 31 years ago. All the stars decamp to Sotogrande for the Gold Cup in August, after the English season. However, the delight is that - notwithstanding the celebrities and social high-flyers who come to watch - the style remains resolutely casual. This is polo for polo's sake.

Santa Maria Polo Club
Ramiro El Monje, Sotogrande, E-11310 Cadiz, Spain
Tel: +34-956-79 64 64   Fax: +34-956-79 41 57

SARLI

In 1959 Fausto Sarli opened a couture workshop in Rome, quickly making a name for himself among the *dolce vita* insiders, with his finely detailed evening dresses, figured from glorious swathes of silk, satin and organza. Clients today include Carol Alt - whose costumes he made for the film *Un Orso Chiamato Arturo* - and grand ladies who favour traditional glamour combined with superb craftsmanship.

Sarli
via Gregoriana 40A, 00187 Rome, Italy
Tel: +39-06-679 5210

SATER

Operating in Milan as well as Rome, Sater's discreet and highly professional chauffeur service counts numerous embassies and banks among its clients, as well as private individuals. Its fleet comprises top-of-the-range Mercedes and Lancias.

Sater
Via Licia 62, 00183 Rome, Italy
Tel: +39-06-77 20 46 42   Fax: +39-06-70 45 03 88

SAUERBRUCH & HUTTON

Husband-and-wife architects Matthias Sauerbruch and Louisa Hutton (he's German, she's English) have established a reputation for themselves as pioneering modernists with a series of bold private commissions in Britain. Their most visible work, however, is for corporate clients in Germany, including the innovative Photonics Centre in Berlin and a new building for the Ministry of the Environment in Dassau.

Sauerbruch & Hutton
57 Lehrer Straße, D-10557 Berlin, Germany
Tel: +49-30-397 8210   Fax: +49-30-39 78 21 30

SAVONLINNA OPERA FESTIVAL

With performances taking place in the 15th-century castle Olavinlinna, built on an islet in Finland's largest lake, this must be one of the most unexpected and dramatic places to hold an opera festival. First directed by Aino Ackté in 1912, it offers a richly varied programme and the chance to see star performers from around the world.

Savonlinna Opera Festival
Puistokacu 1, FIN-57100 Savonlinna, Finland
Tel: +358-15-51 75 10   Fax: +358-15-517 5123

THE SAVOY

A letter addressed to "the manager of the greatest hotel in London" was forwarded by the Post Office with the remark "Try Savoy Hotel, WC2". The Savoy is a London legend. Founded last century by Richard D'Oyly Carte, the Gilbert and Sullivan impresario, its front entrance has become a landmark (and the driveway is the only street in Britain where cars drive on the right). During the 1990s the hotel has been extensively restored, with new rooms and facilities added. Fitness enthusiasts are particularly well catered for, with one of the best gyms in a British hotel and a large roof-top pool.

The Savoy Hotel,
The Strand, London WC2R 0EU, UK
Tel: +44-171-836 4343   Fax: +44-171-240 6040

SCHLOSS WASSERBURG

The charm of this Baroque-style castle, built in the middle of a lake in a wine-growing region near Vienna, is not due just to its setting, its age or its grandiose proportions; it exudes warmth and cosi-

ness. As a young couple with small children, the owners (Count and Countess Seilern) know exactly how to create a house where other families feel at home. There is a special suite of children's rooms and, in the park, a swimming pool and lots of space to run about and climb trees. In winter, skating on the frozen lake is a big attraction and there is skiing an hour's drive away.

Schloß Wasserburg, St Polten, Austria
c/o Villas and Apartments Abroad Ltd,
420 Madison Ave, New York, NY 10017, USA
Tel: +1-212-759 1025   Fax: +1-212-755 8316

SCHLOSSHOTEL LERBACH

Although it opened as a hotel only six years ago, the impossibly romantic Schlosshotel Lerbach feels as if it has been there forever. Built in 1900 by Siemens heiress, Anna Zanders, and restored

by Thomas Althoff in classical country house style, it stands in 28 hectares of ravishing parkland. The honeymoon suite is a dream - tucked into the turret, with a wrap-around balcony from which you can see the spire of Cologne cathedral.

Schloßhotel Lerbach
Lerbacher Weg,
D-51465 Bergisch Gladbach, Germany
Tel: +49-2202-20 40 Fax: +40-2202 20 49 40

SCHLOSSHOTEL KRONBERG

This grand, Tudor-style palace, built in 1889 by the Dowager Empress Friedrich, retains all the glamour of that era. Sensitively restored by the Hesse family and filled with antiques and works of art, it combines great atmosphere with shameless luxury. The terrace overlooks a lovely, Italian-style rose garden and a private, 18-hole golf course.

Schloßhotel Kronberg
Hainstraße 25, D61476 Kronberg/Taunus, Germany
Tel: +49-61-73 70 10   Fax: +49-61-73 70 12 67

SCHLOSSHOTEL VIER JAHRESZEITEN

Set in a lovely garden in Grunewald, this intimate *hôtel particulier* was originally the residence of Kaiser Wilhelm II's personal lawyer. Built in 1912, it was transformed in 1994 by "frustrated decorator" (his own words) Karl

Lagerfeld into a classically-styled haven. The refinement and exquisite detailing of Lagerfeld's décor are echoed precisely by the attentions of the charming staff. The gleaming white swimming pool is splendid.

Schloßhotel Vier Jahreszeiten

Brahmsstraße 10, D-14193 Berlin-Grunewald,
Germany
Tel: +49-30-89 58 40   Fax: +49-30-89 58 48 00

SCHOLTESHOF

As passionate about antiques and gardening as he is about cooking, Roger Souveyrans has created his own little corner of paradise here. He has restored this 18th-century farmhouse with considerable taste and style and, around it, has planted 28 acres of gardens, which produce vegetables and herbs for his cooking. And what cooking. His summer dish, *Crème de pétits pois glacés, carpaccio de coquilles et caviar* is quite out of this world.

Scholteshof

Kermtstraat 130, B-3512 Stevoort Hasselt,Belgium
Tel: +32-11-25 02 02   Fax: +32-11-25 43 28

SCHUBERTIADE FESTIVAL

In late June each year top-class performers, such as Alfred Brendel, Andreas Schiff and Cecilia Bartoli, congregate in Feldkirch, a charming medieval town set among rolling hills and woods in western Austria. Although Schubert *lieder* form the main part of the Festival programme, there are also orchestral concerts. Between performances you can wander in the surrounding flower meadows and pine-scented woods and explore the ancient castles.

Schubertiade Festival GmbH

Villa Rosenthal, Schweizer Straße 1,
A-6845 Hohenems, Austria
Tel: +43-5576-72091   Fax: +43-5576-75450

SCHULE SCHLOSS SALEM

Alma mater of the Duke of Edinburgh and the Queen of Spain, Salem, founded in 1920 by progressive educationalists Kurt Hahn and Prince Max von Baden, is Germany's leading boarding school. It is famous for accepting students from all ethnic backgrounds, encouraging their natural talents and teaching them to take care of people in need as part of their holistic education. Teaching is undertaken in German or English.

Salem College

Schule Schloß Salem, D-88682 Salem,
Germany
Tel: +49-7553-81 317   Fax: +49-7553-81 390

SEABOURN CRUISE LINE

Seabourn's three small, sleek Norwegian-registered ships have established the benchmark for luxury cruising over the past ten years. Not only do the ships offer superb on-board facilities and impeccable service (from a largely Northern European crew that almost matches the maximum of 200 guests on a 1:1 ratio), they sail in exotic waters little visited by other cruise lines; the ships' shallow draft enables them to go into otherwise inaccessible areas. Cruises incorporate special-interest presentations by world-class lecturers, and exceptional land programmes of up to five days' duration.

Most of the beautifully-appointed accommodation comprises suites of 277 square feet, some with private balconies and all with wide picture windows. As well as the expected swimming pool and whirlpools, the ships have a Marina which unfolds from the stern, enabling guests to swim in the ocean and participate in a variety of watersports.

Former motor racing champion, Stirling Moss and his wife, Susie, are typical of the guests - active, highly educated and cosmopolitan (and, in some cases, famous). They happily admit to being "addicted" to Seabourn. In fact, the unusually high percentage of return guests, even more than the clutch of awards that the company has garnered, is proof that Seabourn has a uniquely successful format.

Seabourn Cruise Line (a division of Cunard)

Mountbatten House, Grosvenor Square, Southampton, SO15 2BF, UK
Tel: +44-1703-71 65 00   Fax: +44-1703-22 58 43

SCHWARZWALDSTUBE

The Finkbeiner family's Black Forest retreat is home to virtuoso chef Harald Wohlfart, regarded by many as the best chef in Germany. The restful dining room, with its wood-panelled walls and lovely views of the forests and meadows, is a perfect foil for Wohlfart's sublime, classical cooking. Service, led by maître d' Jean-Luc Poussin and sommelier Stéphane Gass, is, of course, faultless.

Schwarzwaldstube

Hotel Traube Tonbach, 237 Tonbacherstraße, D-72270 Baiersbronn, Germany
Tel: + :49-7442-4920   Fax: +49-7442-49 26 92

SCHWEIZER STUBEN

Roman Schmitt has come home to his family's celebrated inn to take over kitchens first made famous by Dieter Müller. And a very good job he is doing, too, with his inspired versions of great classics. The terrace enjoys blissful views across the peaceful Main river valley in the summer.

Schweizer Stuben

11 Geiselbrunnenweg,
D-97877 Wertheim-Bettingen, Germany
Tel: +49-9342-30 70   Fax: +49-9342-30 71 55

SEAGO

Since establishing their business ten years ago, Timothy and Lindy Seago have gained a reputation as one of Europe's most knowledgeable dealers in garden statuary and ornaments from the 17th- to 19th centuries. The 17th-century Dutch Ovidian-style *Virtue Evading the Embrace of Time* is one of the outstanding pieces which they exhibited at the 1998 Grosvenor House Fair.

Seago

22 Pimlico Road, London SW1W 8LJ, UK
Tel: +44-171-730 7502   Fax: +44-171-730 9179

DR J.L. SEBAGH

Fashion-world insiders on both sides of the Channel love the charming Dr Sebagh for his winning ways with Botox and collagen. Sebagh, who spends half the week in Paris tending to his French *côterie*, undertakes all the serious stuff of plastic surgeons but is best loved for his ability to plump up twilight faces without requiring the knife.

Dr J.L. Sebagh

25 Wimpole Street, London W1M 7AD, UK
Tel: +44-171-637 0548   Fax: +44-171-637 5110
64 rue de Longchamp, 75016 Paris, France
Tel: +33-1-47 04 65 75

SEDDINER SEE
GOLF & COUNTRY CLUB

Its location, just 25 minutes from the centre of Berlin, and its luxurious club-house, overlooking the lake, made this club an instant hit with the great and the good of Germany's capital. In his first foray into Germany, Robert Trent Jones has transformed this flat landscape into the Sudplatz - a testing challenge dotted with natural water hazards; the second course, the Nordplatz, is a Rainer Pressman design.

Golf und Country Club Seddiner See

Zum Weiher 44, D-14552 Wildenbruch, Germany
Tel: +49-33205-7320   Fax: +49-33205-73 229

SELLERIE LOPEZ

The cream of Seville's equestrian circles flock here to kit themselves out with saddles, boots and harnesses, as well as beautiful hand-made shoes for men - all the product of consummate craftsmanship. The traditional saddles, called *vaqueras*, are teamed with the orange and yellow striped fabric *Lola Sarga*.

Sellerie Lopez

Calle Cuna 34, 41001 Seville, Spain
Tel/Fax: +34-95-421 6923

SERENA LE MAISTRE

Answering the burgeoning demand for smart, discreet and highly competent domestic staff, Serena and her team can match you up with anything from butlers and PAs to nannies and estate managers. Rest assured that they have been screened with MI5-type diligence - some 70 per cent of applicants are dismissed before you even see them!

Serena le Maistre & Associates

10 Lower Belgrave Street,
London SW1W OLJ, UK
Tel: +44-171-730 9991   Fax: +44-171-730 9777

SERGIO ROSSI

The son of a shoe-maker, Sergio Rossi started his own business 40 years ago, branching out into fashion shoes with an emphasis on distinctive designs using high-quality materials. The 1980s brought a collection of shoes for men and handbags. Designers such as Gianni Versace and Dolce and Gabbana have chosen Sergio Rossi to produce their footwear.

Sergio Rossi

via Montenapoleone 9, 20121 Milan, Italy
Tel: +39-2-76 00 25 24   Fax: +39-2-76 0146 74

SERGIO VALENTE

Over the course of 30 years, Sergio Valente has built an unassailable reputation as one of Europe's leading hairdressers. Truly charming and an eagle-eyed stickler for detail, Valente himself supervises all of the hair and beauty treatments which are undertaken in his salon. Cocooning his seriously smart clients in luxury, he has lavished as much attention on the aesthetics of his salon as he does on the beauty of his clients. Stepping in from the bustle of the via Condotti, you are enveloped in comfort and calm; the walls are hung with antique prints and he has put a whole library of delicious books on art, jewellery and fashion at his clients' disposal - just one of many thoughtful details.

Sergio Valente

via Condotti 11, 00187 Rome, Italy
Tel: +39-6-679 4515 or 679 1268
Fax: +39-6-69 94 06 96

SESENA

One of the secrets of King Juan Carlos' elegance is the elegant capes that he wears instead of an overcoat. This is where he has them made. They are still cut according to the same patterns and crafted using the same techniques, as they were when Seseña was established over 100 years ago.

Seseña

Cruz 23, 28012 Madrid, Spain
Tel/Fax: +34-91-531 68 40

SHEEN FALLS LODGE

Boasting 15 miles of private salmon and trout fishing on its own stretch of the Sheen River, this is heaven for fishermen. There are plenty of indulgences for non-fishing guests too, but perhaps the best things about Sheen Falls are General Manager, Adrian Baartels and his exceptional staff, and Fergus Moore's Michelin-starred La Cascade restaurant.

Sheen Falls Lodge
Kenmare, Co. Kerry, Ireland
Tel: +353-64-41 600   Fax: +353-64-41 386,

SHEILA PARNESS

As well as marketing a range of luxurious pet toiletries, Sheila Parness creates the most extraordinary beds for dogs and cats. Exact replicas of those made for the pets of the aristocracy and royal court in 18th-century France, they are hand-carved in wood and finished with gold leaf and sumptuous fabrics.

Sheila Parness Ltd.
907 Nell Gwynn House, Sloane Avenue,
London SW3 3HB, UK
Tel: +44-171-584 6474   Fax: +44-171-589 7503

SIETE PUERTAS

The paellas in this great Catalan brasserie are magnificent and the atmosphere is heavy with legend. The small engraved plaques on the walls, above the favourite tables of the illustrious regulars who have passed through its 'seven doors' during its century of existence, say it all: Che Guevara, Maria Callas, Picasso, Orson Welles, Montserrat Caballé, Salvador Dalì and HRH Don Juan de Borbón, to name a few.

Siete Puertas
Passeig Isabel II, 14, 08003 Barcelona, Madrid
Tel: +34-93-319 30 33   Fax: +34-93-319 46 62

SIMPOSIUM

Italy's A-List celebrities love this country-style restaurant. The reason, according to its flamboyant owner-chef, Lucio Pompili, is that "we treat them like normal customers and friends". He treats children very well, too. Having discovered that today's *bambini* prefer breaded escalope of veal with chips and ketchup above all else, he created a sophisticated version to educate their palates: Breast of guinea-fowl with vegetable tempura (looks like chips) and a tomato and balsamic vinegar coulis. It has become a favourite of grown-up children, too, when truffles are not on the menu. In warm weather, ask for a table in the garden (lovely view at lunch time and romantic in the evening).

Simposium Ristorante Quattro Stagioni
via Cartoceto 38, 61030 Cartoceto, Italy
Tel: +39-07-21 89 83 20   Fax: +39-07-21 89 84 93

SMYTHSON OF BOND STREET

With a client list that includes international designers, supermodels, actors and authors, as well as holding three Royal Warrants, Smythson is world famous for the fine quality of its bespoke stationery and for the personal service that it offers to clients. To further enforce its legendary reputation for discretion, Smythson opened a private salon in 1998, which is  available by appointment only and, to help make wedding preparations as painless as possible, the company will make home visits to advise on the most appropriate stationery, as well as correct wedding etiquette.

Established in 1887 in Bond Street by silversmith Frank Smythson, the company introduced its signature blue featherweight paper in 1892 and the first portable diaries soon afterwards. Today there are four Smythson shops, which also stock a fine range of leather products, such as photograph albums, travel and business accessories, pocket-sized record books (for recording your thoughts on everything from shopping and fashion to golf and fishing), and its distinctive and highly covetable *sécretaires*.

Frank Smythson Ltd
40 New Bond Street, London W1Y 0DE, UK
Tel: +44-171-629 8558   Fax: +44-171-495 6111
Smythson by Post
Tel: +44-990-211 311   Fax: +44-171-318 1500

SIR JOHN SOANE'S MUSEUM

The great architect, Sir John Soane (1753-1837), designed and built 13 Lincoln's Inn Fields as his residence and as a showcase for his collection of paintings, drawings, sculpture and antiquities. He established it as a museum in 1833, leaving a rare example of an intact Regency house as well as an astonishing display of his exquisite architectural sense.

Sir John Soane's Museum
13 Lincoln's Inn Fields,
London WC2A 3BP, UK
Tel: +44-171-405 2107

SIMON HORN FURNITURE

Affectionately known as "the bed man", Simon Horn can take credit for the renaissance of the classical bed. His team of English craftsmen produces the most dreamy beds imaginable, based mainly on period French styles, including the classic *Lits Bâteau*, and Empire and Louis XV designs. Cleverest of all is his signature 'Metamorphic Cot', a child's cot-that-turns-into-a-bed-that-turns-into-a-sofa.

Items can be made to order in a variety of woods (including cherry, oak, rosewood, wal-

nut and beech) and finished in a choice of stain and patina. Attention to detail and fine finishing touches are a hallmark of the company - and Mr Horn himself, with his old-school manners, is a delight.

Simon Horn Furniture
117/121 Wandsworth Bridge Road,
London SW6 2TP, UK
Tel: +44-171-731 1279

LE SIRENUSE

Among the charms of this extraordinary little hotel is the swimming pool. Like a box at La Scala, you can see out while the people scurrying about below, in the orchestra pit that is the village of Positano, can most definitely not see in. Originally the family home of Marchese Paolo Sersale, Le Sirenuse still looks - and feels - more like an elegant, clubby summer retreat than a hotel.

Le Sirenuse
via Cristoforo Colombo 30, 84017 Positano, Italy
Tel: +39-089-87 50 66   Fax: +39-089-81 17 98

SOLEDAD LORENZO

Soledad Lorenzo is one of Spain's most respected gallery owners, recognised not only for her *savoir-faire* but also for the special relationships she develops with her artists. By bringing Spanish masters of various generations to the public eye and achieving considerable success

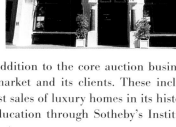

SOTHEBY'S

Founded in 1744, Sotheby's is pre-eminent in the international auction world for the sale of fine art and antiques. The company has a worldwide network of 110 offices located in 46 countries, with principal salerooms in New York and London employing teams of specialists who have expert knowledge in all areas of the decorative and fine arts.

Sotheby's now conducts regular sales in Los Angeles and Chicago, as well as 16 other countries, while an exciting new development in Sotheby's business in Europe is the opening of new auction premises in the historic Galerie Charpentier in Paris. New salerooms are also planned for Zurich and Amsterdam.

Sotheby's was founded as a book auctioneer, so it was fitting that the company's inaugural internet auction, the first by a major auctioneer of fine art, was also for books. In addition to the core auction business, Sotheby's is committed to exploring new services to the market and its clients. These include Sotheby's International Realty, currently enjoying the highest sales of luxury homes in its history, private sales, financial services, fine art restoration and education through Sotheby's Institute, which is an affiliated institution of the University of Manchester.

Sotheby's
35 New Bond Street, London W1A 2AA, UK
Tel: +44-171-293 5000   Fax: +44-171-293 5989

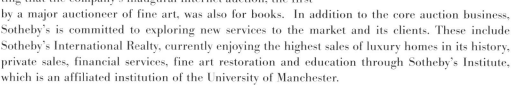

internationally, she has given new vision to the Spanish art world.

Soledad Lorenzo
Orefila 5, 28010 Madrid, Spain
Tel: +34-91-308 2887   Fax: +34-91-308 6830

SOMBRERIA MAQUEDANO

The quintessence of Spanish headgear - the sombrero - has been made and supplied by the house of Maquedano since 1896. Here, you'll find every possible variation in colour and style. Moreover, the hatbox in which your purchase is handed over is one of the most sought-after accessories among Seville's shopping élite.

Sombrería Maquedano
Calle sierpes 40, 41001 Seville, Spain
Tel: +34-95-456 4771

SOTHEBY'S INTERNATIONAL REALTY

For the past 20 years, Sotheby's International Realty has been selling some of Europe's most prestigious properties. Its international network offers property brokerage and marketing services throughout the world. In addition to its London headquarters, it has offices in Paris, the Côte d'Azur and Monaco.

Sotheby's International Realty
34-35 New Bond Street, London W1A 2AA, UK
Tel: +44-171-314 4443   Fax: +44-171-408 5949

SPA'DEUS

California comes to Tuscany with Christina Newburgh's indulgent spa, a favourite of Donna Karan, Marisa Berenson and Franco

Zeffirelli. She promotes a stress-free lifestyle consisting of long walks through the hills, delicious food and blissful treatments, all calculated to help you lose weight with maximum effect and minimum effort.

Spa'Deus
Via Le Piane 35,
53042 Chianciano Terme, Tuscany, Italy
Tel: +39-0578-63 232   Fax: +39-0578-64 329

SPERONE GOLF CLUB

Since 1991 Corsica has been home to one of Europe's most breathtaking golf courses, designed by Robert Trent Jones, on 92 hectares of outstanding natural beauty alongside an exclusive residential development. The second half of the course will bowl you over, with a sequence of four holes (the 12th to 16th) bordering the sea and views all the way to Sardinia. Smart Parisians fly down to play here, as do Italians already familiar with Trent Jones' Pevero on the Costa Smeralda.

Sperone Golf Club
20169 Bonifacio, Corsica, France
Tel: +33-4-95 73 13 69   Fax: +33-4-95 73 06 97

SPIELBANK BADEN-BADEN

Baden-Baden is a place that conjures up pictures of whiskery archdukes, frail contessas and wide-eyed American ingénues, all coming to take the waters during the golden summers before the First World War. Its casino, established in 1855 by Jacques Benazet and described by Marlene Dietrich as "the most beautiful of all casinos", is still redolent of those happy times. Today, in addition to black jack, American roulette and punto blanco, three prestigious international baccarat competitions take place every year.

Spielbank Baden-Baden
Augustaplatz 2, 76530 Baden Baden, Germany
Tel: +49-7221-21 060   Fax: +49-7221-21 06 54

THE SQUARE

Chef-patron Philip Howard has got it absolutely right: inspired cooking and superb service perfectly complemented by a decidedly un-stuffy atmosphere - and two Michelin stars to show for it. Great décor (bright colour, big paintings) and excellent wines add a final flourish. Andrew Lloyd Webber and an eclectic mix of art dealers, bankers and cosmopolitan foodies all love it.

The Square
6-10 Bruton Street, London W1X 7AG, UK
Tel:+44-171-839 8787   Fax:+44-171-495 7150

50 ST JAMES

London's newest and grandest casino lies in the heart of the capital's establishment club-land.

The truly monumental, Grade II-listed building (designed by Benjamin and Philip Watt, who also worked on the Duke of Wellington's Apsley House) has been returned to its long-forgotten status as Britain's first and only purpose-built casino by owners London Clubs International. Its magnificent interior has been restored to the late Regency baroque style of the original by interior designer, the late Robert Lush.

50 St James, London, UK
At the time of writing, UK law prohibits the publication of contact details for British casinos. The law is currently under review.

ST ANDREWS (OLD COURSE)

Known as the 'Home of Golf', this is the only course in the world that everyone who calls himself a golfer must play (it is open to all golfers with a handicap). A caddie is essential if you want to tame the seven double greens and avoid the many hidden bunkers. Every great golfer that has ever lived has walked over the Swilken Bridge on the 18th. The Royal and Ancient Club is a closed shop but, in 1995, the first club-house open to all was inaugurated - providing excellent hospitality and, at last, somewhere to change your shoes!

St Andrews Links Club House
West Sands Road, St. Andrew's,
Fife KY96 9XL, Scotland
Tel: +44-1334-46 66 66   Fax: +44-1334-46 66 64

ST CATHERINE'S COURT

Whenever she took a break filming *Dr Quinn, Medicine Woman*, Jane Seymour would escape back to this beautiful bolt-hole in the Cotswolds, which she created as an antidote to the pressures of Hollywood. It is available for rental to those similarly wishing to find a perfect English hideaway. A 14th-century manor house, it is luxurious, private and romantic, with huge four-poster beds and a dining room lit solely by candles.

St. Catherine's Court, near Bath, UK
c/o Blandings, The Barn, Musgrave Farm,
Horningsea Road, Fen Ditton, Cambs CB5 8SZ, UK
Tel: +44-1223-29 34 44   Fax: +44-1223-29 28 88

ST COLUMBA'S COLLEGE

St. Columba's College is the most 'public' of Ireland's private schools. Established in the 19th century "to furnish the sons of the landed gentry", it is now multi-denominational and co-educational. St. Columba's has often been cited as one of the finest boarding schools in Europe and it has always had a particularly high proportion of foreign students.

St. Columba's College
Whitechurch, Dublin 16, Ireland
Tel: +353-1-490 6791   Fax: +353-1-493 6655

ST MARY'S ASCOT

Established in 1885, St Mary's is the most academic of England's Catholic girls' schools. Its (now entirely secular) teaching staff has a very sound record in arts - especially music - and languages although, despite excellent facilities, it has had less success with the sciences. As well as appealing to smart English families, it attracts a fair smattering of European aristocrats (including, in the past, Princess Caroline of Monaco).

St Mary's School
Ascot, Berkshire SL5 9JF, UK
Tel: +44-1344-623 721   Fax: +44-1344-87 32 81

ST-NOM-LA-BRETECHE

If you want to play golf with the grandees of Paris (antique dealer Jacques Perrin is typical of the members), this is the place. Established in 1959, its two courses play host to the prestigious Lancôme Trophy every September. Fred Hawtree's Blue Course incorporates plenty of water hazards, while his slightly more hilly Red Course has some fast, sloping greens.

St-Nom-la-Bretêche Golf Club
78860 Saint-Nom-la-Bretêche, France
Tel: +33-1-30 80 04 40   Fax: +33-1-34 62 60 44

STEIRERECK (RESTAURANT)

Anyone with a penchant for culinary genius will appreciate the riches of chef Helmut Osterreicher at Austria's premier restaurant. Quite exceptional flavours are the hallmark of his haute cuisine creations - and where better to enjoy them than in the restaurant's devastatingly romantic winter garden? Request your table here well in advance.

Restaurant Steirereck
Rasumofskygaße 2, A-1030, Vienna, Austria
Tel: +43-1-713 3168   Fax: +43-1-71 31 56 82

STEPHEN WOODHAMS

Stephen Woodhams is a young florist and horticulturist whose business has done astonishingly well since he established it in 1986 at the age of 22. His client list now stretches for miles; the likes of Asprey, Vivien Duffield, Robert and Susan Sangster, Elizabeth Taylor and the Royal Household rely on his outstanding creative vision to grace the most high profile events.

Woodhams
3 McKay Trading Estate, 248-300 Kensal Road,
London W10 5BZ, England
Tel: +44-181-964 9818   Fax: +44-181-964 9848

STRATHTYRUM

This grand late 17th-century mansion, adjacent to St Andrew's golf course, is the best possible place to stay if you are playing golf there; originally the Links were owned by the estate

and one of the courses is named 'Strathtyrum'. Set on a 400-acre estate with lovely gardens and woodland walks, the six-bedroom house is filled with paintings and antiques and decorated in classical country style.

Strathtyrum, St Andrews, Scotland
c/o Blandings, The Barn, Musgrave Farm,
Horningsea Road, Fen Ditton,
Cambs CB5 8SZ, UK
Tel: +44-1223-29 34 44   Fax: +44-1223-29 28 88

STOWE SCHOOL

There are many reasons for choosing a school for your child but the words of J.F. Roxburgh, the founding headmaster, are as good as any: "Every boy who goes out from Stowe will know beauty when he sees it for the rest of his life." This mainly boys' school occupies the palatial former home of the Duke of Buckingham, amid grounds (now owned by the National Trust) dotted with Grade-I architectural follies. Drama and sports have always been strong points and the school is enjoying a resurgence in academic standards after slipping in the Eighties.

Stowe School
Buckingham MK18 5EH, UK
Tel: +44-1280-81 31 64   Fax: +44-1280-82 27 69

LE STRESA

Tony and Claudio Faiola's welcome here is irresistible - and so is the food. Valentino and Alain Delon rub shoulders with Alain-Dominique Perrin, John Travolta and the Rothschilds. The first table by the door is particularly sought-after and anyone who wants to be seen must sit in the front room. Pasta is the staple, including Ravioli with white truffles and Carbonara à la Jean-Paul Belmondo (with tomatoes, olives, garlic and spices).

Le Stresa
7 rue de Chambiges, 75008 Paris, France
Tel: +33-1-47 23 51 62

SUNNINGDALE

A favourite haunt for tour professionals and celebrities, Sunningdale is crammed to its traditional rafters with serious golfers. The two courses, Old and New, regularly crop up on people's lists of favourites, since both are wonderfully natural tests through heather and mature trees. A whole day spent here is golfing bliss - a round either side of its famous lunch. A kind of city gentlemen's club in the country.

Sunningdale
Ridgemount Road, Sunningdale,
Berkshire SL5 9RR, UK
Tel: +44-1344-62 16 81   Fax: +44-1344-624 154

SUNSEEKER

Sunseeker produces some of the most desirable power cruising boats around. Their sleek styling never fails to draw admiring glances in the harbours beloved of the jet-set, while the excellence of their build quality has found favour with serious yachting folk. Founded in 1962, Sunseeker is now Europe's largest privately owned and managed powerboat builder.

Sunseeker
27-31 West Quay Road, Poole,
Dorset BH15 1HX, UK
Tel: +44-1202-38 11 11   Fax: +44-1202-38 22 22

SUVRETTA HOUSE

This hotel is beautifully run but rather low-key by St Moritz standards. Smart European families have been coming here for generations - to revel in the Müllers' warm hospitality and to escape the smell of all that new money. Very stylish, very understated and utterly charming.

Suvretta House,
CH-7500 St Moritz, Switzerland
Tel: +41-81-832 1132   Fax: +41-81-833 8524

SWEERTS DE LANDAS

In the stately setting of Dunsborough Park, Baron Dolf Sweerts de Landas and his wife Caroline display their collection of 18th- and 19th-century garden statuary, urns and furniture in a series of restored historical gardens. Regular exhibitors at Basle, they also sell David Williams Ellis' figurative work and act as consultants.

Sweerts de Landas
Dunsborough Park, Ripley,
Surrey GU23 6AL, UK
Tel: +44-1483-22 53 66   Fax: +44-1483-22 45 25

SYDNEY OHANA

For those needing glamorous surroundings when opting for a nip and tuck, the answer lies in a superb *hôtel particulier* in Paris' 16th arrondissement, where Dr Sydney Ohana lifts and remodels faces and breasts with skilfully natural results. The elegant recovery rooms and the staff's sensitivity to their patients' needs make this elegant, art-filled clinic a favourite with celebrities.

Sydney Ohana M.D.
6 square Pétrarque, 75116 Paris, France
Tel: +33-1-53 70 05 05   Fax: +33-1-44 05 97 61

TAILLEVENT and LES CAVES TAILLEVENT

Taillevent is one of the best run restaurants anywhere. The secret is 52 years in the hands of one family. The present owner Jean-Claude Vrinat continues his father's egalitarian approach to the seating plan, as well as insisting on writing up Philippe Legendre's cooking in the simplest terms: 'Pigeon roasted like woodcock', 'Lobster sausage'. So awesome is the cellar that Vrinat has opened a wine shop nearby - an excellent source of hard-to-find vintages, as well as highly-informed advice about less grand wines, which he obtains thanks to his long-standing relationships with the best producers and négociants.

Taillevent
15 rue Lamennais, 75008 Paris, France
Tel: +33-1-44 95 15 01

Les Caves Taillevent
199 rue du Faubourg St-Honoré,
75008 Paris, France
Tel: +33-1-45 61 14 09   Fax: +33-1-45 61 19 68

TAITTINGER

Taittinger's dexterity in regulating the essential elements of champagne - alcohol, bubbles, tannin and flavours - is outstanding. The house's

Comtes de Champagne, made entirely from chardonnay and always a vintage, is its most sophisticated elixir. But look out for Taittinger's special cuvée for the year 2000. Produced only in magnums, it is made from the 1996 harvest - one of the greatest in the last 25 years - and will be available from Spring 1999.

Taittinger
9 Place Saint Nicaise, 51061 Reims, France
Tel: +33-3-26 85 17 46

TALISKER

Not a whisky for the faint-hearted, Talisker shouts its identity and demands to be taken seriously. The flavour is initially light, almost lemony sharp, and then it erupts across the palate, finishing with a peppery kick. The pyrotechnics continue long after it has been swallowed. It leaves an afterglow in its wake, deeply satisfying but also challenging: Have you fortitude enough for another sip?

Talisker
United Distillers, Landmark House,
Hammersmith Bridge Road, London W6 9DP, UK
Tel: +44-181-846 8040   Fax: +44-181-235 2400

TANINO CRISCI

Tanino Crisci began humbly as a small artisan shop in 19th-century Milan, but nowadays bankers, diplomats and the cream of Milanese society - both male and female - are shod here. With a presence in many fashion capitals, its shops are intimate, panelled and clubby, reflecting the classical styling of shoes that are executed in the softest of leathers.

Tanino Crisci
Via Montenapoleone 3, 20121 Milan, Italy
Tel: +39-02-76 02 12 64   Fax: +39-03-83 80 54 48

TANTRIS

With best-selling books behind them, chef Hans Haas and sommelier Paula Bosch are the powerhouses behind Tantris. The name is the Indian word for 'enjoyment' and the décor is Eastern; however, the food's the thing - Haas is a master of subtle flavouring. Join Munich's élite on the terrace in summer.

Tantris
Johann-Fichte-Straße 7, D-80805 Munich, Germany
Tel: +49-89-36 20 61   Fax: +49-89-361 8649

TANNER KROLLE

Although its history stretches back to 1856, Tanner Krolle has become the newly smart name in leather goods since being taken over by Chanel owners Wertheimer. While holding dear its tradition of fine British craftsmanship, its new collection of handbags in nappa, calf and alligator, designed by American Kathy Formby,

is unmistakably contemporary. The company still makes its signature bridle leather luggage but this, too, has been updated by the use of rich colours. Tanner Krolle's first store, opened in London at the end of 1997, will be followed by others in the world's major style capitals.

Tanner Krolle
38 Old Bond Street, London W1X 3AE, UK
Tel: +44-171-491 2243   Fax: +44-171-491 8702

TAPIS ROUGE INTERNATIONAL

This travel agent will appeal to anyone wishing to plunge into an exotic culture while still enjoying five-star comfort from start to finish - albeit at a hefty price. Choose from delights such as a Belle Epoque safari in Tanzania, an Orient Express ride along the Silk Route or a more intensely intellectual tour in the company of renowned historian, Jean de Cars.

Tapis Rouge International
39 rue Marbeuf, 75008 Paris, France
Tel: +33-1-42 56 55 00   Fax: +33-1-45 63 01 51

TAPISSERIE

Needlepoint is suddenly the smart hobby, judging by the number of supermodels stitching away back-stage at the collections. Ahead of her time, Lady Palumbo set up Tapisserie in the mid-Eighties because she couldn't find anything that she liked on the market. Julia Roberts, Sarah, Duchess of York and Countess Leopold von Bismarck are among the regulars who come here for her limited-edition hand-painted canvases.

Tapisserie
54 Walton St, London SW3, UK
Tel: +44-171-581 2715

TASSINARI ET CHATEL

Established in 1680 and owned (since 1998) by the equally august Lelièvre, Tassarini et Chatel works in the grand tradition; its richly coloured silks, velvets and damasks decorate Fontainbleau, Compiègne and Malmaison. Indeed, among the documents from which it still works are an order from Louis XVI for the private rooms at Versailles and patterns from the 18th-century fabric designer Philippe de La Salle.

Tassarini et Chatel
26 rue Danielle-Casanova, 75002 Paris, France
Tel: 33-1-42 62 74 08   Fax: 33-1-42 60 37 15

TATTERSALLS

With an annual turnover of £130 million, Tattersalls accounts for nearly 90 per cent of the British thoroughbred auction market. 10,000 horses are offered for sale each year in 17 sales at Newmarket in England and Fairyhouse in Ireland. The flagship Houghton Yearling sale is unrivalled as a source of Classic winners; last Spring a seven month-old brother of Epsom Derby winner *Generous* fetched £2.6 million.

Tattersalls Ltd.
Terrace House, Newmarket, Suffolk CB8 9BT, UK
Tel: +44-1638-66 59 31 Fax: +44-1638-66 08 50

TAYLOR'S

Taylor's, or Taylor, Fladgate & Yeatman, to give the company its full title, was the first British shipper to own property in the Douro Valley and a succession of magnificent vintage ports bears testimony to its high standards. Serve one of these - perhaps the 1955 or 1963 - after dinner and relax as your guests are enchanted by this most wondrous of wine styles.

Taylor's
rue de Choupelo 250,
4450 Villa Nova Gaia, Portugal
Tel: +35-123-71 99 99 Fax: +35-123-70 73 21

TERENCE DISDALE

One of the world's most sought-after designers, Disdale specialises in the interiors and exteriors of large motor and sailing yachts. Among his 40 projects completed to date are the 52m *Leocrie III*, the 75m *Montkaj* and the 36m ketch *Taramber*. While Disdale's clean-lined 'modern classics' are undeniably beautiful, he insists that they are not made only to look good; form follows function and each is based on a thorough knowledge of how a yacht operates.

Terence Disdale Design
3 Portland Terrace, The Green, Richmond,
Surrey TW9 1QQ, UK
Tel: +44-181-940 1452 Fax: +44-181-940 5964

TERME DEL PARCO SPA

This oasis of calm is set in the midst of a purpose-built Sardinian holiday village. With five pools, it provides state-of-the-art thalassotherapy treatments, the most remarkable of which is the magnesium-rich sea-oil pool, initially developed for the Russian space programme. With a glossy Euro clientele, the atmosphere is relaxed and friendly; however, don't forget to bring your jewellery.

Terme Del Parco Spa
The Forte Village,
09010 Santa Margherita di Pula,
Cagliari, Sardinia, Italy
Tel: +39-0709-21 80 33 Fax: +39-0709-21 246

TEFAF (THE EUROPEAN FINE ART FOUNDATION FAIR) MAASTRICHT

Maastricht is the greatest non-contemporary art fair of all. It attracts visitors from throughout Europe and America and the works are truly international in scope; Johnny van Haeften describes it as "the biggest and best in the world". More than 170 dealers from 13 countries took part in 1998.

The European Fine Arts Foundation
oude Dieze 17, 5211KT, Den Bosch,
The Netherlands
Tel: +31-73-614 5165 Fax: +31-73-614 7360

TERRY O'NEILL

Terry O'Neill started taking pictures in Sixties London when The Holy Trinity of photographers - Bailey, Donovan and Duffy - were in full swing. He takes glamorous and flattering portraits of the rich and famous, explaining, "I don't see wrinkles, crinkles, bags and things that are supposed to make in-depth studies. You don't have to do a Lucian Freud." Past subjects range from The Queen and Lord Olivier to Isabella Rossellini and Frank Sinatra.

Terry O'Neill
34 South Street, London W1Y 5DN, UK
Tel: +44-171-493 1900 Fax: +44-171-493 1221

TGS INTERNATIONAL

Since setting up shop in the Bristol hotel 15 years ago, the charming, bow-tied Thierry Meunier has tended to the grooming of countless movie stars, politicians and chief executives. However, his discretion is as legendary as his talent with the scissors; don't even ask who they are.

TGS International
Le Bristol, 112 rue du Faubourg St-Honoré,
75008 Paris, France
Tel: +33-1-42 66 47 07

THEO FENNELL

Theo Fennell's perfectly judged sense of balance in his jewellery designs (bold but never flash, subtle but never boring) has made him the darling of the fashionocracy. And, as well as making whimsical accessories (a sterling silver ketchup-bottle top, for instance) he has cornered the market in rock star memorabilia, with his scale models of their most precious possessions (guitars, Ferraris, yachts...) executed in precious metals.

Theo Fennell
169 Fulham Road, London SW3 65P, UK
Tel: +44-171-591 5000 Fax: +44-171-591 5001

LES THERMES MARINS

Perched on the cliff beneath Monte Carlo's Hôtel de Paris, this impressive thalassotherapy centre is a Mecca for the Principality's world-weary residents and visitors alike. A palace of pink marble, wood and glass, it offers four levels of therapeutic body (and soul) treatments under the direction of Dr Yves Treguer.

Les Thermes Marins
Société des Bains de Mer, MC 98000 Monaco
Tel: +377-92 16 40 40 Fax: +377-92 16 49 49

DR THIERRY BESINS

This flamboyant individual is one of the most respected cosmetic surgeons in Paris. He is particularly appreciated for his sensitive handling of facial ageing. Whether clients seek his help for drooping eyelids, pouches under the eyes, sagging cheeks or heavily lined necks, they will find themselves safe in his hands.

Dr Thierry Besins
124 rue Faisanderie, 75016 Paris, France
Tel: +33-1-40 72 86 00 Fax: +33-1-40 72 75 23

THIRLSTANE CASTLE

Extending over 15,000 acres in the Lauderdale valley, centred on Captain The Hon. Gerald Maitland-Carew's Thirlstane Castle, this superb shoot delivers what the late Sir Joseph Nickerson (author of *The Shooting Man's Creed*) described as "the most difficult birds". These truly are 5-star pheasants - and the hospitality is of the same level; clients (many of whom are

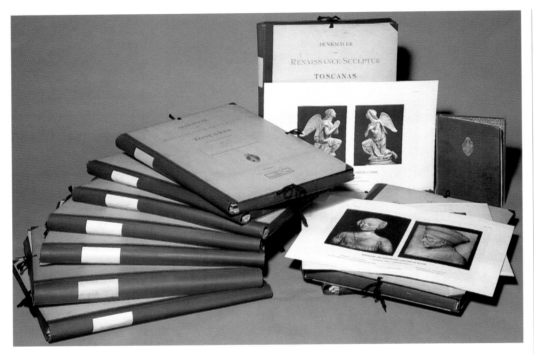

THOMAS HENEAGE ART BOOKS

"I dreamed of becoming one of the world's great art collectors but, unfortunately, didn't have the requisite £30 million pounds to get started," laughs Thomas Heneage. Instead, he appears to have found his true calling. Having begun by working from home in the early 1970s, he has become the best source of information for other collectors. His shop, strategically positioned next to Christie's, is a regular port of call for those in search of advice about anything from Etruscan bronzes to 19th-century drawings, who drop in after the sales and, even more often, before making a buying decision. The personable Heneage, who has an encyclopaedic knowledge of art books, sources rare, antiquarian volumes for collectors all over the world, as well as holding an extraordinarily comprehensive stock of current titles. Heneage regularly exhibits at the Grosvenor House Fair (where he is often called upon to provide a quick reference to items on other exhibitors' stands) and publishes a newsletter three times a year, *The Art Book Survey*, which reviews new and forthcoming art reference books.

Thomas Heneage Art Books
42 Duke Street, St James's, London SW1Y 6JD, UK
Tel: +44-171-930 9223   Fax: +44-171-839 9223

members of the Forbes 500) stay as guests in magnificent castles and country mansions, including Lord Palmerston's Manderston.

Thirlstane Castle, Berwickshire, Scotland
c/o Eskdale Shooting, 3 Market Place, Lauder, Berwickshire TD2 6SR, Scotland
Tel: +44-1578-72 27 03   Fax: +44-1578-72 27 73

THOMAS GIBSON FINE ART LTD.

Despite numerous spectacular deals brokered during the 27 years that he ran his eponymous gallery, Thomas Gibson has always maintained an intensely low profile. Since 1996 this Argentinian-born Old Etonian has been acting as art advisor to a small circle of major collectors. His strength lies in knowing where to find the right work on a client's behalf, whether it is authentic and in good condition, what

should be paid for it and, finally, securing it at the most favourable price.

Thomas Gibson Fine Art Ltd
44 Old Bond Street, London W1X 4HQ, UK
Tel +44-171-499 8572   Fax +44-171-495 1924

TOMASZ STARZEWSKI

Tomasz Starzewski cuts a colourful figure on the London fashion scene and is a great favourite with the city's ladies of leisure, for whom he whips up natty little suits for Ascot and the grandest confections for summer balls. Best friend Tessa Kennedy designed his jewel-box of a shop on Sloane Street. Starzewski cites Yves Saint Laurent and Edith Sitwell as his main influences.

Tomasz Starzewski
177-8 Sloane Street, London SW1X 4AS, UK
Tel: +44-171-235 4526   Fax: +44-171-235 5350

THOMAS GOODE

Founded in 1827, and holder of three Royal Warrants, Thomas Goode is one of the world's greatest china, glass and silver shops. As you enter through the oldest automatic door in London, you are flanked by a unique pair of seven-foot high majolica elephants made by Minton for The Great Exhibition in Paris of 1889.

The elegant show room, illuminated by magnificent chandeliers, houses collections from some of the greatest international china and porcelain manufacturers. Exquisite crystal, silver and linen further enhance the ravishing table displays. Thomas Goode's extensive range of own-brand fine bone china and crystal is unique, ranging from traditional patterns to contemporary designs by Peter Ting. In May 1998, The Victoria and Albert Museum acquired pieces from the Peter Ting range for its permanent collection.

Thomas Goode's knowledgeable staff will offer expert help and advice to clients wishing to create their own bespoke dinner service, which will then be hand crafted in fine English bone china by its own factory. The Bridal Registry provides excellent advice and discreet service for brides-to-be from all over the world. The Goode's Museum houses a fascinating display of historically important china and commemorative glass, commissioned by heads of state and royalty since the firm's earliest years.

Thomas Goode Ltd.
19 South Audley Street, London W1Y 6BN, UK
Tel: +44-171-499 2823   Fax: +44-171-629 4230
Website: www.thomasgoode.co.uk

TONI CORDERO

During his 39-year career, Toni Cordero has designed numerous houses for the great and good (he is too discreet to name names but has collaborated with garden designer Paolo Pejrone). Other credits range from the Turin football stadium to the refurbishment of the Hotel Splendido in Portofino. Always something of a rebel, this architect/interior designer regards minimalism as egocentric and believes in a complex, rather than a simple, architectural language.

Toni Cordero
Strada Communale Mongreno 71,
10132 Turin, Italy
Tel: +39-011-898 9720   Fax: +39-011-898 7295

TORRES

Having been a relatively insignificant operation 40 years ago, Torres is now a world leader. Current president Miguel A. Torres can take much of the credit, having created the company's most famous wine, Gran Coronas Mas La Plana. Its silky texture and great concentration of flavour have led to it being preferred to some of France's finest clarets.

Miguel Torres
Commercio 22, Vilafranca del Penedes,
08720 Barcelona, Spain
Tel: +33-93-817 7400   Fax: +34-93-817 7467

TRASIERRA

Charlotte Scott's 1000-acre estate, set in wild, unspoilt countryside 80km north of Seville, is a perfect hideaway for artists in search of subjects to paint, enervated town-folk pining for tranquillity or celebrities in need of a secure and extremely private bolt-hole (Charlotte won't breathe a word about those who have already stayed). Painting, drawing and photography classes are available on request and parties of eight or more can take the whole place for themselves.

Trasierra
Cazalla de la Sierra, 41370 Seville, Spain
Tel:+34-954-88 43 24   Fax:+34-954-88 33 05

LE TRAVELLERS'

This very 'establishment' club gets an 'A' for architectural merit. Its 800 members (mostly, though by no means all, French) have the run of a marvellous 1870 *hôtel particulier*, built for the Russian-born Marquis de Paiva. It features an exceptional onyx spiral staircase and the original bathroom, which (complete with immaculately preserved silver-plated bronze tub) now serves as a private dining room.

Le Travellers' Club
25 Champs Elysées, 75008 Paris, France
Tel: +33-1-43 59 75 00   Fax:+33-1-45 62 95 16

TRIANON PALACE SPA

A monument to pampering and well-being, the Spa at the Trianon Palace Hotel has it all: luxurious surroundings, first-rate facilities and a mile-long list of treatments (multi-jet hydromassage baths with oil, seaweed and sea water, sudation and hydrojet body treatments, self-heating marine mud, shiatsu massage and something called plantar reflexology, to name just a few).

Trianon Palace Spa
1 boulevard de la Reine, 78000 Versailles, France
Tel: +33-1-30 84 38 00   Fax: +33-1-39 49 88 77

TROISGROS

The twin miracles of this legendary restaurant are its sheer consistency after so many years and the ability of Pierre and Michel Troisgros constantly to tweak what might otherwise become conventionally classical dishes. And the delight is that, despite its exalted position at the very pinnacle of the business, the Troisgros family has never forgotten the importance of a warm welcome.

Troisgros
Place de la Gare, 42300 Roanne, France
Tel: +33-4-77 71 66 97   Fax: +33-4-77 70 39 77

G. F. TRUMPER

London's grandest barber, Trumpers has been tending the hair of courtiers and aristocrats since 1875 (with five royal warrants to show for it). All is traditional here; hair is cut the way hair should be cut and members of staff appear to have been hand-picked for their old-school courtesy.

G. F. Trumper
9 Curzon Street, London W1Y 7FL, UK
Tel: +44-171-499 1850

TRUSSARDI

Originally master glovemakers, Trussardi opted to use the same soft leathers for its famous suitcases, bags and accessories, in a line designed by Nicola Trussardi and launched in 1973. This was followed by expansion into fashion in the mid-70s with the first Trussardi boutique. Leather goods, however, remain the pick of Trussardi's offerings.

Trussardi
Piazza Duse 4, 20122 Milan, Italy
Tel: +39-2-76 06 41   Fax: +39-2-76 06 43 99

TSITOURAS COLLECTION

Dimitris Tsitouras' eponymous Collection is a range of fine decorative accessories in gold, silver, porcelain, glass and fabric, all bearing the laurel-wreath logo designed by Yannis Tsarouchis, one of Greece's most influential artists. It is also a charming hotel on the island of Santorini - five beautifully decorated traditional Cycladic houses, perched on a 1000-foot cliff overlooking the sea.

The Tsitouras Collection
80 Solonos Street, 10680 Athens, Greece
Tel: +30-1-362 2326   Fax: +30-1-363 6738
Hotel: Firostefani, 84700, Thera, Greece
Tel: +30-286-23 747   Fax: +30-286-23 918

THE TURF CLUB

Carlton House Terrace is an entirely appropriate setting for the aristocratic denizens of The Turf Club. Members enjoy a reciprocal arrangement with Paris' Jockey Club and a tradition dating back to the 1860s. A decline in its fortunes was arrested in 1977 when the Marquess of Hartington took the helm and encouraged an influx of younger members.

The Turf Club
5 Carlton House Terrace, London SW1Y 5AQ, UK
Tel: +44-171-930 8555

TURNBERRY

Centred around a grand Edwardian hotel and state-of-the-art spa on the Scottish coast, this is one of the most complete golf resorts in the world. The scenery is beautiful and the tranquillity absolute. It has two courses, the Ailsa (which has hosted the Open Championship three times) and the lesser Arran course. The former has one of golf's most famous landmarks: the lighthouse on a rocky outcrop by the 9th fairway.

Turnberry Hotel & Golf Club
Ayrshire KA26 9LT, Scotland
Tel: +44-1655-33 10 00   Fax: +44-1655-33 17 06

TURNBULL & ASSER

Paul Cuss, head of Turnbull & Asser's Custom Shirt department, counts HRH the Prince of Wales and James Bond (Pierce Brosnan) among his distinguished clients. As well as making beautifully fitting bespoke shirts in the finest cottons, T&A sells a vast range of ready-made shirts, dressing gowns, cashmere sweaters and hand-made silk ties.

Turnbull and Asser Ltd
71/72 Jermyn Street,
London SW1Y 6PF, UK
Tel: +44-171-808 3000   Fax: +44-171-808 3001

ÜBERSEE-CLUB

Housed in a patrician residence, built in 1831 for the great merchant Gottleib Jenish, this discreet private club, was created in 1922 as a meeting place for the leaders of politics and industry. Of its present 1800 members, 100 are women, who have been allowed to join this previously all-male domain since 1951.

Übersee-Club
Jungfernstieg 19, D-20354 Hamburg, Germany
Tel: +49-40-355 2900   Fax: +49-40-34 53 14

UNION BANK OF SWITZERLAND

Adopting a global approach to financial planning and wealth management in its private banking sector, UBS backs up individual service with a team of highly trained professionals in investment banking and trading. With over a century in private banking, its strengths are confidentiality, coupled with strategy and structure.

Union Bank of Switzerland AG
P.O. Box, CH-8098 Zürich, Switzerland
Tel: +41-1-234 1111   Fax: +41-1-236 5111

U ZLATEHO TYGRA

Setting aside any pretensions to stars, rosettes and what-have-you, some of the most eminent Czechs are to be found drinking Pilsner and eating homely cooking at 'The Golden Tiger'. You may be met with disdain if you try to snaffle a table without being accompanied by a regular - Milan Kundera, Milos Forman, or President Havel would do. Frequented by fogey old counts, U Zlateho Tygra has seen and watered a coloured clan ranging from some of the more funky, junior members of the British Royal family to President Clinton.

U Zlateho Tygra
Husova 17, Prague 1, Czech Republic
Tel: + 420-2-24 22 90 20

VACHERON CONSTANTIN

Founded in Geneva in 1755 and deeply proud of its long history, Vacheron Constantin makes expensive and discreet watches in strictly limited numbers, sometimes no more than a few dozen of each type. Indeed, the value of these watches increases after purchase, due to their rarity.

Vacheron Constantin
1 rue des Moulins, 1204 Geneva, Switzerland
Tel: +41-22-310 3227   Fax: +41-22-310 3228

VALDERRAMA

This is Europe's answer to Augusta National. With Bolivian tin billionaire, Jaime Ortiz-Patiño, as its owner and president, this Robert

Trent Jones Sr. course assumed its present incarnation in 1985 (at a reputed cost of $30 million). Nothing is neglected and the owner takes great joy in going out at dawn to oversee the greenkeeping work. Its museum houses some of the rarest items in golf and the sumptuous clubhouse has a Michelin-starred restaurant.

Valderrama
11310 Sotogrande, Cadiz, Spain
Tel: +34-956-79 57 75   Fax: +34-956-79 60 28

C.J. VANDER

For more than a century C.J. Vander has been producing hand-forged silver cutlery of exceptional quality, based primarily on 18th- and 19th-century designs. Special commissions are a forte and its products grace the tables of several royal households. Vander's products are available through fine retailers, including Thomas Goode in London.

C.J. Vander
Vander House, Starnhill Close, Ecclesfield, Sheffield S35 9TG, UK
Tel: +44-114-257 2700   Fax: +44-114-257 2700

VALENTINO

For 38 years Valentino Garavani has been creating supremely ladylike clothes of exquisite cut and quality. With a lifestyle to match that of his couture clients, Valentino's supremacy on the fashion map has always been equalled by his prominence on the social map, as he winters at his magnificent house in Gstaad and summers in Capri and aboard his sumptuous yacht, *T.M. Blue*.

Valentino set up his couture house at the age of 28, with a loan from his parents, having previously worked for Jean Desses and Guy Laroche. Shortly afterwards he met Giancarlo Giametti, an architecture school drop-out, who became the business genius behind the label. Its fortune was assured when ladies like Jacqueline Onassis and Babe Paley discovered his clothes; these days, it is the likes of the Miller girls, Marina Palma, Sharon Stone and Mica Ertegun who carry the torch for him.

At the beginning of 1998 the business was bought for a cool $300 million by the financial conglomerate HdP. It will be business as usual for the partners, however, although they both say that they intend to spend more time in Paris, where Valentino owns the magnificent Château Wideville and Giametti has a fabulous apartment on the Quai d'Orsay.

Valentino
Piazza Mignanelli 22, 00187 Rome, Italy
Tel: +39-06-67 391   Fax: +39-06-679 0275

VANDERVEN & VANDERVEN ORIENTAL ART

Founded in 1968, the van der Ven family's gallery specialises in Asiatic art, particularly Chinese Export porcelain, although its collection also includes bronzes, lacquer-ware and Dutch colonial furniture. The gallery is housed in an Edwardian-style building, with a beautiful garden and French Empire-style tea pavilion.

Vanderven & Vanderven
6 Peperstraat, 5211 KM 's-Hertogenbosch, The Netherlands
Tel: +31-73-614 6251   Fax: +31-73-613 0662
By appointment only

VAN CLEEF & ARPELS

Having established their company in 1906, Alfred Van Cleef and the Arpels brothers (Charles, Julien and Louis) soon became the world's most prestigious jewellers. The two families complemented each other perfectly; Alfred was a clever strategist, Charles and Julien were excellent at choosing stones and Louis was brilliant at public relations. The

Van Cleef & Arpels
LES MONTRES

house's distinctive style emerged from

1922, with the appointment of René Sim Lacaze, who was inspired by the jewels found in Tutankhamen's tomb. From 1925 flower motifs became the main theme, after a bracelet with diamond and ruby roses (designed by Renée Puissant, the daughter of Alfred Van Cleef) won the Grand Prix at the Exposition Internationale des Arts Décoratifs. The unique, mosaic-like designs which appeared in 1933 were made possible thanks to its invention of the *Serti Mystérieux*, a continuing trademark of the house. Many other ingenious ideas followed, such as the *Zip*, which worked as a zipper and a necklace, and the *Passepartout*, a bracelet, necklace, brooch or belt. Today, the house's design team is as innovative as ever, judging from its new *Pendule Mystérieuse Giratoire*, a superb clock created with emeralds, onyx and 2,302 diamonds. The glamour of the pieces has ensured that the company remains a favourite with Hollywood stars, including Sharon Stone.

Van Cleef & Arpels
22 Place Vendôme, 75001 Paris, France
Telephone: +33-1-53 45 45 45   Fax: +33-1-53 45 45 00

THE VARZUGA RIVER

Some of the greatest late spring fishing in Europe is to be had on the Varzuga River. This wide, fast-flowing river, under Russia's 'big sky', yields huge numbers of prime quality salmon - averaging a staggering 81 fish per rod over a week in late May at Kitza during the last five years. The fishing camps provide, according to one habitué, "the best food in Russia".

Roxton Bailey Robinson
25 High Street, Hungerford,
Berkshire RG17 0NF, UK
TEL: +44-1488-68 32 22   Fax: +1488-68 29 77

VAU

This mellow, streamlined restaurant, designed by architect Meinhard von Gerkan and hung, gallery-style, with paintings caused quite a stir when it opened. It attracts a smart business and fashion crowd at lunchtime, opera and theatre folk in the evenings. Excellent game is served in season and the bar in the old coal cellar is a favourite hang-out.

Vau
54-5 Jagerstraße,
D-10117 Berlin, Germany
Tel: +49-30-202 9730   Fax: +49-30-20 29 73 11

VEGA SICILIA

With its plain black and white label, Vega Sicilia does little to announce itself. But it doesn't have to; this famed Spanish wine is in such demand that it has to be allocated rather than sold. It fetches prices more normally associated with fine claret and ages just as well. Keep it for as long as you can. The robustness of its youth gradually softens but it never loses its underlying power.

Vega Sicilia
Ctra. N-122, KM. 322,
47359 Valbuena de Duero, Valladolid, Spain
Tel: +34-983-68 01 47   Fax: +34-983-68 02 63

VENTANA

Inspired by legends like London's Mr Chow and LA's Spago, Ventana follows an Italian-Chinese formula beloved of culinary globetrotters. Klaus Buschbek's food is delicious and it looks perfectly ravishing as well; the Wolfgang Puck-inspired Smoked salmon and caviar pizza is a big hit.

Ventana
77 Grindelhof, D-20146 Hamburg, Germany
Tel: +49-40-45 65 88

VEREL DE BELVAL

Despite the tiny size of this fabric shop, the swathes of magnificent silk in the window will stop you in your tracks; inside, the scintillating colours are as tempting as sweets. In the 18th century, France - and, in particular, Lyon - produced some of the finest patterned silks in the world and this company keeps the craft very much alive.

Verel de Belval
4 rue de Furstenburg, 75006 Paris, France
Tel: +33-1-43 26 17 89

VICTORIA COIFFURE

Antony's precision cutting, hair treatments and special-occasion coiffures make him as sought-after for photo shoots and TV work as he is by Geneva's most stylish women. He trained at Jean-Louis David in Paris and, while there, his clients included Catherine Deneuve and Leslie Caron.

Victoria Coiffure
4 rue Saint Victor, CH-1206 Geneva, Switzerland
Tel: +41-22-346 2512

AU VERGER DE LA MADELEINE

There are barely a dozen bottles of 1895 Château Lafite Rothschild on the world market but you should be able to get one at Jean-Pierre Legras' extraordinary wine shop. He also has hard-to-find wines, such as Jasnières and Château Grillet, and a wide range of reasonably-priced offerings, too.

Au Verger de la Madeleine
4 boulevard Malesherbes, 75008 Paris, France
Tel: +33-1-42 65 51 99   Fax: +33-1-49 24 05 22

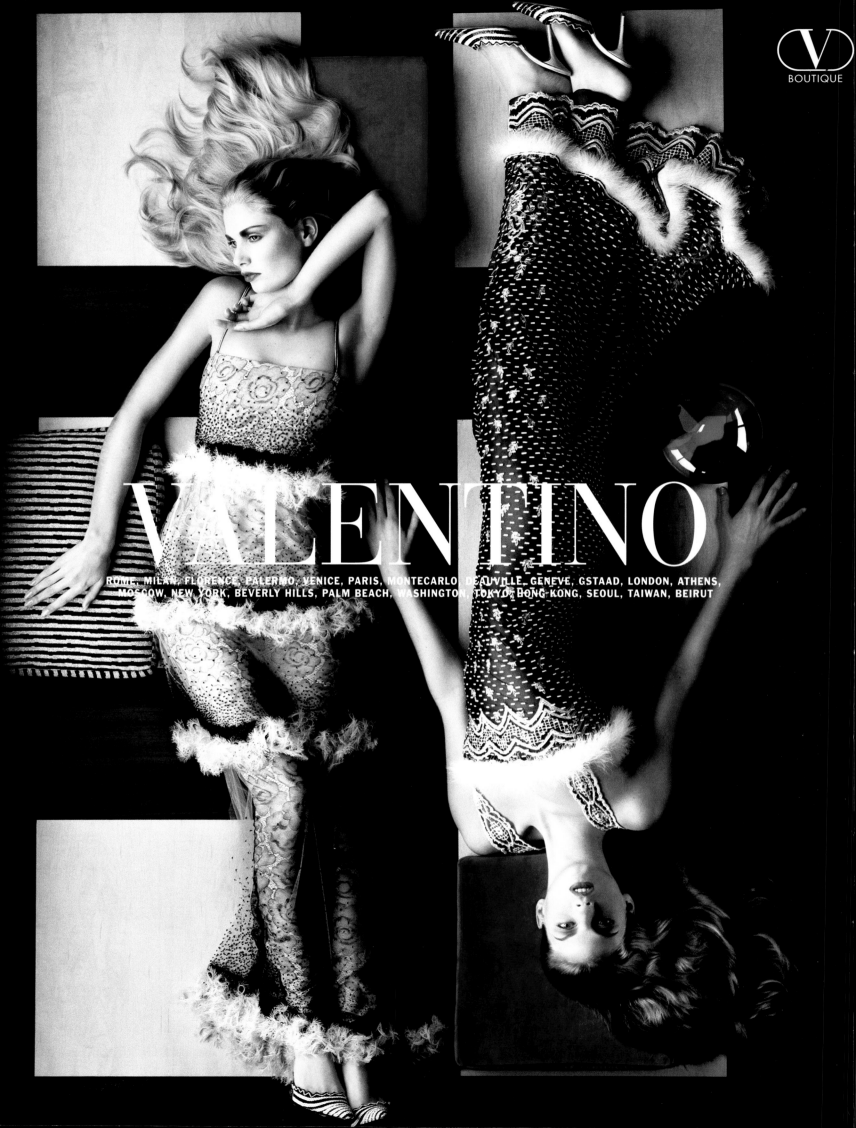

VALENTINO

ROME, MILAN, FLORENCE, PALERMO, VENICE, PARIS, MONTECARLO, DEAUVILLE, GENEVE, GSTAAD, LONDON, ATHENS, MOSCOW, NEW YORK, BEVERLY HILLS, PALM BEACH, WASHINGTON, TOKYO, HONG KONG, SEOUL, TAIWAN, BEIRUT

VICTORIA JUNGFRAU GRAND HOTEL & SPA

The sublime beauty of the forests and lakes make a fitting backdrop to the epitome of the old-style, upmarket Swiss hotel. Sweeping views of the Jungfrau are a treat - request a room with a view - as is the breathtakingly beautiful restaurant, La Terrasse. The hotel is particularly popular with tennis players, as it has four indoor courts.

Victoria Jungfrau Grand Hotel and Spa
CH-3800 Interlaken, Switzerland
Tel: +41-33-828 2828   Fax: +41-33-828 2880

VIERJAHRESZEITEN HAMBURG

The legendary Fritz Haerlin's establishment is a classical grand hotel, though without the intimidating 'grandeur' typical of its genre. Rather than a vast, glittering lobby, there is a cosy, wood-panelled 'lounge hall' and the bedrooms are decorated in discreetly elegant Hanseatic style (those on the upper floors have balconies overlooking the Inner Alster Lake). But, with more than two members of staff per room, service is the real focus; the special preferences of all 15,000 regular guests are kept on file to ensure that they never have to ask for anything twice.

Hotel Vier Jahreszeiten Hamburg
Neuer Jungfernstieg 9, D-20354 Hamburg, Germany
Tel: +49-40-34 940   Fax: +49-40-349 4602

VILLA CIPRIANI

The fortress village of Asolo is described as "the town of a hundred horizons" with good reason. Here, the Villa Cipriani, a 16th-century residence, offers grand hospitality under the inspired management of Giampaolo Burratin. The fragrant garden and timeless vistas are reason enough to justify a visit in their own right.

Villa Cipriani
via Canova 298, 31011 Asolo-Treviso, Italy
Tel: +39-0423-95 21 66   Fax: +39-0423-95 20 95

VILLA DI PILLO

Lavishly restored and decorated by its American owners, this classical 18th-century

VEUVE CLICQUOT-PONSARDIN

Now the second most popular champagne in the United States after Moët et Chandon, this marque has certainly done justice to its founder, Nicole Clicquot. The 1989 and 1990 vintages of its Grande Dame cuvée rival the very best champagnes. The house's 1988 Rosé, which has a deliciously fresh bouquet, despite being aged for nine years, is also a must. Moreover, as Madame Clicquot was the first to produce a rosé champagne, you can be assured of the *savoir faire* behind it. Anybody interested in learning more is always welcome at Veuve Cliquot's headquarters to taste the champagne and tour the cellars (by prior arrangement, of course) however, the most coveted invitation in Champagne is to stay as a house guest at the company's manor in Verzy or its mansion in the centre of Reims.

Veuve Clicquot-Ponsardin
12 rue du Temple, 51100 Reims, France
Tel: +33-3-26 89 54 40   Fax: +33-3-26 40 60 17

hilltop villa enjoys views across its own estate of olive groves and vineyards. Exquisitely comfortable without being overly grand, the villa can accommodate up to ten guests and is set in its own vast park, 45 minutes from Florence.

Villa di Pillo, near San Gimignano, Italy
c/o The Best In Italy,
via Ugo Foscolo 72, 50124 Florence, Italy
Tel: +39-055-33 30 64   Fax: +39-055-229 89 12

VILLA GALLICI

The scent of lavender greets you at the reception desk; 18th century-style *bergère* armchairs are arranged in clusters around the lemon yellow salon and volumes of poetry and art books are heaped on side tables. Little surprise, then, that two of this hotel's directors are ex-interior designers. As Charles Montemarco explains, "For ten years we lived in hotels - it was a terrible sort of life but it finally gave us the idea to start one of our own."

Villa Gallici
avenue de la Violette,
13100 Aix-en-Provence, France
Tel: +33-4-42 23 29 23   Fax: +33-4-42 96 30 45

VILLA LA RIVELLA

Situated in the heart of the Veneto, Villa la Rivella was designed by Andrea Palladio and built by one of his pupils. The villa is decorated in exquisite taste and the gardens are magnificent - with hundreds of different plants (including 30,000 roses) as well as ponds, terraces and a fruit tree-girdled swimming pool.

Villa la Rivella, near Padova, Italy
c/o The Best in Italy,
via Ugo Foscolo 72, 50124 Florence, Italy
Tel: +39-055-22 30 64   Fax: +39-055-229 89 12

VILLA PARADISO

Exclusive but informal, Villa Paradiso is a 19th-century villa on the banks of Lake Garda with

VILLA D'ESTE

How do you describe perfection? Renaissance architecture and pleasure grounds on a magnificent scale? A heated swimming pool that floats directly on the lake? Staff (brilliantly led by Claudio Ceccherelli) that outnumber the guests and who are *genuinely* nice? Truly inspired cooking by Luciano Parolari? A suite in the former villa of Princess Caroline (mistakenly regarded by some guests as 'the annexe') which is one of the most intimate and secluded in all of Europe, with a heartbreakingly beautiful view down the lake? Small wonder, then, that some guests come every year for two months and hardly leave the grounds. Jean-Marc Droulers, whose father bought the hotel in the mid-Sixties, has set the benchmark for 5-star hotels the world over. A single example of his attention to detail: every year during the winter closure, the hotel is not merely cleaned, it is completely repainted.

Villa d'Este
22012 Cernobbio, Lago di Como, Italy
Tel :+39-031-3481   Fax: +39-031-34 88 44

36 pink-washed rooms to which guests retire after a day's pampering at the Preventative Medicine Centre. Doctors, beauticians, nutritionists and physiotherapists are all on hand to restore you to peak fitness.

Villa Paradiso
254 Via Zanardelli,
25080 Fasano del Garda, Italy
Tel: +39-0365-21 883   Fax: +39-0365-20 269

VILLA LA LOGGIA

Built in 1610 by the Brandolini family on the remains of an earlier fortress, Villa La Loggia remains in the hands of the family to this day. Set on a hillside, overlooking the Trevisan-Venetian plain, its lovely garden contains a swimming pool and a charming loggia. Furnished in classical Venetian style the villa contains many rare antiques and 17th-century frescoes.

Villa La Loggia, near Treviso Italy
c/o The Best in Italy
via Ugo Foscolo 72, 50124 Florence, Italy
Tel: +39-055-22 30 64   Fax: +39-055-229 89 12

VILLA SAN MICHELE

In the hills above Florence, surrounded by gardens and woodland, the Villa San Michele (originally a 15th-century monastery with a facade by Michelangelo and an outstanding collection of antiques) is a magical retreat. The fact that, apart from the corner suites, rooms are small-ish in no way compromises the sense of luxury; that is ensured by the marvellous service.

Hotel Villa San Michele
via di Doccia 4, 50014 Fiesole, Florence, Italy
Tel: +39-055-59 451   Fax: +39-055-59 87 34

VILLEROY & BOCH

One of the oldest industrial enterprises in Europe, Villeroy & Boch has, throughout eight generations of family ownership, displayed a remarkable ability to move with the times. As early as the 1850s it took a global approach to marketing and it has consistently improved its manufacturing techniques and materials. However, it is the value which the company has always placed on design which has been a major factor in its success, from its commissioning of Jugendstil artists earlier this century to its association with the likes of Luigi Colani and Paloma Picasso today. Breaking free from the narrow confines of traditional styling, the company today offers a wealth of inspiration, from cheerful country style to subtle elegance.

Villeroy & Boch S.à.r.l.
Rieffstraße 46,
D-66663 Merzig, Germany
Tel: +49-6864-81 42 76   Fax: +49-6864-81 42 93
Email: vbadmin@pt.lu

VILLA REALE

A true showpiece, Villa Reale was created in its present form by Napoleon's sister when she ruled Tuscany. Later it belonged to the King of Italy, then was bought by the present owners in 1918. Its magnificently appointed interiors are rivalled only by the elaborate, romantic gardens, with their grottoes, ponds and sculptures.

Villa Reale, near Lucca, Italy
c/o The Best In Italy,
via Ugo Foscolo 72, 50124 Florence, Italy
Tel: +39-055-22 30 64   Fax: +39-055-229 89 12

VINÇON

When Fernando Amat took over his family's 60 year-old tableware store in 1967, it began to grow...and grow. Now it is a 3,000 sq. metre emporium selling everything for the home. The top floor furniture showroom was once a grand bourgeois apartment and the shopping bags, designed by young artists, are coveted by collectors.

Vinçon
Passeig de Gracia 96, E-08008 Barcelona, Spain
Tel: +34-93-215 6050

VISSANI

His original and highly personalised approach to the ingredients of his native Umbria has made Gianfranco Vissani one of Italy's most exciting chefs; signature dishes, such as Foie gras with caramelised fennel and Pigeon with lentils and white truffles, have diners in raptures. The atmosphere in his rustic, antique-filled restaurant is, however, more pleasantly relaxed than one might expect from such a temple of gastronomy.

Vissani
Strada per Todi, Civitella del Lago,
05020 Baschi, Italy
Tel: +39-0744-95 02 06   Fax: 39-0744-95 03 96

VLADI PRIVATE ISLANDS

In this crowded world the idea of owning a remote island is increasingly attractive. For 25 years Dr Sarhad Vladi has specialised in such properties and has a portfolio of some 3,000 privately-owned islands all over the world, which are available for sale or rental. Edward de Bono and Tony Curtis have both been clients.

Vladi Private Islands
Ballindamm 7, D-20095 Hamburg, Germany
Tel: +49-40-33 89 89   Fax: +49-40-33 00 81

IL VOLTO

Vittorio Fusani's restaurant began, in 1981, as a little *osteria* or tavern. Today, his innovative regional cooking (dishes on the constantly changing menu include marvellous Roasted squab with mustard sauce and Braised beef in olive oil) has earned him a Michelin star. What hasn't changed is the warm ambience and the caring service, under the watchful eye of Mario Archetti.

Il Volto
33 via Mirolte, 25049 Iseo Brescia, Italy
Tel: +39-030-98 14 62   Fax: +39-030-98 18 74

VINCENT CALABRESE

As an entirely self-taught inventor of exceptional skill and imagination, Vincent Calabrese is a watchmaker in the oldest tradition of the craft. Since 1975 he has been waging a one-man crusade against what he terms "the blandness of mass-produced styling", with his highly innovative mechanical timepieces. Having learned all of the trades which would enable him to execute, alone, a complete watch, his first concept

(to create a movement apparently floating in space and unconnected with the watch case) appeared as the Personnelles line, winning a gold medal at the 1977 Geneva International Inventors' Show. The movement, in the form of the initial or symbol prescribed by the buyer, is suspended in a gold and transparent sapphire case. Calabrese has, subsequently, adapted his patented Spatiale technique to numerous other, mostly limited edition, styles, as well as developing other mechanisms and becoming the only watchmaker to produce a platinum movement.

Vincent Calabrese
19a Boulevard de Grancy,
CH-1006 Lausanne, Switzerland
Tel: +41-21-617 0834   Fax: +41-21-617 0835

LES VOYAGES EXCELLENCE

So you own a Rolls Royce and need a hotel with a private garage where you can lock it up for the night? The wide open spaces of Argentina beckon but you haven't a clue where to stay? You'd like to rent a lighthouse somewhere near San Francisco? Simply call Bernard Fromageau, master of the made-to-measure holiday, and all will be arranged. For 15 years he has been cramming his database with the very best travel tips from across the globe. His office is so packed with travel magazines,

hotel brochures, books on sumptuous locations and guides to faraway places that he occasionally disappears from sight. The company's speciality is finding small hideaways around the globe - places that Fromageau says are increasingly in demand, as people have grown tired of the international 5-star hotels that could be anywhere from Cairo to Monte Carlo. His clients have also become more adventurous; he recently arranged for a retired couple to go walking in the Himalayas with their own guide and marvellous accommodation. Les Voyages Excellence produces its own holiday bulletin that is filled with recommendations from his clients.

Les Voyages Excellence
13 rue de Tournon, 75006 Paris, France
Tel: +33-1-46 34 54 54   Fax: +33-1-40 51 03 64

WADDESDON MANOR

Waddesdon Manor was built in French château style to house Baron Ferdinand de Rothschild's world-class collection of French 18th-century furniture, Sèvres porcelain, English and Flemish paintings and decorative arts. Now owned and run by the National Trust, this museum's added attractions include an aviary with exotic birds, the Rothschild wine cellars and marvellous gardens, restored by Beth Rothschild Tomassini.

Waddesdon Manor

Waddesdon, Near Aylesbury,

Buckinghamshire HP18 OJH, UK

Tel: +44-1296-65 12 82

WADDINGTON GALLERIES

Two things distinguish Leslie Waddington from most other leading British art dealers: the size of his operation (his stock reserve has always been worth at least £12 million) and the fact that there is no such thing as a Waddington artist. Beyond a broad 20-century, Modernist tradition, he has never set himself up as the champion of any particular practice, preferring to hunt out the best works within a given genre.

Waddington Galleries

11 Cork Street, London W1X 2LT, UK

Tel: +44-171-437 8611   Fax: +44-171-734 4146

WAGNER FESTIVAL BAYREUTH

Despite accusations of artistic stagnation (which have not, however, dissuaded the world's greatest artists from performing here) and a power struggle between Wolfgang Wagner, the composer's ageing grandson, and rival members of the family, this remains the festival both for deadly serious opera-lovers and for social high-rollers. To escape such intensity, stay in the pretty villages in the countryside nearby.

Wagner Festival Bayreuth

D-95402 Bayreuth, Germany

Tel: +49-921-78 780

WALD & SCHLOSSHOTEL FRIEDRICHSRUHE

It is not just the building (a ravishing, 17th-century summer palace and hunting lodge) or its setting (surrounded by miles of unspoilt countryside) that makes this hotel such a delight. Rather, it is the fact that its owners, Prince and Princess Hohenlohe-Oehringen treat you as if you are guests in their own home. Note that their wine cellar contains such rarities as a 1949 Chambertin.

Wald & Schloßhotel Friedrichsruhe

D-74639 Friedrichsruhe-Zweiflingen, Germany

Tel: +49-7941-60 870   Fax: +49-7941-61 468

THE WALLACE COLLECTION

The Wallace Collection has been described as a mini-Louvre due to its outstanding French 18th-century decorative arts and paintings. Under the terms of the bequest of the Fourth Marquess of Hertford's heir, Lady Wallace, the collection may not be enlarged or loaned, so it perfectly captures the interests of a wealthy late 19th-century family.

The Wallace Collection

Hertford House, Manchester Square,

London W1M 6BN, UK

Tel: +44-171-935 0687   Fax: +44-171-224 2155

WALLY YACHTS

In 1989 industrialist Luca Bassani Antovari decided to build a fast cruising yacht based on

his own requirements: easy handling, flush decks and advanced composite construction. Such was the reaction to *Wallygator* that he established Wally Yachts four years later. Serving as a contracting company, Wally is independent of boatyards, design offices and materials suppliers and, since 1994, has launched 16 craft, from 67 to 107 feet in length.

Wally Yachts

Seaside Plaza, 2 avenue des Ligures,

MC-98000 Monaco

Tel: +377-93 10 00 93   Fax: +377-93 10 00 94

WANNSEE

Established in 1895, Wansee hosted the German Open many times before World War II. Since then Jack Nicklaus and George Bush are among the countless luminaries who have played this mature, par-72 course. The dogleg 7th hole is a real test of nerve, with bunkers strewn the length of the fairway and a tricky green. The stylish clubhouse - in the guise of a traditional German country house - was rebuilt in 1997.

Wannsee

Golf-Weg 22, D-14109 Berlin, Germany

Tel: +49-30-806 70 60   Fax: +49-30-80 67 06 10

WARTSKI

This firm's international reputation for works by Carl Fabergé dates back to the time when the Russian government was selling the Imperial collection to fund industrial expansion. Wartski acquired such masterpieces as the Rosebud, Coronation, Lilies of the Valley, Colonnade, Peacock and Winter Imperial Eggs. It swiftly developed the Fabergé market, selling to Europe's crowned heads and aristocracy. Once a year Wartski brings over some Fabergé, which The Queen enjoys seeing, to Buckingham Palace. Owner Kenneth Snowman has written the essential reference work on Fabergé.

Wartski

14 Grafton Street, London W1X 4DE, UK

Tel: +44-171-493 1141   Fax: +44-171-409 7448

THE WATCH GALLERY

With its pale wood art-deco interior, champagne-and-espresso bar and well-informed staff, this shop has established a new style in watch retailing, successfully targeting both wealthy young professionals and collectors. Its smorgasbord of top timepieces includes Ulysse Nardin, Girard-Perregaux and IWC, as well as first models of limited editions.

The Watch Gallery

129 Fulham Road, London SW3 6RT, UK

Tel: +44-171-581 3239   Fax: +44-171-584 6497

THE WATERSIDE INN

Michel Roux, who trained as a *pâtissier* and worked for the Rothschilds in France, has owned one of Britain's best restaurants for 25 years, becoming a superstar in his adopted country. While the service is occasionally over-attentive, the cooking takes some beating and the delightful riverbank setting is a treat for the senses.

The Waterside Inn

Ferry Road, Bray, Berkshire SL6 2AT, UK

Tel: +44-1628-62 06 91   Fax: +44-1628-67 87 10

WEDHOLM'S FISK

Bengt Wedhom is a chef with a passion - fish and, in particular, sole. Almost a legend (with a Michelin star as confirmation) for what he calls "plain, no-nonsense cooking", his portions are generous and are served by an upbeat staff in this simply decorated restaurant.

Wedholm's Fisk

17 Nybrokajen, 11148 Stockholm, Sweden

Tel: +46-8-10 48 74

WENTWORTH

The car park has Bentleys wall-to-wall and there always seems to be a star golfer or celebrity play-ing or enjoying the ultra-luxe club-house. Wentworth's 700 acres of rhododendron-girdled heathland incorporate three excellent 18-hole courses. The celebrated West Course (which, at £140, has Europe's most expensive green fee) is home to the World Matchplay and PGA championships.

Wentworth Club

Wentworth Drive, Virginia Water,

Surrey GU25 4LS, UK

Tel: +44-1344-84 22 01   Fax: +44-1344-84 28 04

WEXFORD FESTIVAL

Established in 1951, the Wexford Festival is a celebration of less well-known operas in the magical setting of this Irish coastal town. A company of international performers takes to the stage of the small but charming theatre; it is a unique blend of fine artistry and relaxed charm in a house-party atmosphere.

Wexford Festival Opera

Theatre Royal, High Street, Wexford, Ireland

Tel: +353-53-22 144   Fax: +353-53-24 289

WHITE NIGHTS FESTIVAL

St Petersburg's White Nights Festival is so called because it takes place in mid-summer when the sun never sets. Valery Gergiev, Artistic Director of the Mariinsky Theatre, is the driving force behind this programme of opera, ballet and orchestral music. The 1998 programme included Borodin, Tchaikovsky, and Wagner, while 1999 will specialise in music by Berlioz.

White Nights Festival, St Petersburg, Russia

c/o Friends of the Kirov,

95 Aldwych, London WC2B 4JF, UK

Tel: +44-171-831 7547   Fax: +44-171-831 8209

WHITE'S CLUB

With its impressive collection of portraits, celebrated card room and seemingly immutable Grade I headquarters dating from 1674, White's is the club to which every gentleman should belong. Generations of bucks, beaux, gossips and gamblers have watched the world go by from its bay window. Its tent at Ascot is even more sought-after than the Royal Enclosure.

White's Club

37 St James's Street, London SW1 AJG, UK

Tel: +44-171-493 6671

WESTERN & ORIENTAL

As former travel editor of a leading glossy magazine, Bruce Palling - founder of Western & Oriental - knows a thing or two about what people want from travel and pledges to provide "whatever our clients want, wherever and whenever".

His company organises incomparable journeys for those wishing to escape to the perfumed delights of the Far East, South East Asia and the South Pacific in great style. Its Indian itineraries are particularly impressive, as they place great emphasis on showing what makes a specific area unique, which is why the trips are full of little detours to exceptional but rarely visited sites. A recent addition to its schedule is a wildlife journey covering major game reserves in India, to spy on the elusive Bengal Tiger. There are also road

safaris through the majestic mountains of Northern Pakistan and trips to the ancient monuments and superb beaches of Sri Lanka.

The company also takes a great deal of care over accommodation. Believing that many people have more than enough luxury at home and would rather stay in places with atmosphere (as opposed to hotels with every comfort but little ambience), the company offers a marvellous choice of privately-owned homes, forts and palaces.

Western & Oriental

King House, 11 Westbourne Grove, London W2 4UA, UK

Tel: +44-171-313 6600 Fax: +44-171-313 6601

WILDENSTEIN

Together with his sons, Alex and Guy, Daniel Wildenstein is possibly the wealthiest and most powerful art dealer in the world. He heads an awesome company founded in 1875 by his father, George, and now worth an estimated $5 billion. The lead-lined vaults of its Paris headquarters contain Botticellis, Rembrandts, Rubens, Velazquezes, El Grecos, Tintorettos, Fragonards and Watteaus, plus an enormous collection of Impressionists. Today's greatest collectors, such as Paul Mellon, the Annenbergs and the David-Weills shop here.

Wildenstein

57 rue de la Boétie, 75008 Paris, France

Tel: +33-1-45 61 61 61

WILKINSON

Family-owned Wilkinson & Son, with a royal warrant to prove it, is the Rolls Royce of the chandelier business. Its Catford factory manufactures and restores practically every type of grand light fitting, while its Mayfair showroom is a veritable Aladdin's cave of antique chandeliers, mirrors and table candelabra. Winningly, it prides itself on undertaking anything that other companies will not!

Wilkinson & Son
1 Grafton Street, London W1X 3LB, UK
Tel: +44-171-495 2477   Fax: +44-171-491 1737

WILTONS
256 year-old Wiltons is as much an institution as the gentlemen's clubs that surround it. Pullman-style tables are waited upon by demure, nanny-like waitresses serving traditional 'sporting British' food, especially seafood. Clients are similarly upstanding - politicians, journalists and discreet businessmen - lending it the other-worldy air of a bygone era. Famed for its oysters and its equally famous 'Oyster Man', Patrick Flaherty.

Wiltons
55 Jermyn Street, London SW1Y 6LX, UK
Tel: +44-171-629 9955   Fax: +44-171-495 6233

WINGS OF DESIRE
Be whisked to the heliport of your choice in one of this firm's chauffeur-driven Bentleys (Azure, Continental R coupé, Turbo R or Brooklands - you choose) and fly away in its lavishly appointed S76 Agusta. The company also operates a chauffeur motorcycle service and, if you prefer to drive yourself, its portfolio includes Ferraris, Porsches and a Lamborghini roadster. The fantastically stylish livery of the chauffeurs is an added bonus.

Wings of Desire
2-5 Old Bond Street, London W1X 3TB, UK
Tel: +44-171-349 8811   Fax: +44-171-349 8833

WYCOMBE ABBEY SCHOOL
Fiercely academic, Wycombe Abbey has slowly outgrown its bluestocking image to become one of the finest girls' schools anywhere, turning out 'well-rounded' girls - a large proportion of whom win places at the top universities. Drama and music are particularly strong, as are the somewhat esoteric sports of lacrosse and fencing.

Wycombe Abbey School
High Wycombe,
Buckinghamshire HP11 1PE, UK
Tel: +44-1494-52 03 81   Fax: +44-1494-47 38 36

WYKEHAMS
If you cannot wait two years for a new Morgan, you may rent one from this discreet motor dealer - along with other wind-in-the-hair classics, including Aston Martins. And if the love-affair proves terminal, director Charles Eady will happily sell it to you; Wykehams is the only dealership licensed to trade in Morgans.

Wykehams Ltd.
6 Kendrick Place, Reece Mews,
London SW7 3HF, UK
Tel: +44-171-589 6894   Fax: +44-171-589 8886

YACHT CLUB COSTA SMERALDA
Enjoying the patronage of its president, the Aga Khan, The Yacht Club Costa Smeralda lies at the hub of northern Sardinia's marvellous sailing waters. Its members - a mix of Euro-celebrities, socialites and yachting luminaries - have access to two swish club-houses, at Porto Cervo and Porto Rotondo. Club Commodore, Gianfranco Alberini, presides with great charm over several blue-chip regattas each summer, including the Rolex Cup.

Yacht Club Costa Smeralda
07020 Porto Cervo, Sardinia, Italy
Tel: +39-789-90 22 00   Fax: +39-789-91 2 57

YACHT CLUB DE MONACO
Housed in a sleek building tucked into the corner of the Old Port, the Yacht Club de Monaco has, under the energetic direction of Bernard d'Alessandri, emerged from a period as a somewhat snobbish social club to become an active sporting club (with its fair share of glossy parties thrown in for good measure). Prince Albert, himself a passionate sailor, is an enthusiastic and hands-on club President.

Yacht Club de Monaco
16 quai Antoine 1er, MC 98000 Monaco
Tel: +377-93-50 58 39   Fax: +377-93-50 80 88

CHATEAU D'YQUEM

Having owned this legendary château since 1785, the Lur-Saluces family is currently embroiled in a battle with LVMH for ownership of the final 10 per cent of the business that it still retains. Whatever the outcome, Yquem's wines are a masterpiece: rich, elegant and harmonious. And expensive, thanks to the tiny yield (only one glass of wine per vine) and the long ageing (three years in new oak barrels before bottling). Celebrate the millennium with the 1983 Yquem.

Château d'Yquem
33120 Sauternes, France
Tel: +33-5-57 98 07 07   Fax: +33-5-57 98 07 08

YVES SAINT LAURENT

In 40 years of designing, Yves Saint Laurent's vision has remained as steady as a rock. Indeed, he is perhaps the only designer to rely almost entirely on his own resources for inspiration. Not only did he introduce such iconic garments as the see-through blouse and the feminine version of *le smoking* but he pioneered the whole concept of ready-to-wear. With Heidi Slimane in place as menswear designer and Alber Ebaz due to take over the *prêt-à-porter* collection from the end of 1998, Saint Laurent himself will concentrate solely on *haute couture* from now on.

Yves Saint Laurent Couture
5 Avenue Marceau, 75008 Paris, France
Tel: +33-1-44 31 64 00   Fax: +33-1-47 20 62 13

ZAFFERANO

Considering how difficult it is even to get through on the telephone to book a table, this must be London's best neighbourhood restaurant. Belgravia locals and, as the word got out, international celebrities, have been flocking here since 1995, for chef and co-owner Giorgio Locatelli's inspired Italian cooking. Uncomplicated yet interesting, light, modern and comfortable describe the room as well as the cuisine.

Zafferano
15 Lowndes Street, London SW1X 9EY, UK
Tel: +44-171-235 5800

ZOFFANY

When Zoffany began the manufacture of its finely crafted wallpaper for today's great houses it went straight to the original sources for inspiration. Its archives contain countless 18th- and 19th-century documents, on which it bases its elegant and subtly-coloured wall-coverings, many of which are hand printed, as well as a collection of complementary furnishing fabric, carpets and trimming.

Zoffany
63 South Audley Street,
London W1Y 5BF, UK
Tel: +44-171-495 2505   Fax: +44-171-493 7257

ZUBER

With a library of more than 100,000 antique patterns this distinguished company uses traditional printing methods to produce a fabulous range of wallpapers, including *trompe l'oeil* panoramas, ravishing friezes, subtly tinted rose borders and marbled and damask papers. Zuber also produces fabrics in complementary patterns.

Zuber
5 boulevard des Filles-du-Calvaire,
75003 Paris, France
Tel: +33-1-42-77 95 91   Fax: +33-1-42 77 17 98

ZUR TRAUBE

The formal, stucco exterior of this town-house is aptly imposing, for it is home to one of Germany's national treasures - chef Dieter Kaufmann. His cooking is a masterful interpretation of the French classics and his awesome wine cellar contains 30,000 bottles. There are simple but charming rooms upstairs to sleep it all off.

Hotel Restaurant Zur Traube
47 Bahnstrasse, D-41515 Grevenbroich, Germany
Tel: +49-2181-68 767   Fax: +49-2181-61 122

BVLGARI

CONTEMPORARY ITALIAN JEWELLERS

The XL line

In 18kt white gold with amethyst, with blue topaz and with citrine.

Available at Bvlgari stores and at selected jewellery shops.

www.bulgari.it

100 RISING STARS

This selection comprises 100 names which, the Editors believe, will soon make it to the very top in their particular field. Some of them have been around for quite some time and have already achieved a considerable degree of success; others are just starting out. But all, we believe, bear the indefinable mark of true greatness.

HOTEL ADLON

Lorenz Adlon's hotel, inaugurated in 1907, was so luxurious that The Kaiser left his draughty palace in favour of its comforts. Having reopened in 1998 after a long hiatus, it appears that it will live up to its exalted history. The mosaic cupola in the main hall is still a focal point, as is the white mar-

ble staircase down which Marlene Dietrich used to sweep. It has a magnificent spa, the suites are exceptional and its American Bar has, once again, become a favoured Berlin meeting point.

Hotel Adlon
Unter den Linden 77, D-10117 Berlin, Germany
Tel: +49-30-22 610   Fax: +49-30-22 61 11 60

HOTEL AMBASSADE

Blissful floating massages - which take place in a bath filled with health-giving salts - are one of the cosseting services on offer at this lovely hotel. Carved out of a row of buildings overlooking a canal in Amsterdam's 'Golden Century', its rooms are decorated with impeccable taste in Louis XV and XVI style.

Hotel Ambassade
Herengracht 341, 1016AZ, Amsterdam,
The Netherlands
Tel: +31-20-626 23 33   Fax: +31-20-624 53 21

ADONIS

Adonis is the name of Ireland's smartest flower designer. Situated in the oldest quarter of Dublin, between St Patrick's and Christchurch cathedrals, this young company is so hip that it does not produce a brochure - "because we do not have any standard displays". Chief designer Paul Berry is a completely self-taught designer florist, and his partner, Siobhan Downey, is a graduate of Dublin's College of Art and Design.

Together they take their cue from a bewildering array of sources. Influences include "the Dutch Masters, metals and milliner Philip Treacy". *Le tout* Dublin beats a path to their door, not only for distinctive bouquets and posies but also when they require their houses and grand parties decorated in breathtaking style.

As one of the company's recent advertisements admitted, with characteristic honesty, "If you want something special for that special day call us. If you want carnations or chrysanthemums call someone else". The comment is typical of this dynamic and hugely creative young outfit, whose work - and style - is completely unique.

Adonis Flower Designers
59-60 Patrick Street, Dublin 8, Ireland
Tel/Fax: +353-1-454 5973

ANASSA

Situated directly on the unspoilt Askprokemnos Beach at the edge of the Akamas National Park, the brand-new Anassa has been constructed in the traditional, low-rise Cypriot vernacular amid beautiful, scented gardens with sweeping views of the sea and surrounding hills. If initial teething troubles with service are ironed out, this promises to be a special retreat.

Anassa
Latsi, CY-8830 Polis, Cyprus
Tel: +357-6-32 28 00   Fax: +357-6-32 29 00

ANDREA GHIDONI

With loyal clients like Donatella Versace and the director of Moschino couture - and a top-notch range of hair care products to his name - this charming and talented hairdresser looks set to become a Big Thing. Milan's most beautifully sculpted ladies happily drive the 40 minutes out to his lakeside salon.

Andrea Ghidoni
via Verdi 27, 24100 Bergamo, Italy
Tel/Fax: +39-035-24 87 29

ANGEL SCHLESSER

Tipped by the fashion editors as Spain's next big fashion star, 35 year-old Angel Schlesser turns out beautifully crafted, ultra-feminine clothes with a streamlined yet conservative edge.

Angel Schlesser
Claudio Coello 46, E-28001 Madrid, Spain
Tel: +34-91-435 4869

ANTONIO BERARDI

A 1994 graduate of Central St. Martins, Berardi is a hot new name in fashion. The 29 year-old has been approached by Givenchy, Iceberg and Chloé amongst others. His matador-style suits and crocheted and bobbin-lace dresses are sensuous and modern, yet impeccably crafted.

Antonio Berardi
St. Martins House, 59 St. Martins Lane,
London WC2 4JS, UK
Tel: +44-171-836 4265   Fax: +44-171-836 4261

ALEXANDRA BELLINGER

AB
ALEXANDRA BELLINGER
JOYAS DE DISEÑO
JEWELRY DESIGN

Having moved recently from Madrid to London, German-born Alexandra Bellinger continues to offer a discreet, personal service for buyers of her highly original jewellery.

She makes private appointments with her clients and has built up her reputation by word of mouth. Such an individual approach is reflected in her jewellery. "When I design a piece of jewellery, I do not relate to any kind of fashion. I aspire to create something timeless and important by itself and in relation to the person who wears it," she explains.

Alexandra Bellinger absorbed with great attentiveness the environments she enjoyed during her studies of jewellery design and gemology in America, Paris, Hamburg, Bangkok and her extensive private travels. Due to her visual sensitivity, these experiences are now reflected in her creations. Some pieces are decidedly urban: elegant, precious stones, mixed with yellow, pink or white gold. Other pieces draw their inspiration boldly from nature and from *objets trouvés* and fine art curiosities. One of her outstanding designs is the long 'Bomellang' necklace, made of multiple strands of freshwater pearls or coral terminating in two gold spheres applied with delicate gold wirework.

Over the last five years, Alexandra has strengthened her international recognition by launching sales exhibitions of her most recent collections around Europe and the United States.

Alexandra Bellinger
117 Walton Street, London SW3 2HP, UK
Tel: +44-171-225 2004   Fax: +44-171-584 5550
Email: albel@compuserve.com   Website: www.abellinger.com

ANYA HINDMARCH

Anya Hindmarch's distinctive tassel logo adorns the bags of London's young style-setters. Instrumental in developing our taste for dainty little pochettes she also does a mean line in capacious leather shoulder bags. Preferred fabrics for evening are jewel-coloured satins and grosgrain, which can be made to order or customised with clients' monograms.

Anya Hindmarch
15-17 Pont Street, London SW1X 9EH, UK
Tel: +44-171-838 9177   Fax: +44-171-838 9111

APLOMB

Managed by two young, entrepreneurial women, Katia Manenti and Silvia Pierro, Aplomb is a made-to-measure shirt outlet free from stuffiness and old world constrictions. Shirts can be made in 100 types of material and are all cut, sewn and finished by hand. Collars and cuffs are designed strictly to customers' specifications and collar stiffeners can be created in anything from plexiglass to solid gold.

Aplomb
via Monte Vincenzo 50, 20123 Milan, Italy
Tel: +39-02-48 51 91 76

L'ARROSOIR

That L'Arrosoir - opened in December 1997 - is enjoying a *succès fou* is down to the winning combination of Georges Seynave and Jean-Marc Mathez. The former was a banker and brought with him an address book brimming with Geneva's élite; the latter, trained under the great Freddy Giradet, is responsible for the light and imaginative cooking. The restaurant's relaxed ambience is a revelation in this often staid city.

L'Arrosoir
34 Rue Theodore Weber,
CH-1208 Geneva, Switzerland
Tel: +41-22-700 3570

ART AND DECORATION

Increasingly being solicited by international art connoisseurs, Rudolf Pr'hoda specialises in Baroque paintings and furnishings and also has an impressive collection of religious statuary. Potential buyers will be relieved to know that Pr'hoda is adept at organising customs permits - particularly valuable as the government is tightening up art export regulations.

Art and Decoration
Parízská 21, Prague 11000, Czech Republic
Tel: +42-02-24 81 20 86

ATHENEE PALACE HOTEL

As Romania slowly throws off the dark legacy of its communist past, it is being revealed as a magically beautiful country and, having been refurbished at vast expense, the Athenée Palace now provides all the necessary creature comforts. Opened in 1914, when Bucharest was known as the Paris of the East, it was one of the grand hotels of Europe. Now, behind its art-deco façade, it has once again become a slick and polished haven.

Athenée Palace Hotel
1-3 Episcopiei, Sector 1, Bucharest, Romania
Tel: +40-1-315 1212   Fax: +40-1-315 2121

AUBERGE ET CLOS DES CIMES

Régis Marcon trained in France's top restaurants before returning with his wife, Michèle, to run his family's inn. Marcon's Auvergnat roots are clearly evident in dishes like Lamb en croûte with vegetables and cured pork, and a simply perfect Ragoût of puy lentils. The inn - with its cosy bedrooms - like the restaurant, has marvellous views of the Cevennes. As befits the countryside, service is efficient and relaxed. With two Michelin stars already, he is tipped by many for major stardom in the future.

Auberge et Clos des Cimes
Place d l'Eglise, 43290 St Bonnet-le-Froid, France
Tel: +33-4-71 59 93 72   Fax: +33-4-71 59 93 40

BAILEY'S WHISKEY

Bailey's is the name of one of the best-known drinks in the world. What is less well known is that now, in addition to the famed cream liqueur, Bailey's has launched its own whiskey. Aged in barrels that once held a special edition of the liqueur, the spirit is unmistakably Irish but softer than traditional blends. Designed for a younger market, it is fragrant and appealing rather than stern and forbidding.

Bailey's
Nangor House, Nangor Road,
Western Estate, Dublin 12, Ireland
Tel: +353-1-405 1200   Fax: +353-1-405 1222

BAJAZZO

Its relaxed atmosphere and genial staff make Bajazzo one of the most popular restaurants in Athens (you must book ahead for lunch). Star dishes on Klaus Feuerbach's constantly changing, classically-inspired menu include Duck breast with crème de bananes, Sole with salmon mousse and Beef fillets with foie gras and a cognac sauce.

Bajazzo
Anapafseos 14, Mets, 11636 Athens, Greece
Tel/Fax:+30-1-921 3013

LA BASTIDE SAINT-ANTOINE

Once the Midi boasted a number of France's best restaurants, many of which are now resting on their rather withered laurels. So it was heartening to learn that Jacques Chibois, the chef at La Bastide Saint-Antoine in Grasse, had won his country's Chef of the Year award. Although he may not be quite the Marc Veyrat of the South,

Chibois makes up for his more conservative approach with a brilliant balancing of flavours and textures. Try his Kidneys with artichoke hearts and polenta or his dessert of Pistachio macaroons with wild strawberry and liquorice sauce and you will understand why life is looking much rosier in tourist-scarred Provence.

La Bastide Saint-Antoine
48 rue Henri Dunant, 06130 Grasse, France
Tel: +33-4-93 70 94 94   Fax: +33-4-93 70 94 95

BILL AMBERG

Leather designer Bill Amberg blends traditional leather craftsmanship with an insight into the modern-day requirements of bags and luggage for work, travel and leisure, producing classic designs with a contemporary feel. He also takes leather beyond the narrow confines of luggage, using it for furniture, flooring and wall-coverings, undertaking many commissions both privately and for leading interior designers.

Bill Amberg
10 Chepstow Villas, London W2 5BD, UK
Tel: +44-171-727 3560   Fax: +44-171-727 3541

BIBENDUM

Bibendum (Latin for 'time to drink') is a fitting moniker for this company, founded in 1982 by Simon Farr, Ben Collins and Tom Haywood-Lonsdale. Having had great success among the congnoscenti, Bibendum may yet trump the grand old-timers of the trade. Its fine wine desk, which sources rare and fine wines (Cheval Blanc

1945 for a mere £401, for instance), operates a mail order service throughout Europe.

Bibendum Wine
113 Regents Park Road, London NW1 8UR, UK
Tel: +44-171-916 7706   Fax: +44-171-916 7705

BY TERRY

Only a few months after opening, By Terry is a big hit with the film and fashion divas. Hardly surprising, given owner Terry de Gunzburg's background, as creative director of Yves St. Laurent cosmetics. Terry now undertakes personal appraisals and custom-designs make up for each client. The products come in smart pewter containers engraved with the client's name.

By Terry
21 passage Véro-Dodat, 75001 Paris, France
Tel: +33-1-44 76 00 76   Fax: +33-1-44-76 00 79

CAMERON-SHAW

Having joined his sister in her dried-flower business seven years ago, with the intention simply of offering her support, Russell Longmuir discovered his true calling, eventually taking over the business altogether. Entirely self-taught, his creative *tours de force* know no bounds.

Longmuir uses preserved roses to create miniature models inspired by clients' favourite couture gowns or even, as table centrepieces for a celebratory dinner, a whole team of football players. On a larger scale, he creates architectural pieces for leading interior decorators (one of Longmuir's "bare-branch" trees adorns Lord Archer's spectacular London penthouse) and life-size *pierrots*, composed of magnolia leaves and a mosaic of coloured flowers. As well as working for top-flight decorators and private

clients, Cameron Shaw has undertaken commissions for Asprey and Cartier.

Cameron-Shaw
279 New Kings Rd, London SW6 4RD, UK
Tel: +44-171-371 8175   Fax: +44-171-371 8178

THE CARNEGIE CLUB

When entrepreneur Peter de Savary bought this property in 1990 and turned it into a sumptuous private club, he commissioned Donald Steele to extend the existing golf course to 18 holes of championship standard. Bounded on three sides by Dornoch Firth, the result is, according to Ronan Rafferty, "an amazing job". Club members, who stay in the magnificent mansion, former home of Scottish-born tycoon Andrew Carnegie, include royalty, celebrities and Forbes 500 types.

The Carnegie Club
Skibo Castle, Dornoch,
Sutherland IV25 3RQ, Scotland
Tel: +44-1862-89 46 00   Fax: +44-1862-89 46 01

CHARLIE EN PARTICULIER

Previously a top stylist at the legendary salon, Alexandre, Charlie has decided go it alone, followed by many of her most prestigious clients, including Mona Al-Ayoub, who happily pay FF2,000 for her styling skills. The petite brunette's ornate salon will appeal to Christian Dior devotees, as she is licensed to sell its beauty products.

Charlie en Particulier
1 rue Goethe, 75116 Paris, France
Tel: +33-1-47 20 94 01   Fax: +33-1-47 20 94 07

CHEZ TANTE LOUISE

Flush with the continuing success of his excellent Côte d'Or restaurant in Burgundy, Bernard

Loiseau has taken over this traditional-style restaurant opposite the Crillon. As the superchef is known for his rustic yet refined cuisine, Tante Louise's classic dishes, such as *Rémoulade de céleri*, Chestnut soup and Roast pigeon, are likely to be tweaked to perfection.

Chez Tante Louise
41 rue Boissy-d'Anglas, 75008 Paris, France
Tel: +33-1-42 65 06 85

CHRISTOPHE ROUXEL

This 34-year-old couturier (who once assisted Yves Saint Laurent) is one of the few who have said "boo" to Bernard Arnault, the all-powerful president of LVMH. Instead of leaping at Arnault's offer to make him head designer of Givenchy, he decided to go it alone (the job went to Alexander McQueen). *Le style Rouxel* gives more fluidity to the sleeves, shoulders and waist. "Women's bodies have evolved greatly in the past 50 years but many clothes today are as constricting as they were in the 19th century," he says. Parisian high society commissions him

to do wedding dresses, ball gowns and tailored suits. "My clients tell me their secrets," he says. "It is my job to translate them."

Christophe Rouxel
77 rue du Faubourg Saint Honoré,
75008 Paris, France
Tel: +33-1-47 42 33 90

CHATEAU CLIMENS

Only four families have owned this château since it was established by the Roborals in 1547.

Bought in 1971 by Lucien Lurton (who already owned La Louvière and Bouscaut, in Graves), the *domaine* is run by his two younger daughters, Brigitte and Bérénice. Many connoisseurs rate this fine and rich Barsac the equal of Château d'Yquem. Celebrate the millennium with Climens 1988.

Château Climens
33720 Barsac, France
Tel: +33-5-56 27 15 33

D'ANGLETERRE (HOTEL)

With its commanding lake-side position and magnificent views across Lake Geneva to Mont Blanc, this newly refurbished deluxe hotel, dating from 1872, embodies the grand tradition of Swiss hospitality. Small wonder, then, that Michael Jackson and Celine Dion chose it as a base for their European tours last year.

Hotel d'Angleterre
quai du Mont-Blanc 17,
CH-1201 Geneva, Switzerland
Tel: +41-22-906 5555   Fax: +41-22-906 5556

DAVID COLLINS

Interior designer David Collins is a *hot* talent. Having been a prime mover in the recent vogue for elegant but defiantly contemporary restaurant interiors (he has just completed Marco Pierre White's lavish re-invention of Mirabelle), he is becoming increasingly sought-after for residential commissions. Collins' close friends include pop star Madonna.

David Collins Architecture & Design
6-7 Chelsea Wharf, Lots Road,
London SW10 0QJ, UK
Tel: +44-171-349 5900   Fax: +44-171-352 7284

DENISE RENE

A pioneer in avant-garde art, Denise René specialises in French Constructualism and the styles which have developed from this movement. A good range of Constructualist work from the 1940s and '50s, including paintings by Vasarely, Herbin, Claisse and Soto can be found here.

Denise René
196 boulevard Saint Germain,
75007 Paris, France
Tel: +33-1-42 22 77 57

COLLEEN B. ROSENBLAT

"Jewellery is more than a sign of possession; precious stones give power," asserts Colleen Rosenblat. A Quandt (BMW) heiress and trained goldsmith, she is proud that 70 per cent of her customers are women buying their own jewellery. It's easy to see why. Although undeniably contemporary, many of her pieces are reminiscent of

ancient Greek and Roman jewellery. Bold and brave, it's the sort of ornamentation that women choose to make a statement of their confidence in themselves and their good taste.

Colleen B. Rosenblat
Mittelweg 49a, D-20149 Hamburg, Germany
Tel: +49-40-448 0860   Fax: +49-40-44 80 86 64

DOC CHENG'S

Named in honour of the legendary Singaporean medical doctor and world-class *bon viveur* (who spent several years in Hamburg) Doc Cheng's opening in the autumn of 1998 caused a sensation in the city. It is a slick and classy blend of

FAWSLEY HALL

After lying semi-derelict for 70 years, this grand house has been brought back to life by the owners of chic London hideaway, The Halcyon. Set in dreamy, Capability Brown-designed parkland, with lakes, formal gardens and a 14th-century ironstone church, it is surrounded by the serene Northamptonshire countryside.

The atmosphere inside the hotel is a delightful blend of opulence and easy charm (and, remarkably for a hotel of this standard, Fawsley is very child-friendly). That the house has a Tudor core, with Georgian and Victorian additions, has been used to great effect by the designers. Each wing has been decorated in keeping with the period in which it was built and filled with antiques and rich fabrics. The Queen Elizabeth chamber (where Good Queen Bess is reputed to have stayed in the 16th century) is a marvel, with its soaring, arch-braced roof, roaring log fire and stately four-poster bed.

The original Elizabethan kitchen, with its back-to-back hearth has been converted into the restaurant. The cooking here is superlative; celebrated three-Michelin star chef Nico Ladenis is consultant chef at Fawsley and his talented protegé, Tim Johnson, runs the kitchens.

Fawsley Hall
Fawsley, near Daventry, Northamptonshire NN11 3BA, UK
Tel: +44-1327-89 20 00   Fax: +44-1327-89 20 01

East and West, in both its food and décor. John Beriker's star dishes include Tandoori lemongrass chicken with Chinese vegetables and mustard-seed dressing.

Doc Cheng's
Neuer Jungfernstieg 9-14,
D-20354 Hamburg, Germany
Tel: +49-40-34 940   Fax: +49-40-349 4602

EL TOULA

You may already know El Toulà in Rome, a restaurant popular with artists, aristocrats and cardinals alike since it opened in 1966. Further north, don't miss the new El Toulà in Treviso, a rising star thanks to its young chef, who has reintroduced authentic Venetian cooking. The bread and exquisite petits fours are cooked on the premises.

El Toulà
via Collalto 26, 31100 Treviso, Italy
Tel: +39-0422-554 0275

EMILY TODHUNTER

Emily Todhunter trained as a specialist painter before launching into interior design. Starting with chic Manhattan club, Au Bar, she went on to transform high-profile restaurants, including Daphne's, Christopher's and Tamarind. Her private projects are equally impressive, including Sissinghurst Castle and homes for Taki Theodoracopulos, Charles Saatchi and Mogens Tholstrup. Todhunter's success lies in her qui-

etly glamorous style and her ability to reflect each client's personality within her schemes.

Emily Todhunter Ltd.
Chelsea Reach, 1st Floor,
79 Lots Road, London SW10 0KN, UK
Tel: +44-171-349 9999   Fax: +44-171-349 0410

FAIT ACCOMPLI

Camilla Leigh Pemberton is the personable supremo of Fait Accompli, London's up-and-coming party organisers. Working for Krug, Carlton TV and innumerable *branché* private clients, she delights party animals with her young, thrusting team of caterers, florists, decorators and musicians. Together they create some of the most exciting themed events on the social calendar.

Fait Accompli
Victoria House, 1a Gertrude Sreet,
London SW10 0JN, UK
Tel: +44-171-352 2777

FREDDY HEAD

Many times French champion jockey, Head retired from riding last August, stepping off a winner at Deauville, to take up training. Having leased the late, great François Boutin's yard from Boutin's widow, Lucy, he has made a great start. Good-looking and a great charmer (and father of six children), Head's family pedigree and perfect command of English are sure to attract top international owners.

Freddy Head
Le Mont de Po, 60260 Lamorlaye, France
Tel: +33-3-44 58 96 96   Fax: +33-3-44 58 92 22

GAI MATTIOLO

Despite studying science in high school, Gai Mattiolo had been obsessed by fashion since he was ten years old. Having started with a ready-to-wear collection in Milan in 1987, the designer produced his first 'high fashion' range in Rome seven years later and has subsequently been championed in his homeland as a promising young talent.

Gai Mattiolo
128-130 via Leonardo Greppi, 00149 Rome, Italy
Tel: +39-06-559 2686

GALERIA D'ARQUITECTURA EN MINIATURA

Jean-Pierre and Dominique Gault's exquisite architectural miniatures are based on buildings in Venice, Paris, Barcelona and London. Each individually sculpted house is a perfectly-wrought little work of art.

Galeria d'Arquitectura en Miniatura
Calle Boters 8, 08002 Barcelona, Spain
Tel: +34-93-412 2707

FITZWILLIAM HOTEL

Dublin's most chic designer hotel, The Fitzwilliam, opened to great acclaim in summer 1998, in a marvellous location overlooking St Stephen's Green in the heart of Dublin. Designed by Sir Terence Conran's design group (with considerable input from Sir Terence himself), it is a perfect embodiment of contemporary luxury, based on a theme of 'Baronial Modern' - crisp and simple, grand in scale and with a richness of detailing, materials and fabrics. Similar in tone to the rightly-praised Clarence hotel, The Fitzwilliam has raised the Irish capital's designer hotel stakes considerably higher.

A vast double-height entrance hall, with a large fireplace and comfortable leather armchairs, makes the initial statement. The reception area is quite spectacular: black and white marble, green Barcelona limestone, polished steel and American walnut. The 139 bedrooms are fitted with state-of-the-art equipment and have beautiful bathrooms; the best are Rooms 304 and 306, and those on the 5th floor, with balconies overlooking St Stephen's Green. The Fitzwilliam also boasts Ireland's largest roof garden.

Hot young chef, Conrad Gallagher, has moved his renowned Peacock Alley restaurant to the Fitzwilliam and oversees all food outlets within the hotel.

The Fitzwilliam Hotel
St Stephen's Green, Dublin 2, Ireland
Tel: +353-1-478 7000   Fax: +353-1-478 7878

GALERIE 213/MARION DE BEAUPRE

Since Marion de Beaupré opened her gallery in October 1997 with an exhibition of controversial nude portraits by the renowned fashion photographer Mario Sorrenti, 213 has caught the eye of fine-art photography aficionados. The gallery is a showcase for both established photographers such as Ellen von Unwerth and Paolo Roversi and lesser known but equally impressive talents. Previously a fashion photography agent, Marion de Beaupré has impeccable taste and an eye for detail. The gallery's Belle Epoque front room, now a photography and contemporary art bookshop, has a fascinating floor mural by Julian d'Ys, while the gallery's sculpted glass door is by avant-garde furniture maker Robert Carr.

Galerie 213/Marion de Beaupré
213 boulevard Raspail,
75014 Paris, France
Tel: +33-1-43 22 83 23

LE GARAGE

Situated in the 'Amsterdam-Zuid' district, this chic new restaurant headed by Dutch television's socialite celebrity chef, Joop Braakhekke, caters to the social set of this smart neighbourhood. The interior design and furnishings by Cees Dam, who also decorated the city's new Opera, has the effect of making every table feel as if it is the centre of attention.

Le Garage
Ruysdaelstraat 54-56, 1071XE Amsterdam,
The Netherlands
Tel: +31-20-679 7176   Fax +31-20-62 2249

GRAND OPERA

Arkadly Novikov is Moscow's most celebrated restaurateur with 11 restaurants in his chain. (The Tsar's Hunt, one of his more recent ventures, played host to Yeltsin and Chirac last year. Grand Opera's maroon velvet seats, smoky ambience and over-the-top waiting staff are currently all the rage with smart Muscovites, while the Ukranian-Jewish-French cuisine is surprisingly good.

Grand Opera
2/18 Petrovskio Linii, Moscow, Russia
Tel: +7-095-924 0604   Fax: +7-095-923 6196

THE HALE CLINIC

Opened by Prince Charles in 1988 - a worthy endorsement by Britain's New Age champion - the clinic founded by Teresa Hale has been much praised for its complementary therapies and emphasis on preventative medecine. Patients who have derived benefit from the centre's 120 practitioners include Richard Gere, Tina Turner and the late Diana, Princess of Wales.

The Hale Clinic
7 Park Crescent,
London W1N 3HE, UK
Tel: +44-171-631 0156   Fax: +44-171-323 1693

HELMUT LANG

Not to be confused with his namesake and fellow-Austrian, the fashion designer (who would have been among the 'Elite 1000' had he not moved his business to New York), the self-effacing Helmut Lang is content to let his wines speak for themselves. And how they speak! His 1991 Samling 88 Trockenbeerenauslese is a stunner. Burnished gold in appearance, its taste is so concentrated that only a thimbleful on your palate will release a dazzling array of flavours. It can only be a matter of time before the world at large discovers these wines.

Helmut Lang
Quergasse 5, A-7142 Illmitz, Austria
Tel/Fax: +43-2175-29 23

THE HEMPEL

British designer Anouska Hempel (Lady Weinberg) has never shirked a challenge. But her latest creation, The Hempel Hotel in London's Bayswater, is certainly her most daring venture to date. She created the winningly decadent Blakes fifteen years ago but The Hempel couldn't be more different: ultra-minimalist and exceptionally elegant, it is the ultimate Nineties expression of Eastern aesthetics in a Western context. Some people find it all too austere, but the consensus is that The Hempel is one of the most exciting hotels in the British capital. Uncluttered, uncompromising and ineffably cool, The Hempel is not somewhere which can be described in words. It demands to be experienced first hand.

The Hempel
31-35 Craven Hill Gardens, London W2 3EA, UK
Tel: +44-171-298 9000   Fax: +44-171-402 4666

HINDLIP AND PRENTICE

Fiona Hindlip (wife of the Chairman of Christie's) and Nancy Prentice, a London-based New Yorker, combine American and British taste in their design practice. Their style ranges from the traditional to the contemporary and from grand houses to intimate apartments; recent commissions include a Belgravia duplex for a Swedish banker; a country house for a German Countess and a mansion in Greenwich, Connecticut. Before teaming up, Nancy had been with a New York firm of interior designers and Fiona's love of houses had seen her move house 12 times in 26 years.

Hindlip & Prentice
8 Ennismore Street, London SW7 1JE, UK
Tel: +44-171-581 9251   Fax: +44-171-584 6648

HOTEL DE LA MIRANDE

This jewel of a hotel, with its delightful garden, still has all the intimate charm that delighted Madame de Sevigné in the 18th century. The work of superstar decorator François-Joseph Graf, its Provençal furniture is blended with Directoire and Second Empire-style armchairs and sofas and beautiful fabrics. It's a favourite hideaway for French politicians and heads of state, though Chancellor Helmut Kohl may not return; when he was in town for a Euro Summit, he reportedly found himself unable to fit under the shower in his suite.

Hôtel de la Mirande
Place de la Mirande, 84000 Avignon, France
Tel: +33-4-90 85 93 93   Fax: +33-4-90 86 26 85

HURTWOOD POLO CLUB

Having fallen in love with polo, Kenney Jones, drummer with legendary rock bands The Small Faces and The Who, built a pitch for his own amusement. Local people came to watch the 'fun' games he played there and, thus, the club was born. Never mind that many of Jones' rock star chums can be seen here or that the new club-house is one of England's finest; the real delight of this club is its egalitarianism - this is 'village green' polo, just the way it used to be.

Hurtwood Park Polo Club
Horsham Lane, Ewhurst, Surrey GU6 7SW, UK
Tel: +44-1483-26 73 21   Fax: +44-1483-27 26 71

JACOPO FOGGINI

Foggini - a discovery of Romeo Gigli - was the star of the 1997 Furniture Fair, with his unique and colourful pieces created out of materials normally used for road signs. His work, which graces the über-chic homes of Berlin, Tokyo and London, is displayed in a huge three-storey white loft.

Jacopo Foggini
via Sannio 24, 20100 Milan, Italy
Tel/Fax: +39-02-54 10 14 09

JAN JANSEN

A meeting with Roger Vivier in the early 1960s inspired Jansen to become a shoe designer - or rather, "shoe artist". Producing shoes in limited editions of no more than 20 pairs, he fashions unlikely materials into delicate and subtle designs (squirrel fur slippers and knit boots, for instance). His work is regularly exhibited in Amsterdam's Museum of Modern Art.

Jan Jansen
Rokin 42, 1012 KT Amsterdam,
The Netherlands
Tel: +31-20-625 1350   Fax+31-20-624 4557

LES JARDINS DE L'OPERA

This courtyard restaurant's theatrical, Italian-style décor is an ideal stage upon which to play the grand hostess and Maryse Toulousy does so with immense brio. Meanwhile, backstage, her husband Dominique creates virtuoso dishes from the Southwest's finest ingredients. His Fresh foie gras ravioli in truffle juice, Roasted lamb with pink garlic croquettes and, as a grand finale, Plump figs roasted in sweet Banyuls wine, are a fine testament to his talents.

Les Jardins de l'Opéra
1 place du Capitole, 31500 Toulouse, France
Tel: +33-5-61 23 07 76   Fax: +33-5-61 23 63 00

JIMMY CHOO

Malaysian-born Jimmy Choo is the favourite shoe designer of It-girls and young fashion editors alike. The delicate femininity and soft colouring of his creations in fine leather and silk make them a sure hit for dressed-up occasions, while his bespoke service is booked up months in advance. Courtney Love, Madonna and Nicole Kidman are all fans.

Jimmy Choo
20 Motcomb Street, London SW1, UK
Tel: +44-171-235 6008   Fax: +44-171-235 7868

JO MALONE

A second generation beautician, Jo Malone's 2000-strong client list is strictly closed. But disappointed girls-about-town can console themselves with her delicious range of fragrances, bath products and skin-care which simply fly out of her Walton Street shop. Having graduated from filling bottles with rose petals aged seven and, when starting her business, mixing ingredients in her kitchen sink, Malone's success now looks assured.

Jo Malone
154 Walton Street, London SW3 2JL, UK
Tel: +44-171-720 0202   Fax: +44-171-720 0277

JONATHAN PEASE

A youthful-looking Old Etonian, Pease has always been a racing fanatic. Formerly assistant to François Mathet, who was legendary as both a trainer and a martinet, Pease is quite the opposite: easygoing and a trifle shy. Although he has not yet won a Classic, Pease has produced some big winners and is very well-regarded by his peers, fitting easily into the Chantilly scene.

Jonathan Pease
Villa Primrose, Chemin des Aigles,
60500 Chantilly, France
Tel: +33-3-44 58 19 96   Fax: +33-3-44 57 59 90

KELLY HOPPEN

Kelly Hoppen has carved out a remarkably successful career as a decorator in a relatively short time. Her eclectic orientalism - featuring carefully chosen pieces of furniture, sculptural objects and simple fabrics, often counter pointed by orchids or potted topiary - is both sleek and easy on the eye.

Kelly Hoppen
2 Alma Studios, 32 Stratford Road,
London W8 6QF, UK
Tel: +44-171-938 4151   Fax: +44-171-938 1878

KEVIN GOULD

When a food guru such as The River Café's Ruth Rogers calls Kevin Gould in to cook for her parties, there must be something going on. Inspired by the sunny flavours of the Mediterranean, Gould makes a point of using organic ingredients whenever practicable. He also runs a shop, stocked largely with specialist foods from small Italian producers.

Kevin Gould
Joy of Real Food, 511 Finchley Road,
London NW3 7BB, UK
Tel: +44-171-435 7711   Fax: +44-171-435 7007

KIASMA MUSEUM OF CONTEMPORARY ART

Helsinki's new Museum of Contemporary Art (its name, *kiasma*, means crossover, or exchange) has opened to great fanfares, not least for its design. Fanciful interpretations of classically Nordic iconography are worked into the architectural details, for example, in the form of light fittings which resemble melting blocks of ice.

Kiasma
Mannerheiminauko 2, Helsinki, Finland
Tel: +358-9-17 33 65 00

LAURENT BUTTAZONNI

At the start of every *prêt-à-porter* season, this young interior designer waits for John Galliano's call. For the past six years he has been designing the sets for the couturier's runway shows. A protegé of minimalist superstar Andrée Putman, with whom he worked for seven years, Buttazonni seems a surprising choice for such a flamboyant creator, but he explains, "I like him because whatever he does he goes all the way, whether he decides on baroque style or an African influence." His work certainly clicks with fashion designers, as he has decorated houses for Azzedine Alaïa and Helmut Lang.

Laurent Buttazonni
62a rue de Montreuil, 75011 Paris, France
Tel: +33-1-40 09 98 49   Fax: +33-1-40 09 99 24

LARISSA VON WATZDORF

Having grown up in London and studied in Paris and Brussels, where she specialised in decorative paint techniques, Larissa von Watzdorf set up her own design business. Turning her hand to *trompe l'oeil* techniques, wallpaper design, furniture design, hand-painted objects and the creation of whole interior schemes, her

fresh and distinctive approach is inspired by her eclectic background. Clients include Villeroy & Boch, the Interalpen Hotel, Austria, and private clients in Germany, England and the US.

Larissa von Watzdorf
Schumannstraße 8, D-81679 Munich, Germany
Tel: +49-89-688 5196   Fax: +49-89-688 5199

STOKE POGES GOLF CLUB

Set in 350 acres of magnificent, 'Capability' Brown-designed parkland, Stoke Poges' graceful golf course was created in 1908 by the great Harry Shapland Colt. Indeed, Colt's 7th hole here, cut out of a wood to an angled green just across a stream, was the basis of the design for the crucial 12th at Augusta. In addition to its main course, Stoke Poges has recently reopened a further nine holes, thus recreating the original 27-hole format.

Golf, however, is not the only reason to come to this impressive estate. Guests at the 18th-century club house, Stoke Park, will be looked after as if they had dropped into their own stately home. Originally built for John Penn, the founder of Pennsylvania (who commissioned its design from James Wyatt, architect to George III), it has been lavishly restored and provides 21 charmingly-decorated bedrooms. The place is such a blueprint for the English countryside at its most seductive, that scenes from the James Bond classics *Goldfinger* and *Tomorrow Never Dies* were filmed here.

A major attraction, despite the club's rural aspect, is its location, only a seven-mile drive from Heathrow airport and 30 minutes from central London.

Stoke Poges Golf Club

Stoke Park, Park Road, Stoke Poges, Buckinghamshire SL2 4PG, UK

Tel: +44-1753-71 71 71   Fax: +44-1753-71 71 81

Palmer design, will host the German amateur team championship in 2000.

Sporting Club Berlin Bad Saarow

Friedrich-Engels-Damm 300,

15526 Bad Saarow, Berlin, Germany

Tel: +49-33-63 16 35 81   Fax: +49-33-63 16 35 94

STEFANOBI

Although Stefanobi was established only in 1991, its grasp of the finer arts of traditional shoemaking is second to none. The shoes are quite beautiful, chiefly due to the delicate styling, superb leathers and painstaking polishing - the latter takes at least an hour a pair, creating extraordinary colours in the process.

Stefanobi

via Cimarosa 7, 44100 Ferrara, Italy

Tel: +39-0532-90 30 20   Fax: +39-0532-90 18 13

THORNTON'S

Kevin Thornton's Michelin-starred restaurant looks like a neighbourhood bistro from the outside but don't be fooled; anyone who knows anything about good food eats here. Thornton - who trained with Paul Bocuse, among others - cooks for such celebrities as Gregory Peck and Anjelica Huston. Modest and self-effacing, he eschews the spotlight, preferring his food to take all the plaudits (sometime restaurant critic Andrew Lloyd Webber has acclaimed his Suckling pig and trotter as superior to those of Pierre Kaufmann and Marco Pierre White). The mainly French legion of front-of-house staff are expertly led by Alain Chapel-trained maître d' Olivier Meissonave.

Thornton's

1 Portobello Road, Dublin 6, Ireland

Tel: +353-1-454 9067   Fax: +353-1-453 2947

HOTEL TRESANTON

Olga Polizzi has transformed a run-down 1940s hotel into an ultra-chic bastion of contemporary aesthetics and old-fashioned comfort. As the daughter of Lord Forte she spent 16 years with Forte Hotels learning the tricks of the trade, and has now employed this knowledge to build her own business. The Hotel Tresanton is one very personal and stylish outcome of a newly expanding empire.

Hotel Tresanton

St Mawes, Cornwall TR2 5DR, UK

Tel: +44-1326-27 00 55   Fax: +44-1326-27 00 53

VILA BLED

Built in 1947 as a retreat for Tito, this hotel oozes political nostalgia. Kruschev came here to fish, Ceaucescu invited himself for hunting weekends and Indira Ghandi, Willy Brandt and Emperor Akihito are among other past guests. The décor oozes nostalgia, too; it's an extraordinary blend of grandeur and kitsch. Nevertheless, the surrounding countryside is gorgeous and the service, under the direction of Janez Fajar, is exemplary. Incidentally, if you want to sleep in Tito's own room, suite 102 is the number.

Hotel Vila Bled

Cesta svobode 26, SI-4260 Bled, Slovenia

Tel: +386-64-79 15   Fax: +386-64-74 13 20

VILLA LA MASSA

Villa La Massa was once a favourite stopover for English aristocrats on their Grand Tour. Now this refuge, on the banks of the Arno just south of Florence, is being restored by the company which owns the fabled Villa D'Este. An elegant simplicity of line characterises the architecture and decor is in the classic Tuscan villa style.

Villa La Massa

50012 Candeli-Firenze, Italy

Tel: +39-055-62 611   Fax: +39-055-651 0109

LES JARDINS DE L'OPERA

This courtyard restaurant's theatrical, Italian-style décor is an ideal stage upon which to play the grand hostess and Maryse Toulousy does so with immense brio. Meanwhile, backstage, her husband Dominique creates virtuoso dishes from the Southwest's finest ingredients. His Fresh foie gras ravioli in truffle juice, Roasted lamb with pink garlic croquettes and, as a grand finale, Plump figs roasted in sweet Banyuls wine, are a fine testament to his talents.

Les Jardins de l'Opéra
1 place du Capitole, 31500 Toulouse, France
Tel: +33-5-61 23 07 76   Fax: +33-5-61 23 63 00

JIMMY CHOO

Malaysian-born Jimmy Choo is the favourite shoe designer of It-girls and young fashion editors alike. The delicate femininity and soft colouring of his creations in fine leather and silk make them a sure hit for dressed-up occasions, while his bespoke service is booked up months in advance. Courtney Love, Madonna and Nicole Kidman are all fans.

Jimmy Choo
20 Motcomb Street, London SW1, UK
Tel: +44-171-235 6008   Fax: +44-171-235 7868

JO MALONE

A second generation beautician, Jo Malone's 2000-strong client list is strictly closed. But disappointed girls-about-town can console themselves with her delicious range of fragrances, bath products and skin-care which simply fly out of her Walton Street shop. Having graduated from filling bottles with rose petals aged seven and, when starting her business, mixing ingredients in her kitchen sink, Malone's success now looks assured.

Jo Malone
154 Walton Street, London SW3 2JL, UK
Tel: +44-171-720 0202   Fax: +44-171-720 0277

JONATHAN PEASE

A youthful-looking Old Etonian, Pease has always been a racing fanatic. Formerly assistant to François Mathet, who was legendary as both a trainer and a martinet, Pease is quite the opposite: easygoing and a trifle shy. Although he has not yet won a Classic, Pease has produced some big winners and is very well-regarded by his peers, fitting easily into the Chantilly scene.

Jonathan Pease
Villa Primrose, Chemin des Aigles,
60500 Chantilly, France
Tel: +33-3-44 58 19 96   Fax: +33-3-44 57 59 90

KELLY HOPPEN

Kelly Hoppen has carved out a remarkably successful career as a decorator in a relatively short time. Her eclectic orientalism - featauring carefully chosen pieces of furniture, sculptural objects and simple fabrics, often counter pointed by orchids or potted topiary - is both sleek and easy on the eye.

Kelly Hoppen
2 Alma Studios, 32 Stratford Road,
London W8 6QF, UK
Tel: +44-171-938 4151   Fax: +44-171-938 1878

KEVIN GOULD

When a food guru such as The River Café's Ruth Rogers calls Kevin Gould in to cook for her parties, there must be something going on. Inspired by the sunny flavours of the Mediterranean, Gould makes a point of using organic ingredients whenever practicable. He also runs a shop, stocked largely with specialist foods from small Italian producers.

Kevin Gould
Joy of Real Food, 511 Finchley Road,
London NW3 7BB, UK
Tel: +44-171-435 7711   Fax: +44-171-435 7007

KIASMA MUSEUM OF CONTEMPORARY ART

Helsinki's new Museum of Contemporary Art (its name, *kiasma*, means crossover, or exchange) has opened to great fanfares, not least for its design. Fanciful interpretations of classically Nordic iconography are worked into the architectural details, for example, in the form of light fittings which resemble melting blocks of ice.

Kiasma
Mannerheiminauko 2, Helsinki, Finland
Tel: +358-9-17 33 65 00

LAURENT BUTTAZONNI

At the start of every *prêt-à-porter* season, this young interior designer waits for John Galliano's call. For the past six years he has been designing the sets for the couturier's runway shows. A protegé of minimalist superstar Andrée Putman, with whom he worked for seven years, Buttazonni seems a surprising choice for such a flamboyant creator, but he explains, "I like him because whatever he does he goes all the way, whether he decides on baroque style or an African influence." His work certainly clicks with fashion designers, as he has decorated houses for Azzedine Alaïa and Helmut Lang.

Laurent Buttazonni
62a rue de Montreuil, 75011 Paris, France
Tel: +33-1-40 09 98 49   Fax: +33-1-40 09 99 24

LARISSA VON WATZDORF

Having grown up in London and studied in Paris and Brussels, where she specialised in decorative paint techniques, Larissa von Watzdorf set up her own design business. Turning her hand to *trompe l'oeil* techniques, wallpaper design, furniture design, hand-painted objects and the creation of whole interior schemes, her

fresh and distinctive approach is inspired by her eclectic background. Clients include Villeroy & Boch, the Interalpen Hotel, Austria, and private clients in Germany, England and the US.

Larissa von Watzdorf
Schumannstraße 8, D-81679 Munich, Germany
Tel: +49-89-688 5196   Fax: +49-89-688 5199

LAWRENCE STEELE

This Milan-based 35 year-old's great strength as a designer is his meticulous attention to detail and fluid cutting. Steele has repeatedly asserted that he wants his clothes to be "utterly desirable". Judging by his recent collections, he has certainly come close to meeting his own high standards.

Lawrence Steele
via Seprio 2, 20100 Milan, Italy
Tel: +39-02-48 19 51 28

THE LIFE CENTRE

London's smart set comes to this discreet complementary therapy centre for re-balancing, detoxing and general overhauls. Founder Louise White's philosophy was to bring a whole range of life-enhancing therapies together under one roof. These range from the nowadays commonplace - aromatherapy, acupuncture and yoga - to the esoteric - Metamorphic technique, Tibetan Massage and the extraordinary Chavutti Thirumal Massage.

The Life Centre
15 Edge Street, London W8 7PN, UK
Tel: +44-171-221 4602   Fax: +44-171-221 4603

LILIANE SICARD

This is where Geneva's stylish women come for show-stopping, up-to-the-minute piece of jewellery. Sicard's wares are truly democratic - everything from gold and precious stones, to bronze and seashells. She will make up new pieces to order or remodel old ones and also stocks items from such designers as Robert Lee Morris.

Liliane Sicard
10 quai Général-Guisan,
1204 Geneva, Switzerland
Tel: +31-22-311 0055   Fax: +31-22-312 0135

LOCH LOMOND GOLF CLUB

Tom Lehman, 1996 British Open Champion, said of Loch Lomond, "I doubt if there is anywhere in the world which has ever looked more beautiful." A generous description? Perhaps. But this $10 million Tom Weiskopf/Jay Morrish course offers great play; membership is still open and the Georgian pile that is both clubhouse and official residence for members is quite superb.

Loch Lomond Golf Club
Rossdhu House, Luss, near Alexandria,
G83 8NT, Scotland
Tel: +44-14-36 65 55 55   Fax: +44-14-36 65 55 66

THE LUDOVISI COLLECTION

The cool interior of the newly restored Altemps Palace houses one of Italy's most outstanding

LOUISE KENNEDY

This Dublin-based designer has a host of admirers, ranging from Enya and Meryl Streep to former Irish President Mary Robinson and her succesor, Mary McAleese. These women choose her clothes for their gentle sophistication, which is as appropriate for contemporary professional women as it is for those in the public eye. Kennedy herself is her own best advertisement, recognised as a poised, self-made dynamo who wears her marque with aplomb and is articulate on the subject of her design philosophy and success.

With a family background in retailing, Kennedy set her sights early on fashion design. Following studies at the Grafton Academy of Fashion in Dublin, she started her business in the mid-Eighties. Since then Kennedy has become renowned for her daytime tailoring, as well as for the trademark hand-painted silks and printed velvets which are used to such effect in her evening wear. Winner of the Irish Designer of the Year award on two separate occasions, the designer continues to expand into new markets and new areas of creativity.

Louise Kennedy
56 Merrion Square, Dublin 2, Ireland
Tel: +353-1-662 0056   Fax: +353-1-662 0050

displays of statuary. Its Renaissance-style architecture is the perfect backdrop for such treasures - all of which are beautifully presented - making this a true 'find' right in the heart of the capital.

The Ludovisi Collection
Palazzo Altemps,
Piazza Sant'Apollinare 46, 00100 Rome, Italy
Tel: +39-06-52 07 26

MARIANNE ROBIC

Having opened her chic little flower shop in 1991, a stone's throw from that of her former employer, Monsieur Moulié, Kenzo's favourite florist Marianne Robic has garnered her own, exceedingly smart private Parisian clientele. Robic's rich bouquets (wrapped in her signature, pansy-sprinkled paper) emphasise the intrinsic beauty of the flowers themselves, rather than taking off on mad flights of creative fancy.

Marianne Robic
41 rue de Bourgogne, 75007 Paris, France
Tel: +33-1-44 18 03 47   Fax: +33-1-45 55 28 68

MASSIMO DE CARLO

Massimo de Carlo is considered something of a trend-setter in the Milanese art world. The no-nonsense warehouse setting of his cutting-edge gallery perfectly complements the style of its displays. See works by John M. Armelder, Massimo Bartolini and Maurizio Cattelan and marvel at the young gallery owner's prescience.

Massimo de Carlo
viale Corsica 41, 20133 Milan, Italy
Tel: +39-02-70 60 23 81   Fax: +39-02-70 63 41 58

MIRABELLE

Marco Pierre White is reviving this great London gastronomic institution with great flair, installing two of his protegés in the kitchen. Together with interior designer David Collins, he has created a serenely glamorous ambience, overseen by Christophe Capron and (one of London's best sommeliers) Claude Douard. The deceptively simple language of the long menu belies the masterful inventiveness of this great chef.

Mirabelle
56 Curzon Street, London W1Y 8DL, UK
Tel: +44-171-499 4636   Fax: +44-171-499 5449

MODERNA MUSEET
This year-old museum is acclaimed as one of the finest repositories of modern art outside the USA. Founder of the original Stockholm museum, Pontus Hultén, bought up huge chunks of work by such masters as Rauschenberg, Johns, Lichtenstein and Warhol in the '60s. While Pop Art is its great strength, the museum is also strong on surrealism, cubism and abstract expressionism.

Moderna Museet
Skeppsholmen Island,
11149 Stockholm, Sweden
Tel: +46-8-51 95 52 00   Fax: +46-8-51 95 52 16

HOTEL NATIONAL
The Hotel National was built at the turn of the century and every room is steeped in political history. Views of St. Basil's and the Kremlin have been enjoyed by Lenin (room 107 was his), Winston Churchill, H.G. Wells and, more recently, Frederick Forsythe. Four years of intensive renovations have revived the marvellous art nouveau architecture and marbled interior.

Hotel National
15-1 Mokhovaya Ulitsa,
203009 Moscow, Russia
Tel: +7-095-258 7000   Fax: +7-095-258 7100

MARLFIELD HOUSE

Châtelaine of this seductive country house, Mary Bowe, has exquisite taste and her sumptuously decorated retreat - former residence of the Earls of Courtown - combines all the intimacy of a family home with the facilities one expects in a 5-star hotel, as well as excellent fishing and riding. Small wonder, then, that Marlfield has played host to just about every international star who has toured the country for the last twenty years. Peter Ustinov, The Duke of Kent and Steve Martin have all slept at Marlfield, while recent devotees include Tom Hanks and Stephen Spielberg, who stayed in the house for two months while filming *Saving Private Ryan*. Huge log fires, superb Irish art and a truly outstanding garden add to the delight and the service throughout is impeccable, under the charming direction of Mrs. Bowe's daughter, Margaret. Many of the ingredients used in the hotel's restaurant are grown on the estate but that isn't the only reason why food critics fall over themselves to heap praise on the venture; Mrs Bowe has a reputation for nurturing young talent in the kitchen, with many of her 'trainees' going on to become acclaimed chef-proprietors in their own right.

Marlfield House
Gorey, Co. Wexford, Ireland
Tel: +353-55-21 124   Fax: +353-55-21 572

NEIL CUNNINGHAM

Taking his inspiration from *Vogue*, *The Beano* comic, childhood weddings and learning basic sewing skills from his dressmaker mother, Neil Cunningham has turned an interesting education into a profession. Today he translates his nostalgia for glamour into some of the most talked-about party frocks and wedding dresses around, for clients including actress Julie Christie and ballerina Darcey Bussell.

Neil Cunningham
28 Sackville Street, London W1X 1DA, UK
Tel: +44-171-437 5793   Fax: +44-171-437 5794
By appointment only

OSWALD BOATENG
An avowed modernist, Ozwald Boateng has slowly revolutionised fundamental aspects of the bespoke tailoring craft, with his original sense of colour and cut. One of the most flam-

boyant and talented of British designers, Boateng makes suits for Mick Jagger and Spike Lee, among others.

Oswald Boateng
9 Vigo Street, London W1X 1AL, UK
Tel: +44-171-734 6868 Fax: +44-171-734 3737

PALAZZO VIVIANI

Alberta Ferretti discovered this decrepit palace in the centre of a run-down 13th-century village in the Marche region and was enchanted. Together with a group of friends, she has brought the village back to life, turning the palazzo into an enchanting hotel. The magic is enhanced by the sound of music drifting through the streets from the Music Academy established here by Gustav Kuhn.

Palazzo Viviani
47040 Montegridolfo,
Emilia Romagna, Italy
Tel: +39-0541-85 53 50 Fax: +39-0541-85 53 40

PALAZZO GRASSI
The perfect setting for world-class exhibitions, this elegant 18th-century palazzo was bought by Fiat in 1984 - largely at the behest of Gianni Agnelli - and inaugurated two years later. It's a suitably grand venue for sumptuous exhibitions with wide-ranging scope.

Palazzo Grassi
San Marco 3231, 30124 Venice, Italy
Tel: +39-041-522 1375 Fax: +39-041-523 1680

PARADOR DE GRANADA
This enchanting parador hotel is situated in a 15th-century convent in the Alhambra. Its bedrooms, all different, overlook the richly-planted Secano and Albaic'n gardens, whose fountains and arches perfectly illustrate the city's Moorish-Christian heritage.

Parador de Granada
Real de la Alhambra, S/N 19008 Granada, Spain
Tel: +34-958-22 14 40   Fax: +34-958-22 22 64

DR PHILIPPE BERARD
This highly talented cosmetic surgeon is definitely someone to bear in mind for those looking for a natural-looking face lift, especially if a hugely luxurious setting is not required as reassurance. Dr. Berard insists on having a lengthy and wide-ranging discussion with clients before going ahead with an operation, in order to ensure the best possible results.

Dr Philippe Berard
102 rue du Longchamp, 75016 Paris, France
Tel: +33-1-45 53 54 53   Fax: +33-1-45 53 49 68

PIERRE CORTHAY
Having perfected his skills at John Lobb and Berluti, Pierre Corthay branched out on his own. His bench-made shoes have a characteristic sleekness but, if he decides your physique is not suited to a particular model, be prepared for some gentle dissuasion. Trust his advice and he will fit you with a pair that flatters you most.

Pierre Corthay
1 rue Volnay, 75002 Paris, France
Tel: +33-1-42 61 08 89

PIERRE MARCOLINI
This jovial and talented young *chocolatier-pâtissier*, who already counts Fauchon among his clients, is well on the way to becoming one of the greats of his trade. He flavours his fine pralines with liquorice, aniseed, tea and violet and his signature *envol* (crème brulée à l'orange on a bitter chocolate mousse) is truly ambrosial.

Pierre Marcolini
39 place du Grand-Sablon,
1000 Brussels, Belgium
Tel: +32-2-514 1206 Fax: +32-2-511 3321

PIERRE PASSEBON
Current darling of Paris high society, Pierre Passebon has laid out his apartment/gallery with rare finds which have caught his eclectic eye. A Russian art nouveau Talachkino buffet and mirror, contrasting with Jean-Michel Frank straw-woven chairs, adorns one room, while his

collection of Syrian *objets d'art* is exhibited in another.

Galerie Pierre Passebon
39 rue Bourdonnais, 75001 Paris, France
Tel: +33-1-42 36 44 56
By appointment only

PIL-POUL
Although a delicious blend of French and Italian cuisine is served in this enchanting restaurant, the view from the terrace, where dinner is served in the summer, is purely Greek. Khrystos Zieras' signature Pil-Poul salad, an aromatic mix of marinated fish, grilled salmon and strips of pork fillet garnished with parmesan, is excellent.

Pil-Poul
51 Apostolou Pavlou Street, Athens, Greece
Tel: +30-1-345 0803   Fax: +30-1-341 3046

PLANET ORGANIC
Organic produce is the rising star of our future diets - a point which hasn't been lost on Jonathan Dwek (or his backers, members of the Aspinall and Goldsmith clans). His swish, 'organic only' emporium has been a runaway success. No run-of-the-mill 'health food' shop, this; if it's not organically produced, it doesn't get shelf space - and that even goes for the meat.

Planet Organic
42 Westbourne Grove, London W2 5SH, UK
Tel: +44-171-221 7171

LE PUITS SAINT-JACQUES
Twenty minutes outside Toulouse, the talented young Jean-Pierre Retureau is cooking up a storm. His tender Pyrenees lamb, Duck foie gras with caramelised cherries and Pigeon with honey and spices are matched only by the splendid surroundings. Be sure to book a table on the terrace in warm weather.

Les Puits Saint-Jacques
Place de la Mairie, 32600 Pujaudran,
Toulouse, France
Tel: +33-5-62 07 41 11

PULITZER
If you love the elegant merchants' houses that line Amsterdam's canals, book a waterside room at the Pulitzer, a charming luxury hotel created from 24 such historic properties. Much of the buildings' character has been preserved: the warren-like interior retains many quirky original features and the restaurant - housed in a 17th-century former pharmacy - is a joy.

Pulitzer
Prinsengracht 315-331,
1016GZ, Amsterdam, Holland
Tel: +31-20-523 5235   Fax: +31-20-627 6753

RAF SIMONS

There may be a surfeit of Belgian designers currently invading the catwalks but menswear creator Raf Simons looks as if he is here to stay. His slick, sharply cut separates with a slightly futuristic feel are the star attraction at the style-defining Maria Luisa men's boutique in Paris.

Raf Simons
Totem (for stockists)
16 Villa Gaudelet, 75011 Paris, France
Tel: +33-1-49 23 79 79   Fax: +33-1-49 23 79 90

RESOLUMENT DECO

Chantal Payrat loves wrought iron for the freedom of expression that it allows her. This young, self-taught furniture designer creates graceful objects filled with character and humour, inspired by myths and fairy-tale themes.

Résolument Déco
7 rue de Rempart-Saint-Etienne, Toulouse, France
Tel: +33-5-61 21 90 28

RODOLPHE MENUDIER

After a period as a foot soldier for Chloé, Ménudier - young pretender to the shoe-as-coveted-accessory throne - is busy developing his own label, with beautifully balanced, sleekly contoured high heels his forte. Strange, therefore, that he cites the Nike trainer and found objects as major influences on his work.

Rodolphe Ménudier
Laurent Suchel (for stockists only)
4 rue Etienne Marcel, 75002 Paris, France
Tel: +33-1-42 21 34 89

RUSSELL SIMPSON

Alan Russell's property consultancy has grown, to a large extent, by word-of-mouth recommendation. His service is as thorough as it is dis-

creet (eschewing the usual shop-front premises, he operates out of a Chelsea townhouse). Russell sources, sells and lets first class residential properties in the prime areas of London, on behalf of a blue-chip portfolio of international clients. Such is his commitment to matching clients to the right property that he even, on occasion, advises them not to buy.

Russell Simpson
5 Anderson Street, London SW3 3LU, UK
Tel: +44-171-584 7876   Fax: +44-171-581 3859

SAM DE TERAN

Catapulted into the public eye after Tara Palmer-Tomkinson wore her skiwear on holiday with Prince Charles, Sam de Téran has established a cult following amongst style-conscious *sportives* for her state-of-the-art, high-performance sportswear. In addition to skiing, she designs clothes for swimming, aerobics, riding and tennis.

Sam de Téran
151 Fulham Road, London SW3 6SN, UK
Tel: +44-171-584 0902   Fax: +44-171-589 9906

SHILLELAGH

A relatively new shoot, this 3000-acre estate is the only one in Ireland with terrain similar to the legendary Ballinacor and equally high birds; as well as pheasant, woodcock come through on some shoot days. It is supremely well-managed by keeper Anthony Thompson, who worked for seven years at Sir Anthony Bamford's celebrated shoot. A bonus for pressured urban folk is that shooting is allowed here on Sundays.

Shillelagh
c/o Alex Brant, Humewood Castle,
Kiltegan, Co. Wicklow, Ireland
Tel: +353-508-73 215   Fax: +353-508-73 382

SO BY ALEXANDER VAN SOBBLE

Holland's best-known designer, van Sobble is achieving international success with this ready-to-wear 'So' label. In his canal-side studio, he makes his joyous, refined and boldly-cut clothes to order, in vivid colours and multiple tones of white.

So by Alexander Van Sobble
Westerdoksdijk 40C, 1013 AE Amsterdam,
The Netherlands
Tel: +31-20-520 7667   Fax: +31-20-520 7676

SOLANGE AZAGURY-PARTRIDGE

Visiting jeweller Solange Azagury-Partridge's shop is like stepping into a giant jewellery box, laid out in vividly-coloured velvets and leather. The interior, designed by Solange herself, is as original as her jewellery and reflects her approach to design (she had no formal training). Clients include Elton John, Madonna, Noel and Meg Gallagher and Nicole Kidman.

Solange Azagury-Partridge
171 Westbourne Grove, London W11 2RZ, UK
Tel: +44-171-792 0197

SOPHIE HICKS

With every trendsetter in London applauding her interiors for Paul Smith's townhouse retail outlet in Notting Hill, fashion-editor-turned-architect Sophie Hicks is on a roll. The designer responsible for the Sensation exhibition at the Royal Academy, as well as its forthcoming Picasso ceramics show, is an inspired purist; her exuberance betrays itself in the detail.

Sophie Hicks
16-19 Powis Mews, London W11 1JN, UK
Tel: +44-171-792 2631   Fax: +44-171-727 3328

SPORTING CLUB BERLIN BAD SAAROW

One of the newest courses in a country which is undergoing a golf boom of sorts, this club is already being billed as Germany's Number 1. The German Open is played on the Nick Faldo-designed course, which is centred around a plush hotel. The second course, an Arnold

STOKE POGES GOLF CLUB

Set in 350 acres of magnificent, 'Capability' Brown-designed parkland, Stoke Poges' graceful golf course was created in 1908 by the great Harry Shapland Colt. Indeed, Colt's 7th hole here, cut out of a wood to an angled green just across a stream, was the basis of the design for the crucial 12th at Augusta. In addition to its main course, Stoke Poges has recently reopened a further nine holes, thus recreating the original 27-hole format.

Golf, however, is not the only reason to come to this impressive estate. Guests at the 18th-century club house, Stoke Park, will be looked after as if they had dropped into their own stately home. Originally built for John Penn, the founder of Pennsylvania (who commissioned its design from James Wyatt, architect to George III), it has been lavishly restored and provides 21 charmingly-decorated bedrooms. The place is such a blueprint for the English countryside at its most seductive, that scenes from the James Bond classics *Goldfinger* and *Tomorrow Never Dies* were filmed here.

A major attraction, despite the club's rural aspect, is its location, only a seven-mile drive from Heathrow airport and 30 minutes from central London.

Stoke Poges Golf Club
Stoke Park, Park Road, Stoke Poges, Buckinghamshire SL2 4PG, UK

Tel: +44-1753-71 71 71   Fax: +44-1753-71 71 81

Palmer design, will host the German amateur team championship in 2000.

Sporting Club Berlin Bad Saarow
Friedrich-Engels-Damm 300,

15526 Bad Saarow, Berlin, Germany

Tel: +49-33-63 16 35 81   Fax: +49-33-63 16 35 94

STEFANOBI

Although Stefanobi was established only in 1991, its grasp of the finer arts of traditional shoemaking is second to none. The shoes are quite beautiful, chiefly due to the delicate styling, superb leathers and painstaking polishing - the latter takes at least an hour a pair, creating extraordinary colours in the process.

Stefanobi
via Cimarosa 7, 44100 Ferrara, Italy

Tel: +39-0532-90 30 20   Fax: +39-0532-90 18 13

THORNTON'S

Kevin Thornton's Michelin-starred restaurant looks like a neighbourhood bistro from the outside but don't be fooled; anyone who knows anything about good food eats here. Thornton - who trained with Paul Bocuse, among others - cooks for such celebrities as Gregory Peck and Anjelica Huston. Modest and self-effacing, he eschews the spotlight, preferring his food to take all the plaudits (sometime restaurant critic Andrew Lloyd Webber has acclaimed his Suckling pig and trotter as superior to those of Pierre Kaufmann and Marco Pierre White). The mainly French legion of front-of-house staff are expertly led by Alain Chapel-trained maître d' Olivier Meissonave.

Thornton's
1 Portobello Road, Dublin 6, Ireland

Tel: +353-1-454 9067   Fax: +353-1-453 2947

HOTEL TRESANTON

Olga Polizzi has transformed a run-down 1940s hotel into an ultra-chic bastion of contemporary aesthetics and old-fashioned comfort. As the daughter of Lord Forte she spent 16 years with Forte Hotels learning the tricks of the trade, and has now employed this knowledge to build her own business. The Hotel Tresanton is one very personal and stylish outcome of a newly expanding empire.

Hotel Tresanton
St Mawes, Cornwall TR2 5DR, UK

Tel: +44-1326-27 00 55   Fax: +44-1326-27 00 53

VILA BLED

Built in 1947 as a retreat for Tito, this hotel oozes political nostalgia. Kruschev came here to fish, Ceaucescu invited himself for hunting weekends and Indira Ghandi, Willy Brandt and Emperor Akihito are among other past guests. The décor oozes nostalgia, too; it's an extraordinary blend of grandeur and kitsch. Nevertheless, the surrounding countryside is gorgeous and the service, under the direction of Janez Fajar, is exemplary. Incidentally, if you want to sleep in Tito's own room, suite 102 is the number.

Hotel Vila Bled
Cesta svobode 26, SI-4260 Bled, Slovenia

Tel: +386-64-79 15   Fax: +386-64-74 13 20

VILLA LA MASSA

Villa La Massa was once a favourite stopover for English aristocrats on their Grand Tour. Now this refuge, on the banks of the Arno just south of Florence, is being restored by the company which owns the fabled Villa D'Este. An elegant simplicity of line characterises the architecture and decor is in the classic Tuscan villa style.

Villa La Massa
50012 Candeli-Firenze, Italy

Tel: +39-055-62 611   Fax: +39-055-651 0109

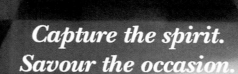

Capture the spirit.
Savour the occasion.

JACK BARCLAY

The world's leading distributor of Rolls-Royce and Bentley motor cars.

• NEW • RE-SALE • AFTER SALES CARE • PRE 1955 PARTS •
BERKELEY SQUARE LONDON W1 • TELEPHONE 0171-629 7444
NINE ELMS LONDON SW8 • TELEPHONE 0171-738 8880

There is only one Blakes

100 BEST-KEPT SECRETS

The 100 names on the following pages are all magical places and specialist shops and services, some of them quirky and most of them hardly known outside the inner circle of Europe's cognoscenti. All of them, however, offer outstanding quality and an indefinable 'something special'.

L'ASTOR

When Joël Robuchon left his remarkable Paris restaurant many critics foolishly assumed that the man who revolutionised restaurant cooking in France had retired. But he now oversees the cooking at this smart little place, where the chef, Eric Lecerf, is one of his best protegés. It is no coincidence that Robuchon's famous mashed potatoes are on the menu.

L'Astor
11 rue d'Astor, 75008 Paris, France
Tel: +33-1-53 05 05 31   Fax: +33-1-53 05 05 30

22 JERMYN STREET

Last year Henry Togna won a Golden Excellence award as one of the best hoteliers in the world. It might seem surprising, then, that he is entirely self-taught and that his hotel only has 13

suites and five rooms. Until, that is, you see quite how hard he works to ensure that every customer is delighted rather than merely satisfied. Togna treats you like his own house guests and will even take you to play tennis at Hurlingham or night-clubbing at Annabel's if the mood takes you. The beauty of 22 Jermyn Street's size - and its lack of public areas - is that it is utterly discreet, a fact much appreciated by Mel Gibson when he stayed there.

22 Jermyn Street
St James's, London SW1Y 6HL, UK
Tel: +44-171-734 2353   Fax: +44-171-734 0750

ACCADEMIA DEL SUPERFLUO

Roberto Lucifero is a one-man cultural phenomenon of sorts. In addition to a sideline business arranging guided tours and lectures in Rome and acting as artistic director for events, he paints décors for exhibitions. Specialising in baroque skies and neo-classical ornamentation, he also paints large canvases to commission, which are sent all over the world. As the final

string to his bow, Lucifero runs classes in *trompe l'oeil*, fresco and gold leaf in his ornate studio in the disused Santa Maria Di Grottapinta church.

Accademia del Superfluo
Via Grottapinta 21, 00186 Rome, Italy
Tel: +39-06-689 6277   Fax: +39-06-830 7356

AGUT D'AVIGNON

Don't be put off by the run-down area where this restaurant is located, for the service is anything but dilapidated, and Pedro Falaganis' menu - comprising many regional dishes - well worthwhile. His Oyster soup, Wild boar with strawberry sauce and the Catalan delicacy, *farcellets de col*, are truly memorable.

Agut d'Avignon
Calle Trinitat 3, 08002 Barcelona, Spain
Tel: +34-93-302 6034   Fax: +34-93-302 5318

ALAIN DE SAINT EXUPERY

In the stables of the Château du Fraysse in the Périgord, this magician of a locksmith - a cousin of the author of the French fable *Le Petit Prince* - restores 17th- and 18th-century locks and keys, and makes anything from a new key for the door of a baronial home to a miniature version for a decorative box.

Alain de Saint Exupéry
Château du Fraysee, 24120 Terrasson, France
Tel/Fax: +33-5-53 50 00 05

ALASTAIR LOCKHART

Having begun in business with The Walton Street Stationery Company, Alastair Lockhart is one of London's finest new-wave stationers with decidedly old world values. The charming premises, run by Alastair and his daughter Olivia, provide full in-house design and type-setting facilities; excellent calligraphy and paper and boards thoughtfully sourced from around the world.

Alastair Lockhart Ltd.
97 Walton Street,
London SW3 2HP, UK
Tel: +44-171-581 8289   Fax: +44-171-912 0652

ALTNAHARRIE INN

The remote north west of Scotland is not somewhere traditionally associated with luxury but Fred Brown has done much to counter this misconception. Altnaharrie lies on the southern shore of Loch Broom. There is no road by which to reach it; rather, a ten minute boat journey in the hotel launch prepares you for the seductively relaxed, homely atmosphere of this eight-bedroomed hideaway.

Altnaharrie Inn
Ullapool, Wester Ross, IV26 2SS, Scotland
Tel: +44-1854-63 32 30

ALZIARI

A source of ambrosial oils and prepared olives, Monsieur Draut's little shop is hidden away near Nice's flower market. The oil, which his family has been making in its own presses since 1869, is mellow and fruity, with a slight hint of almond. Of the seven varieties of olive on offer, the little black *caillette* is particularly delicious. Everything is prettily packaged in blue and decorated with gold stars.

Alziari
14 rue St François de Paul, 06300 Nice, France
Tel: +33-4-93 85 76 92   Fax: +33-4-93 44 45 12

AMIN KADER

Like his former employer, Azzedine Alaïa, Amin Kader has withdrawn from the limelight in order to focus on what really matters to him - perfecting his clothes. The result is a line of fluidly-cut day wear in ultra-luxurious cashmere and fine wool. In keeping with his aesthetic outlook, Kader also stocks the densely aromatic perfumes and pot pourri of the Farmacia Santa Maria Novella in the back room of his boutique.

Amin Kader
2 rue Guisarde, 75006 Paris, France
Tel: +33-1-43 26 27 37

ANTICA BOTTEGA AMANUENSE

Boasting the largest scriptorium in Europe, this building is reminiscent of a medieval Benedictine monastery. Specialised stationery for certificates, invitations and announcements is produced by Màlleus on watermarked, crested paper - written in script dating from the 15th century and embellished with miniatures in gold relief.

Antica Bottega Amanuense
Villa Colloredo, Recanati, 62019 Macerata, Italy
Tel: +39-71-757 4393   Fax: +39-71-757 440

THE ANTIQUE WINE COMPANY

The growing taste for rare vintage wines has been cleverly exploited by Stephen Williams, who specialises in sourcing the oldest and finest wines, often for presentation as gifts. In 1996 he sold a 127-bottle collection of Château d'Yquem (every vintage produced at the château between 1855 and 1990) for the record sum of $1,019,000.

The Antique Wine Company of Great Britain
The Old Stables, Thorpe Hall,
Thorpe Constantine, Staffs, B79 0LH, UK
Tel: +44-1827-83 07 07   Fax: +44-1827-83 05 39

AUBERGE CASA MUSICALE

If you are nostalgic for the villages of Provence before they were overrun by souvenir shops, unspoilt Pigna, in Corsica, seems like bliss.

BELLE ISLE

This is the landscape of Celtic myth: a series of islands on a lake, teeming with fish and surrounded by woods, waterfalls and marvellous caves. On the largest island on the Belle Isle estate, owned by the Duke and Duchess of Abercorn, is a mansion with many enticing delights. Guests may rent the oldest part of the house (early 17th century), which accommodates up to 14 people. It includes a grand hall with minstrels' gallery and a large drawing room, which opens out onto a sunken garden. The wing is decorated in a successful blend of modern and period style. Outside, there is an all-weather tennis court in the charming old

walled garden, shooting and, in addition to salmon fishing (in season), there is pike fishing all year round. A wooden cruiser taking up to 12 people is available for hire on the lake.

Belle Isle Estate
Lisbellaw, Enniskillen, Co. Fermanagh BT94 5HF, Northern Ireland
Tel: +44-1365-38 72 31   Fax: +44-1365-38 72 61

Book a table here and eat delicious regional food, while musicians sing traditional Corsican songs. Bedrooms are painted with frescoes and filled with the scent of mimosa from the terraced gardens which look towards the sea.

Auberge Casa Musicale
20220 Pigna, Corsica, France
Tel: +33-4-95 61 77 31   Fax: +33-4-95 61 74 28

BANK OF IRELAND PRIVATE BANKING

If you are looking for a private bank which is backed by up to 500 retail banking offices world-wide, where a single manager handles both your personal and business accounts, where they don't claim to know all the answers (drawing on the services of the best external specialists) and where they don't insist that expensive dinners are the best way to secure your custom, this is the one. Its discreet Head

Office is in a beautiful Georgian townhouse in Dublin - without so much as a plaque on the door to announce its presence.

Bank of Ireland Private Banking
35 Fitzwilliam Square, Dublin 2, Ireland
Tel: +353-1-676 5566   Fax: +353-1-676 5649

BORGES

In an age when Madeira has become a bland and featureless drink, this tiny family company continues to turn out wines that are models of their kind. All have a thrilling intensity and concentration of flavour. The ten year-olds are superb but, for real excitement, go for the 1935 Boal or 1932 Malmsey and prepare yourself for a ravishing experience.

H.M. Borges Succrs. Lea
Rua 31 Janeiro 83, Apartado 92,
9000 Funchal, Madeira
Tel: +351-91-22 32 47   Fax: +351-91-22 22 81

LA BOTTEGA DISCANTICA

Classical music enthusiasts will be intoxicated by this record store. Such is the quality of its limited edition vinyl, rare compact discs and other sought-after material that celebrated conductors and soloists often drop by when they are in town. Orders can be taken in advance but one must collect in person.

La Bottega Discantica
Via Nirone 5, 20123 Milan, Italy
Tel: +39-02-86 29 66   Fax: +39-02-72 00 06 42

BUÇACO

This marvellous wine is, as insiders know, the product of the Palace Hotel near Coimbra in Portugal. You will have to stay at the hotel if you want to sample a drop and, if you are lucky, they may let you take a bottle or two home. The hotel is a tourist attraction but the lobby is never overrun with sightseers; doormen with a sixth sense for who is a guest - and who is not - see to that.

Buçaco
Hotel Palace Buçaco, 3050 Mealhada, Portugal
Tel: +351-31-93 01 01   Fax: +351-31-93 05 09

CAFE DE CHINITAS

Having drifted out of fashion for some years, this historic *tablao* is right back in style. For over 30 years the flamenco has been performed nightly, with guest artists featured alongside the usual troupe. Skip (the rather ordinary) dinner and go, instead, around midnight for drinks and the show.

Café de Chinitas
Torija 7, 28013 Madrid, Spain
Tel: +34-91-547 1502   Fax: +34-91-542 3669

CASA DE SEZIM

Ambassador António and Maria Francisca Pinto de Mesquita retired here (the estate has been in António's family since the 14th century) having represented Portugal all over the world. Their manor is packed with treasures, from Indo-Portuguese furniture to Baccarat chandeliers. The nine guest bedrooms are deliciously cosy and the long veranda overlooks Maria's lovely gardens and the vineyards, where they produce a distinguished vinho verde.

Casa de Sezim
Nespereira, Guimarães, Portugal
Tel: +351-53-52 30 00

CASA DEL FUNGO E DEL TARTUFFO

This is simply heaven on earth for truffle connoisseurs. Gourmet shoppers are met by the enticing aroma of whichever of these rarefied delights is in season, and can take advantage of Maurizio's words of wisdom in selecting the oils, mushroom creams, terrines and pâtés of their dreams.

Casa Del Fungo E Del Tartuffo
Via Anfossi 13, 20135 Milan, Italy
Tel: +39-02-546 5666 Fax: +39-02-556 4801

CASA GUIDI

Those of a poetic disposition will enjoy staying in the rooms where Robert and Elizabeth Barrett Browning lived, near Florence's Pitti Palace, after their marriage. The Landmark Trust (in association with Eton College) has refurbished the apartment, using Elizabeth Barrett Browning's descriptions of it in her letters as a guide.

Casa Guidi
Landmark Trust, Shottesbrooke, Maidenhead, Berkshire SL6 3SW, UK
Tel: +44-1628-82 59 25 Fax: +44-1628-82 54 17

CASA JUSTO

Traditional Spanish dress has inspired many fashion designers but this is the place for the real thing. The *chaquetillas cortas* (short, fitted jackets), *sombrero cordobés* (flat-brimmed hats), and ruffle-fronted shirts are all-time classics (and will look great with your Saint Laurent).

Casa Justo
La Paz 4, 28012 Madrid, Spain
Tel: +34-91-523 3595 Fax: +34-91-523 3717

CASTOLOVICE

After a glittering, transatlantic social life spanning the past 20 years, Diana Phipps has returned to the Czech Republic where, under her maiden name of Countess Sternberg, she has reclaimed her family's property. Having restored this magnificent Renaissance castle to its original grandeur, she makes it available to carefully vetted clients for private parties.

Zámek Castolovice
Okres Rychnov N., Kneznou,
Hradec Kralove, Czech Republic
Tel: +420-44-21 646 Fax: +420-44-21 729

CERERIA SUBIRA

Originally established as a ladies' fashion store when opened in 1761, this is Barcelona's oldest shop. Maintaining the original décor (worth viewing alone) it is now a candle store, its products equally sought-after by both churches and smart Barcelona residents.

Cereria Subira
Baixada de Libreria 7, 08002 Barcelona, Spain
Tel: +34-93-315 2606 Fax: +34-93-310 3733

47 PARK STREET

For those who would really rather not stay in hotels but who expect a high level of comfort, convenience and privacy, this is a real find. Built originally as a pied-à-terre for gentlemen visiting London, the building has been converted into 52 elegant suites with the atmosphere of a smart Anglo-French 'home away from home'.

As one might expect from an establishment where Albert Roux, founder of Le Gavroche, is the managing director, great attention is paid to culinary arrangements. Each of the one and two bed-

room suites has a private dining room and fully fitted kitchen, which comes complete with shopping list: guests simply mark down their requirements and the concierge will take care of everything. Guests who do not wish to cook for themselves have the benefit of 24-hour room service from the adjoining kitchens of the award-winning restaurant Le Gavroche, a member of Relais Gourmands, and they get priority booking in the restaurant itself (see separate restaurant listing).

47 Park Street
Mayfair, London W1Y 4EB, UK
Tel: +44-171-491 7282 Fax: +44-171-491 7281

LES CHAMPS DE L'OPERA

Two gifted young florists, Olivier Fleury and Patrick Du Martin, decided to join forces a year or so ago, setting up shop on a corner behind the Opera (where flowers are tossed on stage by the dozen). Their lyrically-styled bouquets and imaginative arrangements are the toast of Marseilles' in-crowd.

Les Champs de L'Opéra
rue Francis-Davso 46, 13001 Marseille,
France
Tel/Fax: +33-4-91 33 40 93

CHATEAU EZA

Patti and Terry Giles' 13th-century Château Eza, once the home of Prince William of Sweden,
perches on a dizzying cliff above the Mediterranean. Its ten rooms, all with fireplaces, are enchantingly decorated. Andrew Lloyd-Webber loves the Suite Panoramique, with its roof terrace and rustic beamed ceiling. The terrace restaurant is one of the most romantic dining spots on the entire Côte d'Azur.

Château Eza
06360 Eze Village, France
Tel: +33-4-93 41 12 24 Fax: +33-4-93 41 16 64

CHATEAU DES OLLIERES

In a 3-acre park in the heart of Nice, the former residence of Russian Prince Alexei Lobanov-Rotowsky and his opera-singer wife, the Château des Ollières, has been converted into an exquisite

hotel. It remains richly evocative of the milieu in which the most cultured members of the aristocracy lived between the wars.

Château des Ollières

39 avenue des Baumettes, 06000 Nice, France

Tel: +33-4-92 15 77 99   Fax: +33-4-92 15 77 98

CHRISTIAN BONNET

Tortoiseshell spectacles may seem commonplace - though not if you are looking for the real thing. Christian Bonnet is the third generation artisan specialising in made-to-measure spectacles using this rare material. His father designed pairs for Yves Saint Laurent, Jacqueline Kennedy and Aristotle Onassis, while Christian has claimed François Mitterrand and Jacques Chirac among his clients. All his work is hand-crafted, with great attention paid to a clients' features and personality.

Christian Bonnet

60 rue Lepeletier de Saint-Fargeau,

89100 Sens, France

Tel: +33-3-86 95 22 70

CICERI

If you ever marvelled at how stylish Herbert von Karajan, Riccardo Muti and Claudio Abbado looked on stage, it is thanks to this 100 year-old firm. Soon after its inception Ciceri became leading ceremonial and evening shirt supplier to the Italian royal family and it still uses the same production methods today. After a complex preparatory process, the assembly of a formal set of dress shirt, white tie and waistcoat takes over six hours.

Ciceri

viale Espinasse 82, 80156 Milan, Italy

Tel: +39-02-38 00 19 89   Fax: +39-02-33 40 10 17

CITTA' NASCOSTA

Do you yearn to visit the Sistine Chapel in the solitude for which it was intended? This organisation provides private guides who are both deeply knowledgeable and exceedingly well-connected. They will take you on visits to museums (some of which are entirely closed to the public) and into private castles and villas (where you may be greeted by the owner in person).

Citta' Nascosta

Passeggiata di Ripetta 22, Rome 00186, Italy

Tel/Fax: +39-06-321 6059

DELPHI LODGE

Royals, including The Prince of Wales on his first visit to Ireland, heads of state and stressed-out chief executives in search of solitude and salmon fishing find respite at Peter and Jane Mantle's comfortable country house at the heart of their ruggedly beautiful Connemara estate. The Mantles stress that it is a private home; hence there is no room service and dinner is served around one large table, presided over, rather charmingly, by the captor of the day's biggest fish from the estate's 8km of salmon and sea-trout fisheries.

Delphi Lodge

Leenane, Co Galway, Ireland

Tel: +353-95-42 211 Fax: +353-95-42 296

DOMAINE DE LASTOURS

3,000 of the finest wines are housed in this shop, established in 1893, in a décor which befits their exalted status. Among the treasures are the legendary Cap Corse wines, some exceptional Burgundies, a 1983 Domaine de Jounda and a dry, cask-aged Bas-Armagnac.

Domaine de Lastours

rue de Languedoc 44, 31000 Toulouse, France

Tel: +33-5-61 52 05 20 Fax: +33-5-61 25 65 99

LE DUC DE SAINT SIMON

For quiet comfort and understated elegance, there are few such hotels in Paris to match Le Duc de Saint Simon. Everything from furnishings to flower arrangements has been meticulously planned and every room is individually decorated. Ask for one with a view over the courtyard and 'hidden garden'.

Le Duc de Saint Simon

14 rue de Saint-Simon, 75007 Paris, France

Tel +33-1-44 39 20 20   Fax +33-1-45 48 68 25

DUM HUDEBNICH NASTROJU

A concert grand piano, lovingly fashioned out of maple or mahogany, can be snapped up here for as little as Kc613,000 (£11,500). Baby grands are a modest Kc260,000 (£5,000) - for £100 extra you can have it in Liberace-style

COMBERMERE ABBEY

Eminent art historian John Julius Norwich is typical of the regular guests at Peter and Sarah Beckett's 12th-century Combermere Abbey. With its 1000-acre estate enclosing ancient oak woodlands and the largest privately-owned lake in Britain, the estate offers just three commercial shooting days a year. Traditional driven pheasant and wild duck yield a typical day's bag of up to 200 birds, the emphasis being on relaxed enjoyment rather than mass slaughter.

Combermere Abbey

Whitchurch, Shropshire SY13 4AJ, UK

Tel: +44-1948-87 12 87   Fax: +44-1948-87 16 62

white. Beware, though, if the piano in question is not in stock; you could be kept waiting for six months to a year before setting your fingers on its ivories.

Dum Hudebnich Nastroju
Jungmanovo namesti 17,
110 00 Prague 1, Czech Republic
Tel: +42-2-24 22 25 00   Fax: +42-2-24 22 91 56

ERIC PHILIPPE
A favourite with fashion designers, including Marc Jacobs, Eric Philippe offers a very personal selection of furniture from 1900 to 1950. He is particularly partial to the heavy stylised work of Twenties' Viennese craftsmen, such as Hoffman, the Thirties' furniture maker Ruhlmann, and Jean-Michel Frank.

Eric Philippe
25 Galerie Véro-Dodat, 75001 Paris, France
Tel: +33-1-42 21 17 93

HOTEL EUROPA & REGINA
Only a stone's throw from Saint Mark's Square, this former Tiepolo residence has been beautifully renovated to become a tasteful mini-palace, more discreet than its grand neighbours. The terrace, where traditional Venetian cuisine is served, opens out on to the canal and many rooms have a similarly divine view.

Hotel Europa & Regina
San Marco 2159, 30124 Venice, Italy
Tel: +39-041-520 0477   Fax: +39-041-523 1533

FRANKONIA LOV
The antique guns made by Jaroslov Teichmann - using Holland & Holland mechanics - are the rarest and most valuable of all Central European arms. One client bought an example here for £300 (Kc15,000) and took it to Springer & Co in Vienna for servicing. When the gun was ready Mr Springer offered its owner £15,000 for it. Cartridges made by Selier & Belot (originally deserters from the Napoleonic Army) are also available here, at about 20 per cent of the price in the West.

Frankonia Lov
Manesti IP Pavlova 1/1787,
120 00 Prague, Czech Republic
Tel: +420-2-24 94 25 35 Fax: +420-2-24 94 25 32

LA FRATERIA DI PADRE ELIGIO
Padre Eligio originally restored this ravishingly pretty 13th-century Frateria, which bears his name, as a rehabilitation centre for young people. The result is a charming and well-managed haven, whose restaurant and guest rooms help to finance the community. Breakfasts are heavenly: garden figs and jams, grana and pecorino cheeses and bread fresh from the medieval oven. With no music, TV, radio, papers or phone, La Frateria is perfect for those in need of a tranquil retreat.

La Frateria di Padre Eligio
Il Convento di San Francesco,
53040 Cetona, Italy
Tel: +39-0578-23 80 15   Fax: +39-0578-23 92 20

FUNDACIO ELSA PERETTI
The private collection of Elsa Peretti, Tiffany's celebrated designer, is housed in a secluded Medieval village near Valencia (which is her home for most of the year). Highlights include portraits by Andy Warhol, sculptures from the hand of Xavier Corberó, Ming and Japanese Tang ceramics and photographs by Newton, Scavullo and Mapplethorpe.

Fundació Elsa Peretti
Plaça de l'Església, Sant Martin Vell,
E-46080, Spain
Tel: +34-972-49 02 85
By appointment only.

GAGGIO
Emma Gaggio is the fourth generation to run her family's textile business. Using techniques that were first introduced from the east by Marco Polo, she produces beautiful hand-blocked velvets and painted silks. Specialising in private commissions, she undertakes all manner of decorating projects, from a set of cushions to the interior of Adnan Kashoggi's *Nabila* and several villas in Sardinia and Cortina d'Ampezzo.

FINE ART TRAVEL
After working at Christie's, Lord Charles FitzRoy set up this company, which arranges well thought-out cultural tours to Italy, Spain and France. Tours embrace an eclectic mix of architecture, gardens, paintings and sculpture and Charles FitzRoy effects introductions to private houses and collections for his sophisticated and cultivated clientele, many of whom form lasting friendships on these tours.

Fine Art Travel
15 Savile Row, London W1X 1AE, UK
Tel: +44-171-437 8553   Fax: +44-171-437 1733

Gaggio
Piscian San Samuele, San Marco 3451,
30124 Venice, Italy
Tel: +39-041-522 8574   Fax: +39-041-522 8958

GALERIE ALTERO
Nicole Altéro's charming shop is an excellent source of decorative antiques - especially if you become a friend or regular client, when she will show you into the back room, which is filled with the choicest pieces. Altéro's mother, who opened the shop in 1934, was renowned for 18th-century blown glass, an item which Nicole can still be relied upon to supply.

Galerie Altéro
21 quai Voltaire,
75007 Paris, France
Tel: +33-1-42 61 19 90   Fax: +33-1-40 20 03 30

GALERIE LESTRANGER
After working for almost 30 years in Paris as an art restorer, Catherine Binda-Sterling moved to Saint-Rémy-de-Provence in 1992, having discovered a beautiful late 18th-century house hidden away in the heart of the town. Besides her fascinating collection of artists from 1750-1850, exquisite antique tableware and charming Provençal quilts are for sale.

Galerie Lestranger
Place Jean-de-Renaud,
13210 St-Rémy-de-Provence, France
Tel: +33-04-90 92 57 14

THE GARDEN BOOKSHOP

The only bookshop in Britain to cater for the truly fanatical gardener. From floor to ceiling the store contains volumes appealing to both the expert and novice on subjects ranging from potting to pollination. Stocking new, old and rare editions on diverse specialist subjects, it really is a gardener's paradise.

The Garden Bookshop
11 Blenheim Crescent, London W11, UK
Tel: +44-171-792 0777   Fax: +44-171-792 1991

GELATERIA UMBERTO

If you can negotiate the annual holidays and bizarre opening hours, this *gelateria* is a refreshing must-do pit stop in the bustling heart of Milan. Brave the crowds at the counter to ensure you get a taste of the richest and best ice cream that money can buy - its crème caramel is to die for.

Gelateria Umberto
Piazza Cinque Giornate 4, 20100 Milan, Italy
Tel: +39-02-545 8113

GILBERT AVE

Hundreds of antique clock hands fill this tiny workshop, which was founded in 1855. Gilbert Avé took over from his mother, who established its worldwide reputation, and is now the only remaining clock-hand restorer in France. To restore a treasured antique, Avé will either find a matching example from his archive of 2,000 or he will make an exact replica, ensuring perfect harmony with the clock's mechanics.

Gilbert Avé
14 rue Commines, 75003 Paris, France
Tel: +33-1-42 72 72 29

GIORGIO CLANETTI

Giorgio Clanetti's masks are austere *papier mâché* and leather interpretations of the *commedia dell'arte* sort, inspired by a tradition that originated in Bergamo. He is a mine of information about this fascinating art form and always happy to chat when he is in the shop.

Giorgio Clanetti
Barbaria de la Tole, 6657 Castello, Venice, Italy
Tel/Fax: +39-041-522 3110

THE GOLF FACTOR

Don't be fooled by the un-glamorous address; Ian Woosnam, Mark O'Meara and at least one member of foreign royalty all come here. Golf nut Sam Rogers set up this company three years ago to supply hand made, custom-fitted clubs to golfers seeking an extra edge. There's a virtual reality golf room, where you can watch and analyse your swing with the help of John Palmer, formerly manager of the pro fitting division of Ben Hogan. Other companies provide a similar service, though at a hefty price; here it comes free with your new clubs.

The Golf Factor
7 Delta Park, Smugglers Way,
London SW18 1EG, UK
Tel: +44-171-875 1118   Fax: +44-171-871 9314

LA GROTTE

Famed for its bouillabaisse which it has been serving since the turn of the century, La Grotte is a perennial favourite with the Marseillais. Described as a "chic cabana" with both a terrace and an indoor dining room, it is situated at a tiny port just on the outskirts of the city. Great for fish dishes and fun.

La Grotte
Avenue Pebrons, 13008 Marseille, France
Tel: +33-4-91 73 17 79   Fax: +33-4-91 73 20 54

GUIDO BOSI

As a young man working for his uncle, Bosi began tailoring suits and evening dress for Riccardo Muti, Joan Miró and Herbert von Karajan, amongst others. His jackets, coats and trousers, which he describes as works of art,

JOHNSTON ANTIQUES

Two brothers, Paul and Chris Johnston, run this business, which was started by their father in the 1950s. Until recently they dealt privately, building up a first-class reputation as dealers in fine Irish Georgian antiques, although they have now opened a beautifully appointed shop in the heart of Dublin's antiques district. However, the shop has room for only a fraction of the Johnstons' vast stock at any time and it is always worth enquiring if you are after a specific piece.

Paul travels widely in an effort to repatriate Irish Georgian furniture and unusual examples of the decorative arts - spending a great deal of time in the US, where he has a network of contacts who alert him when interesting items become available. The recent upturn in the Irish economy has created a whole new breed of furniture buyer who is looking for important period pieces. Johnston Antiques is the company to which these buyers turn in order to acquire outstanding examples of important Irish Georgian furniture.

Johnston Brothers
69/70 Francis Street, Dublin 8, Ireland
Tel +353-1-473 2384   Fax +353-1-473 5020

THE HALKIN HOTEL and RESTAURANT STEFANO CAVALLINI

Behind its stately townhouse façade, London's original 'designer hotel' (opened in 1991 by Christina Ong) is all ultra-modern Italian-inspired cool: Armani-uniformed staff, acres of marble and, in the rooms (507 and 105 are the best) clean lines and interesting curves. The mood is reflected also in the restaurant, where Stefano Cavallini's Michelin-starred modern Italian cooking is perfectly complemented by the bright, white space.

The Halkin Hotel and Restaurant Stefano Cavallini

5 Halkin Street, London SW1X 7DJ, UK
Tel: +44-171-333 1000   Fax: +44-171-333 1100

are made in the finest fabrics, including his own exclusive Harrison's cashmere. A lover of the arts, Bosi seldom misses a first night at La Scala or Salzburg.

Guido Bosi

via Farini 3, 40121 Bologna, Italy
Tel: +39-51-58 19 75

HARUMI KLOSSOWSKI

The daughter of artist Balthazar Klossowski de Rola (known as Balthus) and his Japanese wife, Harumi creates exquisite jewellery inspired by her East-West roots: blue topaz and malachite necklaces, rose quartz and pink topaz chokers, for instance. Like her stepbrother Thadée (husband of Loulou de la Falaise, St Laurent's collaborator), she is part of Paris' hard-core fashion circle. Having been associated with John Galliano, she now works independently. However, to possess one of Harumi's pieces takes perseverance, for she is as elusive as her famous father.

Harumi Klossowski

c/o Christian Louboutin
23 Motcomb Street, London SW1X 8LB, UK
Tel: +44-171-823 2234   Fax: +44-171-235 6773

HAVANA

Persevere through this drinks store and you will come to the man you are after. Farouz, who loves to impress clients with his knowledge and to advise on brands, is probably Moscow's most famous cigar merchant. All his smokes are imported directly from Havana, including the Monte Cristo, Cohiba and Romeo y Julieta labels.

Havana

17 Komsomolsky Prospekt,
119021 Moscow, Russia
Tel: +7-095-247 0555

HOTEL LES AMURES

In Geneva unashamed extravagance often goes hand in hand with typical Swiss reserve, as is clearly evident at Les Armures, which once belonged to the city's clergy. A complete overhaul has revealed its former splendour, including magnificent frescoes and ceilings, which sit surprisingly well with the CD players and ISDN lines that travellers now take for granted. Stay in Suite 409 for a real glimpse of the past and the present in unlikely harmony.

Hôtel Les Armures,

1 rue du Puits-Saint-Pierre,
CH-1204 Geneva, Switzerland
Tel: +41-22-310 9172   Fax: +41-22-310 9846

JAR'S

Monsieur Jeannet runs the most discreet of jewellery shops. Unlike its grand neighbours on the Place Vendôme, Jar's has no shop front - just a small plaque on the door leading up to its first floor showroom. However, once inside, there are marvels to be seen: stunning *parures*, rings and bracelets made up of important stones, all in the French classical idiom.

Jar's

7 Place Vendôme,
75001 Paris, France
Tel: +33-1-42 96 33 66

JARANDILLA DE LA VERA

Once a fortress where Charles V lived, the 15th-century Jarandilla de la Vera is one of the best run Parador hotels in Spain. Beautifully restored, this aristocratic establishment charms guests with its pretty setting, rustic interior and hearty regional cooking.

Jarandilla de la Vera

1 Avenida Garcia Prieto,
10450 Jarandilla de la Vera, Spain
Tel: +34-927-56 01 17   Fax: +34-927-56 00 88

JAYME DOS SANTOS

A hotel is fine for a few days, but VIP travellers staying for any length of time often prefer to rent a house or flat. Jayme dos Santos finds such accommodation in London for a clutch of the Hollywood élite. He once gave up his own flat to Lauren Bacall when she arrived at short notice - you can't get more accommodating than that.

Jayme dos Santos

64 Bury Walk, London SW3 6QB, UK
Tel: +44-171-351 7575   Fax: +44-171-351 7272

KEVIN & HOWLIN

Run by Noel Kevin, whose father established the firm in 1936, this traditional shop is a marvellous source of tweeds, both by the length and made up into coats, jackets, scarves and hats as many stylish Italians will confirm. All of the fabrics (including some cashmere blends) are hand-woven in Donegal, many in patterns exclusive to the shop. Its tailors will make up men's clothing to order.

Kevin & Howlin Ltd.

31 Nassau Street,
Dublin 2, Ireland
Tel/Fax: +353-1-677 0257

KRISTINA POPOVITCH

Women of the 'pink city' flock to stylist Kristina Popovitch's exquisite store for her sunny, self-confident clothes. Worked in rich textiles and vivid colours, their spirit owes a great deal more to Christian Lacroix than to either minimalism or grunge.

Kristina Popovitch
rue des Arts 9, 31000 Toulouse, France
Tel: +33-5-61 55 57 63   Fax: +33-5-61 26 15 80

LAURA B

Laura de Chair's clubbish Knightsbridge dress business has a surprising power-base of some 1,500 distinguished clients. Typically, Laura B ladies are high profile but low key - they love the anonymous elegance of outfits that can take them to any social gathering without shrieking 'price' or 'designer'. As an added bonus, Laura never sells two of the same outfits for the same occasion.

Laura B
25B Walton Street, London SW3 2HU, UK
Tel: +44-171-581 4123   Fax: +44-171-581 3833

LAURE BAUDET

Canny decorators make a beeline for this antique dealer's imposing 17th-century townhouse in Toulouse, which once belonged to Louis XVI's Prime Minister, the Comte de Villèle. Baudet has filled the ground floor with treasures found all over Europe, including elaborate Venetian mirrors, vast chandeliers and beautifully crafted furniture. Make a point of seeing her garden while you are there.

Laure Baudet
16 rue Velane,
31000 Toulouse, France
Tel: +33-5-61 25 00 05   Fax: +33-5-62 26 07 41

LIAISONS ABROAD

Liaisons Abroad is the magical ticket merchant for culture vultures. Set up in 1990 by Massimina Caneva, it can source seats for practically any festival or opera house in Europe, as well as for sporting events and pageantry. With particular emphasis on Italy, the company is also involved in hotel representation and makes other travel arrangements on a tailor-made basis.

Liaisons Abroad
Chenil House, 181-3 Kings Road,
London SW3 5EB, UK
Tel: +44-171-376 4020   Fax: +44-171-376 444

LIESBETH ROYAARDS

Liesbeth Royaards' gorgeous showroom occupies the canal-side former home of a grand Dutch merchant. For almost three decades she has been fashioning chic suits and dresses from

McKENNA & Co

Owned and managed by Catherine and Michael McKenna, this delightful little shop deals in top quality antique and period jewellery. With an attractive wood-panelled Regency shop (where a fire burns in the grate on cold days) in a picturesque Knightsbridge thoroughfare, McKenna & Co. is a quintessential 'old-school' jeweller, which makes it all the more surprising to discover that it is only 15 years old. Many of the firm's clients are smart Knightsbridge residents; photographer Koo Stark wrote of her "fascination with the power of gems" in the introduction to the company's last catalogue. She winningly entreated McKenna's customers to "buy for beauty and compatibility. Be empowered by your gems. Therein lies their value!"

McKenna's client list is impressive indeed - and includes royalty, media people, politicians, superstars and top models. However, there is a huge emphasis placed on discretion here and the company would never dream of passing on customers' names or releasing its mailing list, "under any circumstances".

Engagement and wedding rings are a particular speciality. Customers often select a fine period engagement ring from the company's stock and then commission new hand-made wedding rings to match. There is also an impressive range of modern jewellery available, including excellent pearls, at surprisingly modest prices.

McKenna & Co.
28 Beauchamp Place, London SW3 1NJ, UK
Tel: +44-171-584 1966   Fax: +44-171-225 2893

silk, chiffon and taffeta, taking her inspiration from Balenciaga, Patou and Schiaparelli.

Liesbeth Royaards
Herengracht 70, 1015 BR Amsterdam,
The Netherlands
Tel: +31-20-626 5026   Fax: +31-20-427 5867

LULU GUINNESS

Married to brewing heir Valentine, and known for her stylish, magazine-documented home, Lulu Guinness has created an international cult handbag empire in the space of just a few

years. Hers are the rose-topped satin baskets on the arm of young *mondaines* everywhere and other styles are similarly small, perfectly formed and often charmingly embroidered.

Lulu Guinness
66 Ledbury Road, London W11 2AJ, UK
Tel: +44-171-221 9686   Fax: +44-171-243 2167

MARINA SINIBALDI BENATTI

Artist Marina Sinibaldi designed jewellery for Enrica Massei, Missoni and Romeo Gigli before going solo in 1993 and opening her own couture showroom in 1996. She works with cashmere, linen and silk, some of which she handpaints, to create refined clothing that transcends fashion. A constant stream of friends, journalists and clients fill her studio-cum-shop, which is hung with paintings by Dutch artist Martin van der Jaght.

Marina Sinibaldi Benatti
via Soncino 1, 20123 Milan, Italy
Tel: +39-02-805 7152   Fax: +39-02-86 45 46 43

LA MERENDA

There is, as yet, no telephone here (nor are credit cards and cheques an acceptable form of currency); one must make reservations - which are essential - in person. Dominique le Stanc, former head chef at the Hôtel Négresco's celebrated Le Chantecler restaurant, caused a real stir when he decamped last year to take over this tiny bistro. He will cook you the kind of Niçoise lunch that only dreams are made of.

La Mérenda
4 Rue de la Terrasse, Nice, France
No telephone

DR MOSARAF ALI

Dr Ali has set up the only Integrated Medical Centre in Europe, with 25 doctors and therapists offering everything from acupuncture and ayurvedic regimes to irridology and deep-tissue massage. Dubbed "Prince Charles' guru", he is much admired by the heir to the throne and counts many other international royals and celebrities as patients.

Dr Mosaraf Ali
Integrated Medical Centre,
43 New Cavendish Street, London W1M 7RG, UK
Tel: +44-171-224 5111   Fax: +44-171-224 3114

MUSEE CONDE

The Château de Chantilly stands in the middle of a carp-stocked lake in grounds designed by Le Nôtre and houses a collection of French paintings that is second only to the Louvre. Come here to revel in works by artists of the Italian, Northern and French schools (including *Les Très Riches Heures du Berry*), as well as examples of French Orientalism, portrait drawings and illuminated manuscripts.

Musée Condé
Château de Chantilly, 60631 Chantilly, France
Tel: +33-3-44 62 62 60

GALERIE NAÏLA DE MONBRISON

It is only when Naïla de Monbrison slides open one of the dark wood drawers in her jewellery gallery that you realise the full extent of her treasures. She begins by plucking out a ring

made from quail's egg and exotic wood, then comes a silver necklace as solid as a breastplate. On display is a cuff bracelet with topazes stuffed into layers of bronze, next to it antique Indian earrings. Every piece in her collection is unique and, it seems, has a history.

Galerie Naïla de Monbrison
6 rue de Bourgogne, 75007 Paris, France
Tel: +33-1-47 05 11 15

ONE DEVONSHIRE GARDENS

This ultra-chic Glasgow hotel epitomises owner Ken McCulloch's singular good taste and meticulous attention to detail. Three lav-

ishly restored Victorian townhouses, with 27 bedrooms and a Michelin-starred restaurant are the backdrop to what some consider to be *the* British hotel of the 1990s. The service is particularly notable. How did he do it? "Good service isn't a mystery," says McCulloch, "just employ nice people."

One Devonshire Gardens
Glasgow G12 0UX, Scotland
Tel: +44-141-339 2001   Fax: +44-141-337 1663

OMBELINE

Anyone who is nostalgic for Maud Frizon's delectable shoes, as sought-after in the Seventies and Eighties as Manolo Blahnik's today, need pine no more. At Ombeline you can rediscover her timeless Russian high heel boots in exquisitely supple kid leather, her cone-shaped stiletto heels and ultra soft loafers, all hand-made following 19th-century Italian shoemaking traditions. Better still, Mrs Maud Frizon de Marco, as she is now known, may even be there to serve you personally, as

she does such loyal customers as Angelica Houston, Catherine Deneuve and Claudia Schiffer.

Ombeline
17 rue de Bourgogne, 75007 Paris, France
Tel: +33-1-47 05 56 78

OSTERIA DA FIORE

This attractive and friendly family-run restaurant has been an open secret among Venetians for many years. The *seppioline* and *pasticcio di pesce* are prepared far more authentically here than in the city's other seafood restaurants. Despite its back street location it gets packed, so reservations are essential.

Osteria da Fiore
Calle dello Scaleter 2202, Campo San Polo, 30100 Venice, Italy
Tel: +39-041-72 13 08   Fax: +39-041-72 13 43

PACO DE CALHERIOS

The Prime Minister of Holland was one of the Count de Calheiros' first guests at this remarkable 18th-century mansion in the north western corner of Portugal. The house is a veritable treasure trove of colourful antiques and obscure souvenirs of ancient adventures and the Count a charming host, who possesses just the right amount of old world formality and modern ease.

Paço de Calheiros
4990 Ponte de Lima, Portugal
Tel: +351-58-94 71 64   Fax: +351-58-94 72 94

PENSIONE ACCADEMIA

Once you discover this noble *pensione*, you will be intoxicated by its elegance, peace and otherworldliness. Rooms are furnished in an idiosyncratic mix of rural charm and pleasing kitsch - the whole affair has the air of a family house to which you have been invited as a privileged guest.

Pensione Accademia
1058 Dorsoduro, Venice, Italy
Tel: +39-05-23 78 46   Fax: +39-05-23 91 52

LA PETITE MAISON

La Petite Maison is far from Michelin star status but, as the Niçoise bourgeoisie has known for 60 years, this is the place for brilliant local cooking. Succulent *Carré d'agneau* and marvellous fish are complemented by a wine list which, regrettably, does not list the vintages. Tourists are thin on the ground here and, generally, their welcome is, if not frosty, certainly not enthusiastic. However, come back four or five times and Madame will acknowledge your existence with a half smile and a glass of Kir Royale. You will then have joined the very select bunch of non-Niçois who are deemed acceptable.

La Petite Maison
11 rue François de Paul, 06000 Nice, France
Tel: +33-4-93 85 71 53   Fax: +33-4-93 92 28 51

LA PINEDE

This unpretentious seafood restaurant on Cap d'Ail, produces wonderful *loup de mer* at a fraction of the price you would pay five minutes away, in Monte Carlo. Its two open terraces at the foot of the cliffs look directly over the water. Although it's nearly hidden from the road, you'll identify it by the line of parked BMWs with Italian licence plates. It's notoriously difficult to park but, if you phone ahead and are very charming, the owner will arrange for your car to be looked after.

La Pinède
10 boulevard de la Mer, 06320 Cap D'Ail, France
Tel: +33-4-93 78 37 10   Fax: +33-4-93 78 37

THE QUEEN OF SCOTS PRIVATE TRAIN

At the end of the 19th century, the railways provided the last word in luxury for their richest travellers; families would charter whole carriages to transport them to their estates in Scotland. The Queen of Scots uses three beautifully restored carriages from this era to take you anywhere you wish in the British Isles, even to the tiniest station. The Observation Car has, as its livery, the original and beautifully evocative 'plum and spilt milk', which was chosen as the colour scheme for the Royal limousine. The Family Saloon contains a library and the Dining Car, the world's oldest, was originally commissioned for 19th-century cotton barons.

The Scottish Highland Railway Co.
Bedford House, 62 London Road,
Maidstone, Kent ME16 8QL, UK
Tel: +44-1622-68 88 99   Fax: +44-1622-68 88 55

PIPERNO

Run by the Boni Mazzarella family, this is a favourite haunt of Henry Kissinger and Francis Ford Coppola. Gerardo Rubini and Vincenzo Galante's cooking is quintessentially Roman, with Jewish/Italian influences; dishes include marinated anchovies, fried artichokes, zucchini flowers and delicious fish. The tables spill out across the square in summer.

Piperno
Monte de Cenci 9, 00186 Rome, Italy
Tel: +39-06-68 80 66 29

PRIORS DUKKETEATRE

Founded in 1880, Priors Dukketeatre is keeping alive the traditional German craft of making models of buildings from paper. The charming model theatre seen in Ingmar Bergman's *Fanny and Alexander* came from here. There are many designs available, including Copenhagen's Royal Theatre and the Paris Opera House, both ready-assembled or to make up yourself.

Priors Dukketeatre
Kobmagergade 52, 2nd floor,
1150 CopenhagenK, Denmark
Tel: +45-33-15 15 79

PRUHONICE CLINIC

This clinic, run by the distinguished plastic surgeon Vera Satankova and her husband is the only one in the Czech Republic to be devoted entirely to plastic surgery. Clients from all over the world are attracted here by the high quality of surgery and the discreet and pleasant environment in which to recuperate.

Pruhonice Clinic -
MU Dr Vera Satankova
Rikanska ulice,
252 43 Pruhonice, Czech Republic
Tel: +420-2-67 75 00 97   Fax: +420-2-75 25 59

RAMONET

This *domaine* is quintessentially Burgundian: it's tiny, run by two brothers and is superficially chaotic - but it produces some of the most magnificent white wines you'll ever taste. Be enraptured by the panoply of flavours, the superb balance and integration, the lingering finish that goes on and on. Their fabled Montrachet is one of life's great privileges.

Ramonet
11 rue de Grand Puit, 21190 Chassagne, France
Tel: +33-3-80 21 30 88   Fax: +33-3-80 21 35 65

GOOSSENS

Decades after Coco Chanel's demise, her favourite jewellery designer is still producing sumptuous pieces for the Paris *haute couture* collections, as well as his own range. "She worked me very hard and ordered not only jewellery but also tables and sculptures," recalls Goossens. He studied the techniques employed by ancient Greek and Etruscan craftsmen and it is these references that give his gold, bronze and rock crystal pieces such timeless grace.

Goossens
42 avenue George V, 75008 Paris, France
Tel: +33-1-47 23 99 26

LA ROTISSERIE DU BEAUJOLAIS

The little sister of the Tour d'Argent, this restaurant is a must for roasted duck connoisseurs who prefer a more casual ambience than that of France's gastronomic institution. All the roasted poultry is excellent, especially if served with the restaurant's creamy mashed potatoes. You will feel just as pampered as you would next door, since the Tour d'Argent's manager Claude Terrail, now a sprightly 78, often drops in to say hello to the regular clients.

La Rôtisserie du Beaujolais
19 quai de la Tournelle, 75005 Paris, France
Tel: +33-1-43 54 17 47

RUSSKI LYEN

This is a great source of high quality Russian linen at very reasonable prices. The fabric is sold in bolts, in various weights from fine to coarse and is available in natural beige and white. Fine linen products, such as embroidered tablecloths, sheets and towels are also available. Supplies can be erratic, however.

Russki Lyen
29 Komsomolsky Prospekt, Moscow, Russia
Tel: +7-095-242 5925

SALON

The ultimate *blanc de blancs* champagne, Salon is a true rarity, being produced only in fine vintages. Though it is now owned by Laurent Perrier it hasn't lost any of its identity or appeal. Very dry in style, it is intensely flavoured and ages beautifully - a must-have for champagne aficionados willing to go off the beaten track in search of magnificence.

Salon
B.P.3, 51190 Le Mesnil-sur-Oger, France
Tel: +33-3-26 57 51 65   Fax: +33-3-26 57 79 29

LA SCALINATELLA

In the absence of a private house, the best place to stay on back-in-fashion Capri is the small and quirky La Scalinatella. More club than hotel, its immaculate garden overlooks the breathtaking Faraglioni rock formations. Very personal service provides a refreshing antidote to the hit-and-miss grandeur of the more famous Quisisana.

La Scalinatella
via Tragara 10,
80073 Capri, Italy
Tel: +39-81-837 0633   Fax: +39-81-837 8291

LA SIVOLIERE

The fact that this chic little Alpine hotel has only three stars says nothing about the sort of place it is or, for that matter, who stays there. Madeleine Cattelin runs her little fiefdom with great charm and efficiency and studiously avoids publicity. But that's only part of the reason why King Juan Carlos stays there. Tucked away on the edge of Courchevel, La Sivolière has superb skiing, quite literally, on the doorstep.

La Sivolière
73120 Courchevel 1850, France
Tel: +33-4-79 08 08 33   Fax: +33-4-79 08 15 73

SEVEN ONE SEVEN

Seven One Seven is billed as an "exclusive private guest house" and that's just how it feels. It has

only seven bedrooms but each is more charming - and stylish - than the last. Roaring fires and beautiful big bouquets of flowers are to be found scattered around the building and the ambience is warm and studiously personal throughout.

Seven One Seven
Prinsengracht 717,
1017JW Amsterdam, The Netherlands
Tel: +31-20-42 70 717   Fax: +31-20-42 30 717

SWINLEY FOREST

Tucked away amongst the rhododendrons, pines and oaks and indicated by the tiniest of roadside signs, this is one of Europe's most exclusive golf clubs. A small membership of bankers, lawyers, chief executives and a Prince (Andrew) enjoy the beautifully kept heathland course. The only way you can play is either with a member or on one of the limited company days allowed. It is well worth getting to know a member because this is a haven of charm and a little golfing gem.

Swinley Forest
Coronation Road, South Ascot,
Berkshire SL5 9LE, UK
Tel: +44-1344-87 49 79

'T SMALLE

"The Narrow" is indeed a *bruin* café but, more importantly, it is a listed building. Although the cash register has the date 1886 engraved on it, the café actually opened in 1780. And never mind the illicit pleasures found here, the paintings by Flemish 17th-century masters, intriguing antique artefacts and the better-than-excellent beer are quite enough to fuel your imagination.

'T Smalle
The Egelantiersgracht 12,
1015RL Amsterdam, The Netherlands
Tel: +31-20-623 9617

THE THREE OSTRICHES

This delightful hotel is named after the birds that were the stock in trade of its original resident, who was the Prague court's official supplier of ostrich feathers in the 18th century. In 1938 the building, now a listed monument, was bought by the Dundr family, who restored it lovingly, uncovering Renaissance ceilings in the process. Their welcome is unusually warm and courteous.

The Three Ostriches
Drazického námesti 12,
11800 Prague, Czech Republic
Tel: +420-2-57 32 05 65 Fax: +420-2-57 32 06 11

VILLA DI MASER

Designed by Andrea Palladio and decorated with Paolo Veronese frescoes and Andrea Vittoria

WELDON ANTIQUES

Antique Irish silver is much rarer than its English counterpart (for every 150 English teapots there is only one Irish) and there are few good sources of this unique style of silverware, which is characterised by an exceptional fluidity of design. Brothers James and Martin Weldon are two of Ireland's leading authorities on the subject, scions of a well-known family which has specialised in Irish silver, as well as Victorian jewellery, for three generations.

The brothers scour the world - North America, New Zealand, Australia and Britain - for the finest examples of their genre, buying privately and at auction and bringing them back to their warm, intimate shop in the heart of Dublin. Star pieces, such as this rare George I Irish octagonal teapot (Dublin 1714), a 64oz silver basket with a swing handle (c.1755) by Richard Williams and a George III soup tureen (c.1770) by John Lloyd, probably the most celebrated silversmith of his day, are snapped up by Irish and international collectors, many of them Irish-Americans.

Weldon Antiques

55 Clarendon Street, Dublin 2, Ireland
Tel: +353-1-677 1638   Fax: +353-1-670 7958

statuary and stucco-work, the Villa Barbaro di Maser is a fine example of its genre. Its special charm, however, is that it is still lived in year-round by its owners. On the adjoining farm there is a collection of antique carriages and, as a bonus, a 19th-century wine cellar, where tastings of the estate's own wines take place.

Villa di Maser

Maser, 31010 Treviso, Italy
Tel: +39-0423-92 30 04   Fax: +39-0423-92 30 02

VILLA KALLHAGEN

Carl and Diane Kirchner's peaceful haven is where smart Stockholm escapees head for at the weekend. Decorated by Love Arbén, Sweden's ultra-chic interior designer, the 20-roomed hotel profers a mix of relentless modernism with great refinement. During the summertime the owners like to treat guests to their idyllic barbecues - idyllic because they are held on the edge of Djurgardsbrunns Bay.

Villa Kallhagen

Djurgardsbrunnsvägen 10,
11527 Stockholm, Sweden
Tel: +46-8-665 0300   Fax: +46-8-665 0399

WALNUT TREE INN

If Piedmontese roasted peppers, Thai pork or perfectly cooked Salt duck appeal to your palate, make your way to a small whitewashed public house in the Welsh hills and prepare yourself for a truly exceptional meal. The Walnut Tree Inn's Italian proprietor, Franco Taruschio, along with his English wife, Ann, will eagerly welcome you into their ambitious little restaurant with the greatest courtesy and warmth.

The Walnut Tree Inn

Abergavenny NP7 8AW, Wales
Tel: +44-1873-85 27 97

THE WEDDING LIST COMPANY

Nicole Hindmarch set up this invaluable company in 1987 to provide a dedicated and highly personalised present-buying service to prospective couples and their wedding guests. It has an unrivalled and distinctly pukka range of gifts, drawn from its own catalogue of exclusive designs, as well as from the world's leading luxury goods companies.

The Wedding List Company

91 Walton Street, London SW3 2HP, UK
Tel: +44-171-584 1222   Fax: +44-171-581 0440

UNDER THE PATRONAGE OF
HER MAJESTY QUEEN ELIZABETH THE QUEEN MOTH

The Grosvenor House Art & Antiques Fair

9-15 June 1999

Grosvenor House
Park Lane
London W1

Charity Gala Evening: 9 June

For further information
please contact the Organiser's Office
Telephone: +44 (0)171 495 8743
Fax: +44 (0)171 495 8747
E-mail: grosvenor-antiquesfair@msn.com
Web site: www.grosvenor-antiquesfair.co.uk

In association with
The British Antique Dealers' Association

A LIFE OF STYLE

Words by Nicola Mitchell

*Couturier, fine art collector, decorator and gardener extraordinare:
few people have ever embodied French style quite as well as
Hubert de Givenchy.*

Hubert de Givenchy is a name that conjures up the most lavish of settings. So it is a surprise to find the six-foot-six-inch frame of this ineffably elegant gentleman folded behind a desk in a tiny office at 6 rue Paul Baudry. Then again, the new President of Christie's France presides over even this cramped space so graciously that we might just as easily be sitting in an ante-chamber at Versailles. In fact, Givenchy's transition from legendary couturier to ambassador of one of the world's leading auction houses has been as natural to him as changing for dinner. "If I hadn't become a designer I would have been an architect or a decorator," he says. "Furnishing a room is like designing a dress, you choose fabrics and objects which will work harmoniously together so the place is comfortable to live in."

A devoted collector of 18th century art and antiques, Givenchy must certainly feel at home in this building filled with art treasures, situated in such a familiar street. His grandfather, after training with Paul Baudry, was chief administrator of the celebrated Gobelins and Beauvais tapestries, as well as a passionate collector of costumes and all kinds of *objets d'art*. So Givenchy had a love of fabrics and fine craftsmanship instilled in him from childhood.

Indeed, aged four, he was already making dolls for his sisters from discarded material and, by seven, had begun drawing clothes for the women he saw in fashion magazines. His visit to the Pavillion de l'Elegance at the Exposition Internationale in 1937, when he was 10, was the turning point in his young

In December 1993 Hubert de Givenchy sold the contents of his then Paris residence, the hôtel d'Orrouer in St. Germain. A collection of splendid antiques and furniture, amassed over 30 years, it is a perfect reflection of both M. de Givenchy's faultless taste and his exceptional connoisseurship of the decorative arts. OPPOSITE: The gentle colours in the hôtel d'Orruer's salon blanc are echoed by the green of the trees in the garden, seen through the tall windows.
ABOVE: The sumptuous salon vert bears witness to M. de Givenchy's search not only for the finest individual examples of their genre but for items that harmonise perfectly with each other. A Louis XIV bureau plat by André-Charles Boulle stands in the foreground.

life. Confronted with the extravagant designs of Elsa Schiaparelli, the sculptural dresses of Madame Gres, Mainbocher's trousseau for the Duchess of Windsor and other marvels of this brilliant fashion decade, he made up his mind to become a couturier.

Although he was enchanted by the couture world, there was only one person whose work made a deep impression on him: the Spanish couturier Cristobal Balenciaga. After completing his *baccalauréat*, he decided to go and see this formidable designer in Paris with a selection of his best drawings. "There was no question of me asking Balenciaga for work," Givenchy hastens to point out. "I simply wanted him to say, 'Yes, young man, your sketches are good.' Or, 'They are worthless, there is no point in continuing." Unfortunately, the couturier's notoriously fierce manager, Madame Renée, wouldn't let him through the door.

Disappointed, but determined not to go home empty handed, Givenchy went to see Jacques Fath, who was very much in vogue at the time. Much to Givenchy's surprise, he was hired on the spot. "It was an extraordinary opportunity for me to work for Fath as I was only 17 and had no training." He remembers his first months there as being like exploring "a sensual, dangerous universe." As his job was mainly research, he was delighted to find that he could spend many hours sketching designs in museums, art galleries and libraries.

A year later, in 1946, he joined the Swiss couturier Robert Piguet, known for his uncompromisingly classic approach and purity of line. Christian Dior had trained with the designer, one reason why Givenchy was attracted to the house. Better still, Piguet, like the young designer's family, was a staunch Protestant, and from that point they accepted his choice of career with more equanimity. On Dior's recommendation, he then went to work for Lucien Lelong, but, unhappy with the atmosphere there, he left after six months. Encouraged by a friend, the celebrated fashion illustrator René Gruau, he joined Elsa Schiaparelli. The four years Givenchy spent running the boutique of this rebellious genius, had a lasting effect on his approach to couture.

As his 25th birthday present to himself, Givenchy set up his own fashion house at 8 rue Alfred de Vigny, overlooking the Parc Monceau, in February 1952. "I only had the means to open in a very modest way, so I decided to establish a luxury boutique offering separates, rather than a couture house," he explains. More to the point, he was convinced that there was a demand for this type of fashion. "The clients I looked after for Schiaparelli, such as Comtesse Edie von Bismarck, the Duchess of Windsor and Gloria Guinness, already felt the need for accessories which were not haute couture but inspired from it. They wanted to create their own individual style, whether it was by throwing a sweater over a shirt or finding a chic belt to set off an outfit. I felt that this was the right formula for me." Added to that: "No one was doing anything like it at the time," he says.

ABOVE: A pair of Louis XV lidded porphyry vases stands on a pair of Languedoc marble pedestals. OPPOSITE: In the salon vert, the rich dark green silk velvet is a perfect foil for a Louis XVI low bookcase, signed by Etienne Lavasseur, a pair of Louis XIV guéridons by Boulle from the Duchess of Talleyrand's Palais Rose, and Samuel van Hoogstraten's Interior Scene.

Givenchy chose the most beautiful models of the day to present his first collection, among them Suzy Parker, Ivy Nicholson, Sophie Malga and Bettina Graziani, who doubled as his public relations manager. Every design in the collection was made of gingham because, he says, "It was fresh and inexpensive". The show was a triumph. "Afterwards everyone said, 'Great, but now you must open a real couture house'. This didn't interest me at all. I wanted to create a new way of dressing."

Right on cue, the muse who was to make this possible appeared at his boutique. Givenchy was busy

showing his latest collection when he was informed that Mademoiselle Hepburn would like to meet him. Expecting to see Katherine Hepburn, an actress he greatly admired, he rushed into the reception area, only to be greeted by a tall, very thin girl in cotton slacks and a T-shirt, who explained that she would like him to help her choose costumes for her starring role in Billy Wilder's film *Sabrina*. "Her gentle look and exquisite manners seduced me immediately," Givenchy says. As for Hepburn, she remembers: "He was adorable right from the start. I had never seen a haute couture dress, let alone worn one, but he took the time to choose a suit with such a spiritual quality to it and a superb dress in white organza with black embroidery which I wore when I danced with William Holden in the winter garden..." From that time on, she felt she was born to wear Givenchy.

The actress represented a revolutionary image of 'youth, gaiety and elegance' for the couturier. "After the huge success of the film I became very well known in the United States; and every film I dressed her for after this, such as *Funny Face*, *Ariane*, *Breakfast at Tiffany's*, brought me a huge amount of publicity. Audrey always remained loyal to me, even though she could have asked anyone she liked to design her clothes." Her generosity in letting him use her name when he launched his perfume for young women *Fleur Interdit* in 1994 particularly moved him. "We didn't have a contract, which wouldn't be possible with actresses like Catherine Deneuve or Carole Bouquet. She showed nothing but integrity and friendship towards me."

Besides being the couturier synonymous with Hollywood's most angelic actress, Givenchy says his career was blessed with one other 'great privilege'. This was his friendship with Balenciaga, whom he finally met in New York in 1954. On that day, Givenchy says, "He told me that he had seen and admired my work for some time and regretted that no one had introduced us." The young designer was so overwhelmed by this tribute that he considered closing down his house and going to work for him.

"In terms of technical skills, Balenciaga was the greatest couturier, well in advance of any other designer at the time. His clothes had an architectural quality and style that was unsurpassed. He wanted each piece to be as beautifully produced inside as it was on the outside. There was never a false note." Givenchy valued him as much as a friend and confidant as a tutor and mentor. "If I had a problem, he would say, 'Come round on Saturday and we will sort it out over a drink.' After he retired, he would telephone me late in the evening and say: 'Still working? Go home and it will make more sense in the morning.' He was always right." Almost ingenuously he asks: "Can you imagine the luck I had with someone like that to guide me?"

OPPOSITE: *Capucine wearing Givenchy in 1952.* ABOVE: *Hubert de Givenchy takes a bow with his seamstresses at the end of his autumn/winter '95/'96 haute couture show.*

Luckier still, perhaps, were all the very wealthy women who wore his creations. Whether they chose his earlier designs, such as his revolutionary shirt dress or "Bettina" blouse, the bias-cut dresses and shirts, the sculpted little coats and seductive cocktail dresses with bare backs or, best of all, his legendary evening gowns, they couldn't fail to look ravishing. Explaining his vision, he says: "A dress must be like a breath of air. It must follow the movements of its wearer. That is the art of our profession. Just like an artist who gives the impression that the inspiration for his paintings came all at once." With such an aesthetic approach, it is not surprising that the cantatrice Frederika Von Stade once confided to him: "When I wear your clothes, I sing better."

Despite the success of his collections, Givenchy decided to bolster his income by setting up a perfume company, launching the scent *De* in 1957. It was well received, as were the six other perfumes for men and women which followed. Henri Recamier, the chairman of Louis Vuitton, was particularly impressed by Parfums Givenchy's performance and, after wooing the couturier for two years, finally convinced him to sell him first the perfume company in 1986, then his couture house two years later. "He was a grand *monsieur*," says Givenchy, significantly. "Given our good relations, as well as the fact that I had no partner and that my nephew wasn't interest in the business, I decided to go ahead. It meant that I could concentrate entirely on my collections and have more time in general."

By 1988, however, his couture and perfume companies were owned by LVMH: Moët-Hennessy Louis Vuitton and a bloody boardroom battle had begun for the presidency of the group. The victor was neither Henri Recamier nor Alain Chevalier of Moët-Hennessy, both respected figures in the closed world of the French luxury goods industry, but an outsider, the brilliant young strategist Bernard Arnault, who had bought the failing Christian Dior couture house in 1984. A property developer earlier in his career, Arnault had little time for the complex etiquette and gentlemen's agreements which had kept the companies ticking over demurely in the past.

Givenchy had signed a seven-year contract with the group in 1988 and had six years to go after Arnault became president. Those years saw the spectacular return of haute couture largely thanks to Arnault, who had rapaciously bought up and revamped one fashion house after another. But for Givenchy, who remembered couture in its purest form, before licensing agreements became the buzz word in the boardrooms, the clothes were parodies of the real thing. Finally in 1995, although he was asked to stay on, Givenchy decided to retire. "I thought it would be better if I withdrew," he says, looking as if he had swallowed a neat, unsugared citron pressé in one go.

After 50 years as a couturier, Givenchy slipped quietly out of the fashion world, aside, that is, from the occasional, irrepressible public jibe at his successors in the couture house. However, he was far from at a loose end, thanks to his appetite for collecting antiques and love of

decorating. A sense of volume, purity of line and a great sensibility in the form are the recurrent characteristics in his exquisite 18th century collection of fine objects and furnishings, including magnificent André-Charles Boulle cabinets and Louis XVI chairs. He is particularly fond of armchairs: "They are like humans: they have arms and legs and are either introverted or welcoming, solid or fragile."

As for the splendid homes he has filled with his treasures, he says: "I love houses not because I like to give parties or impress people but because I love beautiful objects and like to place them in surroundings that do them justice." He devotes just as much time to perfecting his gardens. At Jonchet, his 17th century manor house near Tours, he completely redesigned the grounds, creating a park inspired by the Venetian gardens of the San Giorgio Maggiore monastery, thought to have been designed by Palladio, as well as a vegetable area and a herb garden. In these he placed great glass bells over the plants to protect them from frost. "Each season I dress the garden differently, exactly like a collection," he once said.

Many of Givenchy's couture clients, however, would have preferred that he carried on dressing them rather than his gardens. When he took over his new role at Christie's last year, though, it gave them an opportunity to get in touch. "I was very moved by the number of letters I received," Givenchy says. He chuckles when he remembers the reaction of Bunny Mellon, who was one of his most loyal clients: "She said to her husband, who is a great art collector, 'Do you know that Hubert is going to Christie's in Paris?' He replied, 'That's wonderful, for years you were dressed by him, now he can decorate for you.' I said: 'Of course, and if Paul has any pictures or other things he would like to sell, tell him to think of me, just as you thought of me for your clothes.'"

If these encounters bring back memories of more glorious days, he keeps his feelings under wraps. "I was passionate about my work, but you can't make time stop. Fashion was different in my day, women wore hats and gloves: it was another era." Still, he can't repress his distaste for fashion in the Nineties: the hair "plastered to the face", the huge wedge shoes, but worst of all, he says, "If young women don't look exactly the same as their friends they laugh at them." Style, he believes, is all about "being in harmony with yourself, this is what makes you look good". Describing his assistant Bettina Graziani he says: "She would come to work in a man's shirt, a simple skirt and moccasins and look exquisite."

As for today's cinema stars, he looks bewildered at the mere idea of finding a muse in Hollywood today. "I went to see *Titanic*, which was quite a good film, but I didn't see one pretty dress, even though it was a great period for fashion. There was far more attention paid to the boat's decoration than the costumes. If Visconti had made the film the clothes would have been wonderful."

For a moment, he seems in danger of drifting into a wistful reverie over the days when he dressed Lauren Bacall, Elizabeth Taylor, Princess Grace, Marlene Dietrich, not to mention Audrey Hepburn, but then he throws back his silver-haired head and says defiantly, "Why should I cry? Paris is beautiful, the sky is blue... and there are some things they can't change, like the trees and gardens."

OPPOSITE: *A stunningly simple black evening gown from Givenchy's autumn/winter '92/'93 collection.* ABOVE: *Hubert de Givenchy and an assistant fit a dress destined for Audrey Hepburn, in the mid-1950's.* ABOVE RIGHT: *Audrey Hepburn with Hubert de Givenchy in 1988.*

escape

Nusa Dua
Bali, Indonesia

experience

HOTEL MEURICE
rue de Rivoli
Paris, France

work

relax

THE DORCHESTER
Park Lane
London, England

The Beverly Hills Hotel
and Bungalows

Beverly Hills
Sunset Boulevard, USA

THE AUDLEY GROUP

'A connoisseur's collection
of the world's
most perfect hotels.'

THE MEANING OF LUXURY

Words by Lucia van der Post

The definition of luxury has changed at the end of the 20th century, evolving from the overt status symbols of the Eighties into a discreet blend of functionalism and high craftsmanship.

It is odd how notions of luxury change. "Luxury has been wrongly associated with the unattainable," Andrée Putman, the French interior designer, has said. And she's right. It is not so long ago that most of us, if asked to define what luxury meant to us, would have had no trouble at all in indulging in a little private day dreaming. A private jet. A string of racehorses. A box at the opera. Unlimited Krug. A villa in Tuscany. But these are grand luxuries, expensive luxuries, luxuries whose most beguiling characteristic, to those that have access to them, is that they tell the world at large that they are rich.

This is the world of obvious opulence - of yachts with panelled drawing rooms and a battalion of staff, of mirrored hallways and crystal chandeliers, of taps coated in gold, of Lamborghinis and Château Petrus. It's the world of matching sets of hand-stitched leather luggage, of swanky furs and high-gloss jewels. It's a world where the accumulation of instantly recogniseable, even iconic, consumer goods and artefacts seems to confer power and status.

But that was then and now is now. Expensive and self-affirming though all these things may be, tastes, even among the very rich, have changed. They may still (because, of course, it is so handy and it really does save time and the very real frustration of airport queues) board their Gulfstream jets - but they wouldn't dream of letting everybody know. Where once their women may have sashayed down the shopping streets of the world swathed in fur, today they know it's so much more chic to wear their fur on the *inside* of the coat. It keeps them just as warm, it still feels just as soft but it then becomes a

PREVIOUS PAGE: *The new, discreet luxury - as interpreted by Chopard.* ABOVE: *Master craftsman Gianni Grassi, at work in the Asprey & Garrard atelier.* OPPOSITE: *Princess Magna is a superb example of fine craftsmanship married to high technology; however, to charter is smarter than to buy.*

private, personal pleasure, not a way of establishing their pecking order in the world. Even the rich these days no longer want to take refuge in a steady stream of internationally recognisable symbols of wealth. They prefer to plot a more singular path. Luxury, as defined by the old, obviously swanky models, has begun to seem about as cool as a nylon anorak.

As economies boomed and stockmarkets soared in the late 20th century, much of the world has got richer. Large numbers of consumers outside the previously small and privileged circle have become sophisticated shoppers. They have had the means to become familiar with the allure of butter-soft leather, the beguiling warmth and lightness of double-faced cashmere, the sweet smell of linen sheets, the tantalizing delights of silken underwear and of embroidery that takes 100 woman-hours to work by hand. In the affluent shop-till-you-drop years they learned about quality, about why a Kelly handbag is so enduringly desired, why a kid-glove-soft loafer costs more than three times its high street copy, why Guerlain scents have life-long admirers who will wear nothing else, why there are women who will spend more than a month's salary on a jacket that comes with a pedigree and a little gilt chain sewn inside the hem.

They may have started buying grand names because they liked the reassurance of their status but, in the process, they became addicted to the quality that they offered. Once you feel the lightness of the cloth, the comfort of the cut and see, up close, the perfect line of seam and button, then - but only then - does the charm of a dead-plain Jil Sander double-faced cashmere coat become blindingly clear. Once you've felt the softness of a Gucci leather jacket, the comfort of a lean little Hermès cashmere or swathed a feather-light pashmina around your shoulders you're spoiled forever. Nobody but a fool could fail to appreciate their quality.

But this new shopper, though she understands the seductive pull of class and quality, doesn't want the old-fashioned luxury of the large

logo, the glitzy jewels, the obviously expensive trimming, the flash furs - she wants her luxury new and hip and almost monastically understated. That's why she loves the pashmina - made from the finest and, centimetre for centimetre, costliest fibres in the world; only the inner circle would know that. It's the combination of sumptuous luxury and near-anonymity that makes it so perfect a paradigm for this new approach to luxury. At their most chic when absolutely plain, pashminas look like nothing but a simple scarf but - crucially - the inner circle knows that it has cost nearly as much as the monthly mortgage. That's also why Jil Sander is the new shoppers' patron saint; she uses nothing but the finest, most luxurious materials and cuts them impeccably, subtly and ever-so-discreetly. If you saw a Jil Sander hanging on a rack and you didn't know its secret you could quite easily pass it by. It has a subtle cachet that you have to be not only rich but also knowledgeable and sophisticated to enjoy - and therein lies its power.

All the well-managed luxury goods companies have realised for some time that the whole business is undergoing a profound change. Not only have the tastes of their shoppers changed - becoming more subtle, more refined, more obsessed with real quality - but the customers themselves have become

OPPOSITE PAGE: *The exquisite luxury of fine Frette bed linen.* ABOVE: *Calvin Klein slip dress - discreet, sexy and stylish.*

younger. The old bourgeois assumptions, the air of middle-aged stuffiness, that lay behind many of the products has had to be abandoned. These sophisticated younger customers no longer feel the need to proclaim their membership of a club dominated by conspicuous wealth; they may still respond to the reassurance of a grand name but, unless it comes underpinned by real quality, they won't be flexing their credit cards. They can recognise the ersatz and the second-rate at 30 paces. And, on top of that, they want a certain (but not too much) fashionability, some real design and an indefinable cachet.

It's quite a package to deliver but, when a company (such as Gucci, which did it so spectacularly when it took a dead-beat label and revived it as one of the hippest luxury labels around) gets it right, the rewards come rolling in. It's that irresistible combination of effortless class, serious glamour and a certain sexiness that is delivered by something like a Manolo Blahnik shoe, an Elspeth Williamson dress or a Paloma Picasso necklace. This is the reason why almost all the grand, established purveyors of luxury goods have gone out and found younger, newer designers to freshen up their image. It's why Louis Vuitton got Marc Jacobs, the sweater and sneaker-clad designer from New York, to produce a line of sleek clothing so understated that it's not until you get up close that you realise that the sweatshirt is in three-ply cashmere, the zipped jacket in softest suede, the shirts in finest silk. It's also the reason why you can now buy Louis Vuitton leather without a single logo in sight. It's why Loewe has got Narciso Rodriguez to zap up its fashion and its accessories so that, together with the quality that the name of Loewe underwrites, their customers will get glamour and luxury with an utterly modern edge.

But, though nobody would deny the thrill there is in owning your very first Gucci (or Hermès or Chanel or Louis Vuitton) handbag or the exquisite sense of enjoyment that comes from a tissue-wrapped wisp of silk with a grand name attached, luxury doesn't reside only in the long-established names and in the large and expensive purchases. It also resides - most satisfactorily - in some of the smaller every-day things that are available to one and all. These are often the just upgraded versions of life's daily necessities. They often cost very little more than their more everyday relations but oh, how they're worth it and oh, what a difference they make. It's about choosing the finest and the best over the mundane or the merely adequate.

A John Smedley sweater, for instance, costs more than other similar-looking versions - but not that much more - and, when you put one on, when you feel its softness, its silkiness, you wonder why you ever wore anything else. Like many of the new luxuries it isn't anything very much to look at; see it residing upon a shelf and you would probably not give it a second glance. But it's not for nothing that John Smedley is a label whose name is passed around amongst many of the world's most discriminating shoppers. Once you own one you can't wait to buy more. The pleasure it gives derives from knowing that you are wearing the finest wool or the most refined Sea Island cotton that the world can provide.

Luxury can take in bespoke shoes from Lobb or Berluti, a made-to-measure shirt from Turnbull & Asser or Borrelli, a stainless steel kitchen, a weekly manicure, Cutler & Gross spectacles or Lorna Wing to cook your dinner party. It resides in little touches of individuality. Where once the buyers of

RIGHT: *Made of the finest Merino or Sea Island cotton but completelt understated, the classical John Smedly sweater is highly sought-after by sophistaced shoppers.* OPPOSITE PAGE: *An exceptionally high level of workmanship goes into making even the simplest bowl at Christofle; several of its craftsmen have been awarded the accolade 'Meilleur Ouvrier de France'.*

the finest perfumes would have sought the security of the big international names, today they might turn to the smaller perfume houses, to names such as Jo Malone or Les Senteurs or Creed's *Fleurs de Bulgarie* or the exquisite fragrances from the chic little French perfumier, Les Parfums de Rosine. Or to lesser-known scents from a grand house, such as Chanel's *Vol de Nuit* or *Cuir de Russie*.

Luxury can be found, too, in something as small as a fine bar of soap; once you have used a bar of triple-milled soap made of nothing but natural oils and subtly perfumed with only herbs or essential oils, once you have sampled the heady delights of a Guerlain, a Farmacia Santa Maria Novella, or Hermès' delicious *24 Faubourg* you will never want to use a cheaper, coarser brand.

Whether you are penning a thank-you note or merely a shopping list, there is intense pleasure to be got, too, from good quality stationery - watermarked and with engraved addresses. Open a letter that arrives in a lined Smythson envelope, unfold that heavy paper and your local stationer's best will never seem the same again. A good pen - a Mont Blanc, a Parker 51 or a Dunhill - where its weight and the alignment of its nib are nothing less than perfect, gives pleasure every single day.

And then there are country roses in a jug, instead of the stiff, hothouse versions, or filling the house with the scent of a Rigaud candle - neither are cheap but nor are they luxuries which will break the bank. Or what about Blue Mountain coffee from Jamaica, so mellow, so smooth that the pleasure per sip makes it cheap at the price? First-pressing virgin olive oil is another of life's luxuries that won't break the bank. Nor will first-class mature cheddar or truly fresh herbs. And no man can resist the heady delight of owning a really good quality pen-knife. Pick up a traditional French shepherd's knife by Lagioule, made in the mountains of the Aveyron, feel its handle of horn, finger its brass rivets and fine blade and merely peeling a peach becomes an aesthetic experience.

Proper beeswax candles won't cost a fortune but how sweetly they smell and how nicely they burn. Then there is the exquisite pleasure of sleeping in proper linen sheets, of laying one's head on pillows filled with down - neither are cheap but nor are they only for the seriously rich.

It's the little luxuries - things like hardback books, fine music, good-quality wine, fresh flowers, face creams that don't come from the supermarket, teas from Whittard of Chelsea - that, in the end, make more difference to one's daily life than the grand ones. There is a time when small children play havoc with timetables and the only luxury worth having is a good night's sleep. To a harassed mother, a manicure and a massage in a proper beauty salon or a weekend away at a country-house hotel would be more welcome than a fancy piece of jewellery.

Which isn't to say that some of the grand luxuries would not come amiss. Few of us these days long for diamond necklaces (too showy), our own yachts (it's easier to hire) or wardrobes full of furs (too swanky) but offer us limitless first-class air travel and there you've got us. Offer us a week in an Eastern spa, a Ben Nicholson painting, an Elizabeth Frink horse, a wardrobe filled with Chanel or Yohji Yamamoto and we have to admit that, affordable though many of life's best treats may be, the definition of luxury as "the unattainable" will never be *entirely* out of date. **E**

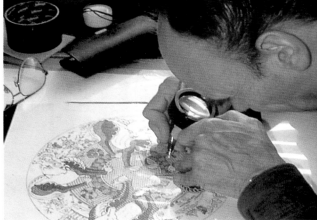

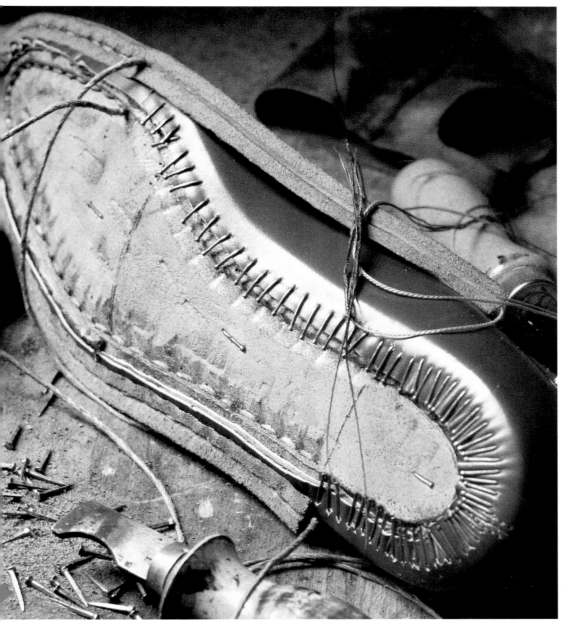

OPPOSITE PAGE, *above: Hermés' classic Kelly bag - much imitated, never equalled. Below: The combination of near-anonymity and sumptuous luxury make the pashmina shawl a perfect paradigm for the new approach to luxury. THIS PAGE, top: Manolo Blahnik's beautifully crafted 'Numi' day shoe in two-tone kid. Above: A craftsman at Thomas Goode's workshop hand paints a plate for a special order. Left: Berluti shoes are as comfortable as they are beautiful, thanks to the quality of workmanship involved in their making.*

CHEWTON GLEN

THE HOTEL, HEALTH & COUNTRY CLUB

FOR FULL DETAILS SEE PAGE 85

THE
MIGHTY MARK

Words by Alexander von Schönburg

The German economy has been the powerhouse of Europe and the mighty Mark the dominant currency. However, outsiders know little of how the German élite lives.

According to the Sunday Times Rich List, of the ten richest Europeans practically all are German. But have you ever heard of any of them? Does the name Karl Albrecht ring a bell? Or Curt Engelholm? Apart from the fact that you may hardly be able to pronounce their names properly, it is most unlikely that any of them will have crossed your path on the social circuit, because the richer a German is, the more he will live in hiding. And the last place you will find him is in Germany. For tax reasons Switzerland is a preferred place of residence, although most merely reside there while actually living in Florida.

One of these, Otto Beisheim, lives in Miami. Were you to meet him in the street, you would think of him as one of those elderly gentlemen who dutifully cuts out tokens from newspapers to get two bottles of window-cleaner for the price of one. And if you were to speak to him, you would realise that this is exactly what he does. He owns the biggest retail chain in Europe and is said to be worth about 20 billion Marks but he does not drive an expensive car (just an Audi), takes commercial flights, his suits are not tailored and his wife uses the window-cleaner he got the price-break for to clean the windows herself.

The super-rich Germans generally do not believe in spending money on themselves, unless they want to prove a point. Otto Beisheim wanted to buy an apartment in Miami, in a building he happened to like, but his offer was refused and the apartment went to another buyer. So Mr. Beisheim bought the whole block – and the two neighbouring ones as well.

Just like Beisheim, the Albrecht brothers and Erivan Haub (another one of these obscure billionaires) have made their money in retailing, owing much to Germany's post-war *Wirtschaftswunder* (economic miracle). These fortunes are still in the hands of the founding generation, which probably explains why they are so cautious in spending it. Their fathers had been humble drugstore owners, so they do not feel entitled to spend their money on luxuries, no matter how rich they are. If one looks for a little bit of lifestyle, a hint of *savoir vivre*, one has to consider the families that are not among the ten richest but which have had money for at least two or three generations.

The fortunes that were made in the industrial revolution are the glamorous ones. The Flicks, Thyssens, Sachs and Krupps are those who joined up with the aristocracy in the pastime of blowing money at the end of the last century and now are completely at ease with it. The Krupps learned from the aristocracy so thoroughly that they degenerated at a rate that would have taken an aristocratic family hundreds of years and are now extinct. But the Flicks, Thyssens and Sachs are still very much around.

ABOVE: *Mick Flick.*

Gunter Sachs, of all the heirs of these fortunes, made the most of it by developing the chasing of women into an art form. His greatest coup was the capture of Brigitte Bardot, then the most desirable woman in the world. Apparently, BB's resistance waned when he chartered a plane, dropped roses over her house in St. Tropez, then parachuted a case containing his underwear and shaving kit into her garden before floating in himself. Even today, notwithstanding his happy marriage to the lovely Mirja, he is unrivalled in his skill. He has written a book scientifically proving the relevance of astrological star signs. I recently went to Gunter's chalet in Gstaad and realised why he had written it when I saw a bunch of young blondes queuing up to sit on his lap, eagerly asking him about their star signs.

The other dynasty that is so old and so rich that it practically qualifies as aristocracy is the Thyssens. In fact, the Thyssens were the first to realise that the best way of acquiring a taste for the sweet things in life is to mingle with the aristocracy. The newcomers realise that families like mine have had a good time over hundreds of years and can teach them a trick or two. The old families, on the other hand, welcome the newcomers, as we have so efficiently blown our fortunes in this long pursuit of pleasure that an injection of new money is highly appreciated. Heini Thyssen's grandfather married a Hungarian Baroness and merged her name with his in order to make his own sound grander. Heini Thyssen-Bornemisza's daughter Francesca, a few years back, married the scion of the grandest dynasty in Europe, Archduke Karl von Habsburg. Heini himself first married Princess Teresa zur Lippe then, after some more wives, fell prey to a Spanish lady of distinctly non-aristocratic background, who now spends his money for him. In his heyday, Heini continued to add to his father's magnificent art collection, amassing so many great works of art that he could afford to donate a whole

ABOVE: *The opera house at Bayreuth; the Wagner Festival here continues to attract both the social heavyweights and the musical élite.*

museum to the Spanish government and still have enough left over to have Picassos hanging in his bathroom.

The Flicks took a little longer to catch up with the lifestyle of the German upper class (though they made up for it by marrying into my own family). Friedrich, the founder of the Flick iron and steel empire, made his fortune buying up bankrupt companies and scrap yards and became so rich that no matter how hard his son tried, he could not succeed in seriously diminishing it. This son, Friedrich-Karl ("F.-K.") decided to cash in his 29 per cent share of Daimler-Benz (today Daimler-Chrysler) in the mid-Eighties – a rash move, with hindsight, given that the share prices have been climbing ever since. In his attempt to save taxes in this transaction he triggered the biggest corruption scandal in German post-war history by bribing virtually every politician he came across, wasting millions. When a news magazine uncovered the 'Flick Scandal' the credibility of the political class in Germany was undermined to such a degree that it gave rise to the anti-establishment Green Party. In an awkward way at least, F.-K. has left his imprint on history, just as he has on the interiors of various Munich restaurants that he demolished (…"Just put it on my bill, please!").

In line with my theory of growing sophistication over the generations, F.-K.'s nephews, Mick and Muck, are much more refined than their uncle. In fact, you will not find me making any rude remarks about them because I would like to be invited back to Mick's chalet in Gstaad (from which I am currently banned because of things I wrote some time ago). So let me make it clear: these Flicks are both very charming. Muck has written a book on lost Old Master paintings and Mick collects impressive works of modern art. He also took part in last year's Paris to Peking rally and was one of the few to make it…..in a vintage Mercedes (what else!).

F.-K.'s daughters, Alexandra and Elisabeth, in line with my theory of growing sophistication over the generations, are also very agreeable, though they ought to be handled carefully since, should you ever aggravate them, they still have enough funds to take over your company and dismantle it before you have the chance to say, "Have a nice d…" Alexandra is already married, while Elisabeth, the younger one, is still single. Judging by the boys she goes out with, it seems that she has grasped the principle of mingling with old names, understanding it to be essential to any serious attempts at social climbing in a country like Germany, where pedigrees still count as much as bank balances.

Evidently, the most effective way to merge money and blue blood is marriage. The role model is the present wife of the Aga Khan. Her mother, an able businesswoman who had become a self-made millionaire by the age of 22, comes from a town in the industrial Ruhr area, called Bottrop, a place so dark and bleak that it makes Newcastle or Detroit look like Florence. But she made her way out of there by marrying five times – every time a little bit further up the social ladder. Her daughter Gaby has changed her name even more often than she has changed her face starting as Gaby Homey, she became Gaby Thyssen (nothing to do with *the* Thyssens though), then Gaby Wunderlich (she always took on the name of the man her mother married). Then she advanced to Princess by marrying Prince Karl-Emich zu Leiningen, divorced him and has now arrived at the illustrious name, Begum Inaara Aga Khan.

ABOVE RIGHT: The Begum Inaara Aga Khan (formerly Gabriele Homey-Thyssen-Wunderlich-von Leiningen). BELOW: Archduke Karl von Habsburg, his wife, Francesca (née Thyssen) and their children. OPPOSITE: Princess Gloria von Thurn und Taxis, with her children, Elisabeth and Albert.

ABOVE: *Karl-Eduard and Celia von Bismarck.*
LEFT: *Alexandra Flick, daughter of Karl-Friedrich.*

The family struggling most in its efforts to climb the social ladder is the Piëchs. They are the heirs of the Porsche-Volkswagen empire but history has placed their roots in Wolfsburg – the least likely place from which to launch a social career. Had they done as the Thyssens and the Flicks did and mingled more over the years, they would have had friends to tell them not to go to the Vienna Opera Ball, for example, which used to be elegant before the war, but is social death to attend today. An attempt to introduce their daughters to members of the upper classes failed recently, when the Piëchs chartered a boat on the Nile for a week-long party. Unfortunately, the 12-page invitation they concocted was so overblown that every hoped-for blue-blood stayed away. One wonders if Ferdinand Piëch, who carried through the Volkswagen takeover of Rolls Royce, might secretly hope that ownership of the most elegant of car manufacturers will raise his social status.

The art of spending money in style is such a delicate one that it requires careful instruction. Central European life is full of traps. How does one know, for example, not to sing the praises of Düsseldorf to someone who knows that the only smart city in Germany is Munich (because Bavaria had the most full-on royal court with a properly mad king and snobbish courtiers)? While Munich, Salzburg and Vienna still conserve some of the glamour of Imperial times and, thus, a courteous (and courtly) social scene, places like Hamburg and Frankfurt have a distinctively bourgeois attitude. Hamburg is certainly smart – but in a low-profile way typical of the north, rather than the overtly glamorous southern way. Berlin is becoming a more exciting place but, socially, has not yet reached the standing of a metropolis like London or Paris, notwithstanding the newly rich Russians, who have chosen the city as their Western El Dorado. It will be at least a generation before Berlin's real social position becomes clear.

But, once you have sorted out your cities, what advice bureau explains which fixtures of the social season to attend and which to skip? Here is a start. Do go to the opera festivals in Bayreuth and Salzburg (July and August). But, in Salzburg, you must be invited by Princess Manni Sayn-Wittgenstein and Thaddeus Ropac or you don't exist socially. Do not turn down an invitation to the annual summer party hosted by the Chancellor (Helmut Kohl at the time of writing). Optional are the Bambi Awards (December), the Munich Oktoberfest (but only at Käfer's tent, not among the lager-louts), the Love Parade in Berlin (June) and the Rennwoche in Hamburg (Germany's horse-racing highlight). Strict no-go areas for those who aspire to the social elite are the Ball des Sports, the Frankfurt and Vienna Opera Balls, charity parties hosted by a certain Ute Ohoven and an annual piss-up called Hamburger Nächte.

Something that one should take into account when dealing with Germans is the fact that there are only a few of them who can be considered properly smart, in the English upper class or American 'Wasp' kind of way. The overriding characteristic of German society is its incredibly large and wealthy middle class – a middle class that is far more urban and cosmopolitan, far more affluent and well-travelled than that of any other European country (the average wealth of a German is 400,000 Marks). It is a middle class that dwarfs the few hundred 'elegant elite', not only in size but also in influence and relevance.

As the attentive reader has probably figured out by now, in Germany it is an alliance of old names and assimilated nouveaux that socially calls the shots. There are a few households whose parties are an absolute must: the Fürstenbergs, one of the few very old families who are still very rich (the source of the Danube is located in their palace's park), the Toerrings (German cousins of the English and Spanish royal family), known for the colourful blend of guests at their pretty Schloss Winhöring near

ABOVE: *Baron Heini von Thyssen, Pilar Fovez-Acebo and Baroness Thyssen (née Carmen Cervera).*

ABOVE: *The Hemmerle jewellery store on Munich's Maximilianstrasse, a favoured port of call for Germany's élite.* RIGHT: *Gunter and Mirja Sachs.*

Munich, the Bismarcks, with their social head-quarters Friedrichsruh (near Hamburg), who uphold a social siege on Marbella (and partly London) that would make the Iron Chancellor proud, the Henkells (industry), Schöllers (banking) and of course my sister, Princess Thurn und Taxis. The party that she gave for her late husband, Prince Johannes, for his 60th birthday in 1986 is regarded as a classic in the history of 20th century bashes. Guests like Malcolm Forbes, the old Begum Aga Khan, Adnan Khashoggi, Mick Jagger, all in Rococo costumes, had to walk through a time-warp leading them into the courtyard of Regensburg Palace, which had been turned into a village scene where farmers bowed deeply to the arriving guests. The theme of the evening being *Don Giovanni*, this mother of all masked balls culminated with an abridged performance of Mozart's opera, with my sister interrupting the disheartening finale to give the story a happy end with her rendering of the Marlene Dietrich song *Johnny, It's Your Birthday Tonight*.

As far as style is concerned, Germans look abroad for inspiration. This attitude is one of the refreshingly pleasant streaks of post-war Germany. The Germans had been humbled so much by the experience of losing two wars and were so impressed by the lifestyle of their occupiers after the last (the Americans, the British and the French) that they decided that anything German is tacky (apart from Mercedes cars; even Porsches are driven only by dentists in Germany). A smart German would brag about staying at the Mercer in New York, talk about L.A. like his backyard and flaunt foreign status symbols to gain credibility. The fashion idols of rich Germans are not Wolfgang Joop and Jil Sander, but Alexander McQueen and Christian Lacroix. Karl Lagerfeld is fine, because he has been internationalised and is no longer regarded as German. One's tailors are in London and Milan, one's lover in Paris, one's money in US bonds, one's house in St. Tropez or in Porto Cervo. The Germans are so obsessed with being international that they even had their new parliament in Berlin, the Reichstag, re-built by an Englishman, Sir Norman Foster, who himself was puzzled when chosen as the architect.

ABOVE: *Stephanie von Bismarck.*

One of the richest and nicest Germans I ever met lives in a beautiful house overlooking the bay of St. Tropez. He is extraordinarily rich, yet he lives in total obscurity. As he has managed to hide so well from public attention, I will certainly not spoil it for him now but I have to tell the tale of how he impressed another rich German. He is married to a charming lady but, unfortunately, they have no children. They therefore treat their dog, a cute white terrier, as if it were their daughter. The dog has its own little house, covered with photos: dog in Paris (behind it the Eiffel Tower), dog in Pisa (behind it the Leaning Tower), in Venice and so on. At lunch, the fellow billionaire tried to impress them by saying, "The flight connections between Nice and London are such a drag, I had to have my children's nanny flown down by private plane the other day, because we were going out for dinner and couldn't leave the kids alone at home." "Yes, you're so right," said my friend, "I too had my dog flown in by private plane the other day." E

Calvin Klein

100 LEADING EUROPEANS

Research by Kevin Kelly, Sandra Lane, Nicola Mitchell, Giulia Pessani,
Alexander von Schönburg, Caroline zu Waldburg-Wolfegg, Trevor White.

Stylish, charismatic, erudite, entrepreneural, flamboyant and cerebral – some
of the virtues of our leading Europeans. The totality of Europe's talent and the
strengths of its differing cultures are reflected in our choice of 100 Europeans.

AGNELLI

When Gianni Agnelli stepped down as chairman of Fiat in 1996, many commentators speculated that it was the end of an era. But the man affectionately known as l'Avvocato still has a huge influence on the way both Fiat and Italy are run today. In his last speech to board members he said, "Fiat has managed to maintain and consolidate a world presence for Italian cars." If anything, that is an understatement. Fiat is now 14 times larger in terms of annual sales than when he took over 30 years ago. Its turnover is equivalent to three per cent of Italian gross domestic product.

Charismatic, immensely stylish and a pivotal figure among the jet set for four decades, Agnelli enjoys setting trends. When, for example, he started wearing his wristwatch over his shirt cuff, thousands of Italians followed suit and, as long ago as the Sixties, when he wore them to go sailing, he made 'driving shoes' a chic accessory. His opinions on matters as mundane as bus strikes and as profound as the future of Europe are treated with equal reverence. Giovanni's wife, Marella, is a charming hostess, renowned for her faultless taste, who has sustained her own successful career as a photographer, writer and designer.

Sixty-four year old Umberto, Gianni's younger brother, is often described as 'the man who might have been' although that label looks more and more redundant in the wake of his recent performance. Passed over in favour of his late son, Giovanni Alberto, to inherit Fiat's leadership, he looked set to enjoy a comparatively quiet retirement until his son's tragic death from cancer at the age of 37. 'The Bean Counter' (as some critics have unfairly dubbed him) now plays two hugely important roles: CEO of IFI, the vehicle for the

Agnelli family's shareholding in Fiat, and Chairman of IFIL, the industrial holding company for the Agnelli group. This latter interest includes extensive holdings in food, retail, tourism, telecommunications, banking and even a share in the famed Château Margaux. Together, the family's two 'safeboxes' are worth an estimated $450m.

A Senator of the Italian Republic from 1976 to 1979, he is a ferocious critic of the inward-looking nature of many Italian firms. In a recent interview he said, "There was a moment in the Eighties when the economy was strong and industry was working flat-out for the national market. At that moment we lost the opportunity to look abroad."

Comments like these and his track record in investing overseas have not always been welcomed at home, although the Italian media have applauded Umberto for his astute management and leadership skills in the last year. On the international stage he has long been held in high esteem. In 1996, for instance, he was awarded the Grand Cordon of the Order of the Sacred Treasure from the Japanese government and he has won equally impressive plaudits in the many countries where the Agnellis do business.

A qualified lawyer, Umberto is married to Allegra Caracciolo di Castagneto and they have two children, Andrea and Anna. In his spare time Umberto enjoys playing golf and watching football. He has been Chairman of both Juventus Football Club and the Italian Football Association. ◄

ALMODOVAR

Spain's most celebrated film director since Luis Bunuel, Pedro Almodovar was born in La Mancha in 1951 and spent the early years of his life loathing the Catholic priests who were supposed to be educating him. That they have subsequently been caricatured in his films is hardly surprising, for this is a man whose passions and interests are constantly re-invented for the benefit of his audiences.

At 16 he moved, alone, to Madrid, where he dedicated himself to living well at a time when Franco had most of Spain in a stranglehold. To the young man, the capital represented everything that the provinces didn't: liberty, culture and sex. After drifting through several inconsequential jobs, he landed his first 'respectable' position - with the National Telephone Company. To celebrate, he bought himself a Super-8 camera. After work every day he produced short films and plays with Los Gollardos, an independent theatre group.

His first film, *Pepi, Luci, Bom*, shot on 16mm film, was released in 1980. This was followed by such contemporary classics as *Matador*, which introduced the world to Antonio Banderas, and *Tie Me Up! Tie Me Down!*, which earned him the vitriol of American feminists. *Women on the Verge of a Nervous Breakdown* was nominated for an Oscar as Best Foreign Language film of 1988 and is still the most successful Spanish film ever. His 1996 film *The Flower of My Secret* marked a new maturity, which is particularly evident in his last film, *Live Flesh*. British critic Alexander Walker concluded that it "has freed Almodovar from the campness, the kitsch and the high decibel dialogues of his previous pathological-farcical-tragical farragos."

ANTINORI

Scion of one of the world's most influential wine dynasties, Marchese Antinori controls a vast empire that includes three estates in Chianti, two in Umbria and holdings in Piedmont, Hungary, Malta and the Napa Valley. In addition to its extensive Chianti Classico estates, the company is expanding into the Tuscan wine regions of Montepulciano, Montalcino and Bolgheri, "where we want to be a major player," he says. His company has an estimated turnover of 85 billion lire, employs over 200 people and produces nearly 15 million bottles of wine a year.

Innovation and attention to detail are the buzzwords which Antinori uses to account for his success. "We have always focused on improving quality while at the same time trying to reduce costs," he explained in a recent interview. Marketing savvy has helped too, of course. Indeed, Antinori is celebrated in the industry as the man who almost single-handedly established the international reputation of Chianti.

Antinori is renowned as an exceptionally hard worker who is invariably at his desk in the Palazzo Antinori, his 15th-century headquarters in the heart of Florence, before the rest of his staff arrive. The Marchese doesn't travel as much as he used to - an integral part of any wine maker's agenda nowadays - preferring to let his deputies promote Antinori abroad while he concentrates on ensuring its quality at home. Don't be surprised, however, if you bump into the amicable 60 year-old at smart soirées around Italy - gregarious and fun-loving, he always has something to bring to the party. The Marchese's three attractive daughters - Albiera, Allegra and Alessandra - are all involved in the family business.

ARNAULT

Bernard Arnault relaxes by playing Chopin on the piano - and he plays it to concert standard. Surprising, perhaps, for a corporate chieftain who has, in the last decade, gobbled up some of France's most revered champagne, fashion and perfume houses under the banner of LVMH (Louis Vuitton-Moët Hennessy). His activities are seen, particularly by his competitors in the French luxury goods business, as exciting but also as disturbing, largely because he is so good at American-style marketing and merchandising. However, it seems to be just the shot in the arm that the sector needed, inspiring many of his peers to both modernise and internationalise their thinking. LVMH itself is, today, the largest luxury goods business in the world, with earnings of $860 million from operations in 1997.

Arnault's background didn't mark him out for particular greatness. A native of France's uninspiring Northern flatlands, he began his professional career in 1971, working for Ferinel, his family's property company. After three years spent establishing the firm in America in the early Eighties (he never really settled into the US and is said to have come back to France every two weeks) he returned home in 1984. But he came armed with a wealth of new business ideas and, just as importantly, the contacts who would help him to buy Boussac, the bankrupt textile empire that counted Christian Dior among its brands. It was this small foothold that eventually led him to the top of LVMH, his final accession following a bitter battle with Henri Racamier, a gentleman's gentleman of the old school and erstwhile boss of Louis Vuitton.

Despite his portrayal by the media as being ruthlessly aggressive, a company insider describes Arnault as a charming, though somewhat diffident individual, with a passion for the finer things in life and a deep discomfort at having become so public a figure. Socially, his glamorous blonde wife, Hélène Mercier, a respected Canadian pianist, is a perfect foil for him.

While each of the LVMH brands is run and marketed independently, Arnault has always insisted on keeping a close eye on all of his operations. Too close, according to his detractors, who resent his disregard for the traditional French old-business-school network in favour of managers who produce results. As a profile in *Forbes* magazine put it last year: "Don't let the snooty labels deceive you; this is hard-nosed business." V

ARMANI

The name is as big as a name can get. The man embodies a style that is quintessentially Italian, modern, unhurried and irresistibly understated. Born in 1934 in Piacenza, Giorgio Armani gave up his medical studies at university to pursue his interest in clothes. He first joined the department store, Rinascente, as a buyer, then spent six years at Cerruti. From there he went into freelance design, eventually launching Giorgio Armani S.p.A. in 1975, in partnership with Sergio Galeotti. Informed by a philosophy of stressing what he terms "the elegance of the essential" in his clothes, Armani believes that his designs are influenced by what his audience inspires. "Drastically imposing a fashion......would mean having no respect for the consumer," he has said. "The goal I seek is to have people refine their style through my clothing, without having them become victims of fashion." This philosophy has taken Armani's annual worldwide sales, through some 2,000 stores, to an estimated 1.876 billion lire today. Λ

BALLESTEROS

George Bernard Shaw famously described golf as "a good walk...spoiled." But he never witnessed the sort of characters who have revitalised the game in the modern era. Severiano Ballesteros is a perfect example. One of the most charismatic professionals in the game's history, he was born in Pedrena, Spain, in 1957 and began to play golf at the age of four with his uncle, who was the professional at his local club. By the time he was seven, young 'Seve' would saunter brazenly in and offer his services as a caddie to anyone who would listen; a year later he was sneaking on to the course to play in the early mornings. He turned pro in 1973 at the age of 16, and soon injected new vivacity into the circuit, with his breathtaking performances and breezy personality. The unpredictability of his game has made him both the despair and the delight of his fans; among his unforgettable moments of real brilliance was the approach shot he played to the 16th green at the British Open - from a spectators' car park.

Ballesteros first came to prominence at the US Open in 1976, when he tied for second place with Jack Nicklaus. His first US Open victory came three years later, when he became the youngest ever player to win the title. A year later he repeated the feat at the US Masters. He has not, however, been without his critics. Although universally recognised as the supreme master of the recovery shot, Ballesteros has never translated his enormous natural talent into a bagful of victories at the Majors and persistent back troubles have plagued his form for the past few years.

Unusually in sport, Ballesteros is not merely respected by his fellow competitors but universally loved; never was that more evident than when he captained the European team to victory in the 1997 Ryder Cup at Valderrama.

BAMFORD

Sir Anthony Bamford is the Chairman and Managing Director of JCB, the hugely successful construction equipment company founded by his father in 1945. Bamford Senior retired to Switzerland 23 years ago, leaving his son (who originally wanted to become a professional photographer) at the helm of a company that had enormous scope for expansion. The bright yellow JCB digger is ubiquitous in Britain and, while 70 per cent of the company's production is already exported, Bamford is keen to replicate its home-grown success in emerging markets around the world. Despite the impact of the Asian economic crisis, the company has been valued at £1.2 billion, while internal estimates put an even higher price on it.

Educated at Ampleforth College, England, and Grenoble University, France, Bamford has a reputation for great civility but prefers to keep a low public profile. His glamorous blonde wife, Carol, is renowned as a society hostess at Daylesford, the magnificent Oxfordshire home which they bought from Baron Heini Thyssen-Bornemisza (qv) in 1988. They recently spent £14 million on *The Virginian*, formerly John Kluge's yacht, and their other assets include an impressive array of vintage cars, farms and a lavishly appointed holiday home in Barbados.

Bamford's firm belief in the 'enterprise ethic' has, curiously enough, endeared him to both Margaret Thatcher and Tony Blair, who both cite his company as a template for potential employers.

BARILLA

Known in Italy as the King of Pasta, 40-year-old Guido Barilla has been chairman of Barilla Group, the family's food business, since 1993. On graduating from university with a degree in philosophy, Barilla spent two years working in one of the family's subsidiary operations in the United States, before returning to Italy in 1988. His rapid ascent through the ranks has led to charges of nepotism but neutral observers invariably concede that he has never been less than an able candidate for promotion. He lives in Parma with his wife Federica and their two sons. A very competent golfer, he also enjoys skiing and literature.

BARTOLI

An ambitious and beautiful young woman, whose parents were also professional singers, the outstanding Italian mezzo-soprano, Cecilia Bartoli, was introduced to the world on Italian television at the age of 19 by soprano Katia Ricciarelli and baritone Leo Nucci, before being 'discovered' the following year by conductor Daniel Barenboim. But her career really took off when impresario Jack Mastroianni took over her exclusive worldwide management five years later, in 1989. He has cunningly promoted her on the classic principle of scarcity - the less she's heard, the more we'll clamour for her.

Bartoli's range and ability are best illustrated in roles that divas don't normally consider. As a performer, she often fares better in productions in which she is part of an ensemble; as a recent newspaper profile put it, she is "the star among many, who has her turn then recedes into the dramatic whole." Bartoli, then, is not the sort of singer who single-handedly carries an opera, as a dramatic soprano must in works like *Tosca*. "I am a person of the 18th century," she has often said, when asked about her voice, repertoire and style. In those days singers performed exceptionally demanding roles that called for coloratura virtuosity rather than dramatic heft. That explains her favourite composers - Rossini, Mozart, Haydn, Monteverdi and Vivaldi.

She sings only two or three operas a year from a repertoire of only six roles. The rest of her work comprises recitals, concerts and recording. Restricting her performances keeps her, she says, on top form: "Working a bit less is the only way to hold on to one's pleasure in singing. You can only enjoy yourself by not singing every night."

Not surprisingly, Bartoli's greatest influences are singers of the past such as Conchita Supervia, whose singing she describes as "very modern - one can like or dislike the voice but that's not the most important aspect. You can see the personality. It's the personality behind the voice which makes the artist." That is the sort of praise that critics have repeatedly heaped on Bartoli herself. ⋁

BECKENBAUER

Unlike many football stars who vanished into obscurity after their career on the pitch, Franz Beckenbauer went on to become the most popular man in Germany, whose opinions on matters ranging from Zen Buddhism to politics are sought and respected. Referred to as 'the Kaiser', in the eyes of his countrymen, he is virtually incapable of putting a foot wrong; if he ran for political office, there is no doubt that he would be elected. However, for tax reasons his main residence is Kitzbühl in Austria and his favourite activity is playing golf. With mobile phone companies and car-makers queuing up to sign him as an 'adviser' and promoter, it's a lifestyle he can easily afford.

Multiple German and European Champion with Bayern Munich in the Seventies, captain and coach of the national team and now President of Germany's most successful soccer club, FC Bayern Munich, Beckenbauer is the only footballer to have won the World Cup both as a player (1974) and as a coach (1990). The fact that he refuses to take part in FIFA, the world football association, is seen only as further proof of his magic. ⋏

BENETTON

Born in 1935 in Treviso, Luciano Benetton, together with his brothers, Gilberto and Carlo, and sister, Giuliana, founded the family firm in 1965. Currently President of the Benetton group, he has always had a global vision for his company, considering Europe a "domestic" market and looking to the Far East as an area of great potential and rapid growth. Today, the company's brands - United Colours of Benetton, Sisley, 012 and, since 1997, Benetton Sportsystem - are sold in over 120 countries.

A father of four children (it was Luciano's son, Alessandro, who took Benetton into Formula 1 racing), Benetton is also on the Board of Directors of Edizione Holding, the family-owned financial holding company, and was an Italian Senator from 1992 to 1994. ◄

BERLUSCONI

A combination of business acumen, extensive media interests and opportunistic politics has ensured Silvio Berlusconi's rise to prominence. Under the banner Freedom Alliance, his Forza Italia (together with neo fascist allies, the AN and LN) formed the Italian government for nine months in 1994, with Berlusconi as President of the Council of Ministers. This rise to political power was particularly controversial, given his control of such a large portion of the Italian media.

Born in Milan in 1936, Berlusconi graduated in law from the University of Milan before becoming General Manager of a building contracting firm when he was only 23 years old. It was Berlusconi who proposed 'the city without cars', a concept that has since found favour with many urban planners. In 1976 he established his investment vehicle, Fininvest, and became a major shareholder in and, later, publisher of the daily *Il Giornale*. Having launched his first private TV channel in 1974, he set up Canale 5 four years later, extending that network and acquiring further television interests throughout the Eighties. In 1994 he resigned from the board of Fininvest to pursue his political interests.

Described by acquaintances as "easygoing" in private, Berlusconi's nature sometimes appears contradictory. Sufficiently aware of his own importance to surround himself with bodyguards at all times, he nevertheless treats them as family. Invite him to dinner and, chances are, you will find yourself entertaining 'the boys' as well. He goes jogging religiously every day (those bodyguards in tow) and his other enthusiasms include tennis, sailing, playing the piano and football (he bought the first division football team, AC Milan, in 1986).

Always a colourful figure, Berlusconi has been dogged by corruption allegations for more than two years, culminating in a judgement against him for tax evasion in mid-1998. However, while that may make his future in politics questionable, the Byzantine workings of the Italian judicial system may well mean that he can avoid serving his sentence.

BIBERSON

President of Médecins Sans Frontières (MSF), Philippe Biberson was born in 1955 in Bangkok, to French parents. After graduating from medical school in 1982 he became a company physician in Cameroon before joining MSF in 1984. During his first six months with the organisation, spent as a physician in charge of health services at a Salvadorian refugee camp, he first witnessed the dreadful side effects of civil unrest in developing countries and resolved to devote his career to the organisation. (Established in 1971 by a group of French doctors, it has become one of the world's most effective non-governmental aid organisations.) Ten years later, having led a series of MSF missions in trouble spots throughout the Third World, he became the organisation's president.

Dynamic and determined, Biberson distinguishes himself from many other leading aid workers through his robust approach and his publicly stated belief that many humanitarian organisations are overly reticent in the face of the legal and administrative obstacles to the provision of effective relief. It is this 'can do, will do' spirit that characterises his approach to his work and earns him huge respect in his field. When not travelling, Biberson lives with his wife and four children in Paris. ⋏

BINOCHE

Juliette Binoche was born in Paris in 1964 into a theatrical family; her father, Jean-Marie Binoche, is a theatre director and her mother, Monique Stalens, is a French teacher and theatre actress. They divorced when Juliette was still an infant and it was her mother who encouraged her into acting.

Although she has become one of the few French actresses successfully to make the transition to Hollywood, her career path has been far from smooth. Having graduated from the Conservatoire de Paris, she initially dedicated herself to the stage. Like most young theatre actors, she struggled, working as a cashier in the local store to make ends meet.

Binoche's movie debut was in Pascal Kanés' *Liberty Belle*, in which she uttered a single line, "Sale Con!" (meaning "You dirty bastard!"). Hardly an auspicious start. However, following her first real role, in Jean-Luc Godard's *Je Vous Salue, Marie*, she decided to concentrate on screen rather than stage acting, and her performance in *Rendez-vous* was rewarded with the Romy Schneider Prize for the most outstanding actress of the year.

Her international career took off in 1987, with *The Unbearable Lightness of Being*. Then, during a six-year relationship with director Léos Carax, she had a starring role in two of his films: *Mauvais Sang* and the controversial *Les Amants du Pont Neuf*. After the decidedly mixed response to that film, Binoche accepted the lead in *Wuthering Heights* - a film that was neither a commercial nor a critical success.

In 1994 things improved immeasurably when Binoche played the lead in Krzystof Kieslowski's acclaimed *Three Colours: Blue*, which won a César for best film. She at last seemed destined for greatness, but her next project, *Lucie Aubrac*, was a disaster; following repeated clashes with director Claude Berri, Binoche was replaced by Carole Bouquet after two weeks of shooting. Miss Binoche finally hit the big time with her next film, *The English Patient*, for which she scooped one of its nine Oscars, as Best Supporting Actress. ➤

BONO

It is not often that rock stars find themselves on the cover of *Time* magazine, an honour achieved by Bono, leader of the Irish-based supergroup U2. On his band's spectacular world tours, this hyperactive Dubliner dominates an awe-inspiring, futuristic stage production.

However, Bono (real name Paul Hewson) is not your average rock star with attitude or a brain scrambled by chemicals; he is a serious figurehead for a range of important causes. He has consistently campaigned against dumping by the British nuclear reactor plant at Sellafield, while supporting the work of his wife, Ali Hewson, a long-term activist working with Russian children affected by the Chernobyl disaster and, in collaboration with Luciano Pavarotti, was the first rock star to bring a major concert to Sarajevo. Most recently, Bono masterminded a concert to support the 'Yes' vote in the Northern Ireland. With a fortune estimated in excess of $100 million, Bono has a château on the Cote d'Azur, a mansion overlooking the sea in Killiney (dubbed 'Dublin's Beverly Hills' by the locals) and a shooting lodge in Connemara. A great survivor in the notoriously fickle world of popular music, Bono seems set to retain his mantle as Europe's most influential rock star for some time yet.

BRANAGH

The leading British actor-director of his generation, Kenneth Branagh was born in Belfast and raised in England. Only six weeks after leaving The Royal Academy of Dramatic Art (RADA), Branagh made his West End debut in *Another Country*, for which he won the Society of West End Theatres' Award for most promising newcomer of 1982.

Two years later he played the title role in *Henry V* with the Royal Shakespeare Company, a role which he would later repeat on camera in his directorial debut. The film, released in 1988, was nominated for four Academy Awards, including two for Branagh, as Best Actor and Best Director. It was on the set of the BBC's Fortunes of War that Branagh met his future wife Emma Thompson. The pair were soon being compared to Laurence Olivier and Vivien Leigh, including comparisons surrounding their subsequent break-up. Not surprisingly, Branagh was immediately invited to Hollywood to direct his next film, *Dead Again*, in which he played dual roles as a gumshoe detective in 1990s Los Angeles and a European composer in the 1940s. In 1992 he co-produced, directed and starred in the low budget *Peter's Friends*, an amiable romp through British middle-class mores.

The same year he also co-produced, directed and starred in *Much Ado About Nothing*, which was screened in competition at the 1993 Cannes Film Festival. Starring Denzel Washington, Michael Keaton, Keanu Reeves and Emma Thompson, it was a critical and commercial success. Perhaps most importantly, it spawned a wave of Shakespeare films that has brought the great dramatist to a huge international audience. In this respect, Branagh has succeeded where many eminent actor-directors (with the exception, perhaps, of Olivier) have tried and failed. It is ironic that his efforts to popularise Shakespeare - which reached their conclusion in his film version of *Hamlet* (1996) - were initially dismissed as naive and idealistic. His success has changed all that.

BRANSON

Despite his right-on anti-establishment credentials and penchant for woolly jumpers, Richard Branson, founder and chairman of the Virgin Group of Companies, is a formidable business talent; in 1995 the combined sales of the various Virgin holding companies exceeded £1.5 billion.

Born in 1950 and educated at Stowe School in England, Branson showed his colours early, establishing a national magazine called *Student* and setting up a student advisory service centre to help young people. In 1970 he founded Virgin as a mail-order record company and, shortly afterwards, opened a record shop in London. Virgin subsequently became one of the biggest record companies in the world, representing artists such as Phil Collins, Janet Jackson and The Rolling Stones. The equity of Virgin Music Group was sold to Thorn EMI in 1992 in a $1 billion deal. Branson established Virgin Atlantic Airways in 1984, with one 747 plying the London-New York route. His concept of offering what he calls "a competitive and high-quality" service has made it the second largest British long-haul carrier and brought numerous travel industry awards.

However, Branson owes his prominence as much to his very public non-business activities, although his most outrageous antics (such as appearing in a wedding dress and high heels to launch his bridal shops) were, he claims, simply an effort to secure cheap publicity. A daredevil in true *Boys' Own* style, he has been involved in several world record-breaking exploits. In 1986, on his second attempt, he won the Blue Riband by crossing the Atlantic in the fastest ever recorded time in his power boat *Virgin Atlantic Challenger II*.

This was followed a year later by the epic hot air balloon crossing in *Virgin Atlantic Flyer*. He has subsequently tried, and failed, and continues to try to circumnavigate the world by balloon - testimony, perhaps, to the time-honoured notion that you can't win 'em all.

Branson lives in Oxfordshire and London with his wife Joan and their two children. An accomplished networker, he is renowned for his unstinting good humour, sociability and almost manic energy. It has been reported that, even on holiday on Necker, his idyllic private island in the Caribbean, his companions are never given a moment's rest; competitions are organised for the children, the adults have sailing races and there are frantic tennis tournaments and much frenzied swimming. ∧

CONRAN

If you are British and are inordinately fond of your duvet, have ever owned (as a student, perhaps?) a piece of flat-pack, self-assembly furniture and relish an Oriental stir-fry in a reliable flame-blackened wok, it is thanks to the man who introduced these fabulous inventions to Britain: Terence Conran.

He did so through his retail chain of home-furnishing shops, Habitat, which has since spread across Europe. To an absurdly naive, post-war British public, the arrival of the Habitat 'look' was nothing short of a revolution. Habitat is a name that goes hand-in-hand with Mary Quant, The Beatles and the mini-skirt as being emblematic of swinging London in the Sixties. Its catalogue, launched in 1964, was even voted by the Sunday Telegraph as one of the Ten Books That Changed Your Life.

Today Conran's empire is large and diverse. In addition to his retail interests (he sold his interest in Habitat during the Eighties) his Conran Shop, selling high-quality furniture and accessories (which now has branches in Germany, Japan, Melbourne and Paris) and publishing interests (Conran Octopus books), the man who worked as a plongeur in a Paris restaurant in the Fifties has built up a restaurant empire that has become almost ubiquitous in London.

Chummy with Richard Rogers and the rest of the design/architecture aristocracy, this notable admirer of beautiful women has received numerous design awards and was knighted in 1983. An ardent Francophile, he was made Commandeur des Arts et des Lettres in 1992. ∀

CHRISTIE

In 1934, when Sir George Christie's father John built an auditorium for his opera-singer wife, Audrey, in the grounds of their estate, nobody imagined that it would not only give birth to a major fixture on the English social calendar but would also gain a worldwide musical reputation, helping to launch the careers of many performers in the process - Thomas Allen, Simon Rattle and Kiri Te Kanawa among them. One of the delights of the Glyndebourne Festival, now run by Sir George, is that it retains a country-house feel. Here, during the interval, people sit stoically on damp rugs in a field, in full evening dress, eating their picnic suppers as if it were the most natural and jolly thing to do in the world.

Sir George is, as you might expect, an unashamedly upper-class character but his grandee's accent belies a refreshingly informal personality. The 62-year-old's office, for instance, is delightfully untidy, littered with pictures, portraits, mementoes and thousands of books and CDs. However, the carefree image is superficial at best. Christie is an extremely shrewd businessman who, in the early 1990s, managed to raise £34 million in corporate and private donations to build a spanking new 1,150-seat theatre to replace the one built by his father. It is the only purpose-built British opera house since the war not to be funded, at least in part, with public money; neither has the festival itself ever claimed a penny of subsidy.

Christie and his wife, Mary, have three sons - Hector, Augustus and Ptolemy - and a daughter, Louise. As well as sharing a passion for music, the whole family is notoriously fond of that peculiarly English breed of dog, the pug, even instigating pug tea parties. Invitations to these events show every sign of becoming as sought-after as tickets for the opera.

D'ORNANO

When Isabelle d'Ornano talks of the therapeutic qualities of Sisley cosmetics, you almost feel better just listening to her. An elegant ambassador for the company that she owns and runs with her husband, Count Hubert d'Ornano (whose father was a part-owner of Lancôme), she is responsible for communications and product development.

D'Ornano was born in Poland, brought up in Portugal and Spain, worked in England and married in France. Together with her husband (they married in 1963), she travels the world promoting the Sisley message with admirable gusto and no shortage of good old-fashioned panache. When, for instance, she was first introduced to Giscard d'Estaing, then French President, she is said to have told him, "Sisley is your ally, because we're keeping up the morale of the masses. If governing means making the people happier, then cosmetics firms are very important."

The d'Ornano's opulent Paris apartment, on the Quai d'Orsay, is the venue for parties that invariably attract a vibrant mix of European aristocracy and whichever Hollywood celebrities happen to be in town. Away from the capital, the family escapes to a serene 6,000 acre hunting estate on the edge of the Loire valley.

But this mother of five children (one of her daughters, Elisabeth, is the model for Sisley's publicity shots and her son, Philippe, is Assistant General Manager) is anything but a socialite. Rather, the Comtesse d'Ornano is a serious businesswoman, who happens to combine a penchant for entertaining with a successful career as the head of the $150 million company that produced one of the first international cosmetic and skincare ranges based on plants and herbs. ➢

DE BOTTON

The founder and Chairman of Global Asset Management, Swiss-born Gilbert de Botton has a first-class pedigree as an investment manager and an impressive roster of clients who trust his judgement implicitly. Graduating from Columbia University in 1957, de Botton became Chief Executive of Rothschild Bank AG, Zurich, ten years later and then President of Rothschild Inc, New York, in 1981-1982. In 1983 he moved to London, where he established Global Asset Management. The following year it had $2 million dollars of funds under management; it now has $12.6 billion of clients' money to play with in its search for lucrative mutual funds.

De Botton's personal beliefs have a huge influence on the company's corporate philosophy, although he has always insisted on having a hands-off approach towards his fund managers. As he said in a recent interview, "I am an extremely patient orchestrator of fund managers' talents...... By being hands-off we let them fend for themselves. The soft edge to that is that we give them comfort and nurse them along. Part of our trade secret is that we have a balance between extreme discipline and hanging loose."

What this often means in practice is that de Botton monitors his internal teams' portfolio strategies and asset allocation and then enhances them by hiring outside help in the form of fund managers with suitably stellar track records. The principle is based on his belief that a single organisation is unlikely to attract the top managers in every market. It also ensures that creativity is always high within the organisation, and the benefits of this cross-fertilisation are more than apparent to anyone who has watched Global Asset Management's rapid ascent.

An immensely cultured man (he speaks seven languages, is a major authority on Chaucer and lists reading Seneca in Latin among his leisure activities), de Botton is a philanthropist of the first order, although he keeps that quiet. His coolly elegant wife, Janet (a Wolfson heiress), is a major collector of contemporary art in her own right and his son, Alain, a precociously talented novelist.

DE RIBES

Yves Saint Laurent (qv) once called the Comtesse de Ribes "the pearl in the King of Poland's ear, the Queen of Sheba's tallow-drop emerald… a tall black swan, a royal blue orchid, an ivory unicorn." But most people know her simply as one of the most elegant women in Europe. Married to banker Edouard de Ribes, she lives in Paris and, from there, conducts a life which one commentator has described as "supremely glamorous."

Jacqueline de Ribes' mother, the impossibly sophisticated Comtesse de Beaumont (whose achievements included the translation of all of Tennessee Williams' works into French) was a strong influence on the young Jacqueline, who started to design her own clothes at the age of 16. Four years later she topped the list of the world's best-dressed women and has continued to prove that the judges' choice was right.

In the 1980s she decided that, knowing *haute couture* so well (she was a key client of Saint Laurent and Chanel in particular), she would design and produce her own collections. De Ribes soon found herself at the helm of a successful business. But she decided, towards the end of that decade, that mass production was taking her away from her original philosophy of creating what she calls "couture clothing, but in sizes" and, since then, has concentrated on producing pure haute couture for a small circle of similarly elegant women.

Now in her Sixties, Jacqueline de Ribes is still extremely active - as she said in a recent interview, "I don't imagine myself as old. The only thing that has changed in my life is needing reading glasses." A highly intelligent, worldly woman - and a great beauty with a blue-chip aristocratic pedigree - she is one of Europe's best hostesses, renowned as *the* social fixer in Paris. ⅄

DE SOLE

Italian-born Domenico De Sole, who made his name as a brilliant attorney with the New York firm Patton, Boggs and Blow (of which he became a partner in 1979) came to Gucci in 1984, when he was appointed chairman and CEO of Gucci America Inc.

De Sole, married and a father of two, was born in 1944. In 1970, after receiving his law degree, he moved to the United States, earning a masters at Harvard.

He remained in the US until 1994, at which time Bahrain-based Investcorp (which had bought Gucci at the end of the Eighties, after a byzantine struggle between the late Maurizio Gucci and his cousins had brought the firm to its knees) hired him as General Manager of Gucci Group N.V., based in Florence. De Sole became its chairman and CEO in 1995.

Under his leadership, the group has been transformed into a hugely successful public company, thanks to the placement of Gucci shares on the New York and Amsterdam stock exchanges.

To re-establish the label, De Sole has restored the exclusive nature of the Gucci trademark, thanks in no small part to his inspired hiring of maverick American designer Tom Ford and former Bergdorf Goodman merchandising supremo, Dawn Mello, who have brilliantly re-styled the brand.

De Sole travels extensively to maintain close ties among the various group companies worldwide. He is well liked within the group and has a reputation for unflagging commitment to anything he gets involved in. So far, so good, although it remains to be seen what will happen if Prada, the largest single shareholder in the company, increases its stake.

DEL VECCHIO

Until 1991, Leonardo Del Vecchio kept a very low public profile in Italy. That year, however, he topped the list of Italian taxpayers - and was quickly dubbed Signor Nessuno (Mr Nobody) by the Italian newspapers. With a personal fortune of almost $2 billion, you may well ask how he managed to retain his privacy for so long, but this quietly spoken workaholic has always shied away from the gossip columns - he is far too busy at Luxottica, the company he founded in 1961 to manufacture components for eyeglass frames. Nowadays, the company has 19,400 employees and its net profit last year was $147 million. At its factory in Agordo, a postcard-pretty town in the Alps, Luxottica produces 14 million frames a year, or one in five of all designer-brand glasses; among the designers it works with are Armani, Saint Laurent, Valentino and Brooks Brothers.

Life hasn't always been so rosy for Del Vecchio. When he was seven his father died, leaving his mother to bring up seven children. Young Leonardo was sent to a Milan orphanage before being apprenticed to a factory, where he trained to become a tool-maker. He married while still in his early Twenties (he says he prefers his wife's cooking to dining out) and, at the age of 23, decided to open his own mould shop, which led in turn to the move to Agordo.

Del Vecchio's three children are all involved in the family business. When in America (where Luxottica recently acquired Lens Crafters, the largest eye-wear retailer in the US, for $900 million) Del Vecchio is based in an apartment in the Trump Tower in Manhattan. Apart from the prestigious address, however, there is nothing about this 62-year-old that suggests ostentation. He is the seriously hard-working head of an empire that looks set to dominate the optical business for many years to come. ≺

DELLA VALLE

For her role in Robert Redford's latest movie, *The Horse Whisperer*, Kristen Scott Thomas insisted on wearing a pair of J.P. Tod's. It's ironic that, after 30 years in business, J.P. Tod's is suddenly the height of fashion, thanks to these classic loafers. Much of their present status is due to Diego Della Valle. He is Managing Director of the company, founded by his father, whose clients also include Sharon Stone, Catherine Deneuve (qv) and Jemima Khan.

A stylish figurehead and a smooth operator - both financially and socially - his ability and energy have propelled his company to an annual turnover of 320 billion lire, 50 billion net profit and almost 2,000 employees.

The two abiding passions of this youthful 44 year-old are sailing and motor racing. Della Valle's best pal - and partner in two other businesses, Acqua di Parma perfumes and Web Sunglasses - is Ferrari's Luca Cordero di Montezemolo (qv). In Della Valle's office, housed in an 18th century palazzo, a photograph of his maxi racing yacht, *Il Moro di Venezia*, jostles for space with a plaque commemorating the Cavaliere del Lavoro honour which he was awarded by the Italian government in recognition of his achievements.

A collector of contemporary art (Fontana and Calder are among his favourites) Della Valle is a gracious host. It has been suggested that the re-emergence of Capri as a 'hot' destination has more than a little to do with Della Valle and di Montezemolo's patronage of the island. Della Valle is also a great animal lover (as his two Labradors will doubtless confirm) and a keen fan of - wait for it - Seventies pop music!

DENCH

Judi Dench, the doyenne of English stage and screen, is still much in demand after nearly 40 years in the profession. Having won every possible award in the theatre, and with film credits as diverse as *A Room with a View* and *Goldeneye*, she has distinguished herself time and again with her versatility and the elegance of her performances. But Dench is a remarkably modest character, preferring to heap praise on her cohorts: the screenwriters, directors and her fellow cast members.

The daughter of an English country doctor, Dame Judi has enjoyed consistent success almost since the moment she launched herself as an actress on the English stage. Almost, because her debut, as Ophelia, was notable only for the panning she received at the hands of her critics. One famously wrote of her performance, "She stepped out into the limelight, tripped over her advance publicity and fell flat on her pretty face".

Nowadays, Dench is renowned as one of the most diligent and inspiring professionals in the business.

She is extremely methodical in her research, insisting on entering into the mind-set of every character she plays. For her recent role in *Mrs Brown*, for instance, Dench immersed herself in the life of Queen Victoria; she can now quote reams from the Queen's Highland Journal.

The elaborate costumes she wore in that film are, however, nothing like the simple, low-key clothes that the actress wears in real life. They are typical of this modest, entirely unassuming woman, whose nomination for an Academy Award in *Mrs Brown* was greeted with characteristic astonishment. ➤

DEMARCHELIER

The first non-British photographer to be invited to photograph a member of the Royal Family, Patrick Demarchelier's photographs of Diana, Princess of Wales, first appeared in the December 1989 issue of British *Vogue* and he subsequently photographed her on four separate occasions.

Demarchelier has published two acclaimed books of photographs and an exhibition of his work is currently touring the globe. Married, with three boys, his principal interests outside photography are sailing and collecting contemporary art. Based in New York - his favourite city - the 54-year-old Frenchman commutes constantly between Europe, Asia and America.

Regarded by many as the hottest photographer working today, Demarchelier was hired in 1992 to work exclusively for *Harper's Bazaar* magazine, published by Hearst, putting an end to his extensive work for other publications, including *Vogue, Time, Newsweek, Rolling Stone* and *Life*.

His commercial client roster - traditionally where the big bucks are made - includes names like Revlon, L'Oréal, Ralph Lauren, Calvin Klein, Yves St Laurent and Chanel. He has directed television advertisements for these major luxury goods names, as well as doing still photography for them. ◄

DENEUVE

Catherine Deneuve's 'fire and ice' persona has lent real drama to her diverse film roles, as well as perpetuating her mystique in the public eye. Virtually an icon in France, she loathes personal publicity, yet leads a very public social life, not least as a close friend and confidante of Yves Saint Laurent (qv).

The daughter of a voice-over artist (her father dubbed films into French) and an actress, Deneuve's own career started while she was still at school in Paris, with a couple of minor roles in long forgotten films. In 1961 she met the director Roger Vadim, whom she subsequently married, on the set of *Les Parisiennes*. However, neither of the two films they made together proved to be her launching pad. Her breakthrough came with *Les Parapluies de Cherbourg*.

Fêted by critics and punters alike for her portrayal of a sweet, if senseless, young bourgeois girl, she followed this success two years later with a role that could not have been more different: a sexually repressed schizophrenic in Roman Polanski's *Repulsion*. But it was her role as a coolly ambiguous rich man's wife in Bûnuel's *Belle de Jour* which was, perhaps, her finest performance.

Deneuve's films in English have generally been pretty forgettable - unless, that is, you remember *March or Die*, *Hustle* or *The April Fools* - but Deneuve's reputation in France was copper-fastened by her mesmerising performance in *Indochine*, for which she received an Oscar nomination in 1992.

Married for three years to photographer David Bailey, whom she met in 1965, Deneuve has two children: Christian, by Roger Vadim, and Chiara, by the late Marcello Mastroianni. They are both actors. Deneuve is working a little less than she used to - and the roles she chooses increasingly reflect her feminist sympathies - although she has become active in the promotion of French cinema abroad.

DEPARDIEU

One of the most successful actors in the history of French cinema, Gerard Depardieu has appeared in more than 70 films since his debut in 1971. In typical fashion Depardieu says he lost count years ago, although that number is certainly close to the mark.

A colossus of a man, with an instantly recognisable profile, he cannot be described as handsome, although his brooding physicality certainly makes him a hunk in the traditional sense of the word. But the dark, poetic intensity which he brings to his roles - quite likely influenced by his tough upbringing - separates him from the horde of character actors who litter the European film scene.

His cuddly vulnerability and mellifluous voice have endeared him to audiences, both French and international, in films as diverse as the magical *Cyrano de Bergerac*, for which he received a Best Actor Oscar nomination, *Green Card* (his charming but soppy US debut) and *Danton*, the 1982 film that firmly established him among the pantheon of truly great French actors. His portrait of a doomed idealist during the French revolution was imbued with pathos and, for many, it remains the definitive Depardieu performance: extravagant, brooding, romantic and hugely sympathetic. ◄

DETTORI

Frankie Dettori is the sort of sporting champion who comes on the scene once every 50 years. Born in Italy but based in England, he is adored as much for his charisma as his huge talent as a jockey. His numerous big race victories include winning The Magnificent Seven at Ascot in 1996, when he won all seven races on the card. It was a racing correspondent's dream and the media lapped him up. The 28-year-old Dettori also has a strong philanthropic streak. Disillusioned with the way money to many aid agencies is siphoned off to cover 'expenses', he set up Direct Aid For Africa, together with Irish trainer and professional gambler Barney Curley, to fund educational projects and hospices in East Africa. The money donated goes directly to the places where it is needed, as the charity has no office expenses and is staffed entirely by volunteers. ⅄

DI MONTEZEMOLO

When asked to list his occupation for the likes of Who's Who In Italy, Luca Cordero di Montezemolo could be forgiven for pausing a moment. He has had such a variety of jobs and has such overwhelming enthusiasm for anything with which he is associated, that the word 'occupation' seems inadequate for a man whose passions dictate his behaviour. He has organised Italy's America's Cup entry, was Managing Editor of *La Stampa* newspaper, worked for Cinzano, coordinated the football World Cup in Italy and now - in one of several positions that he still holds - is President of both the retail and the racing arms of Ferrari. It hardly seems surprising, then, that this laid-back Italian is hard to track down. One place, however, where you will rarely find the president and chairman is beside the race track - at 51, his heart is in poor shape and, as he told a British newspaper last year, "It's very bad for me, because I sometimes want to get my hands dirty. But it's easier to stay away. I am not needed."

Di Montezemolo is a nephew of Gianni Agnelli (qv), a connection that has inevitably led to charges of nepotism, but his track record is surely enough to dispel the illusion. His own business interests, in partnership with best pal Diego della Valle (qv), include sunglasses manufacturer Web and perfume house Acqua di Parma. He bought the latter, which produces his favourite aftershave, when he discovered that it was going bankrupt. He aggressively restructured it, expanding its lines to include soaps, toiletries, candles and potpourri as well as, of course, the original aftershave. ➤

DOMINGO

To the general public, Placido Domingo is best known as one of the three tenors who, through their landmark concerts and subsequent recordings, have done more to popularise opera than almost anyone in living memory.

But, as an individual, his achievements are equally glittering. He has appeared in 111 different roles, more than any other tenor in the history of music, with a repertoire that runs the gamut from Mozart to Verdi, Berlioz to Puccini, Wagner to Ginastera. He regularly sings in every important opera house in the world, has made well over 100 recordings, of which 93 are full-length operas (for which he has earned eight Grammys) and has starred in full length cinematic versions of such operas as *La Traviata* and *Carmen* as well as his classic interpretation of Verdi's *Otello*. He has made more than 50 videos and his telecast of *Tosca* was seen by more than 1 billion people in 117 different countries.

Born in Madrid, Domingo moved with his family to Mexico at the age of eight. After studying voice and piano, he made his début as Alfredo in *La Traviata* before spending two years with the Israel National Opera. Since his Met début in 1968, he has appeared there in close to 400 performances, in 38 different roles, and is now in his 30th consecutive season with the company. Warm and big-hearted, Domingo is hugely popular among his fellow singers - not least, they say, because he never tries to upstage them (all the more surprising, in view of most opera stars' egos). On the contrary, he is renowned for nurturing the talents of others, as with his mentorship of rising star Josè Cura.

Unlike many of his colleagues, Domingo continually broadens his repertoire with new roles, like his leads in last year's productions of Ginastera's *Don Rodrigo* and Meyerbeer's *Le Prophète*. In addition to singing and an ever-growing presence as a conductor, Domingo is also the man behind the biggest international vocal competition, Operalia, which is to be held in Puerto Rico in 1999. He is, rightly, one of the most decorated and honoured performers in the music business today. ◄

DUCASSE

With an unprecedented six Michelin stars to his credit in three restaurants, Alain Ducasse has enormous influence on the way discerning Europeans eat today. At Le Louis XV in Monaco, where he gained his first trio of stars, his eponymous restaurant in Paris - a richly decorated townhouse in the 16th arrondissement, which he took over from Joel Robuchon - and La Bastide de Moustiers, a country inn in Haute Provence, Ducasse has provided a template for the future of gourmet dining. Behind the deceptively simple names of dishes such as *Poulette des Landes*, *Langoustines* and *Dos de Merlu*, there lurks a meticulous perfectionist. But it is Ducasse's flair that separates him from the legions of good (rather than truly great) chefs working in France today. Since he came to Paris, Ducasse has surprised many critics by refusing to capitulate to the whims of fashion. Instead, he has served resolutely classical dishes - always, however, with the inimitable Ducasse touch.

A leader of the movement to use only the freshest local ingredients in his cooking - now a cliché in gourmet circles - he has repeatedly stressed that "the product alone is the truth. The produce alone is the star, and not the cook." This may explain why - rather like offering theatre seats in the middle of the stage - he installed a table in one of his kitchens, allowing his most privileged clients to see how his beloved ingredients are translated into such delicious results.

DUISENBERG

As first head of the newly formed European Central Bank, Wim Duisenberg has a curiously unenviable task. He is bound to come in for enormous criticism over the remaining seven years of his eight-year term - if, that is, he lasts the distance. At the time of writing, Duisenberg would concede only that "the duration of my term of office is still open and, given good health, who knows, I may serve for eight years." The French, however, are adamant that he will step down in four years to make way for the governor of the Bank of France, Jean-Claude Trichet.

From the moment his appointment was described as "a political fudge", the 63 year-old Dutchman has been given a bumpy ride but, so far, he has performed his Herculean task admirably. His six-member executive board includes bankers from France and Germany but he is the real power horse, providing the stability and credibility that the financial markets demanded of the head of the new institution. But, as *The European* newspaper warned after his first month of office, "Duisenberg's good start must not be allowed to obscure the fact that treacherous shoals lie ahead for the euro. The bank alone cannot be a government and the black hole of political accountability at its centre has yet to be addressed."

Duisenberg's pin-striped, chain-smoking exterior, along with his half-moon glasses, distinctive white hair and stern demeanour, belie his love of country music and relaxed off-stage manner. His tall and elegant wife, Greta, reputedly caused quite a stir at the Bank's launch – as, indeed, did the Riverdance troupe who even had the normally staid bankers clicking their heels.

DUMAS-HERMES

A poet and philosopher manqué, Jean-Louis Dumas' conversation is peppered with quotes and esoteric references - not to appear clever, you sense, but simply for his own enjoyment. Warm, wily and wickedly funny, with a worldly, old-school manner, Dumas-Hermès is a highly cultured man. But don't let that fool you; he is also a brilliant strategist.

Last spring he shocked the fashion world with his appointment of iconoclastic womenswear designer Martin Margiela. It was seen as the death-knell of Hermès' timeless and quintessentially *bon chic bon genre* image. However, by the time Margiela launched his first collection, Dumas was being hailed as a visionary; the designer had delivered the perfect synthesis of traditional and modern *savoir faire*. This was merely the latest step in Dumas' brilliant handling of his family firm's expansion. When he became its fifth-generation chairman in 1978, the company's growth rate had slowed considerably. However, he positioned the business perfectly to capitalise on the status-crazed Eighties, emphasising the illustrious history of the saddle-making firm (founded by Thierry Hermès in 1837) in order to appeal to a new generation. He continued the company's transformation (begun in the 1930s by Emile Hermès) into a luxury accessories business, acquiring Puiforcat silver, St Louis crystal and John Lobb shoes along the way. Now he is pushing it further in the direction of fashion.

Although he is steeped in the family tradition (his father, Robert, whom he succeeded as chairman, married into the Hermès family), Dumas' background was far from insular. After graduating with degrees in law and economics (as a student, he was the drummer in a jazz band) he left France to become a buyer at Bloomingdales before returning to the family firm in 1964. His wife of 36 years, Rena, is an architect; in addition to her own highly successful practice, she has redesigned the Hermès stores, as well as their own stunning house in Morocco.

While Dumas' overriding passion is for 'the genius contained in craftsmanship' (he regularly sends members of the sales teams to the ateliers to understand better how the products are made) he is very proud of his own creative input. Every year he concocts a theme - in 1998 the tree, before that, Africa - to inspire his artisans and designers. He carries a notebook with him constantly, entries from which are published in the house magazine, Le Monde d'Hermès. "I do it the old way," he has said. "Everything that is signed Hermès is signed with my OK."

Jean-Louis Dumas' unconventionality as a boss is underlined by a story that Karl Lagerfeld relates. One Christmas Eve at 7pm Lagerfeld dropped into the flagship store in search of a last-minute present. "There was Jean-Louis, supervising everything. No big Paris boss would be at that place at that moment. Nobody except him. I was very impressed."

ECCLESTONE

Bernie Ecclestone, the 67 year-old son of a trawler fisherman, has been described, accurately enough, as the ringmaster of Grand Prix racing. A highly controversial figure who, until now, has effectively 'owned' the sport (largely through his control of television rights), Ecclestone was, until recently, regarded simply as a tough and wily wheeler-dealer who pulled all the strings and kept a very low profile. However, the revelation that he had donated £1 million to the British Labour Party before the last General Election sparked a row of epic proportions, as it coincided with the new government's decision to exempt Formula 1 from a tobacco advertising ban in sport. Ecclestone was unrepentant, claiming that he had donated the money because Tony Blair had promised to keep down top tax rates. "I personally would have gained substantially from a ban on tobacco sponsorship," he maintained. In the event, the embarrassed government returned the cash, further incensing the notoriously prickly Ecclestone.

At the time of writing, his future looks uncertain. Plans to float Formula 1 Holdings are bedevilled by frenzied speculation in much of the British media that the business may, after all, be a house of cards. His contract with FIA, the sport's governing body, has been under intense scrutiny in recent times and some commentators believe that he will be less than graciously received by the European Commission's Competition Department. However, even if he does meet an impasse, Ecclestone will retire a rich man. Since 1989 he has taken £142 million in salaries and dividends from his various companies associated with F1. But, with a personal fortune estimated at £1,500 million, he could easily afford to indulge himself in his recent purchase of a BA-e 146 jet to ease the commute between the homes in London and Gstaad that he shares with his lofty wife, Slavica, and their two children. Since large chunks of his business are registered in Croation-born Slavica's name, the 39-year-old former model should be included in that calculation.

ECO Umberto Eco is a jovial, chain-smoking academic who happens also to be a best-selling author. Ostensibly Professor of Semiotics, the study of communications through signs and symbols, at the University of Bologna, Eco has enjoyed phenomenal success at almost everything to which he has turned his hand in an illustrious 30-year career. He has been acclaimed variously as a philosopher, an historian, a literary critic and an aesthetician. He is also an avid book collector, who owns more than 30,000 volumes. The bewildering array of subjects on which Eco has written include St. Thomas Aquinas, James Joyce and Superman. However, in a public context, his name is most regularly cited as the author of *The Name of the Rose*, a medieval murder mystery, which was successfully turned into a film starring Sean Connery. Many critics have cited another of his books, *Foucault's Pendulum*, as one of the century's best novels. Ⱥ

FERRAGAMO

Shoemaker to the stars, shoemaker of dreams - the plaudits to awarded the man who turned shoe design into a visionary art have grown, rather than decreased, with time. We have Salvatore Ferragamo to thank for the wedge and the cork heel; he even designed an 'invisible' shoe and one made of pure gold for an Indian princess. His fascination with the anatomy of the foot and his determination to stretch the boundaries of shoe design made him one of the greatest shoemakers of all time. Not bad for a poor boy from Naples, who hand-made his first pair of shoes when he was only eight - a small white pair for his sister to wear for her first communion.

Today Salvatore's widow, Wanda, is head of this exceptionally elegant family. Operating from a magnificent 15th-century palazzo in Florence, it owns 100 per cent of the shares in this shoes-to-silks business, which turned over £300 million last year. How have they done it? Being Italian helps. The family embodies a specifically Italian style of business management - close-knit and family run. Wanda's six children, three boys and three girls, each occupy key roles within the company whose product line has expanded to include clothes and accessories.

Among the more recent moves have been the 1996 purchase of Emanuel Ungaro and a 1997 joint venture with Bulgari to manufacture and market perfume and cosmetics. The principal benefit of the family's independence, according to Chief Executive Ferrucio Ferragamo, is that it enables them to put money back into the business rather than into shareholder dividends. ▲

FISCHER

The leader of the German Green Party may not be the most important German politician but, in a way he symbolises modern Germany more than anyone else. Joska Fischer is the outstanding example of how the leaders of the student revolts of the Sixties and Seventies have been integrated into the country's establishment. He began his career in politics as a taxi driver in Frankfurt, rallying on the street against US intervention in Vietnam; 20 years later he was the first anti-establishment minister, responsible for the environment in the cabinet of the federal state of Hessen. Banks and industries in the Frankfurt area who threatened to move out of Hessen soon calmed down when they saw that Fischer was a realist. His practical approach has, in turn, not only had a significant influence on how the Green lobby pitches itself in other countries but has also made the establishment in those countries marginally less suspicious of its agenda.

Due largely to the fact that the Social Democrats have become increasingly conservative, aping the strategy of Britain's Tony Blair, the charismatic Fischer has become a figurehead of the German Left.

FOSTER

Along with his close friend and ex-business partner, Richard Rogers (qv), Sir Norman Foster is at the helm of British architecture and is responsible for many cutting-edge buildings around the world. They include the Hong Kong and Shanghai Bank headquarters in Hong Kong, Stansted Airport in England, the Reichstag in Berlin, the Torre de Collemosa in Barcelona and the new Hong Kong airport at Chek Lap Kok. The latter - built at an estimated cost of £12 billion - has been universally acclaimed as one of the great architectural landmarks of the century. All of Foster's work is characterised by its sleekness and brilliant engineering - reflecting his passion for aircraft design.

Born in Manchester in 1935, Foster and his third wife, Elena, a Spanish psychologist, live 'above the shop', in a magnificent, glass-walled penthouse overlooking Chelsea from the southern bank of the Thames. Despite being in his Sixties, Foster is extremely fit, with the energy of a schoolboy. When not flying his private helicopter, he enjoys cross-country skiing and mountain biking. The couple have an immensely busy social life which revolves around a shared love of food and the theatre.

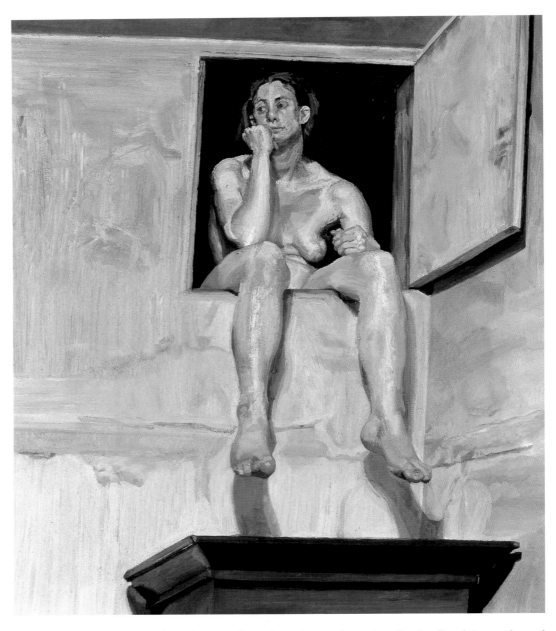

FREUD

One of the foremost figurative painters of our time, Lucian Freud (a grandson of Sigmund Freud, the father of psychoanalysis) was born in Berlin in 1922 and moved to Britain with his family at the age of 11. He briefly attended the Central School of Art in 1938 and Cedric Morris' School of Painting and Drawing between 1939 and 1941. Freud has a huge international following, particularly in America, France and Italy. In 1998 his *Large Interior, W11* was sold to a private American collector for £3,572,410 - the highest price ever paid for a living British artist.

Freud's early paintings were notable for their intensely focused observation and a precision of line that led Herbert Read to describe him as "the Ingres of Existentialism." From the mid Fifties, when he swapped his sable brushes for hog's hair, the surfaces of his paintings became more animated, as he sought to find in paint a material equivalent for human flesh. To this day his work is characterised by an uncompromising adherence to this principle.

A famously private and elusive man, whose sartorial style tends towards discreet cashmere sports jackets, Freud can, however, be found lunching - always at the same table - in Wilton's restaurant several times a week. Interviews are extremely rare and he looks genuinely startled if approached by admirers. Twice-married, Freud has eight children, one of whom, Bella, is a successful fashion designer. His brother is Sir Clement Freud, the writer, broadcaster, caterer and former Liberal MP; they have not spoken for at least ten years.

Art critic Adrian Searle has written: "To look at Freud's paintings is to look into the painter's lair. Perhaps people look in the hope of finding Freud the misfit, the difficult old man, trailed by the rumours, the mythical quarrels, the list of lovers, the gambling, the dining habits." ⚑

Perini Navi, Blue-Water Sailing Yachts

March 1998: the 52 metre *S/Y Liberty* sailing off Tortola, BVI

PERINI NAVI   Via M. Coppino, 114 - 55049 Viareggio - Italia - Tel. +39 0584 4241   Fax +39 0584 424200
PERINI NAVI USA   One Maritime Drive - Portsmouth, RI 02871- U.S.A. - Tel. 401-683-5600   Fax. 401-683-5611

GERGIEV

Valery Gergiev's passion and charisma have made him one of the most sought-after conductors on the international music circuit and the darling of the social set that swirls around it. Ostensibly, his chief position is Director of the Mariinsky Theatre in St Petersburg - home to the Kirov Opera and Ballet - but this brilliantly talented and maniacally energetic native of Ossetia in the Caucasus is also the principal guest conductor of the New York Metropolitan Opera and principal conductor of the Rotterdam Philharmonic Orchestra.

Gergiev studied conducting with Ilya Musin at the Leningrad Conservatory, winning the Herbert von Karajan Conductors' Competition in Berlin at the age of 23. Since his 1978 Kirov début with *War and Peace*, he has gone from strength to strength, conducting all the leading orchestras of the former Soviet Union; for four years he was chief conductor of the Armenian State Orchestra.

His American début came in 1991 with a new production of *War and Peace* at the San Francisco Opera. In London he was Artistic Director of the Mariinsky-Kirov Series from 1993-95 and, as a guest conductor, Gergiev has performed with leading orchestras around the world, including those of Los Angeles, New York, Amsterdam, Rome and Berlin.

The conductor is hugely popular with artists and audiences alike and the winner of countless awards in Europe

and America (including People's Artist of Russia, that country's highest cultural accolade). Gergiev has gained respect and enemies in equal measure for his determination to stamp out the corruption that has remained entrenched in much of the Russian musical establishment since communist days. ⋀

GALL

In 1995 Hugues Gall, then general administrator of the Geneva Opera, took up a new role as head of Paris' operatic institutions, with a contract running until 2001. Charged with sorting out the bureaucratic, political and financial chaos in which they were mired, he assumed autocratic power over both the Bastille and the Palais Garnier, the centres for opera and ballet respectively. Indeed, unlike his predecessor Pierre Bergé, he managed to resolve many of the problems which had dogged the venues for years.

The 58 year-old was born in Normandy. His early career saw him in the Ministry of Agriculture (where he distinguished himself as a whiz-kid) and then at the Ministry of Culture. He credits as a mentor another man gifted with the art of replacing chaos with order - Rolf Liebermann, who was in charge of the Palais Garnier in the Seventies.

Gall is credited with bringing an international style to the two houses he runs and for favouring a reasonable degree of experimentation - an increasingly rare quality in the world of money-spinning, corporate-friendly opera. He is a great scout, too - Ruggiero Raimondi and Samuel Ramey are among his finds. But he will need his wits about him to revolutionise life fully at the Opera Bastille. As a recent profile of him concluded, "There have been 11 different administrators in Paris since Rolf Liebermann left the opera in 1980 and the notoriously militant theatre unions have become stronger with each one's passing." Rumour has it that the Royal Opera, Covent Garden, is courting him to come and sort out its own dire mess when his present contract expires; as his success so far in Paris demonstrates, he is one of the few who might be capable of doing so. ⋀

GOTTSCHALK

The guru of German television entertainment, Thomas Gottschalk started as a radio host on Munich's Bayern-3 Radio, moved on to TV and became the darling of Saturday prime-time entertainment, with ratings that are still unrivalled. In the Eighties he established the first daily Letterman-style late-night show on German television. He is now based in Malibu with his beautiful wife, Thea, and their children. From there he produces films and television shows but only appears on German TV when he is needed to boost ratings.

GUIGOU

The French Justice Minister in Lionel Jospin's government, 51 year-old Elisabeth Guigou is sometimes referred to as 'Madame Maastricht' for her central role in drafting the treaty for European monetary union in 1992. She can, it is rumoured, quote the entire treaty verbatim. Strikingly attractive, she regularly upstages every woman in the room, thanks to her excellent taste in designer clothes. However, it is her *hauteur* and razor-sharp intellect that make her feared, even by powerful leaders, in political corridors all over Europe.

GUILLEM

Paris-born Sylvie Guillem is currently Principal Guest Artist at the Royal Ballet. Regarding rumours that she is one of the highest paid dancers in the world, she told one journalist, "Don't ask me. I don't know how much everyone else gets." Since her move from the Paris Opera Ballet in 1989, she has wowed both the critics and the punters. Indeed, one critic gushed, "Has the Covent Garden stage ever seen a more erotic sight?", while the London Times drooled over "the sumptuous embroidery of her unparalleled technique. She is a ballerina typecast to play sexy."

At the age of 11, Guillem took a short course at the Paris Opéra Ballet, before entering the corps de ballet as a *quadrille*. In 1983 she fulfilled her early promise by winning the prestigious Varna Competition. The following year she was promoted to the rank of *première danseuse* and, only five days later, was promoted yet again - to *étoile* - after a performance of *Swan Lake*. In 1988 she was awarded the Prix Andersen (Copenhagen), Commandeur des Arts et Lettres and the Grand Prix de la Danse (Ministère de la Culture, France). When she appeared in Paris with the Royal Ballet in June 1993, she was presented with the Médaille de la Ville de Paris after dancing Odette/Odile.

For her Covent Garden début in January 1988, Guillem danced the title role in *Giselle*, partnered by Rudolf Nureyev. At the time he said of her, "She is the only woman I would consider marrying." ➤

HARLECH

Born Amanda Grieve, daughter of a successful London lawyer, Lady Harlech rose rapidly through the ranks of London's style magazines, working on *Harpers & Queen*, before marrying Francis Ormsby Gore, the 6th Lord Harlech, in a lavish society wedding. She was adopted as a muse by John Galliano when he took over as designer at Christian Dior. Galliano reportedly used her as a term of reference in much the same fashion that Givenchy used Audrey Hepburn earlier this century. But disaster, for Galliano, at least, struck when Karl Lagerfeld (qv) poached Harlech for Chanel, a move that threw couture-watchers into a flurry of bitching and back-stabbing.

What, then, does she do for Lagerfeld? Harlech is suspicious of the word muse, although she does concede that it "probably fits better than anything else, because of what it suggests about working within the dream." In a recent interview she said, "I use the word 'collaborator' to describe my role, but it has commercial connotations which I don't think are right. It doesn't encompass the enthusiasm for the work which is necessary, and which cannot be bought." Harlech was chosen by Lagerfeld because she is, according to the designer, "the modern Chanel. That is why I look at her and work with her and talk to her." She is, it seems, the driving spirit of the house.

Until recently Harlech spent half the year in Paris and the rest of her time on the family estate in Wales with her husband and two children. But she is constantly in touch with Lagerfeld. "Amanda is all-important," he confirms. "Her style, her beauty, her wit, her spirit brings life to the studio, and it would be gloomier without her." In the wake of all this exuberance, Lord Harlech cuts a lonely figure. Last year he admitted to a newspaper that his wife "runs her own life", adding that, "the only way I know how to contact her is through Mr Lagerfeld." ◄

HEANEY

In the wake of Seamus Heaney's 1995 Nobel Prize for Literature, Robert Lowell's description of him as the "most important Irish poet since Yeats" seems wholly accurate. He is certainly the most popular poet writing in English today; his books sell by the tens of thousands and, in Ireland, where poetry has always enjoyed an unusually large following, he is a national hero.

Born in Northern Ireland in 1939, he graduated in 1961 with a first-class degree in English from Queen's University, Belfast. While working as a lecturer in English Literature at St Joseph's College, Belfast, he first published his poetry under the pseudonym Incertus. His first volume of poems, *Death of a Naturalist*, was published in 1966, earning him a host of awards including the Geoffrey Faber Memorial Prize. Heaney's second volume, *Door into the Dark*, was published in 1969 and became the Poetry Book Society's Choice for the Year. He continued teaching in Ireland until 1981, when he became a visiting professor at Harvard, before publishing the highly acclaimed *Station Island* collection in 1984.

Heaney had always been very close to his parents and his mother's death that same year prompted *Clearances*, a magnificent sonnet sequence memorialising her. His equally mesmerising 1991 collection, *Seeing Things*, contains many similarly affectionate memories of his father, who had died the year before the book was published. In 1989 Heaney was elected to a five-year post as Professor of Poetry at Oxford University. He currently lives in Dublin with his wife, Marie Devlin, whom he married in 1965. He has two sons and a charming daughter. ◄

HINGIS

The father of Martina Hingis lives in a soulless apartment block in the Czech Republic; he earns £170 a month as a caretaker at the local tennis club. His Slovakia-born daughter, now a Swiss national, has made more than £4 million in career winnings and almost £10 million in endorsements. They see each other a couple of times a year but, otherwise, live separate lives. Why? At the age of four Martina's parents split up, a result, according to the gossip columns, of Melanie Hingis' overweening ambition for her daughter. A broken home is the price that Martina Hingis has paid for her glittering tennis career. Career? She is only 17.

Among the countless tournaments that Hingis has already won, two achievements stand out: she is the youngest player - man or woman - to win a Grand Slam this century and she is the youngest number one woman tennis player since the rankings began.

Martina - named after her parents' idol, Navratilova - is a remarkably unassuming young woman, whose bouncy personality seems unaffected by her achievements. When she is not playing tennis she enjoys precarious hobbies, such as in-line skating, skiing and horse riding. Although a riding accident is said to have cost her the French Open Final in 1997, she has no plans to give up her risky pleasures. In an interview last year she said, "I love showjumping and falling off is one of the risks." The girl who admits to having played for up to 16 hours a day before turning pro at 14 then added, "Tennis is important to me but that doesn't mean it should stop me from doing everything else." ▲

JOHN

Elton John's genius for unforgettable melodies and outrageous visual extravagance have captured the spirit of the moment throughout the last three decades. He has built a back catalogue of songs worth at least £100 million. However, according to music industry observers, John is more of a bankable proposition now than at any time in his career. His current success is a tribute to the man's ability to reinvent himself, and follows over two decades of emotional upheaval, alcohol and drug abuse and the deaths of his beloved mother and several close friends, including Gianni Versace and Diana, Princess of Wales.

Christened Reginald Dwight, John grew up on the outskirts of London, and entered the Royal Academy of Music at the age of 11. He left, just before graduating, to launch himself into rock music with Bluesology, a backing group for singer John Baldry. It was his 1967 meeting with lyricist Bernie Taupin - through a local newspaper advertisement - that proved seminal. Four years later, the pair had become the first musical act since The Beatles to have four albums in the top ten of the American charts and, in 1975, he graced the cover of *Time* magazine.

In 1977 his partnership with Taupin fell apart and John retired, blaming the pressure of fame and the gruelling touring. But not for long. In 1979 he became the first Western singer to tour the Soviet Union and, the following year, Taupin and John re-united. Throughout the Eighties, John's public successes were a cruel mirror of his private tragedies, which included a failed, four-year marriage and the death of his close companion, Ryan White. Shortly after White's death, John checked into a rehabilitation clinic and emerged leaner and fitter. From that moment he developed a more cultured persona.

This complex character is renowned for his extraordinary generosity, not just towards friends and acquaintances, whom he entertains royally and showers with gifts and flowers, but to good causes. In 1992 he set up the Elton John AIDS Foundation, to which he has since donated all profits from the sales of his singles and, last year, he handed over to the Diana, Princess of Wales Memorial Fund royalties of £20 million-plus on the re-worked version of *Candle in the Wind*, which he sang at her funeral.

Together with his generosity and gift for friendship, Elton John is remarkable for his unswerving loyalty to those around him. This made even more surprising his acrimonious split last year with John Reid, the manager who, for 30 years, had masterminded his success. V

JUAN CARLOS

King Juan Carlos has defined, better than anybody, the perfect demeanour for a late 20th century monarch. If the institution is to continue successfully in other countries, his example should be the template: not too lacking in the common touch, yet retaining a sense of royal mystique; he and his family have become neither gossip-column fodder nor ordinary bicycling citizens. This achievement is perhaps as significant in historic terms as his success in uniting the Spanish people under his leadership since the Franco years.

Born in 1938 in Rome, where the Spanish Royal Family had fled when the Republic was proclaimed in 1931, Juan Carlos was, at the express wish of his father, Don Juan de Borbon y Battenberg, educated in Spain from the age of ten onwards. In 1955 he joined the Academies and Military Colleges of the Army, the Navy and the Air Force, qualifying as a military pilot. He then completed his education at Madrid's Complutense University, where he studied constitutional and international law, economics and taxation.

Following his 1962 marriage to Princess Sofia of Greece, the couple set up home at the Palacio de la Zarzuela, on the outskirts of Madrid, which is still their residence. The next year their first child, Princess Elena, was born, followed by Princess Cristina and finally, in 1968, by Prince Felipe. A great sportsman, the King is passionate about skiing and sailing and he has a reputation for being warm-hearted and utterly unpretentious. Among his many honorary doctorates are those from the Universities of Bologna, Oxford, Cambridge and Harvard. He is an associate member of the Institut de France and the American Philosophical Society and is also honorary President of the Board of Trustees of the Cervantes Institute, which is dedicated to the dissemination of the Spanish language worldwide.

In the 18 years since he was proclaimed King (having been designated Successor to the Head of State by Franco himself in 1969), Juan Carlos has enjoyed great popularity at home, both personally and politically. In 1981, his actions saved the Constitution (which had been established as the cornerstone of Spain's transition to democracy in 1976) in the face of an attempted coup. On the international stage, he is respected as intelligent and progressive. As well as being a committed pro-European, he has encouraged a new style in conducting relations with Latin America, emphasising the advantages of collaborating with countries that share the same language and pointing out the need to generate common initiatives. A

KIEFER

Anslem Kiefer is the most eminent German contemporary artist, not only because his subject matter is essentially German - history and mythology - but because he represents Germany's ethnic and cultural identity through his paintings and sculptures. At the beginning of this century, the futurist art theorist Marinetti claimed that classic art was dead and that technology was the real contemporary art. "An aeroplane is more beautiful than the Venus de Milo," he claimed. Kiefer fulfilled Marinetti's vision and made aeroplanes out of lead - as a reference, perhaps, to Germany's militarism. He has also made a library out of lead, which was possibly a reflection on Germany as a country of thinkers and poets. Kiefer does not celebrate 'art for art's sake' but takes art as serious as politics. Typically German.

KIRCH

Ironically, given that he is Germany's mightiest media mogul, Leo Kirch never steps into the public eye. Forty years ago, the unknown Kirch bought the rights for Fellini's *La Strada* on credit. It became a classic and Kirch continued to buy up film rights.

Today he holds the biggest stock of movies in Germany, although he suffered a setback when the Monopolies Commission in Brussels prevented him from entering a joint venture with Bertelsmann. Kirch has poured hundreds of millions into digital television, believing it to be the future, but so far the investments have not paid off. The Kirch Group is estimated to be worth at least $4 billion, although it is surrounded by an aura of mystery, as Kirch runs it very much as a one-man show.

KOPPER

If Russia is looking for foreign investment, its first point of reference should be Hilmar Kopper, not any Head of State. As Chairman of DeutscheBank, he is one of the most powerful people in Europe. Kopper has widened the traditional areas of Deutsche's activities; besides its traditional vast community of private clients, it is now among the big players in corporate and institutional banking, as well as investment banking. Deutsche also has direct investment in private industry (including 10 per cent of insurer Allianz and 11 per cent of car maker Daimer-Chrysler).

LAGERFELD

As influential as he is talented, Karl Lagerfeld was born into a prosperous Hamburg family in 1938 (his father was the founder of the dairy chain Glucksklee Milch). He was educated privately, first in Hamburg then, from the age of 14, in Paris. His dream of being a fashion designer became reality when he won a prize for a wool coat in the International Wool Secretariat design competition in 1954. In the same competition a young man called Yves Saint Laurent (qv) won first prize in three out of four categories.

Lagerfeld first worked for Pierre Balmain (1954-'57) then, in 1958, moved to Jean Patou. From 1963 he was head designer at Chloé and, during his time there, also began designing furs for Fendi and launched his own company. Lagerfeld designed independently from 1978 to 1982, when Alain Wertheimer hired him to produce *haute couture* at Chanel. The following year, in conjunction with Gilles Dufour, he took on Chanel's ready-to-wear lines. Affectionately dubbed 'Kaiser Karl' by Women's Wear Daily, Lagerfeld transformed the fortunes of the then moribund house, a precursor to the flurry of prestigious hirings within a number of prominent couture houses in the last few years.

A gifted photographer, Lagerfeld styles and shoots his own publicity campaigns. He effectively invented the concept of the supermodel, by hiring a 'face' to represent the house - first, Inès de la Fressange (whom he famously dumped when she was chosen as the model for Marianne, symbol of France's nationhood), then Claudia Schiffer, Stella Tennant and now Karen Elson.

The prolific Lagerfeld, who speaks four languages fluently, has also designed costumes for 20 films and operas, put his stamp on the Schlosshotel Vierjahreszeiten in Berlin and recently finished decorating his spectacular villa in Biarritz. ⋀

LLOYD WEBBER

From *Cats* to *Phantom of the Opera*, *Evita* to *Starlight Express*, Andrew Lloyd Webber's music is as ubiquitous as Cole Porter's was in a previous era. Today there is hardly anyone left on the planet who can't hum a Lloyd Webber tune.

Son of the composer, William, and brother of cellist, Julian, Andrew Lloyd Webber was born in 1948. It was his partnership with lyricist Sir Tim Rice that led to a string of spectacular musical successes from the 1960s onwards. In 1982 he became the first person ever to have three musicals running concurrently in New York and three in London. To add to his Grammys, Tonys and an Oscar, Lloyd Webber has been awarded a fellowship of the Royal College of Music and, in 1992, a knighthood, followed five years later by a life peerage. In 1996 the London production of *Cats* became the longest running musical in history. His latest musical, *Whistle Down the Wind*, opened in London's West End in June 1998.

Lord Lloyd Webber has been married three times. His present wife, Madeleine, is an accomplished horsewoman. Together they have homes in Berkshire and Tipperary, which they use as a base when racing in Ireland. Last year Lloyd Webber sold his Eaton Square house in London for a reported £12.5 million. His other interests include wine - before selling off a large portion of it, he had one of the finest private cellars in Europe - and dining out; his restaurant review column in *The Sunday Telegraph* has become compulsory reading for literate gourmets. 𝒜

LUPU

Pianist Radu Lupu's modest stage presence and cuddly bear looks have prompted more than one reviewer to note that he looks as if he is playing for his own amusement rather than anyone else's. But his private, almost detached manner belies a virtuosity that has catapulted him to the upper echelons of his profession. In constant demand as a soloist, chamber musician and concert artist, his interpretations of the core 19th-century repertoire have garnered huge international acclaim.

He was born in 1945 in Romania and, from an early age, exhibited the curious combination of discipline and flair that distinguishes the truly gifted musicians from the merely good. He made his public début with a performance of his own music at the age of 12, before winning a scholarship to the Moscow Conservatoire. International stardom soon followed when he won the 1966 Van Cliburn Prize and, three years later, the Leeds International Piano Competition. In addition to playing with the world's greatest orchestras, Lupu has made extensive recordings over the last 15 years. His 1995 albums for Decca, of Schubert sonatas and works by Schumann, won Grammy and Edison awards respectively.

At a gala concert held to commemorate the life of Peter Diamond, Lupu paid tribute to the late impresario's "intelligence and warmth, friendship and laughter, wit and charm." In the rarefied world of classical music, where egos often run all too rampant, these are exactly the sort of qualities that differentiate Lupu from many of his peers. ➤

MACGREGOR

Director of the British National Gallery for over ten years, 52-year-old Neill MacGregor was born in Glasgow, Scotland. After graduating in French and German from New College, Oxford, he read Philosophy at the Ecole Normale Supérieure in Paris for a year. He then took an LLB in Law at the University of Edinburgh, where he was Green Prizeman, before being called to the Scottish Bar. But, foregoing his legal training, MacGregor obtained yet another degree, an MA in 17th- and 19th-century art from the Courtauld Institute.

In 1981 he became Editor of the art magazine Burlington, where he remained until he assumed his present post. MacGregor has an unimpeachable professional reputation and is invariably tipped as a candidate whenever the top spot at any of Europe's more prestigious galleries becomes available. His unassuming style - he takes the underground to work and walks home - has endeared him to both his colleagues and the media. When he isn't managing a space which attracts five million visitors a year, MacGregor is usually found on the side of a hill. As he said in a recent interview, "I love mountain walking. It's very quiet, away from towns and beaches. There are no crowds, no telephones. And no art!" ◄

MACKINTOSH

Cameron Mackintosh is a disarmingly casual character, whose low-key lifestyle belies his huge success. With his production of lavish, large-scale musicals, he has, almost singlehandedly, revolutionised both London's West End and musical theatre world wide.

His reputation is that of a thoroughly decent person of almost legendary generosity. In 1989 Mackintosh gave Oxford University £2 million to establish a Chair of Contemporary Theatre, which has been held by the likes of Sir Ian McKellen and Lord Attenborough. His parties are equally generous; he hired a large private jet to take a group of friends to the opening night of *Miss Saigon* in Stuttgart and spent £125,000 preparing the venue for his party for *Oliver!*

On leaving Ampleforth - alma mater of Sir Anthony Bamford (qv) - Mackintosh enrolled in London's Central School of Speech and Drama. After an undistinguished spell there, he had several less than successful outings as a producer before his first break, in 1976, with *Side by Side by Sondheim*. But it was a famously long lunch with Andrew Lloyd Webber which kick-started their collaboration, beginning with *Cats*, the longest running musical of all time. To finance the production, Mackintosh persuaded 200 people to invest £750 each - in retrospect an exceptionally good buy. Nowadays he regularly gets cold calls from people offering a million pounds to finance his next venture.

What next, then, for the man who had 50 productions running around the world last summer and who has amassed career earnings of around £250 million? Although he has received a knighthood for his services to the theatre, awards are clearly not an incentive. As he told a journalist recently, "I'm not one for honours but my mother is very proud. I've just got this great fear of changing, because I've thoroughly enjoyed being me."

MAGNIER

The master of Coolmore, John Magnier has built up the world's most successful bloodstock empire. The quietly-spoken former Irish Senator has surpassed the might of the Al Maktoums, the Wildensteins and others who aspire to dominate the sport of Kings. Despite Magnier's deep aversion to publicity, the extraordinary success of his Coolmore operation attracts ever-increasing media interest. The in-word at Coolmore is globalisation. From its attractive, tax-free Irish base (Coolmore also has properties in the US and Australia), stallions are flown around the world. The Coolmore list of breeding stallions reads like an equine Debretts: *Sadler's Wells, Danehill, Be My Guest, Caerlean, Desert King* and *Entrepreneur* are among its exceptional portfolio. Magnier's owners, partners and associates include the likes of Monaco-based entrepreneur Michael Tabor, Chanel's Alain Wertheimer, the reclusive financier Joe Lewis, Robert Sangster, J.P. McManus (the Swiss based former Irish bookmaker who is now one of the world's top currency traders), Lord Weinstock and Wafic Said.

Magnier, whose family has a long tradition of breeding and racing horses in Ireland, married one of the beautiful daughters of legendary trainer Dr Vincent O'Brien, late master of Ballydoyle. In O'Brien's place there, Magnier has installed another brilliant trainer, 28 year-old wunderkind Aidan O'Brien (no relation). Despite his low public profile, Magnier has a typically Irish propensity for enjoyment. A superb host, only the finest champagnes and first growth clarets are served at Ballydoyle. He is also a generous supporter of several cancer charities, a keen golfer (who is known to bet heavily on the success of a shot) and an avid follower of hurling. Magnier is part of the consortium which purchased the Sandy Lane Hotel in Barbados and has built for himself, nearby, a spectacular house, decorated by London-based Jane Churchill.

MIDDELHOFF

Thanks to an old in-house rule at media empire Bertelsmann, which demands that the CEO cannot be older than 62, Thomas Middelhoff was appointed in 1998 to succeed Mark Wossner as Chairman and Chief Executive. The latter had built the organisation into the world's third-largest media company, behind Time-Warner and Disney, and is now Chairman of the Supervisory Board. Middelhoff joined Bertelsmann in 1986, beginning by managing printing plants and rising to become a member of the Board of both Bertelsmann and America Online (AOL) in 1994. Middelhoff is regarded as an innovator so, if you own a media business, brace yourself for take-overs. Just remember what happened to Random House.

MILLER

A doctor of medicine by training, Jonathan Miller is also an author, lecturer, television producer and presenter, as well as a film and opera director. Born in London, he obtained his medical degree from Cambridge University in 1959, where he got to know Alan Bennett, Peter Cook and Dudley Moore, with whom he co-authored and appeared in the cult classic *Beyond the Fringe* from 1961 to 1964.

Diversifying into theatre directing, Miller's many outstanding productions include a legendary *Merchant of Venice* at the National Theatre, with Sir Laurence Olivier and Joan Plowright. As Artistic Director of the Old Vic from 1988-'90, he directed several highly-acclaimed productions, including *Andromache*, with Janet Suzman, and *The Tempest*, with Max von Sydow.

Since making his début as an opera director in 1973, Miller has worked at most of the world's great houses, including La Scala, The Met, Covent Garden, The Vienna State Opera and at the Salzburg Festival. He established a particularly close relationship with the Maggio Musicale in Florence, through his productions of *Tosca*, *Don Giovanni*, *Cosi fan Tutti* and *The Marriage of Figaro*.

On television, Miller's series on the history of medicine, *The Body in Question*, made him a household name. This was followed by two acclaimed series, *Born Talking* and *Museums of Madness*. Miller gives frequent lectures on a wide variety of subjects, including, in 1994, a series at the National Gallery, London, entitled *From the Look of Things*, which he also delivered at the Metropolitan Museum, New York. In 1996 Jonathan Miller was awarded an honorary Doctor of Letters by Cambridge University and, in 1997, he was elected as a Fellow of the Royal College of Physicians. ◄

MONTAIGNER

A giant among the late 20th century's medical researchers, Luc Montaigner was born in 1932 in Chablis, France. After studying in Paris, he became a researcher at the National Centre for Scientific Findings. This was followed by three-and-a-half years with the Medical Research Council in Britain, where he discovered a new property of cancer cells, which led to a now-routine technique in laboratories working on transformation and oncogenes.

Montaigner returned to France to work for the Pasteur Institute, where he has made a breathtaking number of contributions to the way in which doctors around the world are working today, including opening the way for the cloning of interferon genes. But it is for his pioneering work on the AIDS virus that he will probably be best remembered. In 1983 he discovered HIV-1 and demonstrated its role in AIDS. Two years later he isolated the second human AIDS virus (HIV-2) from West African patients. Since 1986 he has concentrated on identifying the complex mechanisms of AIDS pathogenesis. ▲

MUTTER

After Herbert von Karajan discovered Anne-Sophie Mutter at the age of 13, violin playing was never quite the same again. Her beauty and spirit, coupled with the incomparable sounds that she coaxes from her instrument - soft but strict, displaying heartfelt and soulful perfection - have made her much imitated, though never equalled.

Miss Mutter masters the 18th century concertos as if they were written for her but she is also an ardent champion of contemporary music, believing that she has a responsibility to expand the repertory for her instrument. As a result, she has premièred several works written specially for her by composers such as Witold Lutoslawski, Krzysztof Penderecki and Sebastian Currier. In 1998 she undertook the most important project of her career to date, devoting the year to performing Beethoven's ten sonatas for violin and piano worldwide with pianist Lambert Orkis, all of which were recorded live.

Miss Mutter also has a strong philanthropic bent. In 1987 she established the Rudolf Eberle Endowment (recently incorporated into the Anne-Sophie Mutter Foundation and Friends Circle), which supports talented young string musicians throughout Europe. Her strong commitment to social and health problems is manifested in regular benefit concerts. In 1998, for example, the proceeds from one of her Beethoven evenings in Munich went to the Christiane-Herzog-Stiftung for sufferers of cystic fibrosis, while she also performed a benefit concert for the German Red Cross, on behalf of a Romanian orphanage.

'The Mother', as she is known in her native Germany (where she holds the Order of Merit of the Federal Republic), is indeed a mother of two, although already a widow, following the death in 1997 of her husband, the respected lawyer Detlev Wunderlich. ➤

NAEGELLEN

In gastronomic circles, Bernard Naegellen is the most feared in France. The annual publication of the Michelin Guide, of which he is Editor-in-Chief, is "a defining moment in French culture", as one newspaper put it. It is a time when chefs as great as Alain Ducasse can be reduced to panic attacks and one that heralds feverish discussion in the national press. The award or loss of a star in France is, literally, front-page news and the Guide's decisions influence the dining habits of gourmets the world over.

Michelin is secretive and works hard to maintain its mystique. In keeping with that style, Naegellen is publicity-shy and impossible to track down; he even refuses to send his biographical details to the French *Who's Who*. He has a background in five-star hotel and restaurant management, is in his mid-fifties, mildly spoken, looks more like an ascetic academic than a *bon viveur* and is, apparently, amused by the dread fear that he can inspire in the most illustrious chefs when he chooses to pay them an anonymous visit.

The almost paranoid secrecy that characterises the Michelin style is the Guide's magic ingredient; it is the only one that really matters to chefs. Decisions are final and the barest crumbs of information are offered by way of explanation for a rating. As Naegellen once said, in a rare moment of openness, "We never explain and we never change our minds."

O'REILLY

In 1979 when Tony O'Reilly took over as CEO of Heinz, the American food giant was valued at $900 million; when he stepped down from its day-to-day running in 1998 it was worth $23 billion. O'Reilly's own 2 per cent stake is valued at $460 million. Independent Newspapers, O'Reilly's Dublin-based company, has media interests as far afield as Australia, South Africa and Britain (his holding in that company is worth at least £200 million) and he has also made an impressive contribution at porcelain and crystal group Waterford Wedgwood. But this 61 year-old, Jesuit-educated lawyer's achievements seem all the more impressive, given the fact that he started out with a passion for sport but no real connections. His celebrated career as an Irish rugby international - he also had a trial for Arsenal football club - was the unlikely platform on which he amassed an empire worth at least £700 million.

As well as possessing an exceptional business brain, the charismatic O'Reilly (or Dr AJF, as his employees call him) is a world-class networker, a marvellous after-dinner speaker and a talented raconteur, with an unbelievable knack of remembering not only people's names but their interests and life stories. When in Ireland he entertains lavishly. Invitations to his parties on the night of big sporting events are highly prized. Here, Hollywood (Paul Newman and Gregory Peck) mixes with politics (the Kissingers, Nelson Mandela and George Bush - an O'Reilly tennis partner) and the media (Ben Bradlee and Sally Quinn). Add to that the pick of the *Fortune 500*, poets, writers, musicians and philosophers, not to mention rugby heroes both past and present. As one guest noted, "to see O'Reilly work the room is to see a master at work."

With his second wife, 51 year-old Chryss Goulandris (the Greek shipping heiress and, in her own right, a successful racehorse breeder) he shares Castlemartin, a lavish County Kildare estate, a home in Pittsburgh and a stud farm near Deauville. O'Reillly also has a home on Fitzwilliam Square, Dublin's smartest residential address.

Tony O'Reilly is the principal force behind the development of The Ireland Fund, which raises money from successful people of Irish extraction around the world for peace and reconciliation. He has also, almost single-handedly, saved the Wexford Opera Festival.

Always a great man for the one-liner, O'Reilly suggested, when asked by a group of Irish university students how to succeed in business, "Look Irish, dress British, think Yiddish." Clearly a man who has taken his own advice. ≺

OCKRENT

Christened 'La Reine Christine' by viewers, Christine Ockrent currently presents Soir 3 on France's Channel 3 every Sunday - a heavyweight current affairs programme with an intellectual following. The French are obsessed with her; it is not only her cool demeanour and glacial good looks that have endeared her to them but her uncompromising reporting style, which has delivered a sharp blow to the non-investigative world of French journalism.

Born in 1944, the daughter of a Belgian ambassador, she grew up in Paris, went to a smart girls' school, spent a year in Cambridge to learn English and, before going to Harvard University to take up a prestigious Harkness fellowship, joined NBC television in Paris on work experience. There was just one problem - the journalism bug bit and Harvard never happened.

Ockrent's training in a hard-hitting Anglo-Saxon style of journalism caused consternation from the start. "People were horrified because I asked direct questions," she once said. "In France the code of politeness is such that you barely touch the subject." Her journalistic coups include editing *L'Express* magazine (improving its circulation by a third) and pulling off an interview with Saddam Hussein in the middle of the Gulf War. She is currently editor of the new French weekly magazine *L'Européen*, owned by the Barclay brothers (who also own *The European* in Britain). The *Nouvel Observateur* magazine described Ockrent in action thus: "[She] delivers the news like battle orders. When you hear her, you think, 'That's serious. The world might end tomorrow.'"

Ockrent has a 12 year-old son, Alexandre, with socialist MP Bernard Kouchner, a founder of Médecins Sans Frontières. A bona fide rebel in every sense, ten years ago she smoked cigars, wore leathers and rode to work on a motorbike. Today, to maintain her coiffure for the cameras, she has given up her crash helmet but she is still refreshingly uninterested in her looks and loathes shopping. This hasn't detracted from her appeal; the French vote Ockrent alongside Deneuve and Bardot as the embodiment of national beauty. ⋀

OETKER

In partnership with his brother, Richard, Rudolph Oetker heads August Oetker KG, one of Germany's best-known companies. There is probably no country in the world where one cannot find Oetker's baking powder. Widely respected in Germany, Oetker is a central figure in the Association of Industries and the Board of Employers. Following a kidnapping case in the family, he is rarely seen in public and lives reclusively in Dusseldorf. However, Oetker is clearly a man of some taste and culture, using his fortune to buy up such jewels as Brenner's Park Hotel, The Hôtel du Cap, Le Bristol in Paris and the distinguished London art dealer, Colnaghi.

PANERAI

A key figure in Milan society, Paolo Panerai is, thanks to his publishing interests, close to all the major political and business figures in Italy. Born in Milan in 1946, he graduated from the University of Genoa with a degree in jurisprudence. He played professional football as a young man (as an attacking half back for Fiorentina and Fioggia) before becoming a financial journalist and, subsequently, establishing a series of highly respected publications. These include the weekly *Milan Finanza* (1986), the daily *Italia Oggi* (1991), where his inclusion of daily financial reportage on Italy's huge fashion industry has doubled the paper's circulation, and the widely acclaimed *Class*, described as "a mix of *Forbes* and *Town and Country*." Turning his interest increasingly to publishing joint ventures in France and the United States, in 1996 Panerai became a majority shareholder in the prestigious *Global Finance* magazine, based in New York, Hong Kong and London.

But this modest and unassuming man's talents go beyond publishing. A notable *bon viveur*, in 1980 he bought Castellare di Castellina, a Chianti vineyard, where he produces a range of award-winning wines. The *Wine Spectator* recently gave his I Sodi di S.Niccolo 96 points out of 100, while Robert Parker, the American wine guru whose opinion can make or break a company, gave his 100 per cent Cabernet Sauvignon, Coniale, 92 points out of 100, both great testaments to Panerai's ability as a producer. Castellare also produces a range of olive oils, which are used in prominent restaurants throughout the world. A stylish, intelligent and highly creative man, Panerai is an excellent host; invitations to sail with him on board his Swan yacht are particularly treasured. ⋁

PAJARES

One of Europe's most distinguished hoteliers, Ramon Pajares is only the sixth Managing Director of The Savoy Group of Hotels since 1889. A Spanish citizen, his career in the hospitality industry brought him to London by way of the Canary Islands, Germany, Switzerland, Canada and the US. He joined London's Four Seasons Hotel as Executive Assistant Manager when it opened in 1970, becoming General Manager in 1975 and, subsequently, Regional Vice President, Europe of the Four Seasons group.

With a reputation for toughness, albeit cloaked in great charm, when Pajares took over at The Savoy, there was much grumbling amongst the old guard (both staff and guests) that 'things would never be the same.' However, while tightening up what he perceived as lax management practices, he has spearheaded a major investment in improvements to the group's properties and modernisation of its systems. This has resulted in an acknowledged improvement in service.

As Pajares has explained, "The Savoy Group has always epitomised excellence..... But the hotel business and the needs of our guests are constantly evolving, so our job is to make sure that we keep abreast of every change."

Pajares has received a host of awards in recognition of his ability, including, in 1980, the Cruz de Oficial de la Orden del Merito Civil from King Juan Carlos of Spain. In 1988 he became a Freeman of the City of London. With his English wife, Jean, Pajares has three children. He is a keen fan of classical music - a suitably soothing interest for someone who works so hard to make others relax. ◄

PIECH

Ferdinand Piëch is Chief Executive of Europe's leading car maker, Volkswagen, which produces more than four million cars annually through its VW, Audi, Rolls Royce, Lamborghini, Seat and Skoda divisions.

As the grandson of Ferdinand Porsche, founder of Porsche cars and inventor of the VW Beetle, Piëch grew up in the business and holds a significant block of its shares. Born in Vienna in 1937, his mother was Louise Porsche and his father Anton Piëch, chairman of VW during the war. After studying in Austria and Switzerland, Piëch entered the Porsche family business at the age of 26. Later he moved to Audi, where he became CEO in 1988. Having turned Audi around, ridding the company of its middle-class image and making it a competitor of Mercedes and BMW, he was taken onto the VW board in 1992, becoming Chief Executive of the parent company a year later.

One of Piëch's coups, when he headhunted Jose Ignacio Lopez from General Motors, resulted in a fierce legal battle, with GM accusing Lopez of taking confidential   material over to its rival. The matter was finally settled out of court, when VW paid $100 million to GM. Given Piëch's belief that there will be only three or four car companies left in the world in a few years' time, his recent takeover frenzy (Rolls Royce and Lamborghini in 1998) is clear evidence of his determination that VW should be one of them.

PIANO

One of the leading architects of his generation, Renzo Piano is the son of a Genoa builder. Born in 1937, he graduated from the school of architecture, Milan Polytechnic, in 1964. During his studies he worked under the design guidance of Franco Albini and, when he wasn't at college, gained practical knowledge by working on his father's building sites. From 1965 to 1970 he worked with Louis I. Kahn in Philadelphia and Z.S. Makowsky in London.

His collaboration with Richard Rogers (qv) dates from 1971; their most important work together was the Pompidou Centre in 1973. In 1977 he established a partnership with Peter Rice (Atelier Piano & Rice) and he currently has offices in Genoa, Paris and Berlin, under the name Renzo Piano Building Workshop.

In 1998 Piano won the world's most prestigious architecture award, The Pritzker Prize. He has had over 20 exhibitions of his work, in places as diverse as Australia, Japan, the Netherlands and Israel, and has written over 30 books on architecture. Renzo Piano's recent projects include the breathtaking new airport at Osaka, Japan, for which an island was specially constructed. Although Piano works in a determinedly high-tech idiom, his work has been described as more 'poetic' or 'lyrical' than that of Rogers or Sir Norman Foster (qv), and his 'environmentally balanced' buildings look set to have a seminal influence on the architecture of the next 50 years. ➤

PINAULT

Born in Brittany in 1936, the son of a timber trader, François Pinault left school at 16 to work in the family business. After his father's death Pinault created his own timber business with a family loan of £10,000 and spent most of his early career expanding its distribution network. From these obscure origins Pinault has created a huge business empire extending across three continents. The French newspapers have estimated that he is personally worth at least £1.2 billion and an American magazine recently suggested that he is the world's 82nd richest person.

Commentators marvel at his shrewdness. In 1973, for instance, he sold 80 per cent of one of his businesses for Fr30 million, only to buy it back two years later for a mere Fr5 million. That Fr25 million profit was the plank on which this tall, blond 63 year-old built his way to huge riches in the 1980s. He is still as acquisitive as ever, spending much of his working day in the search for 'good buys', while his team of executives tend to the day-to-day affairs of his holding company, Artémis, which includes, among other prizes, outright ownership of the Château Latour winery, a majority share in auction house Christie's and a controlling interest in FNAC, France's leading chain of book, record and electronic stores.

Pinault has had close links with France's most prominent politicians for at least two decades; when Jacques Chirac moved into the Elysée Palace commentators speculated that Pinault would be one of the few people with access to his hotline number.

Pinault has three children from his first marriage, the eldest of whom, François-Henri Pinault, is being groomed as the next head of Artémis. He also has a step-child, the daughter of his second wife Maryvonne from her first marriage. While his chief leisure pursuits are walking and cycling, Pinault clearly also has a taste for the good life; immaculately tailored and a famously good host, he is also a noted collector of French fine art and furniture and of contemporary American art, owning work by Rothko, Rauschenberg and Jasper Johns. His impressive collection of sculpture includes Picasso's *A Seated Woman* and Henry Moore's *Two Forms*.

PININFARINA

Europe's most renowned car designer, Sergio Pininfarina was born in Turin in 1926 and educated in the UK and the US. After gaining a degree in mechanical engineering from Turin Polytechnic, to which he returned as Professor of Car Design in the 1970s, he joined Carrozzeria Pinin Farina, the firm which had been founded by his father, Battista. He became Managing Director in 1961 and, on his father's death in 1966, took over as Chairman.

Under his leadership the Pininfarina Group has enjoyed an enormous increase in technical and production development; some 30,000 car bodies are now produced each year by the company in its factories in Italy and Germany. Many of Pininfarina's designs for cars are modern classics. Great names like Ferrari, Alfa Romeo and Fiat, as well as Cadillac (the Allanté) and Peugeot all owe a huge debt to this extrodinarily innovative designer. His contribution to the motor industry has been recognised by innumerable awards, including France's Chevalier de la Légion d'Honneur and Italy's Cavaliere del Lavoro.

The father of three adult children, Pininfarina is a keen golfer and sailor in his spare time and lives with his wife in Turin. A committed pro-European, from 1979 to 1988 he was a member of the European Parliament (liberal and democratic group) and, from 1989 to 1994, a board member of the Association for Monetary Union of Europe. ⋀

PISCHETSRIEDER

One of the great ironies of the traditionally inward-looking British motor industry is the fact that a German is spearheading its revival. That man is Bernd Pischetsrieder, Chairman of BMW, which bought Rover Cars. The purchase, coupled with its ongoing interest in Rolls Royce (the subject of a complex agreement with new owner, VW) and huge investment in its British plants, has reinvigorated the British car industry.

This most cosmopolitan man, who speaks perfect English with a South African accent, a legacy of his time as the head of BMW's African operations, is known as a people person.

His father, the head of a successful advertising agency, ensured that his son "did not have to go without anything", as he revealed recently. But this pampering did nothing to blunt the young man's ambition, as his ascent to the top of BMW illustrates. He started his career as a production planning engineer at BMW after studying mechanical engineering at Munich Technical University. Within a few years he had become Director of Operations at the company's Dingolfing factory. His African sojourn (1982-'85) was followed by further promotions - first to Head of Quality Assurance, then Head of Technical Planning, culminating in his appointment, in 1991, to the BMW board. He became Chairman of the Board of Management in 1993. His achievements are particularly impressive when you consider that he has just turned 50.

Pischetsrieder is a remarkably approachable man. Straightforward, polite and energetic, he works a 16-hour day. He is married with two grown-up children and, to relax, he enjoys snowboarding, skiing and climbing. ⋀

POLKE

No other German artist currently fetches such high prices on the international art market. Sigmar Polke's importance as an artist lies in his continuation of Joseph Bueys' artistic heritage and in his profound influence on other artists of his generation. In the Sixties he created German pop art, calling it 'capitalist realism.' Since then Polke has painted mainly abstract works, using prefabricated materials, such as textiles and polyester tiles. He has also experimented with a material that reacts visibly to room humidity and with radioactive stones.

PUIG

A new generation has taken over at Spain's most successful fashion and cosmetics company. One of the few family-owned businesses remaining at the top of the luxury goods industry, Puig has maintained its position through shrewd marketing, competent management and a robust, hands-on style which has seen three generations of the family at its helm. Mariano Puig Sr, Chief Executive for three decades, stepped down last year to allow a new team (two sons, Marc and Mariano Jr, a cousin and an outsider) to embark on an ambitious expansion programme which will, if all goes according to plan, see the company's sales of $750 million soar to $1.3 billion by the year 2006. A little optimistic? Time will tell – but one thing is certain: the new generation is determined to build on its predecessors' success.

While perfume brands like Agua Brava, which have traditionally enjoyed huge success in their home market, continue to account for an impressive proportion of Puig's revenue, further investment in fragrance-to-fashion brands is seen as a key element in the strategy to boost sales. Close friends with the Spanish Royal Family - although they refuse to discuss that relationship publicly - the family sails with King Juan Carlos (qv) and his children in the Copa del Rey in Palma de Majorca. Both keen sailors and waterskiers (their father was once a champion at the latter sport) Marc and Mariano Jr maintain close ties with the rest of their family. They get together frequently at Les Ginesteres, the family home, which houses their impressive collection of Catalan art. The house - at Vila Sal, in the hills north of Barcelona - was built by their father. ∀

RAUSING

There was a time when the names Hans and Gad Rausing were almost inseparable. But in 1995 the brothers parted ways (if only financially) when Hans, 72, sold his stake in their business to his brother for an estimated $4.5 billion. Tetra Laval, the business which was started by their father in Sweden some 50 years ago, has been built up by his sons.

Since delivering its first liquid food packaging in 1952, it has developed various new types of container, of which the Tetrapak milk carton has become familiar throughout the world. Tetra Laval is now the world's biggest packaging group, with annual revenues of around 55 billion Swedish crowns.

The Rausings came to Britain as tax exiles in the early 1980s. Notoriously secretive, they rarely give interviews although we do know that they have donated at least £10 million to various charities and have set up two vehicles to further their philanthropic activities, the Nikeno Trust and the Ruben & Elizabeth Rausing Trust. In the early 1990s the brothers gave £2.5 million to fund the construction of a new mathematics centre at Cambridge University. Recently, a Rausing family member was reported to have spent almost £20 million buying one of London's most expensive houses.

Dr Hans Rausing has honorary doctorates from the Royal Institute of Technology in Stockholm and the Stockholm School of Economics. He is married to Marit Norrby, and they have one son and two daughters. Hans has traditionally been the face of the company but, having taken a back seat since the sale of his interest, his even more shy and retiring brother Gad is taking an increasingly public role.

REZA

Yasmina Reza has never had much time for intermissions. Given the breathtaking speed of her rise to prominence as a leading European dramatist, this hardly seems surprising. *Art*, her brilliantly witty 90-minute (intermission-free) reflection on the destruction of friendship, has catapulted her into the upper echelons of her profession. The young French writer, whose mother was Hungarian and father a Russian Jew, wrote the play in 1993. Its opening premise, that a character called Serge has paid a fortune for an all-white painting, is emblematic, it seems, of the 1990s. With society's increasing acceptance of the superficial, the distinction between worth and worthless seems ever murkier.

The attractive and vivacious Reza came to writing after a short, undistinguished career as an actress. She has clearly found her feet. *Art* opened in 1994 in Paris, where the foreign rights were quickly snapped up by actor Sean Connery on the prompting of his wife, Micheline. It has since played to packed houses in 20 languages world wide. Reza has written two more plays since then and, last year, published a series of sketches about her friends called *Hammerklavier*. A winning portrait of the sophisticated milieu which Reza inhabits, it has none of the self indulgence which often surfaces in follow-up memoirs.

ROBINSON

Donegal-based Gerry Robinson's curriculum vitae is a clear riposte to those who allege that Britain will never be classless. After a brief stint as a seminarian, Robinson began his career in 1965 as an accountant in Lesney Products, manufacturers of matchbox toys. Climbing the corporate ladder and moving to London, he got his first really big break in 1980, when he was appointed Finance Director of Grand Metropolitan's UK Coca-Cola business. Within two years he had become its Managing Director. Robinson, however, was restless. In 1983 he became Chief Executive of the Contract Services division at Grand Metropolitan. Four years later he led the UK's then-largest management buy-out, with the £163 million purchase of the division, subsequently renamed the Compass Group.

In 1991 he joined Granada as Chief Executive, taking over as Chairman in 1996. His appointment prompted angry letters to *The Times* from distinguished film producers, wringing their hands in horror at the thought of a carpenter's son controlling a company which produced some of the most intellectually challenging documentaries on television. But, in time, even these critics began to respect Robinson's ability. Meanwhile, the City of London saw him as Britain's rising financial star. In a poll of analysts from the top international financial institutions, Robinson was named as the man most people would like to have lunch with. His epic takeover battle with Forte plc (which included a majority stake in the prestigious Savoy group of hotels) was tagged as one of the great coups of the 90s. It pitted working class Robinson against privileged public schoolboy Rocco Forte, scion of the Forte family. The bid was launched on a bank holiday, while the hapless Forte was shooting partridge on the Yorkshire moors. (Forte, however recovered strongly from a disastrous start and emerged from the battle with his dignity, if not his company, intact.)

Robinson, an avuncular, laid-back Irishman is typically modest about his achievements and that, perhaps, is the key to his success. His rise, against the odds - though with apparent ease - to the highest echelons of British society has been crowned by his Chairmanship of both BSkyB and The Arts Council. Robinson's leisure activities include music, particularly opera, painting, skiing and golf. ⋀

ROBINSON

After seven years as President of the Republic of Ireland, liberal lawyer and former Harvard Law School lecturer, Mary Robinson, resigned to become Commissioner for Human Rights at the United Nations.

Articulate, highly intelligent and multi-lingual, Robinson had been an outstanding Irish President. A great networker, she was hailed as a feminist icon and picked up an impressive array of honorary degrees and other intellectual accolades during her term. She moderated her left-liberal political bias during her presidency and achieved an unprecedented 95 per cent popularity rating. Mrs Robinson was the first Head of State to visit Rwanda in the aftermath of the genocide there and, during her Presidency, placed special emphasis on the needs of developing countries, linking the history of the Irish Famine to today's poverty issues, thus creating a bridge between developed and developing countries. But in her new role, although she is hugely committed to problems of famine and disease in Africa, initial reports indicate that Robinson is struggling with both the UN bureaucracy and the notoriously endemic corruption of certain African governments.

Whether this tough lawyer will succeed where others have failed is a matter of speculation, but it certainly won't be for the lack of commitment and steely determination. She has an outstanding background in the area of human rights, with special expertise in Constitutional and European Human Rights Law. Born in 1944 in County Mayo, Ireland, Mrs Robinson was educated at Trinity College, Dublin, where she later served as Professor of Constitutional and Criminal Law. With her art historian husband, Nick, she has three children, the eldest of whom, Tessa, recently qualified as a barrister in Ireland. ➤

ROGERS

Lord Rogers of Riverside, as he became on his elevation to the peerage in 1997, has, together with Norman Foster (qv), put contemporary British architecture on the world map. His work is visionary and often controversial; the Pompidou Centre in Paris, created with his friend and partner, Renzo Piano, and the Lloyds building in London are the best known. Rogers also has the somewhat unenviable task of designing the beleaguered Millennium Dome in Greenwich, London.

He is quintessentially European, (his family moved to England from Florence) - from his relaxed style of dressing, to his legendary sex appeal, which appears not to be fading with age. He is married to Ruthie Rogers, co-founder of the River Café, which evolved from being her husband's office canteen to one of London's best restaurants. Food is an abiding obsession with both and they entertain frequently at their villa in Tuscany and home in Chelsea - a spectacular double-height loft-style space carved out of two adjoining stucco-fronted houses.

Rogers has close links with the UK's major arts and public organisations. He has been Chairman of the Tate Gallery, Deputy Chairman of The Arts Council and is Chairman of the Architecture Foundation. He has published and lectured widely and is passionate about cities, campaigning vigorously for their design to be put at the heart of the public and political agenda.

ST. LAURENT

One of the 20th century's most influential fashion designers, Yves Saint Laurent was born in Algeria in 1936. Coming to Paris as a teenager, he showed some of his drawings to Michel de Brunhoff, director of *Vogue*, who selected several of them for his magazine. De Brunhoff subsequently introduced the young man to Christian Dior, for whom he worked until the latter's death in 1957, when he took over from his mentor as Head Designer. His first collection, the *Ligne Trapèze*, was a resounding success.

In 1958 he met Pierre Bergé, who is, to this day, his business partner and closest confidant. Three years later they opened their own fashion house, presenting their first collection in September 1962. Since then, Saint Laurent has experimented with a tremendous array of styles. Many ideas which are now part of the common fashion vocabulary - the military and naval looks, the Russian collection, the Mondrians, the ethnic look, and, perhaps most memorably, *le smoking* - were pioneered by him. Unlike many couture houses, whose main business is selling perfume rather than clothes, Saint Laurent continues to exert an enormous influence on fashion and, just as importantly, his *haute couture* clothes are worn by real women, rather than simply being splashed across the front pages of newspapers.

But, even as his star shone ever brighter, Saint Laurent's always delicate health seemed to be getting worse. Although he still enjoys subsidiary pleasures like designing stage settings and costumes for ballets, shows and plays, he now makes few public appearances, preferring to let his personality speak through his eternally elegant clothes.

In 1998 Saint Laurent retired from designing ready-to-wear to concentrate on *haute couture*. Nevertheless, it was a busy year for him. He opened a room in London's National Gallery devoted to 17th century French art, which he had restored at a personal cost of around a million pounds. And he masterminded a show of 300 of his designs at the Stade de France for the finale of the World Cup.

SCHREMPP

Jurgen Schrempp is Co-Chairman and Co-Chief Executive of Daimler-Chrysler, the huge company created by the ongoing merger of Chrysler and Daimler-Benz. What was extraordinary about the deal was not only its scale - it is the largest industrial merger ever - but the fact that it was a German powerhouse enveloping an American one. Times have changed. Europe is bigger and stronger than it used to be and America now knows it.

Schrempp is a man made for the task: tough, ruthlessly ambitious and someone who likes to be in absolute charge. He started working as an apprentice in his home town of Freiburg 30 years ago and scaled the corporate ladder with admirable gusto, joining the board of Daimler-Benz in 1989. Schrempp has turned the company into a leaner, more productive organisation by introducing many of the values he absorbed while working in the United States in the 1980s, running Daimler-Benz's Euclid heavy truck division. A no-nonsense, blunt-talking executive, he is renowned for his unwavering attention to detail, qualities which served him well in the run up to the merger with Chrysler. Under Schrempp, Daimler-Benz was one of the first European companies to present its end-of-year figures in full compliance with American accounting standards. His justification for what seemed, at the time, like unnecessarily fastidious book-keeping was simple enough - he was studiously preparing for the company's listing on the New York Stock Exchange.

Known for his distinctive taste in spectacles, Jurgen Schrempp will also, before long, become known as the highest paid executive in German industry. If the merger is finalised, he is likely to receive a hefty whack of between $10 million and $20 million. Ⱥ

SCHUMACHER

Born in 1969 in Kerpin-Manheim, a working-class town near Cologne, the sometimes controversial but always exciting Michael Schumacher has been the pre-eminent driver in Formula 1 for the last four years.

At the age of four he was given a go-kart powered by an old lawn-mower engine by his father. The boy's passion soon became an obsession, fed by the initiative of the elder Schumacher, whose mechanical ability led him to work part-time repairing other go-karts at the local track. In 1980 he traveled to Nivelles, Belgium, for the World Karting Championship and saw, for the first time, the legendary Ayrton Senna, who made a huge impression on him. Four years later Schumacher won the German Junior Championship and the European Karting Championship came his way in 1987. Schumacher then made the transition to Formula Ford, winning nine out of ten rounds in his first full year competing in the series. The following year he joined the Mercedes junior team and, under the watchful eyes of Jochen Neerspasch and Jochen Maas, was schooled in the art of race-car driving. During this period Schumacher learned much of what would later become his trademark smoothness on the track.

When Jordan's Formula 1 driver Bertrand Gachot landed himself in jail Schumacher was given a test with the Irish team. Jordan wanted to sign the young driver to a three-year contract but Schumacher's advisors urged caution. A temporary deal was done and he made a brilliant debut, qualifying ahead of his more experienced teammate. The following year he won his first race at Spa in Belgium. In 1994 he became World Champion with Benetton and, in 1995, after an arduous battle with Damon Hill, became the youngest double champion ever. More recently Schumacher has spearheaded Ferrari's revival.

Considered the most courageous and talented driver in the wet, he has been dubbed the *rainmeister* by his legions of fans. Will he go down in history as one of the very best? Only time will tell. Ⅴ

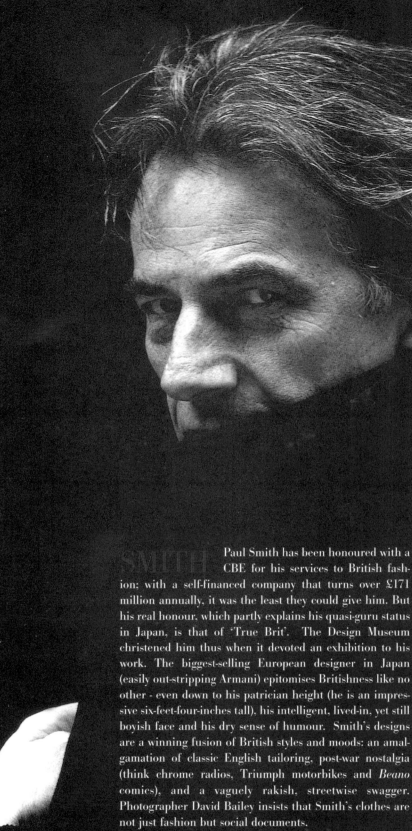

SMITH

Paul Smith has been honoured with a CBE for his services to British fashion; with a self-financed company that turns over £171 million annually, it was the least they could give him. But his real honour, which partly explains his quasi-guru status in Japan, is that of 'True Brit'. The Design Museum christened him thus when it devoted an exhibition to his work. The biggest-selling European designer in Japan (easily out-stripping Armani) epitomises Britishness like no other - even down to his patrician height (he is an impressive six-feet-four-inches tall), his intelligent, lived-in, yet still boyish face and his dry sense of humour. Smith's designs are a winning fusion of British styles and moods: an amalgamation of classic English tailoring, post-war nostalgia (think chrome radios, Triumph motorbikes and *Beano* comics), and a vaguely rakish, streetwise swagger. Photographer David Bailey insists that Smith's clothes are not just fashion but social documents.

Paul Smith's website exploits and builds on his iconic status: here you will find lists of Paul's ten favourite restaurants and Paul's five favourite films. Signs of a rampant ego? Not in Smith's case. Born in Nottingham where his company is still based, he remains very much "a Northern lad who happened to do rather well." A cycling fanatic, when he's not riding the seven miles to work every morning, Smith drives a Bristol; and he eschews "proper literature" in favour of comic-strip character, Denis the Menace. He lives in London's Holland Park and in Tuscany, with his companion of 25 years, Pauline Denyer.

SMURFIT

Michael Smurfit's company, Jefferson Smurfit, the world's largest producer of corrugated packaging and container board, operates in more than 20 countries and has earned Smurfit and his family an estimated fortune of almost £250 million.

Proudly Irish, Smurfit nevertheless comes from 'North of England stock' (he was born in Lancashire), a fact which he readily admits has had an enormous influence on the way he has done business over 40 years. Integrity, loyalty, ability, trust, motivation - these key values have served him well in a career which has seen him turn the fledgling Irish shoebox maker - founded by his father - into a global corporation. Smurfit was appointed Joint Managing Director of the company in 1966. Eleven years later he became Chairman and Chief Executive, a position he has occupied ever since.

His interests include golf (he is a member of eight exclusive clubs in four countries), tennis, riding and horse racing. The latter has brought him success on race tracks across the world. He owns *Vintage Crop*, the Dermot Weld-trained horse which won the Melbourne Cup at odds of 16-1 in 1994. He is also an avid art collector, particularly of Irish art, with one of the largest collections of Jack B. Yeats' paintings in private hands.

Twice-married, 61 year-old Smurfit is based in Monaco, where he is the honorary Irish Consul. His talent for hospitality is clearly evident at his Kildare Hotel and Country Club, which he uses as a base when working in Ireland and which is hotly tipped to host the Ryder Cup in 2005. Smurfit's philanthropic endeavours include donations to an impressive array of concerns, most notably education. The Michael Smurfit Graduate School of Business, at University College Dublin, is one of Europe's largest. Λ

SOROS

George Soros needs little introduction. He is the financial genius who made a fortune by anticipating the fall of the pound and its departure from the Exchange Rate Mechanism in 1992. Dubbed "the man who broke the Bank of England," he is known to have made at least $1 billion on that one extraordinarily skilful gamble. Furthermore, he recently sent stock market shares in Russia tumbling when he announced that, if the rouble was not devalued, the Russian economy would crumble. But he is much more than a man with a nose for money and a good hunch.

Born into a Jewish family in Budapest in 1930, Soros emigrated to England in 1947, where he studied at the London School of Economics. Here, he came into contact with the philosopher Karl Popper, who was to have a profound influence on his thinking and, in particular, his philanthropic work later in life. By the mid-1950s, Soros had moved to the US where he founded a highly successful international investment fund.

Soros campaigns fervently for political and economic freedom in repressed countries, with a particular interest in Eastern Europe. He funds a network of foundations that operate in 31 countries throughout Eastern and Central Europe, the former Soviet Union, Central Eurasia, South Africa, Haiti, Guatemala and the United States, which are dedicated to building and maintaining the infrastructure and institutions of an open society. In one year alone, his foundation spent around $362 million. In 1995, the University of Bologna, Italy, awarded Soros its highest honour, the Laurea Honoris Causa, in recognition of his efforts to promote open societies throughout the world.

Soros is Chairman of Soros Fund Management, a private investment management firm, which is principal adviser to the Quantum Group of Funds. The Quantum Fund NV has had the best performance record of any investment fund in the world in its 28-year history. ➤

STARCK

The term 'design guru' was surely invented for Philippe Starck. At 49, the French designer and full-time *enfant terrible* induces a hushed reverence from art students and an eager parting of cash from everyone from high-street shoppers to five-star hotel groups. His best-known contributions to 20th century life include his Juicy Salif lemon squeezer, those sweetly cartoon-like little plastic lamps, a mail-order house for self assembly furniture and some rather spectacular room interiors. No one who has walked into The Paramount or The Royalton in New York, or Felix restaurant at the Peninsula in Hong Kong, can forget the impact of his organic, surreal, surprise-packed visions. Starck deserves to be called a genius because he has changed the way we look at things.

Starck has four homes - three in France and a houseboat off Ibiza. The important thing about an object, he says, "is the joy [it] gives to the person using it." It is therefore not entirely surprising that he insists on certain details and objects being identical in all his homes: taps, towels, toothbrushes, books, CDs, scent (Dyptique, as a matter of fact). His beds must all be the same height (67cm) and they must face south.

He also can't survive, apparently, without indestructible tracing paper and a pack of 28 Japanese pencils. Starck lives with his fiancée Patricia Bailer and has two children, a daughter, Ara, and a son, Oa. ◄

STOPPARD

One of Britain's finest living playwrights, Tom Stoppard was born in Czechoslovakia in 1937 and spent much of his formative years travelling the globe. He wrote his first play, *Enter a Free Man*, while working as a journalist in the English provinces, but it was the first of his plays to be staged, *Rosencrantz and Guildenstern Are Dead*, a verbal tour de force, that established his reputation. Thirty years later, he has a remarkable body of work behind him and continues to produce plays, for both radio and stage, as well as screen plays, with apparent ease.

Among his more notable achievements are the 1995 New York Drama Critics' Circle Award for *Arcadia*, three Tony Awards, seven Evening Standard Awards and the Prix D'Or at the Venice Film Festival for his film version of *Rosencrantz and Guildenstern Are Dead*. He has been married twice (his second wife was Dr Miriam Stoppard, the forceful writer and broadcaster) and lives in London. Stoppard is regularly described in the British press as one of the most intelligent men in the country and his work rate at the time of writing (he was working on a play and three screenplay adaptations) certainly suggests as much.

His work brims with intellectual *joie de vivre*, as his latest play, *The Invention of Love*, brilliantly illustrates. As one reviewer concluded, "The sheer richness of Stoppard's dramatic imagination leaves you gasping." He was knighted in 1997 and, last year, the French government made him an Officier de l'Ordre des Arts et des Lettres. ⋎

SÜSKIND

Being famous is one thing but Patrick Süskind, author of the fantastically successful book *Perfume*, is more. He has mythical status in Munich, where he lives, sometimes contributing witty but anonymous commentaries to the local paper *Suddeutsche Zeitung* and writing screen plays. But, so far at least, he is a one-book-wonderboy. But what a wonder: his lust-and-crime story, telling the life and fate of an overly sensual genius, is already a contemporary classic.

SUTHERLAND

Rumour has it that the only opposition among the equity partners of Goldman Sachs to the appointment of an outside Chairman came from a few somewhat effete Americans, who were horrified that Peter Sutherland insisted, as part of the deal, that he could continue to smoke his beloved Havana cigars. This highly regarded former EC Commissioner is a charming, articulate, Jesuit-educated barrister who, in his earlier days, was a formidable front-row forward with Landsdowne Rugby Football Club in Dublin.

Born in Ireland in 1946, Sutherland was admitted to the Irish Bar (Kings' Inns), the English Bar (Middle Temple) and the New York Bar. In a glittering career he has served variously as Attorney General of Ireland, Director General of the World Trade Organisation, and on the boards of Investor A.B., ABB-Asea Brown Boveri Ltd and LM Ericsson. He has received honorary doctorates from nine universities in Europe and the United States.

Well-read and a keen sportsman - he is a member of Fitzwilliam, the exclusive Irish tennis club - Sutherland and his elegant Spanish wife have three children and live in Dublin and London. With the impending flotation of Goldman Sachs and the birth to of BP Amoco (he is chairman of both companies), Peter Sutherland joins the ranks of the seriously rich. But Irish commentators remain convinced that the pull of politics is never far away for Sutherland and a return to Strasbourg or even a further foray into Irish domestic politics, can never be ruled out. ➤

TAVENER

John Tavener sprang into the public consciousness as the composer of the haunting piece that brought to a close the funeral of Diana, Princess of Wales. But his reputation in the musical world had been established long before that day.

Born in London in 1944, he showed his talent at an early age, composing his first work at the age of three. Tavener has always shown an originality of concept and an intensely personal idiom - described as "holy minimalist" - which make his voice easily distinguishable from those of his contemporaries. Over the years the contemplative side of his nature has led him in a more spiritual direction and his commitment to the Greek Orthodox Church, which he joined in 1977, is now evident in all his work.

An unusually tall man, Bentley-driving Tavener divides his time between a large house in Sussex and a small Greek island. Combined with his reflective spirit and eccentric dress sense (don't be surprised if you meet him in an Armani scarf and tatty green plimsolls) Tavener has an engaging humour, which is never far from the surface.

His major pieces over the last decade include *The Akathist*, which was given a standing ovation in a packed Westminster Abbey at its première in 1988, and two large-scale choral and orchestral works, *Resurrection* and *We Shall See Him As He Is*.

THIELEMANN

He is German. That is what the young conductor's critics say. Born in Berlin, Thielemann loves the bombastic depth in music. This he celebrates when he plays Wagner, but also Schoenberg, Beethoven and Strauss. He translates his musical passion into the sound he conjures from his orchestra at the Deutsche Opera in Berlin, which he has made Germany's most outstanding opera house. A bachelor, Thielemann is perhaps the only conductor in Europe who stands in the same tradition as Furtwangler and Karajan.

THURN UND TAXIS

Germany's most glamorous woman has also proved a natural genius in business. When she married the renowned practical joker, Prince Johannes, in 1980, she exploded into society with her extravagant punk hairdos and Paco Rabanne evening dresses. To *W* and *Vanity Fair* magazines she was simply 'Princess TNT'. But her life changed drastically after the death of her husband in 1990. Despite having never worked in business, she looked at the family's diverse concerns and decided, with not much more than common sense, that the TNT empire held more prestigious objects than profitable ones. She took private lessons in micro and macro-economics, sought advisors (including Swatch inventor Nicolas Hayek), fired her board of directors, sold off unprofitable companies (the private bank, brewery and some industrial interests) and reduced the business to its core: vast forests all over southern Germany, real estate and other conservative investments. Her two daughters, Maria-Theresia and Elisabeth, 17 and 16 respectively, are raw diamonds on the circuit of the European jeunesse dorée and their brother, 15 year-old Prince Albert, will one day inherit a thriving family business. ⋎

THYSSEN-BORNEMISZA

Baron Hans-Heinrich (Heini) Thyssen-Bornemisza has amassed one of the greatest art collections in the world today. His decision, made in 1993 at the behest of his Spanish wife, Carmen Cervera (whom he married in 1985), to allow the Kingdom of Spain to acquire the collection, safeguards the future of a priceless cultural artefact for future generations of art lovers.

Born in Holland in 1921, the baron is the son of a German industrialist father and aristocratic Hungarian mother. His father made a series of cunning moves in the world of high finance and, having revived the Thyssen family fortunes, which had originated in the German industrial heartland, promptly set about assembling the great collection of Old Masters which is now the core of the Thyssen collection. After completing his university studies in Switzerland, Hans-Heinrich dedicated his life to expanding and enriching his father's collection.

A keen skier, Thyssen is a Life Member of the Eagle Club in Gstaad and also of the Knickerbocker Club, New York, and the World Wildlife Fund. He is an Emeritus member of the Trustees Council of the National Gallery of Art, Washington D.C., and a member of the Sotheby's Holdings Advisory Board. He maintains homes in Madrid, London and Lugano. ⋏

TRAPANI

The driving force behind Bulgari, Francesco Trapani, is a fourth-generation descendant of the company's founder Sotirios Boulgaris, who emigrated from Greece to Rome in 1884. His nomination as head of the company came in 1984, at the time when one of the founder's grandsons, Gianni Bulgari, parted company with his two brothers, Paolo and Nicola, prompting them to ask their nephew, Trapani, to take over.

The appointment may have raised eyebrows in some quarters; neither of Trapani's parents had been involved in the company (his mother was a Bulgari, his father a doctor) and he himself, still only 27 years-old, had been working there for just three years. While, to his credit, Trapani has acknowledged publicly that his inexperience was a disadvantage in the early days, his first-class degrees in commerce and economics from Naples University have clearly stood him in good stead. He has turned what was a small (albeit highly prestigious) family business into a high-profile global group - the third-largest jewellery firm in the world - with 43 per cent of the shares in public hands, a burgeoning asset base and huge potential for expansion. A confident and affable man, renowned as a good host and a snappy dresser, Trapani is described by company insiders as serious and tough, yet great fun to work with.

Now 41, Trapani lives unostentatiously in the Piazza Navona, in the heart of Rome, with his wife, Mariangela, a former model, and their two small children. Apart from family weekends at his country house and a sailing holiday each August, Trapani has little care for the trappings of success or the wealth that his personal 5 per cent shareholding provides. He describes his hobbies simply as "my work and my family."

WAGNER

The grandson of composer Richard Wagner presides over his grandfather's musical heritage in a way that even his enemies have to admire. And they are numerous, including even his own family, which is fighting bitterly over who will succeed him when his contract as Director of the Bayreuth Festival ends only on his death.

The opera festival, which he and his wife Gudrun manage, is artistically and financially the soundest in the world; each year he could sell 500,000 tickets - but only 50,000 are available. Wagner is accused of having too little enthusiasm for innovation or experiment but, when new productions do come to Bayreuth, the musical world holds its breath. Whatever Wagner's perceived faults, stars such as Barenboim, Levine and the greatest orchestral musicians happily give up their summer holidays to play for him, even though he pays them far less than any other opera house.

WERTHEIMER

Alain Wertheimer is the Chairman of Chanel, the company which was founded by Gabrielle 'Coco' Chanel in the early years of the century. Since 1924 it has been in the hands of the Wertheimer family, who used the proceeds from its ownership of both the Chanel perfume brands and the middle-of-the-road Bourjois cosmetics company to buy the fashion house. Although the group is notoriously reticent about releasing figures, it is known to achieve annual sales in excess of $1.8 billion for its perfume sector alone, with Chanel No.5, launched in 1921, commanding almost 5 per cent of the world market share.

Wertheimer, who took over the company from his father in the 70s, is renowned as a hard worker, a firm but fair boss and a fan of fine wine. This last interest manifested itself most prominently with his recent purchase of Château Rauzan-Segla, which produces a superb second-growth claret. Commentators have speculated that this purchase may signal a bid to diversify. But those who know Wertheimer well are less sure. "Diversification?" said one. "That is an ugly word for such a worthy indulgence." A possible symptom of Wertheimer's anglophilia (he lived in London for several years) is his purchase, during the late 1990s, of British firms, Tanner Krolle and Holland & Holland, both of which are being built into leading luxury brands.

WALLENBERG

This pre-eminent financial dynasty is renowned as a secretive and conservative organisation with very long tentacles. So it came as a surprise to seasoned Wallenberg watchers when someone from outside the family was appointed, in 1997, as the head of Investor, the family's chief holding company. But Peter Barnevik, previously chief executive of Asea Brown Boveri (itself a Wallenberg company) enjoys only a certain amount of control. Much of the real power apparently remains in the hands of Jakob and Marcus, the son and nephew respectively of Peter Wallenberg, patriarch and chief executive of Investor for 15 years, until he handed over the reins to Barnevik.

The Wallenberg empire has traditionally been concentrated in banking, pharmaceuticals, airlines, automobiles, television and mining. Among the companies in which it has a substantial holding are S-E Banken, Saab, Scania Trucks, TV4 television station, SAS airline and Electrolux.

Jakob Wallenberg's title is Managing Director of S-E Banken, and Marcus, his first cousin, is Deputy Chief Executive and Chief Financial Officer of Investor. Over the past few years the two men, who are both 42, have established themselves as major players in the family "sphere", as the Wallenbergs prefer to call their empire, by winning the confidence of the investment community through a series of shrewd decisions. Neither of the men are in any way reckless, but they have both stressed the importance of grasping the opportunities presented by emerging industries. Ericsson, the hugely successful mobile phone manufacturer, is perhaps the most obvious example of the young Wallenbergs' acumen. Having bought into the company when it was a fledgling operator, they are now poised to make yet another fortune from their small, initial investment.

INDEX I

LISTING BY ALPHABET

ALPHABETICAL INDEX

PLEASE NOTE:
Entries which begin with a definite article (*The, Le, La, Il, El, Der, Die* etc.) appear under the first letter of the name proper, as do entries which begin with initials.

Hotels and Restaurants normally appear under the first letter of the name proper, except in a few cases where the name cannot stand alone. (For example, Hôtel du Cap is listed under 'H', whereas the Hotel Imperial and the Hotel Cala di Volpe are listed under 'I' and 'C' respectively.)

Wine châteaux and domaines are listed under the name proper; however, entries such as hotels or properties whose name begins with Château or Domaine are listed under 'C' or 'D' respectively.

PREVIOUS PAGE: *Classic Stationery from Smythson.*

INDEX I

INDEX I

INDEX II

LISTING BY COUNTRY

INDEX BY COUNTRY

PLEASE NOTE:

Entries which begin with a definite article (*The, Le, La, Il, El, Der, Die etc.*) appear under the first letter of the name proper, as do entries which begin with initials.

Hotels and Restaurants normally appear under the first letter of the name proper, except in a few cases where the name cannot stand alone. (For example, Hôtel du Cap is listed under 'H', whereas the Hotel Imperial and the Hotel Cala di Volpe are listed under 'I' and 'C' respectively.)

Wine châteaux and domaines are listed under the name proper; however, entries such as hotels or properties whose name begins with Château or Domaine are listed under 'C' or 'D' respectively.

(RS) and (BKS) denotes entries which appear in the Rising Stars and Best Kept Secrets listings respectively. The category of each entry appears in block letters after its index listing.

PREVIOUS PAGE: 24 *Opera from Riva.*

INDEX II

INDEX II

INDEX II

AEROLEASING

Europe's finest fleet of business jets.
Ready whenever you are.

Aeroleasing can take you practically anywhere in the world. With matchless safety and convenience.
In Europe's largest fleet of advanced aircraft devoted exclusively to custom air service.
With Aeroleasing you're in charge. You decide when to take off, where to land. You save precious hours, even days.
Superb on board and on-the-ground services assure your every comfort. You can be still more creative, more efficient.
In your position, can you afford to settle for less?

One Swiss telephone number for superb world-wide service.

AEROLEASING

GENEVA · P.O.Box 36 · 1215 Geneva 15 Airport, Switzerland
Tel.: +41 (22) 717 00 00 · Fax: +41 (22) 717 00 07 · http://www.aeroleasing.ch

INDEX III

LISTING BY PRODUCT CATEGORY

INDEX BY PRODUCT CATEGORY

PLEASE NOTE:

Entries which begin with a definite article (*The, Le, La, Il, El, Der, Die etc.*) appear under the first letter of the name proper, as do entries which begin with initials.

Hotels and Restaurants normally appear under the first letter of the name proper, except in a few cases where the name cannot stand alone. (For example, Hôtel du Cap is listed under 'H', whereas the Hotel Imperial and the Hotel Cala di Volpe are listed under 'I' and 'C' respectively.)

Wine châteaux and domaines are listed under the name proper; however, entries such as hotels or properties whose name begins with Château or Domaine are listed under 'C' or 'D' respectively.

(RS) and (BKS) denotes entries which appear in the Rising Stars and Best Kept Secrets listings respectively.

PREVIOUS PAGE: *Restaurant Patrick Guilbaud, Dublin.*

INDEX III

INDEX III

Europe's Elite 1000

The Ultimate List
1999

PUBLISHER
Kevin Kelly
Associate Publisher: Patricia McEntee

EDITOR
Sandra Lane
Managing Editor: Lynda Weatherhead
Associate Editor: Jason Cooke

Editor, France: Nicola Mitchell
Editor, Germany: Caroline Gräfin zu Waldburg-Wolfegg
Editor, Italy: Giulia Pessani
Editor, Art & Antiques: Anna Somers Cocks
Contributing Editor: Caroline Kellett
Contributing Editor: Trevor White

ART EDITOR
Phyl Clarke
Picture Editor: Nicole Bettelley
Contributing Designers: Pat Moroney, Conor Swanton

CONTRIBUTING WRITERS & RESEARCHERS
The Duchess of Abercorn, Kari Ardissone, Charles Benson, Raymond Blake,
Radha Burgess, Steve Carr, Rosie Clayton Stancer, Nessrin Gräfin zu Königsegg,
Barbara Gurawska, Jeremy Jones, James O'Connell, Ferga O'Neill
Kate Quill, Michèle Reichenbach, Bronwen Riley, Alexander von Schönburg

FEATURE WRITERS
TOM DOAK is President of Renaissance Golf Design Inc, Traverse City, Michigan and the author of *The Confidential Guide to Golf Courses.*
JANE ELLIOTT is a contributor to many leading British and international publications.
ALISTAIR McALPINE: Lord McAlpine is the author of several books and an inveterate collector and traveller. His latest book is *Collecting and Display.*
LUCIA VAN DER POST is the Editor of *How To Spend It,* for the *Financial Times.*
ALEXANDER VON SCHÖNBURG is an author, a contributor to *Die Zeit* and a columnist for *Bunte* and *B.Z.*

PHOTOGRAPHIC CREDITS
David J.Whyte: *Pages 36,37,38,40,42,45*
Renaissance Golf Design: *Pages 35, 37, 38, 39, 40, 42*
Allsport: *Pages 35, 41, 43, 44*
Robert Harding: *Pages 49 (Adam Wolfitt), 50 (Alain Evrard, Ellen Rooney),*
51 (J. Dupont, Roy Rainford), 52 (John Miller), 53 (Simon Harris)
Henry Naim Dallal: *Page 55*
Raghubir Singh: *Page 189*
Givenchy Archives & Christie's France: *Pages 223-231*
People in Pictures: *Page 230*
Christian Coigny for Chopard & Cie. S.A: *Page 233*
Will White: *Page 234*
Jainie Cowham for Nigel Burgess Ltd.: *Page 235*
Berluti: *Page: 241*
Sabine Brauer: *Pages 243-251*
Rex Features: *Pages 253-295 (excluding Biberson page 258,*
di Montezemolo page 267)
Frank Spooner Pictures: *Pages 258, 267*
Clare Bankcroft: *Page 267*

VIVRE · AUCTION HOUSES · CASINOS · CASTLES &
TIC SURGEONS · DOMESTIC EMPLOYMENT AGEN
S · GOLD CLUBS · HAIR & BEAUTY · HOTELS · JEWEL
TY ORGANISERS & CATERERS · PICTURE DEALERS
LTANTS · RACING TRAINERS & BLOODSTOCK AGE
HOOLS · SECURITY CONSULTANTS · SPAS & CLINIC
MS · TRAVEL CONSULTANTS · WINE MERCHANTS ·
BUILDERS · YACHT CLUBS · AIR CHARTER · ANTIQU
IRS · ARTS DE LA TABLE · ARTS DE VIVRE · AUCTION
OOKERY SCHOOLS · COSMETIC SURGEONS · DOM
ORISTS · GARDEN DESIGNERS · GOLD CLUBS · HAI
USIC FESTIVALS · NANNIES · PARTY ORGANISERS &
TE BANKS · PROPERTY CONSULTANTS · RACING TR
TIQUE & PICTURE RESTORERS · SCHOOLS · SECURI
ORTING ESTATES · SPORTS CLUBS & GYMS · TRAVE
IRITS · YACHT BROKERS, DESIGNERS & BUILDERS
CTS & DECORATORS · ART & ANTIQUE FAIRS · ARTS
ASTLES & VILLAS · CHAUFFEUR SERVICES · COOKERY
ENCIES · FASHION & ACCESSORIES · FLORISTS · GA
WELLERY & WATCHES · MUSEUMS · MUSIC FESTIVAL
S · POLO CLUBS · PORTRAITS · PRIVATE BANKS · PR
ENTS · RESTAURANTS & BARS · ANTIQUE & PICTUR
ICS · SPECIALIST SHOPS · SPORTING ESTATES · S
HANTS · WINES, CHAMPAGNES & SPIRITS · YACHT
R · ANTIQUE DEALERS · ARCHITECTS & DECORATO
UCTION HOUSES · CASINOS · CASTLES & VILLAS · CH
EONS · DOMESTIC EMPLOYMENT AGENCIES · FASHI
LUBS · HAIR & BEAUTY · HOTELS · JEWELLERY & WAT
RGANISERS & CATERERS · PICTURE DEALERS · POLO
NTS · RACING TRAINERS & BLOODSTOCK AGENTS